SHEPPARD'S BOOK DEALERS
IN THE BRITISH ISLES

Companion Volumes

SHEPPARD'S DIRECTORIES

Directories of Antiquarian & Secondhand Book Dealers

SHEPPARD'S BOOK DEALERS
IN EUROPE

SHEPPARD'S BOOK DEALERS
IN JAPAN

SHEPPARD'S BOOK DEALERS
IN AUSTRALIA & NEW ZEALAND

SHEPPARD'S BOOK DEALERS
IN NORTH AMERICA

SHEPPARD'S BOOK DEALERS
IN INDIA AND THE ORIENT

SHEPPARD'S BOOK DEALERS
IN LATIN AMERICA & SOUTHERN AFRICA

Other Directories
SHEPPARD'S INTERNATIONAL
DIRECTORY OF PRINT AND
MAP SELLERS
A DIRECTORY OF BUSINESSES IN THIRTY-EIGHT COUNTRIES

SHEPPARD'S INTERNATIONAL
DIRECTORY OF EPHEMERA DEALERS
A DIRECTORY OF BUSINESSES IN TWENTY-ONE COUNTRIES

Companion Web Sites

www.sheppardsdirectories.com
www.sheppardsworld.co.uk

SHEPPARD'S

BOOK DEALERS IN THE BRITISH ISLES

**A DIRECTORY OF
ANTIQUARIAN AND SECONDHAND
BOOK DEALERS IN THE
UNITED KINGDOM,
THE CHANNEL ISLANDS,
THE ISLE OF MAN AND THE
REPUBLIC OF IRELAND**

TWENTY-EIGHTH EDITION

RICHARD
JOSEPH
PUBLISHERS

First Edition published 1951
Twenty-eighth published 2005

RICHARD JOSEPH PUBLISHERS LIMITED
P.O. BOX 15, TORRINGTON
DEVON EX38 8ZJ
ENGLAND
TEL: 01805 625750 FAX: 01805 625376

E-MAIL:

For book sales:
office@sheppardsworld.co.uk

For Sheppard's Booksearch and UK registering
of businesses in the British Isles:
booksearch@sheppardsdirectories.com

For enquiries and subscription to
Sheppard's World
info@sheppardsworld.co.uk

I.S.S.N. 0950-0715
I.S.B.N. 1 872699 83 9

MADE IN ENGLAND

Database advisor - Kevin Grimshire
Printed and bound by
Antony Rowe Ltd., Bumpers Farm, Chippenham, Wiltshire SN14 6LH

CONTENTS

ENGLAND (by Counties)

ENGLAND (by Unitary Authorities)

To locate a dealer within a Unitary Authority, use the page references shown below in conjuction with the County Index shown above.

SPECIALITY INDEX

The following list has been created from the subjects
provided by dealers' entry forms.

INTRODUCTION

If the trade wants a comprehensive reference source of dealers published regularly each year, the majority of dealers must cooperate. We are acutely conscious that this edition appears nearly five months late and most dealers know that we aim to publish at the end of each year. Dealers who do not respond to our repeated requests to update their entry simply delay publication, for it is self defeating to publish a half completed directory, and a late publication affects every user in this country as well as overseas. These delays do not help our many users – the very people who are your customers.

Three years ago, all entries were created from our printed forms sent back by dealers. From our records, in an average year about half would be returned within four weeks of mailing but the rest took another three months to gather. With increasing costs, we turned to the Internet and created an environment in which dealers could change their details quickly, and at little or no cost. For those with broadband, this cost is less than the price of postage. So we have pursued this course and when we send out mass e-mails, approximately 15% respond within five days but 30% fail to get through for reasons I list later. We do know that a large percentage of e-mails are read by the recipient as we receive confirmation that the e-mail has been read. Some might argue that we should return to sending out forms by post but if we were to do this, either the cost of the book would rise to £45 a copy or we would have to charge dealers for an entry. Both options would be counter productive – but we do send still forms out to those not on the Internet – and both options depend on dealers' responses.

In the past where dealers have not responded to our e-mails, our policy has been to reduce their details to 'one-liners'. For this year, we have repeated dealers' entries but this time they are in full but where e-mail addresses previously appeared, they have been omitted on the basis that if we cannot obtain an answer, it is safe to assume that no one else can either. It may be that they were correct but the user has allowed (accidentally we hope) their anti-spam program to block them. But our policy is that if we cannot get an e-mail through, then users of this directory contacting the dealer by e-mail will also fail and that will be equally frustrating.

Significantly, 451 dealers whose details had been shown as 'one-liners' in the last edition did take the time to visit their page on the web site. Others might have retired, ceased trading, or died, but it cannot account for all of them. So we have decided to take a course of action that might encourage this trend to continue.

All dealers who updated their details since the last edition are indicated by '[Updated]' at the end of their entry. All others have the date in brackets when they last updated their entry, or their information was amended here from other instructions received. Users can therefore take a view on the current data shown remaining valid today.

This phenomenon, people not answering e-mails, is not confined to our trade. It appears to be widespread across many industries which is a surprise considering the massive increase in the use of the Internet. On this subject, I was asked to submit an article for the December/January edition of *Rare Book Review* in which I outlined eight possible reasons for e-mails not being answered. These were (1) a dealer changes his e-mail address and does not amend it on the site, therefore no automatic reminders of passwords will ever reach the dealer; (2) our e-mails are accidentally deleted or blocked by anti-spam programmes; (3) Dealers forget their password and user name and don't bother to contact us; (4) our e-mails are ignored; (5) dealers or their staff might not recognize the name of Sheppard in the subject line; (6) dealers' mail boxes are full and will not accept any more;

(7) Dealers recognize the name *Sheppard*, plan to deal with it later, then forget; and (8) the dealer moves premises and does not let us know. Then our last ditch postal reminder is bound to fail too and no answer means omission.

If we are to publish the next edition in December 2005, then dealers should make a note to update their details now – and check their details on www.sheppardsdirectories.com The best time to do this is in July or August.

Some interesting statistics have been drawn from the current database. This edition has a total of 1,867 dealers listed, down on previous years. But 451 dealers previously been shown as one-liners have now been dropped which if added would return the total to the stable total of 2,300. Our database is actually much larger than this. Of the total listed, 1,403 have e-mail addresses and 832 have web sites. There are 80 new subjects in the Subject Classification, a higher than usual figure for an annual change. In the 2001 edition of this directory, we recorded that there were 1,269 businesses trading from shops (as well as private premises). This year the number of businesses trading from shops is 620 which confirms that the trade is going through a dramatic change and traditional methods of trading are disappearing. If dealers are becoming reliant on the Internet, then e-mails become even more important.

With the majority of dealers now trading from private premises, storerooms, or warehouses, is there a reluctance to have their businesses listed in a trade directory? It is too easy to assume the Internet is the main reason but other issues may affect their decision such as fear of burglary; officialdom and even nosey neighbours. Dealers opting not to be listed means that they miss out on free publicity and make it harder for people to find dealers when house clearances are required, or specialist collections are for sale?

New dealers can always register their business on-line – and existing dealers can re-register – on www.sheppardsdirectories.com. For those not linked to the Internet, please send your details, or ask for the form, to The Editor, Sheppard's Book Dealers in the British Isles, Richard Joseph Publishers Ltd, PO Box 15, Torrington, Devon EX38 8ZJ.

Sheppard's International Directories

Dealers and collectors will be pleased to learn that all our other directories are now being compiled concurrently – only possible via a new website on the Internet:

www.sheppardsworld.co.uk

Any dealer of ephemera or any print and map seller can register their details. The site is also designed for all overseas book dealers previously listed in a Sheppard's Directory. Once sufficient names have been registered, a new edition of each regional directory will be published in book form.

Sheppardsworld is searchable on line, and dealers can be located by subject classification of the stocks they hold – or by location country, state, city and town. The information shown in the search results is similar to that shown in printed directories. As this site builds, it will prove to be useful search tool and the cost – the annual subscription is £30 – will be a huge saving over buying the seven printed directories. While most dealers listed will have access to the Internet, we will be adding those that are not to the database, thus searches will show these too but obviously contact must be made my telephone, fax or post. To find out more – visit www.sheppardsworld.co.uk

Richard Joseph
April 2005

ABBREVIATIONS
USED IN DESCRIBING BOOKS

Some booksellers and buyers use highly individualistic systems of abbreviations and others have adapted traditional terms for the Internet. The following are sufficiently well known to be generally used, but all other words should be written in full, and the whole typed if possible. Condition is described by the following scale:– Mint – Fine – Very good – Good – Fair – Poor

A.D.	Autograph document	Lea.	Leather
A.D.s.	Autograph document, signed	Ll.	Levant Morocco
A.D.*	Autograph document with seal	Ll.	Leaves
A.e.g.	All edges gilt	L.P.	Large paper
A.L.s.	Autograph letter, signed	M.	Mint
a.v.	Authorized version	Mco., mor	Morocco
B.A.R.	Book Auction Records	M.e.	Marbled edges
Bd.	Bound	M.S.(S.)	Manuscripts
Bdg.	Binding	N.d.	No date
Bds.	Boards	n.ed.	new edition
B.L.	Black letter	n.p.	no place (of publication)
C., ca.	Circa (approximately)	Ob., obl.	Oblong
C. & p.	Collated and perfect	Oct.	Octavo
Cat.	Catalogue	O.p.	Out of print
Cent.	Century	P.	Page
Cf.	Calf	P.f.	Post free
C.I.F.	Cost, insurance and freight	Pict.	Pictorial
Cl.	Cloth	Pl(s).	Plate(s)
Col(d).	Colour(ed)	Port.	Portrait
C.O.D.	Cash on delivery	P.P.	Printed privately
Cont.	Contemporary	Pp.	Pages
C.O.R.	Cash on receipt	Prelims.	Preliminary pages
Cr. 8vo.	Crown octavo	Pseud.	Pseudonym(ous)
d.e.	Deckle edges	Ptd.	Printed
Dec.	Decorated	q.v.	Quod Vide (which see)
D-j., d-w.	Dust jacket, dust wrapper	Qto.	Quarto
E.D.L.	Edition de luxe	Rev.	Revised
Edn.	Edition	Rom.	Roman letter
Endp., e.p.	Endpaper(s)	S.L.	Sine loco (without place of publication)
Eng., engr.	Engraved, engraving		
Ex-lib.	Ex-library	Sgd.	Signed
Facs.	Facsimile	Sig.	Signature
Fcp.	Foolscap	S.N.	Sine nomine (without name of printer)
F.	Fine		
F.,ff.	Folio, folios	Spr.	Sprinkled
Fo., fol.	Folio (book size)	T.e.g.	Top edge gilt
F.O.B.	Free on board	Thk.	Thick
Fp., front.	Frontispiece	T.L.s.	Typed letter, signed
Free	Post Free	T.p.	Title page
G.	Good	T.S.	Typescript
G., gt.	Gilt edges	Unbd.	Unbound
G.L.	Gothic letter	Uncut	Uncut (pages not trimmed)
Hf. bd.	Half bound	Und.	Undated
Illum.	Illuminated	V.d.	Various dates
Ill(s).	Illustrated, illustrations	V.g..	Very good
Imp.	Imperial	Vol,	Volume
Impft.	Imperfect	W.a.f.	With all faults
Inscr.	Inscribed, inscription	Wraps.	Wrappers
Ital.	Italic letter		

SIZES OF BOOKS

These are only approximate, as trimming varies and all sizes ignore the overlap of a book case.

	Octavo (8vo)		Quarto (4to)	
	Inches	*Centimetres*	*Inches*	*Centimetres*
FOOLSCAP	$6^3/_4$ x $4^1/_4$	17.1 x 10.8	$8^1/_2$ x $6^3/_4$	21.5 x 17.1
CROWN	$7^1/_2$ x 5	19.0 x 12.7	10 x $7^1/_2$	25.4 x 19.0
LARGE POST	$8^1/_4$ x $5^1/_4$	20.9 x 13.3	$10^1/_2$ x $8^1/_4$	26.6 x 20.9
DEMY	$8^3/_8$ x $5^5/_8$	22.3 x 14.2	$11^1/_4$ x $8^3/_4$	28.5 x 22.2
MEDIUM	9 x $5^3/_4$	22.8 x 14.6	$11^1/_2$ x 9	29.2 x 22.8
ROYAL	10 x $6^1/_4$	25.4 x 15.8	$12^1/_2$ x 10	31.7 x 25.4
SUPER ROYAL	$10^1/_4$ x $6^3/_4$	26.0 x 17.5	$13^3/_4$ x $10^1/_4$	34.9 x 26.0
IMPERIAL	11 x $7^1/_2$	27.9 x 19.0	15 x 11	38.0 x 27.9
FOOLSCAP FOLIO			$13^1/_2$ x $8^1/_2$	34.2 x 21.5
METRIC A5	$8^1/_4$ x $5^7/_8$	21.0 x 14.8		
A4	$11^3/_4$ x $8^1/_4$	29.7 x 21.0		
'A' FORMAT PAPERBACK		17.8 X 11.1		
'B' FORMAT PAPERBACK		19.8 X 12.9		

BRITISH PAPER SIZES (untrimmed)

Sizes of Printing Papers

	Inches	*Centimetres*
Foolscap	17 x $13^1/_2$	43.2 x 34.3
Double Foolscap	27 x 17	68.6 x 43.2
Crown	20 x 15	50.8 x 38.1
Double Crown	30 x 20	76.2 x 50.8
Quad Crown	40 x 30	101.6 x 76.2
Double Quad Crown	60 x 40	152.4 x 101.6
Post	$19^1/_4$ x $15^1/_2$	48.9 x 39.4
Double Post	$31^1/_2$ x $19^1/_2$	80.0 x 49.5
Double Large Post	33 x 21	83.8 x 53.3
Sheet and $^1/_2$ Post	$23^1/_2$ x $19^1/_2$	59.7 x 49.5
Demy	$22^1/_2$ x $17^1/_2$	57.2 x 44.5
Double Demy	35 x $22^1/_2$	88.9 x 57.2
Quad Demy	45 x 35	114.3 x 88.9
Music Demy	20 x $15^1/_2$	50.8 x 39.4
Medium	23 x 18	58.4 x 45.7
Royal	25 x 20	63.5 x 50.8
Super Royal	$27^1/_2$ x $20^1/_2$	69.9 x 52.1
Elephant	28 x 23	71.1 x 58.4
Imperial	30 x 22	76.2 x 55.9

METRIC CONVERSIONS

SIZES

inches	m.m.	inches	m.m.
$1/4$	6	$7^3/4$	197
$1/2$	13	8	203
$3/4$	19	$8^1/4$	210
1	25	$8^1/2$	216
$1^1/4$	32	$8^3/4$	222
$1^1/2$	38	9	229
$1^3/4$	44	$9^1/4$	235
2	51	$9^1/2$	241
$2^1/4$	57	$9^3/4$	248
$2^1/2$	64	10	254
$2^3/4$	70	$10^1/4$	260
3	76	$10^1/2$	267
$3^1/4$	83	$10^3/4$	273
$3^1/2$	89	11	279
$3^3/4$	95	$11^1/4$	286
4	102	$11^1/2$	292
$4^1/4$	108	$11^3/4$	298
$4^1/2$	114	12	305
$4^3/4$	121	$12^1/4$	311
5	127	$12^1/2$	318
$5^1/4$	133	$12^3/4$	324
$5^1/2$	140	13	330
$5^3/4$	146	$13^1/4$	337
6	152	$13^1/2$	343
$6^1/4$	159	$13^3/4$	349
$6^1/2$	165	14	356
$6^3/4$	171	$14^1/4$	362
7	178	$14^1/2$	368
$7^1/4$	184	$14^3/4$	375
$7^1/2$	191	15	381

WEIGHTS

lbs.	kgs.
1	0.45
2	0.91
3	1.36
4	1.81
5	2.27
6	2.72
7	3.18
8	3.63
9	4.08
10	4.54
11	4.99
12	5.44
13	5.90
14	6.35
15	6.80
16	7.26
17	7.71
18	8.16
19	8.62
20	9.07
21	9.53
22	9.98
23	10.43
24	10.89
25	11.34
26	11.79
27	12.25
28	12.70
56	25.40
112	50.80

To convert inches to millimetres multiply by 25.4. Millimetres to inches may be found by multiplying by .0394.

To convert pounds to kilogrammes multiply by .4536. Kilogrammes to pounds may be found by multiplying by 2.205.

THE BRITISH BOOK TRADE

NEW BOOKS

In the United Kingdom, marketing of new books is well organised and controlled by individual publishers. However, the British Book Trade has two highly organised trade associations, The Publishers Association and The Booksellers Association which represent a vast majority of their respective parts of the trade.

The Booksellers Association publishes an annual directory of members, listing 'over 3,000 bookselling outlets' in the current edition. This is an essential reference source used by all publishers. In addition, the Booksellers Association publishes an annual directory of book publishers, distributors and wholesalers.

The directory of B.A. Members includes not only general booksellers, but businesses that concentrate on specific subjects. Although, in fact, it confers no right to buy books at trade terms, entry in this directory confirms to publishers that they are eligible for trade terms.

Bibliographic information is supplied to the book trade through Nielsen BookData Ltd. Publishers supply information on the titles they have published and this is disseminated by these two companies to booksellers. Users of this directory will note the growing importance of this information in relation to the secondhand book trade.

THE BOOKSELLERS ASSOCIATION OF THE UNITED KINGDOM AND IRELAND LIMITED, 272 Vauxhall Bridge Road, London SW1V 1BA. Tel: (020) 7802-0802. Fax: (020) 7802-0803. E-Mail: mail@booksellers.org.uk. Web Site: www.booksellers.org.uk. Est: 1895 as the Associated Booksellers of Great Britain and Ireland and changed to its present name in 1999. Chief Executive: Tim Godfray. The Association's aims are: to provide services to help members increase book sales and develop the market for new books; to assist members to reduce costs; to improve distribution between publishers, booksellers and consumers; to represent booksellers' interests; and to provide a forum for members to discuss matters of common interest. It is not concerned with the secondhand or antiquarian trade: membership is open to all those engaged in the sale of new books, some of whom also sell secondhand and antiquarian books. The Association is governed by an Annual Conference and a Council which meets four times a year, delegating much work to specialist committees and encouraging members to join groups concerned with academic bookselling, Christian bookselling, children's bookselling etc. Book Tokens, and batch.co.uk - an electronic clearing house for the payment of accounts – are some of the services provided for members. The Association is linked with similar bodies overseas.

THE PUBLISHERS ASSOCIATION, 29B Montague Street, London WC1B 5BWH. Tel: (020) 7691-9191. Fax: 7691-9199. E-Mail: mail@publishers.org.uk. Est: 1896. President: Henry Reece. Chief Executive: Ronnie Williams. Including the Trade Publishers Council, International Division (BDCI), the Educational Publishers Council (School Books division), the Council of Academic and Professional Publishers and the Electronic Publishers Forum. The Association represents the interests of UK publishers of books, electronic publications and journals to governments, other bodies in the trade and the public at large. It seeks to promote the sales of British books by all suitable means, and provides members with a wide range of services and help on publishing problems and opportunities.

SECONDHAND AND ANTIQUARIAN BOOKS

Anyone who is so minded can enter this branch of the trade without any formality at all and, indeed, book lovers and collectors, buying items for their own libraries and selling duplicate or unwanted copies, have sometimes, almost unwittingly, drifted into a habit of rather casual regular dealing. This sounds easy and pleasant but, to enter seriously into business and make a profit in any way commensurate with the work involved, a great deal of expert knowledge is required.

Some dealers have large and handsome premises, but retail shops are now relatively few as most dealers now work from warehouses, storerooms, and private premises. In addition to these sales outlets, there are numerous book fairs of varying size around the country from which dealers trade. Many more though are trading via the Internet. While most dealers in secondhand and antiquarian books will try to obtain for a customer any required item which they do not have in stock, many specialists will now refer requests outside their speciality to other dealers.

Dealers offer titles for sale and advertise for titles wanted in the weekly magazine *Bookdealer*. Perhaps a word of advice may be given here: if a book is required, ask for it from as many dealers as possible, but make it clear whether you wish the bookdealer to advertise for it, and ask only one to do this. If a book-buyer goes from dealer to dealer asking to see if they can get a copy of some book for him, the probability is that six advertisements for it will appear in the next week's *Bookdealer*; the law of supply and demand will begin to operate, and the man who has a copy will feel that he has put too low a price on a book that is so eagerly sought, and will increase it accordingly.

The Internet has become a very useful tool to search for titles. In some respects, web sites devoted to the secondhand and antiquarian book trade are better organised than those for the new book trade. Those seeking information about this aspect will find *Sheppard's Booksearch* **(www.sheppardsdirectories.com) and** *Sheppard's World*\(www.sheppardsworld.co.uk) **very useful but also see the list on page forty-four.**

Booksellers whose principal business is in new books must, nearly always, maintain a general stock. There are a few in large towns that do not, but, generally speaking, if anyone requires any recently published book, he goes to the nearest bookshop and it can be obtained as easily from there as from anywhere else; if it is not in stock it will come from the publishers in a few days at a known cost.

A distinctive feature of the secondhand book trade, however, is its high degree of specialisation. Almost every dealer has a particular interest, and some will be found who deal only in books on one subject, or indeed in the works of one author or group of authors. If one requires a secondhand or antiquarian book he should go or write directly to the specialist. This directory is intended to provide a handy guide that will enable the booklover to do this with the minimum of trouble, to fill its place as an essential reference book for the trade.

There are two national trade associations for antiquarian book dealers:

THE ANTIQUARIAN BOOKSELLERS' ASSOCIATION, Sackville House, 40 Piccadilly, London W1J 0DR. Tel: (020) 7439-3118. Fax: 7439-3119. E-Mail: admin@aba.org.uk. Web Site: www.ABAinternational.com. Est: 1906. President: Jonathan Potter. Vice President: Robert Frew. Treasurer: Paul Minet. Administrators: John Critchley, Philippa Gibson, and Marianne Harwood. The Antiquarian Booksellers' Association includes the leading dealers in antiquarian, fine and scarce secondhand books throughout Great Britain as well as in some other countries. It is the founding member of the twenty similar associations, scattered throughout Europe, the Americas, and the Far East which together form the International League of Antiquarian Booksellers.

The Association seeks to provide a comprehensive service to its members. It organises the prestigious and renowned Antiquarian Book Fair each June at Olympia, London and a more broadly-based Book Fair at Chelsea Town Hall every autumn. Branch fairs are also held in Edinburgh. All members receive an informative newsletter each month and there is a fine reference library ready to answer their bibliographical queries. Their interests are further looked after by representatives sitting on various government bodies and dealing with such  subjects as the export of manuscripts, the future of the British Library, the National Book League, the monitoring of V.A.T. and customs regulations both here and in the Common Market. The Association organises, through the year, a series of events – sporting, social, and educational – aimed at promoting friendship and understanding among colleagues at both national and international levels. There is a Benevolent Fund upon which members may call in times of financial difficulty. Members may also benefit from advantageous rates on credit card processing, postal and delivery services and insurance negotiated on their behalf by the Association.

There are various ways in which the Association looks after the interest of the general public. By requiring of all its members a good experience of the trade, and high professional standards and ethics, it ensures that the public may approach with confidence any dealer displaying the A.B.A. badge. In rare cases of difficulty or dispute, the Association stands ready to arbitrate between dealer and client.

The public, especially institutions and public libraries, are further served by a sophisticated security system founded and developed by the Association and now copied throughout the world. It has already accounted for the apprehension of an impressive list of book-thieves and for the recovery and restoration to their rightful owners of many hundreds of stolen books.

From within its ranks, the Antiquarian Booksellers' Association can produce experts on most aspects of bibliography and book-collecting, and their collective expertise is available to the general public through the Association's office. A list of Members is published annually and is available on request from the Administrators, or through the website.

PROVINCIAL BOOKSELLERS' FAIRS ASSOCIATION, The Old Coach House, 16 Melbourn Street, Royston, Hertfordshire SG8 7BZ. Tel: (01763) 248400. Fax: 248921. Fairs information line: 249212. E-Mail: info@pbfa.org. URL: www.pbfa.org. Est: 1974. Chairman: Alex Alec-Smith. Vice-Chairman: George Newlands. Honorary Secretary: Phil Salin. Honorary Treasurer: Clare Brightman. Honorary Membership Secretary: Bob Date. Administrator: Gina Dolan. Over 730 members.

The PBFA is the largest association of antiquarian and secondhand booksellers in Great Britain. With over 700 members it is also the largest in the world. It is non-profit making and co-operatively managed by its members through national and regional committees. The full-time administrative headquarters are in Royston.

The Association organises book fairs throughout the country – 140 in all – each year. Central to this programme are the monthly fairs held at the Hotel Russell in London and the international fairs held each June, at the Hotel Russell and Novotel London West.

Support for members and their dependents is available at times of distress through the Association's own charity, the Richard Condon Memorial Fund. The size of the membership allows the PBFA to negotiate advantageous rates for credit card processing, postal services, insurance and bulk purchasing.

The PBFA caters for a wide range of book collecting interests and aims to promote a broader interest in antiquarian and secondhand books. The PBFA provides safeguards for the public buying from its members and is committed to maintaining the highest trading standards. In addition a monthly newsletter is published for members and an annual Directory of Members *(£5.00 inc. p&p)* and a nationwide calendar of book fairs *(free)* is available from the Royston office.

There is also an antiquarian and secondhand book-trade association for Wales:

WELSH BOOKSELLERS ASSOCIATION, c/o 44 Lion Street, Hay-on-Wye, Herefordshire HR3 5AA. Tel: (01497) 820322. Fax: 821150. Est: 1987. Chairman: Richard Booth. Secretary & Treasurer: Anna Cooper. The Association aims to encourage the development of secondhand and antiquarian bookselling in Wales. Books, maps, prints, manuscripts and ephemera all come within the scope of the Association. An annual leaflet giving details of each member is available by subscription from the Secretary, or any member.

PRIVATE LIBRARIES ASSOCIATION, Ravelston, South View Road, Pinner, Middlesex HA5 3YD. Est: 1956. The Private Libraries Association is an international society of book collectors with about 650 private members (about one quarter of them in America) and about 150 institutional members. The Association publishes a quarterly journal (*The Private Library*, which contains articles, notes and other items), an annual checklist of Private Press Books, a quarterly *Newsletter and Exchange List*, a *Members' List*, and other books about various aspects of book collecting. Annual subscription £25.

ANTIQUARIAN BOOKSELLERS' ASSOCIATIONS

Australia and New Zealand

AUSTRALIAN AND NEW ZEALAND ASSOCIATION OF ANTIQUARIAN BOOKSELLERS, 69 Broadway, Nedlands 6009, Western Australia. Tel: (618) 9386-6103. Fax: (618) 9386-8211. E-mail: anzaab@iinet.net.au. Internet: www.anzaab.com.au/~anzaab. Est 1977. President: Louella Kerr. Vice-Presidents: Peter Tinsley. Secretary: Sam Haynes. Treasurer: Michael Sprod. 70 members.

Austria

VERBAND DER ANTIQUARE ÖSTERREICHS, Grünangergasse 4, A-1010 Wien, Austria. Tel: (01) 512 15 35. Fax: (01) 512 84 82. E-mail: sekretariat@ hvb.at. Internet: http://www.buecher.at. President: Norbert Donhofer

Belgium

CHAMBRE PROFESSIONNELLE BELGE DE LA LIBRAIRIE ANCIENNE ET MODERNE (C.L.A.M.). BELGISCHE BEROEPSKAMER VAN ANTIQUAREN (B.B.A.). Secretary: Michael Lhomme. Secretary CLAM-BBA, p/a Rue des Carmes 9, B-4000 Liege, Belgium. Tel: (+ +32) (04) 223 24 63. Fax: (+ +32) (0)4 223 24 19. E-Mail: libraire@ michel-lhomme.com. Est: 1946. President: Henri Godts. Vice President: Jan Ceuleers. Treasurer: Alain Ferraton. The CLAM-BBA, the Belgium Antiquarian Booksellers' Association is affiliated to the International League of Antiquarian Booksellers (I.L.A.B)

Brazil

ASSOCIAÇÃO BRASILEIRA DE LIVERIROS ANTIQUÁRIOS, Rua Santos Dumont 677 25625-090 Centro Petrópolis, Brazil. Tel: (242) 42 03 76. Fax: (242) 31 16 95. Est: 1945 President: Mrs Ana Maria Bocayuva de Miranda Jordão. E-mail: sebofino@uol.com.br. 9 members.

Canada

ANTIQUARIAN BOOKSELLERS' ASSOCIATION OF CANADA, (A.B.A.C). c/o 783 Bank Street, Ottawa, Ontario K1S 3V5 Canada. President: Wilfrid M. de Freitas. Secretary: Charles Purpora (Tel: 604 320-0375). E-mail: charles@purporabooks.com. 70 members.

Czech Republic

SVAZ ANTIKVÁRU CR, Karlova 2, 110 00 Praha 1, Czech Republic. Tel: & Fax: (02) 22 22 02 86, 22 22 02 88. Est: 1922. President: Petr Meissner. E-mail: info@meissner.cz. 5 members

Denmark

DEN DANSKE ANTIKVARBOGHANDLERFORENING, P.O. Box 2028, DK-1012 Copenhagen K, Denmark. E-mail: info@antikvat.dk. Internet: www.antikvar.dk. Est: 1920. President: Poul Jan Poulsen. 35 members.

PROVINCIAL BY NAME

The PBFA has been running quality book fairs for more than quarter of a century. From our first event, held in London in 1972, and intended as a shop window for provincial book dealers (hence the name), to our current programme of fairs all round the country we offer the book collecting public and the secondhand book trade an unparalleled range of events to suit every taste and every pocket - large fairs, small fairs, in the North and in the South; specialist fairs, and general fairs with books on all subjects at prices ranging from £5 to £10,000. A PBFA book fair, large or small, stands out by its quality - quality of presentation, quality of organisation and quality of items offered.

Our fairs held at the Hotel Russell have a well-deserved reputation as **the** place to buy books in London, but each area of the United Kingdom now boasts its own regular major event; from Aberdeeen through Edinburgh, York, Harrogate, Cambridge, Oxford and Bath.

Visit our website www.pbfa.org to see our full programme of quality fairs, lists of exhibitors, detailed information and maps for all fairs. Our published calendar is also available post free from our HQ address below.

All PBFA members are established bookdealers who abide by a code of practice. Their trading details are readily accessible in the Directory of Members available at £4.00 (p + p extra) and through our online directory.

The PBFA relies on volunteers to run its affairs, be it on committees, managing a fair, or helping out with putting up posters or clearing up afterwards. We could not function without these hardworking members and however large we grow, we will retain our founding principles of working co-operatively to sell quality books at quality events.

WORLDWIDE BY REPUTATION

For further information on our renowned book fairs or how to join the PBFA contact:
Gina Dolan, PBFA, The Old Coach House, 16 Melbourn St, Royston, Herts, SG8 7BZ.
Tel: 01763 248400, Fax: 01762 248921,
email: info@pbfa.org or visit our website at www.pbfa.org

Finland

SUOMEN ANTIKVARIAATTIYHDISTYS. (Finnish Antiquarian Booksellers Association), c/o Kampintorin Antikvaarinen Kirjakauppa, Fredrikinkatu 63, Helsinki, Finland. Tel: (09) 694 3306. Est: 1941. E-mail: timo .surojegin@pp.inet.fi. 23 members.

France

SYNDICAT NATIONAL DE LA LIBRAIRIE ANCIENNE ET MODERNE, 4 rue Gît-le-Cœur, F-75006 Paris, France. Tel: (01) 43 29 46 38. Fax: (01) 43 25 41 63. E-mail: slam-livre@wanadoo.fr. Internet: www.slam-livre.fr. Est: 1914. President: Mr Frederic Castaing. 225 members.

Germany

VERBAND DEUTSCHER ANTIQUARE e.V., P.O. Box 10 10 20, D-50450 Köln, Kreuzgasse 2-4, D-50667, Köln, Germany. Tel: (06034) 908495. Fax: (0221) ? E-mail: pirckheimer@nanoweb.de. Internet: www.antiquare.de. Est: 1949. 278 members.

Italy

ASSOCIAZIONE LIBRAI ANTIQUARI D'ITALIA, via Jacopo Nardi 6, I-50122 Firenze, Italy. Tel: & Fax: (055) 243 253. E-mail: alai@tzm.it. Internet: www.tzm.it/alai. Est: 1947. President: Giuliano Gallini. Vice President: Umberto Pregliasco. Treasurer: Piero Crini. 120 members.

Japan

THE ANTIQUARIAN BOOKSELLERS' ASSOCIATION OF JAPAN (ABAJ), 29 San-ei-cho, Shinjuku-ku, Tokyo 160-0008, Japan. Tel: (03) 3357-1411. Fax: (03) 3351-5855. Est: 1963. President: Mr Mitsuo Nitta. E-mail: rarebook@yushodo.co.jp. 30 members.

Korea

ANTIQUARIAN BOOKSELLERS' ASSOCIATION OF KOREA (A.B.A.K.), 33, Gwan-Hoon-Dong, Chongro-Ku, 110-300 Seoul, Korea. Tel: & Fax: (02) 735 2772. 31 members.

Netherlands

NEDERLANDSCHE VEREENIGING VAN ANTIQUAREN, Secretary: Drs. P.A.G.W.E. Pruimers. Van Stockum's Veilingen B.V., Prinsengracht 15, 2512 EW's-Gravenhage, The Netherlands. Tel: (070) 364 98 40/41. Fax: (070) 364 33 40. Est: 1935. President: Mr Ton Kok (E-mail: kok@xs4all.nl). 88 Members.

Norway

NORSK ANTIKVARBOKHANDLERFORENING, Postboks 1420, Vika N-0115 Oslo, Norway. Tel: (47) 23 31 02 80. Internet: www.antikvariat.no. President: Kamilla Aslaksen. (E-mail: kamilla.aslaken@cappelensantokvariat .no). 21 members.

Spain

ADSCRIPTO IBERICA LIBRARIAE ANTIQUARIORUM (A.I.L.A.), San Miguel 12, E-07002 Palma de Mallorca, Spain. Tel: (971) 72 13 55. Fax: (971) 71 74 36. Internet: www.libreriaripoll.com.

Sweden

SVENSKA ANTIKVARIATFÖRENINGEN, Box 22549, SE-104 22 Stockholm, Sweden. Tel: (08) 653 08 08. Fax: (08) 654 80 06. E-Mail: main@svaf.se. Internet: www.svaf.se.

Switzerland

VEREINIGUNG DER BUCHANTIQUARE UND KUPFER-STICHHÄNDLER IN DER SCHWEIZ (V.E.B.U.K.U.) / SYNDICAT DE LA LIBRARIE ANCIENNE ET DU COMMERCE DE L'ESTAMPE EN SUISSE (S.L.A.C.E.S.), Restelbergstr. 82, CH-8044 Zürich, Switzerland. Tel: (01) 350 14 41. Fax: (01) 350 14 43. E-mail: mail@fluehmann.com. Internet: www.vebuku.ch and www.slaces.ch. President: Marcus Benz. Secretary: Francoise Bloch.

United Kingdom

THE ANTIQUARIAN BOOKSELLERS' ASSOCIATION, Sackville House, 40 Piccadilly, London W1J 0DR. Tel: (020) 7439-3118. Fax: 7439-3119. E-Mail: admin@aba.org.uk. Web Site: www.ABAinternational.com. Est: 1906. President: Jonathan Potter. Director: John Critchley. Events Officer: Philippa Gibson. Administration: Marianne Harwood.

PRIVATE LIBRARIES ASSOCIATION, Ravelston, South View Road, Pinner, Middlesex HA5 3YD. Est: 1956. The Private Libraries Association is an international society of book collectors with about 650 private members (about one third of them in America) and about 150 library members.

PROVINCIAL BOOKSELLERS FAIRS ASSOCIATION, The Old Coach House, 16 Melbourn Street, Royston, Hertfordshire SG8 7BZ. Tel: (01763) 248400. Fax: (01763) 248921. Fairs information line: (01763) 249212. E-Mail: info@pbfa.org. Web Site: www.pbfa.org. Est: 1974. Chairman: Alex Alec-Smith. Vice-Chairman: George Newlands. Honorary Secretary: Phil Salin. Honorary Treasurer: Clare Brightman. Honorary Membership Secretary: Bob Date. Administrator: Gina Dolan. Over 730 members.

WELSH BOOKSELLERS ASSOCIATION, c/o 44 Lion Street, Hay-on-Wye, Herefordshire HR3 5AA. Tel: (01497) 820322. Fax: 821150. E-Mail: WBA@richardbooth.demon.co.uk. Est: 1987. Chairman: Richard Booth. 29 members.

United States of America

ANTIQUARIAN BOOKSELLERS' ASSOCIATION OF AMERICA (A.B.A.A.), 20 West 44th Street, Fourth Floor, New York, N.Y. 10036-6604, U.S.A. Tel: (212) 944-8291. Fax: 944-8293. E-Mail: inquiries@abaa.org. Web Site: www.abaa.org. Est: 1949. President: John Crichton. Treasurer: Rob Rulon-Miller. Over 457 members.

INTERNATIONAL LEAGUE OF ANTIQUARIAN BOOKSELLERS (I.L.A.B.) to which most national associations belong. President: Robert D. Fleck, 310 Delaware Street, Newcastle, DE 19720 USA. E-mail: oakknoll@oakknoll.com. General Secretary: Steven Temple, Steven Temple Books, 489 Queen Street West, Toronto, ON M5V 2B4 Canada. E-mail: books@steventemplebooks.com.

PERIODICALS

Literary Magazines and Book Trade Papers

Please note that magazine prices and subscriptions are given as a guide only, and are liable to change.

THE AFRICAN BOOK PUBLISHING RECORD (ABPR). Covers new and forthcoming African publications, as well as publishing articles & news. Est: 1975. Quarterly. Subscription: EURO 328.00 (price for 2004). Editor: Cécile Lomer. Published by: K.G. Saur Verlag GmbH, Ortlerstrasse 8, 81373 Muenchen, Germany; Postfach 70 16 20, 81316 Muenchen, Germany. Tel: +49-89-76902-0; Fax: +49-89-76902-150; E-mail: saur.info@thomson.com. Subscription enquiries to K.G. Saur Verlag.

ALMANACCO DEL BIBLIOFILO. Yearly. Published at: Edizioni Rovello di Mario Scognamiglio, P.za Castello, 11, 20121 Milano, Italy. Tel: (02) 86464661 or (02) 866532. Fax: (02) 72022884. E-mail: edirovello@libero.it

ANTIQUES FAIRS AND CENTRES GUIDE. Six monthly. £1.50 per copy plus 50p p&p. (5 year subscription only £16.00 - as 4 year subscription). Published by: H.P. Publishing, 2, Hampton Court Road, Harborne, Birmingham B17 9AE. Tel: (0121) 681-8000 (Ad Sales); -8001 (Accounts); -8002 (Editorial). Subscriptions: Tel: (0121) 681 8003; Fax: (0121) 681-8005. E-Mail: subscriptions@antiquesmagazine.com. Web Site: www.antiquesfairsguide.com.

ANTIQUES MAGAZINE. Weekly or fortnightly. Subscription. £52.00 – 45 issues, plus 2 Antiques Fairs & Centres Guide (U.K.). Fortnightly £28.00 (U.K.); please call for overseas rates. Published by: H.P. Publishing, 2, Hampton Court Road, Harborne, Birmingham B17 9AE. Tel: (0121) 681-8000 (Ad Sales); -8001 (Accounts); -8002 (Editorial). Subscriptions: Tel: (0121) 681 8003; Fax: (0121) 681-8005. E-Mail: subscriptions@antiques magazine.com. Web Site: www.antiquesmagazine.com.

ANTIQUES TRADE GAZETTE. Contains comprehensive weekly reports on antiquarian book sales world-wide plus auction calendar. Est: 1971. Weekly. Subscription: £76.00 (£158.00 North America and rest of world, £120.00 Europe) a year. Published by: Metropress Ltd., 115 Shaftesbury Avenue, London WC2H 8AD. Tel: (020) 7420-6601. Editor: Ivan Macquisten. Antiquarian Books Editor: Ian McKay. Tel: (01795) 890475. Fax: 890014. E-mail: ianmckay1@btinternet.com

AUS DEM ANTIQUARIAT. German journal on Antiquarian booktrade by subscription. Published six times a year by MVB Marketing- und Verlagservice des Buchhandels GmbH, Grosser Hirschgraben 17-21, 60311 Frankfurt am Main (Postfach 100442, 60004 Frankfurt am Main), Germany. Tel: +49 (69) 1306 469. Fax: 1306 394. E-mail: antiquariat@mvb-online.de. Internet www.buch-antiquariat.de

BOOK AND MAGAZINE COLLECTOR. Biographies and bibliographies of collectable 19th and 20th century authors and illustrators, plus lists of books for sale and wanted. Est: 1984. Monthly. Subscription: £39.50 a year (13 issues, U.K.), £43.00 (Europe, Airmail), £50.00 (Rest of the World). Editor: Jonathan Scott. Publisher: John Dean. Published by: Diamond Publishing, Metropolis Int., Unit 101, Wales Farm Road, London W3 6UG Tel: (0870) 732-8080. Fax: (0870) 732-6060. E-mail: bmceditor@metropolis.co.uk

THE BOOK COLLECTOR. Est: 1952. Quarterly. Subscription: £42.00 (overseas £45.00, U.S. $75.00) a year. Editor: Nicolas Barker. Published by: The Collector Ltd., 20 Maple Grove, London NW9 8QY. Tel: & Fax: (020) 8200-5004. E-mail: info@thebookcollector.co.uk.

THE BOOKDEALER. Trade weekly for secondhand and antiquarian books for sale and wanted. £52.00 a year or £26.00 for six months (incl. p. & p. within U.K.). Editor: Barry Shaw. Published by: Alacrity, Eastern Wing, Banwell Castle, Weston-super-Mare BS29 6NX. Tel: (01934) 822971. Fax: 820682. E-mail: alacrity@dial.pipex.com.

BOOKS FROM FINLAND. English-language journal presenting Finnish literature and writers. Est: 1976. Editor-in-chief: Kristina Carlson. Editors: Soila Lehtonen & Hildi Hawkins. Quarterly. Subscription: 20 euros a year (Finland and Scandinavia), 27 euros (all other countries). Published by: Finnish Literature Society, P.O. Box 259 FIN-00171, Helsinki, Finland. Tel: & Fax: (09) 135-7942. E-Mail: booksfromfinland@finlit.fi. Web Site: www.finlit.fi/fili/bff.

THE BOOKSELLER. Journal of the book trade in Great Britain. Weekly. Subscription: £170.00 a year (U.K.), £185.00 (overseas, airmail extra). Editor: To be announced. Published by: VNU Entertainment Media UK Ltd., 189 Shaftesbury Avenue, London WC2H 8TJ. Tel: (020) 7420-6006. Fax: 7420-6103.

BOOK SOURCE MAGAZINE. Published since 1985, contains articles, news, reviews and information for the secondhand/antiquarian book trade in the USA. Subscription bi-monthly: $20.00 (1st class USA); $24.00 (library rate, Canada and Mexico); $48/£28.00 (overseas airmail). Editor: John C. Huckans. Published at: 2007 Syossett Drive, Cazenovia, NY 13035-9753. Tel: & Fax: (315) 655-8499. E-Mail: books@dreamscape.com. Web Site: www.booksourcemagazine.com.

BOOK WORLD. Articles, reviews, advertisements and news of the book world in general. Monthly. Subscription: £50.00 (U.K.), $100.00 (surface mail U.S.), $140.00 (air mail U.S.). Published by: Christchurch Publishers Ltd., 2 Caversham Street, Chelsea, London SW3 4AH. Tel: & Fax: (020) 7351-4995.

CONTEMPORARY REVIEW. On politics, current affairs, theology, social questions, literature and the arts. Monthly. Subscription: £49.00 a year (U.K. surface mail), $195.00 (U.S.A. and Canada, airfreight), others on application. Editor: Dr. Richard Mullen. Published by: The Contemporary Review Co. Ltd., P.O. Box 1242, Oxford, OX1 4FJ, England. Tel: & Fax: (01865) 201529. E-mail: subscriptions@ comtemporaryreview.co.uk. Editorial office: editorial@comtemporaryreview.co.uk.

L'ESOPO. Bibliophile magazine. Quarterly. Published at: Edizioni Rovello di Mario Scognamiglio, P.za Castello, 11, 20121 Milano, Italy. Tel: (02) 86464661 or (02) 866532. Fax: (02) 72022884. E-mail: edirovello@libero.it

FINE BOOKS & COLLECTIONS (formerly OP Magazine). Dedicated to the out-of-print, collectible, and antiquarian book world. Six full colour issues a year. US Subscription $25. Published by FB&C, 4905 Pine Cone Drive, Suite 2, Durham NC 27707. E-mail: subscriptions@finebooksmagazine.com.

FOLIO. Produced 3-4 times a year, to members only. Editor: Kit Shepherd. Published by: The Folio Society Ltd., 44 Eagle Street, London WC1R 4FS. Tel: (020) 7400-4222.

THE LITERARY REVIEW. Covers books, arts and poetry. Est: 1978. Monthly. Subscription: £32.00 a year (U.K.), £39.00 (Europe), £39.00 (U.S.A. & Canada Airspeed), £54.00 (rest of the world Air Mail). Editor: Nancy Sladek. Published by: The Literary Review, 44 Lexington Street, London W1F 0LW. Tel: (020) 7437-9392. Fax: (020) 7734-1844.

MINIATURE BOOK NEWS. Est: 1965. Quarterly. (Now incorporated in the Miniature Book Society Newsletter – Subscription to both: $30.00 oer year, US, $35.00 Canada and $45.00 Overseas). Editor: Julian I. Edison. Published at: 8 St. Andrews Drive, St. Louis, Missouri 63124, U.S.A.

THE PRIVATE LIBRARY. Established 1957. Quarterly. Distributed free to members of the Private Libraries Association, annual subscription £25.00 ($40.00). Editors: David Chambers & Paul W. Nash. Sample copy free on request. Published by: The Private Libraries Association, Ravelston, South View Road, Pinner, Middlesex HA5 3YD.

PRIVATE PRESS BOOKS. An annual bibliography of books printed by private presses in the English speaking world. 1999 edition: 96 pp,;2000 edition 95pp; 2001 edition 64pp. £10.00 or $20.00 (£5.00 or $10.00 to PLA members) Editor: Paul W. Nash. Published by: The Private Libraries Association, Ravelston, South View Road, Pinner, Middlesex HA5 3YD.

QUILL AND QUIRE. Keeps its readers up-to-date on Canada's exciting book publishing scene and provides the earliest and most complete look at new Canadian books, with more than 500 titles reviewed each year. In addition, the Canadian Publishers Directory, which puts the book industry at your fingertips, is delivered free bi-annually. 12 issues a year for $64.15; USA and Overseas $95CDN (includes postage). Est: 1935. Editor: Derek Weiler. Published at: 111 Queen Street East, 3rd Floor, Toronto, Ontario M5C 1S2 Canada. Subscriptions tel: (905) 946-0406. Fax: 905 946-0410. Email: subscriptions@ quillandquire.com. Web Site: www.quillandquire.com.

RBR (RARE BOOK REVIEW). Magazine containing articles, book reviews, auction reports and catalogue news. Est: 1974. Subscription: £28.50 a year (U.K.), £36.00 (Europe), £44.00 (Rest of the World). Rare Book Review, 24 Maddox Street, London W15 1PP Tel: +44 (0) 20 7529 4220. Fax: +44 (0) 20 4229. E-mail: crispin@rarebookreview.couk

TRIBUNE. Books Editor: Chris McLaughlin. Published by: Tribune Publications Ltd., 9 Arkright Road, London NW3 6AN. Tel: (020) 7433-6410. E-mail: george@tribpub.demon.co.uk.

The Book Collector

In its fifty years of publication THE BOOK COLLECTOR has firmly established itself as the most interesting and lively current journal for collectors, bibliographers, antiquarian booksellers and custodians of rare books. Leading authorities contribute regularly on all aspects of bibliophily, from medieval manuscripts to modern first editions and each issue offers new and original insight into the world of books

Some back numbers of issues from 1956 to 1979 are available
We hold complete volumes from 1980 to date.

Subscription rates and detailed list and prices from:

The Book Collector

20 MAPLE GROVE, LONDON NW9 8QY

Tel/fax 020-8200 5004

E-mail: info@thebookcollector.co.uk

Website: www.thebookcollector.co.uk

CURRENT REFERENCE BOOKS

ABC OF BOOKBINDING. By Jane Greenfield. $39.95. Published by: Oak Knoll Press, 310 Delaware Street, New Castle, DE 19720, U.S.A. Tel: (302) 328-7232. Fax: 328-7274. E-Mail: oakknoll@ oakknoll.com. Sales rights: Worldwide outside of UK. Available in the UK from The Plough Press.

AMERICAN BOOK PRICES CURRENT 2004. The auction season September 2003 to August 2004. $156.90. Published by: Bancroft Parkman Inc., P.O. Box 1236, Washington, CT 06793, U.S.A. Tel: (860) 868-7408. Fax: (860) 868-0080. E-Mail: abpc@snet.net. Web Site: http://www.bookpricescurrent.com.

AMERICAN BOOKS ON FOOD & DRINK. By William R. Cagle & Lisa Killion Stafford. $95.00. Published by: Oak Knoll Press, 310 Delaware Street, New Castle, DE 19720, U.S.A. Tel: (302) 328-7232. Fax: 328-7274. E-Mail: oakknoll@oakknoll.com.

AMERICAN BOOK TRADE DIRECTORY. Profiles retail and antiquarian book dealers plus book and magazine wholesalers, distributors and jobbers in the United States. 2004/2005: £245 plus £15 post and handling. Available from: Information Today Ltd., Woodside, Hinksey Hill, Oxford OX1 5BE. Tel: (01865) 327813. Fax: (01865) 730232. E-mail: info@infotoday.com. Web Site: www.infotoday.com.

THE ART & HISTORY OF BOOKS. By Norma Levarie. Paperback $29.95. Published by: Oak Knoll Press, 310 Delaware Street, New Castle, DE 19720, USA. Tel: (302) 328-7232. Fax: 328-7274. E-Mail: oakknoll@oakknoll.com.

THE ART OF BOOK–BINDING. By Edward Walker. $30.00. Published by: Oak Knoll Press, 310 Delaware Street, New Castle, DE 19720, U.S.A. Tel: (302) 328-7232. Fax: 328-7274. E-Mail: oakknoll@ oakknoll.com.

AT HOME WITH BOOKS. How book lovers live with and care for their libraries. By: Estelle Ellis, Caroline Seebohm, Christopher Simon Sykes. £29.95. Published by: Thames & Hudson, 181A High Holborn, London WC1V 7QX. Tel: (020) 7845-5000. Fax: 7845-5050.

BEFORE PHOTOCOPYING: THE ART & HISTORY OF MECHANICAL COPYING 1780 - 1938. By William Streeter & Barbara Rhodes. $75.00. Published by: Oak Knoll Press, 310 Delaware Street, New Castle, DE 19720, U.S.A. Tel: (302) 328-7232. Fax: 328-7274. E-Mail: oakknoll@oakknoll.com.

A & C BLACK COLOUR BOOKS. A collector's guide and bibliography 1900–1930. Author: Colin Inman. £30.00. Published in 1990 by Werner Shaw Ltd and distributed by Alacrity, Eastern Wing, Banwell Castle, Banwell, Weston-Super-Mare, Somerset BS29 6NX. Tel: (01934) 820644, or 820478. Fax: (01934) 820682. E-mail: alacrity@dial.pipex.com. A bibliogrpahy covering 800 books in 50 series, with full historical account of this great publishing venture.

A BOOK OF BOOKSELLERS. By Sheila Markham. Conversations with the Antiquarian Book Trade. Price £25.00 plus postage. Orders to: Shiela Markham Rare Books, P.O. 214, London SE3 9XS. E-mail: markham@endpaper.demon.co.uk

BOOKBINDING & CONSERVATION BY HAND: A working guide. By Laura S. Young. Hardback $35.00. Paperback $24.95. Published by: Oak Knoll Press, 310 Delaware Street, New Castle, DE 19720, U.S.A. Tel: (302) 328-7232. Fax: 328-7274. E-Mail: oakknoll@oakknoll.com.

BOOKDEALING FOR PROFIT. By Paul Minet. The philosophy behind the business as well as a look into the future and how the Internet is having a major effect on the trade. Hardback £10.00. Published by Richard Joseph Publishers Ltd, P.O. Box 15, Torrington, Devon EX38 8ZJ. UK. Tel: (01805) 625750. Fax: (01805) 625376. E-mail: admin@sheppardsworld.eclipse.co.uk. Web Site: www.sheppardsdirectories.com; and www.sheppardsworld.co.uk

BRITISH NATIONAL BIBLIOGRAPHY. Records new and forthcoming publications in the UK and Ireland. Options include: print (weekly list with cumulations), CD-ROM (monthly disc, fully cumulated) and MARC (weekly data file). Published by: The British Library, The Bibliographic Standards and Systems, Boston Spa, Wetherby, West Yorkshire LS23 7BQ. ENGLAND. Tel: (01937) 546548. Fax: 546586. E-mail: bss-info@bl.uk. Web Site: www.bl.uk. Orders and subscriptions: Turpin Distribution Services Ltd., Blackhorse Road, Letchworth, Herts SG6 1HN. ENGLAND. Tel: (01462) 672555. Fax: 480947. E-mail: turpin@turpinltd.com.

LEWIS CARROLL AND THE PRESS. By Charles Lovett. $35.00. Published by: Oak Knoll Press & The British Library. Information from: Oak Knoll Press, 310 Delaware Street, New Castle, DE 19720, U.S.A. Tel: (302) 328-7232. Fax: 328-7274. E-Mail: oakknoll@oakknoll.com.

CHILDREN'S BOOKS IN ENGLAND. By F.J. Harvey Darton. $49.95. Published by: The British Library & Oak Knoll Press. Information from: Oak Knoll Press, 310 Delaware Street, New Castle, DE 19720, U.S.A. Tel: (302) 328-7232. Fax: 328-7274. E-Mail: oakknoll@oakknoll.com.

W.H. DAVIES, A BIBLIOGRAPHY. By Sylvia Harlow. $78.00. Published by: Oak Knoll Press, 310 Delaware Street, New Castle, DE 19720, U.S.A. Tel: (302) 328-7232. Fax: 328-7274. E-Mail: oakknoll@oakknoll.com.

DIRECTORY OF PUBLISHING: United Kingdom & Republic of Ireland. 2004/5 30th Ed. 216pp £69.95. ISBN: 0 8264 7528 0. Published by Continuum, The Tower Building, 11 York Road, London SE1 7NX. ENGLAND. Tel: (020) 7922-0880. Fax: 7922-0881. Orders and distribution: The Orca Book Services, Stanley House, 3 Fleets Lane, Poole, Dorset BH15 3AJ. Tel: (01202) 665432.

THE ENCYCLOPEDIA OF PAPERMAKING AND BOOKBINDING: the definitive guide to making, embellishing and repairing paper and books by Heidi Reimer-Epp and Mary Reimer. 160 pages with 200m colour illustrations. Hardback £16.95. Published by The British Library; available from Turpin Distribution Ltd., Blackhorse Road, Letchworth, Hertfordshire SG6 1HN. E-mail turpin@tuirpinltd.com

THOMAS FROGNALL DIBDIN, 1776 - 1847: A BIBLIOGRAPHY. By John Windle & Karma Pippin. $85.00. Published by: Oak Knoll Press, 310 Delaware Street, New Castle, DE 19720, U.S.A. Tel: (302) 328-7232. Fax: 328-7274. E-Mail: oakknoll@oakknoll.com.

THE DICTIONARY OF 19TH CENTURY BOOK ILLUSTRATORS. By Simon Houfe. £39.50. Published by: Antique Collectors Club, Sandy Lane, Old Martlesham, Woodbridge, Suffolk IP12 4SD. Tel: (01394) 389950. Fax: 389999.

THE DICTIONARY OF 20TH CENTURY BRITISH BOOK ILLUSTRATORS. By Alan Horne. £45.00. Published by: Antique Collectors Club, Sandy Lane, Old Martlesham, Woodbridge, Suffolk IP12 4SD. Tel: (01394) 389950. Fax: 389999.

DIRECTORY OF RARE BOOK AND SPECIAL COLLECTIONS IN THE UNITED KINGDOM AND REPUBLIC OF IRELAND. Editor: B.C. Bloomfield. 1997. £99.95. Published by: Facet Publishing, 7 Ridgmount Street, London WC1E 7AE. Tel: (020) 7255-0590. Fax: 7255-0591. E-Mail: info@facetpublishing.co.uk. Web Site: www.facetpublishing.co.uk.

ENCYCLOPEDIA OF THE BOOK. By: Geoffrey Ashall Glaister. Hardcover $75.00, Paperback $49.95. Published by Oak Knoll Press, 310 Delaware Street, New Castle, DE 19720, U.S.A. Tel: (302) 328-7232. Fax: 328-7274. E-Mail: oakknoll@oakknoll.com.

THE ENGLISH AS COLLECTORS. By Frank Herrmann. $49.95. Published by: Oak Knoll Press & John Murray Ltd. Information from: Oak Knoll Press, 310 Delaware Street, New Castle, DE 19720, U.S.A. Tel: (302) 328-7232. Fax: 328-7274. E-Mail: oakknoll@oakknoll.com. Sales Rights: Worldwide outside of the UK. Available in the UK from The Plough Press.

FIRST EDITIONS: A GUIDE TO IDENTIFICATION. 4th edition for 2001. $60.00. Editor: Edward N. Zempel. Published by: Spoon River Press, P.O. Box 3635, Peoria, IL 61612-3635, U.S.A. Tel: (309) 672-2665.

T.N. FOULIS: The History and Bibliography of an Edinburgh Publishing House. By Ian Elfick & Paul Harris. £30.00. Published by Werner Shaw Ltd and distributed by Alacrity, Eastern Wing, Banwell Castle, Banwell, Weston-Super-Mare, Somerset BS29 6NX. Tel: (01934) 820644, or 820478. Fax: (01934) 820682. E-mail: alacrity@dial.pipex.com

ERIC GILL, A BIBLIOGRAPHY. By Evan Gill. $60.00. Published by: Oak Knoll Press, 310 Delaware Street, New Castle, DE 19720, U.S.A. Tel: (302) 328-7232. Fax: 328-7274.

GREATER LONDON HISTORY AND HERITAGE HANDBOOK: the millennium guide to historical, heritage and environmental networks and publications. 1999 edition, 189pp, £20 + £2p&p. Editor: Peter Marcan. Published by: Peter Marcan Publications, P.O. Box 3158, London SE1 4RA. Tel: (020) 7357-0368.

A GUIDE TO WORLD LANGUAGE DICTIONAIRIES. Andrew Dalby. 1998. £69.95. Published by Facet Publishing, 7 Ridgmount Street, London WC1E 7AE. Tel: (020) 7255 0590. Fax: (0)20 7255 0591. E-mail: info@facetpublishing.co.uk. Web Site: www.facetpublishing.co.uk.

HISTORY OF ENGLISH CRAFT BOOKBINDING TECHNIQUE. By Bernard C. Middleton. $55.00. Published by: Oak Knoll Press, 310 Delaware Street, New Castle, DE 19720, U.S.A. Tel: (302) 328-7232. Fax: 328-7274. E-Mail: oakknoll@oakknoll.com. Sales rights: Worldwide outside of UK. Available in the UK from The British Library

ELSPETH HUXLEY, A BIBLIOGRAPHY. By Robert Cross & Michael Perkin. $78.00. Published by: Oak Knoll Press, 310 Delaware Street, New Castle, DE 19720, U.S.A. Tel: (302) 328-7232. Fax: 328-7274. E-Mail: oakknoll@oakknoll.com

THE ILLUSTRATIONS OF W. HEATH ROBINSON: A COMMENTARY AND BIBLIOGRAPHY. By Geoffrey Beare. The bibliography which follows the long introduction to Heath Robinson's work as an illustrator, was compiled from primary sources. £18.95. Published by Werner Shaw Ltd and distributed by Alacrity, Eastern Wing, Banwell Castle, Banwell, Weston-Super-Mare, Somerset BS29 6NX. Tel: (01934) 820644, or 820478. Fax: (01934) 820682. E-mail: alacrity@dial.pipex.com

INTERNATIONAL DIRECTORY OF ANTIQUARIAN BOOKSELLERS. A world list of members of organisations belonging to the International League of Antiquarian Booksellers (I.L.A.B.). Published every 2 years: 2004-5 edition available October 2004. £15.00 + £2.00 p&p. Published by: I.L.A.B. Distributed in the UK by: The Antiquarian Booksellers' Association, Sackville House, 40 Piccadilly, London W1J 0DR. Tel: (020 7439-3118. Fax: (020) 7439-3119. E-mail: admin@aba.org.uk.

BIBLIOGRAPHY OF HENRY JAMES. By Leon Edel & Dan Laurence. $80.00. Published by: Oak Knoll Press, 310 Delaware Street, New Castle, DE 19720, U.S.A. Tel: (302) 328-7232. Fax: 328-7274. E-Mail: oakknoll@oakknoll.com.

LIBRARIES AND INFORMATION SERVICES IN THE UNITED KINGDOM AND REPUBLIC OF IRELAND, 2004. £39.95. Published by: Facet Publishing, 7 Ridgmount Street, London WC1E 7AE. Tel: (020) 7255-0590. Fax: 7255-0591. E-mail: info@facetpublishing.co.uk. Web Site: www.facetpublishing.co.uk.

CILIP: the Chartered Institute of. 2004–2005. £44.95. Compilers: Kathryn Beecroft (ed.). Published by: Facet Publishing, 7 Ridgmount Street, London WC1E 7AE. Tel: (020) 7255-0590. Fax: 7255-0591. E-Mail: info@facetpublishing.co.uk. Web Site: www.facetpublishing.co.uk..

LITERARY MARKET PLACE. The directory of the book publishing industry for America and Canada. Published annually. 2004 edition. Priced £215 plus £15 post and handling. Orders outside the USA via Information Today Ltd., Woodside, Hinksey Hill, Oxford OX1 5BE. Tel: (01865) 327813. Fax: (01865) 730232. E-mail: info@infotoday.com. Web Site: www.infotoday.com.

LOCAL STUDIES LIBRARIANSHIP: A WORLD BIBLIOGRAPHY. Editor: Diana Dixon. 2001. £49.95. Published by Facet Publishing, 7 Ridgmount Street, London WC1E 7AE. Tel: (020) 7255 0590. Fax: (020) 7255 0591. E-mail: info@facetpublishing.co.uk. Web Site: www.facetpublishing.co.uk.

MARCAN HANDBOOK OF ARTS ORGANISATIONS: A compendium of information on the activities and publications of national (U.K. & Ireland), regional and international arts & cultural organisations. New 5th edition June 2001. £35 + £3.00 p&p. First published as 'Arts Address Book' in 1982. New edition planned. Published by: Peter Marcan Publications, P.O. Box 3158, London SE1 4RA. Tel: (020) 7357-0368.

A MATTER OF TASTE. By William R. Cagle & Lisa Killion Stafford. $95.00. Published by: Oak Knoll Press, 310 Delaware Street, New Castle, DE 19720, U.S.A. Tel: (302) 328-7232. Fax: 328-7274. E-Mail: oakknoll@oakknoll.com.

THOMAS BIRD MOSHER: PIRATE PRINCE OF PUBLISHERS. By Philip R. Bishop. $125.00. Published by: Oak Knoll Press & The British Library. Information from: Oak Knoll Press, 310 Delaware Street, New Castle, DE 19720, U.S.A. Tel: (302) 328-7232. Fax: 328-7274. Sales rights: Worldwide outside of UK. Available in the UK from The British Library.

NEW SCIENCE OUT OF OLD BOOKS. Studies in manuscripts and early printed books in honour of A.I. Doyle. £77.50. Edited by: Richard Beadle and A.J. Piper. Published by: Ashgate Publishing Ltd., Gower House, Croft Road, Aldershot, Hampshire GU11 3HR. Distributed by Bookpoint. Tel: (01235) 827730. Fax: 400454.

NEW WORLDS IN OLD BOOKS. By Leona Rostenberg & Madeleine Stern. $29.95. Published by: Oak Knoll Press, 310 Delaware Street, New Castle, DE 19720, U.S.A. Tel: (302) 328-7232. Fax: 328-7274. E-Mail: oakknoll@oakknoll.com.

OLD BOOKS IN THE OLD WORLD. Reminiscences of book buying abroad. By: Leona Rostenburg and Madeleine B. Stern. $22.95. Published by Oak Knoll Press, 310 Delaware Street, New Castle, DE 19720, USA. Tel: (302) 328-7232. Fax: 328-7274. E-Mail: oakknoll@oakknoll.com.

A POCKET GUIDE TO THE IDENTIFICATION OF FIRST EDITIONS. An essential guide to identifying first editions for collectors, dealers, librarians, cataloguers and auctioneers. 6th Edition $15.95 per copy plus $1 shipping 40% discount on 5 or more copies; shipping for 5 copies is $4 by Priority Mail. International orders: single copies shipping $2.50; five copies $6 by Air/Printed Matter. Published by: The Jumping Frog, McBride/Publisher, 141 South Street, West Hartford, CT 06110, U.S.A. Tel: (860) 523–1622. Web Site: www.mcbridepublisher.com.

PRINCE OF FORGERS. By Joseph Rosenblum. $39.95. Published by: Oak Knoll Press, 310 Delaware Street, New Castle, DE 19720, U.S.A. Tel: (302) 328-7232. Fax: 328-7274.

PROVENANCE RESEARCH IN BOOK HISTORY. By David Pearson. Hardback $49.95, paperback $29.95. Published by: Oak Knoll Press & The British Library. Information from: Oak Knoll Press, 310 Delaware Street, New Castle, DE 19720, U.S.A. Tel: (302) 328-7232. Fax: 328-7274. Sales Rights: North and South America; elsewhere, The British Library.

RESTORATION OF LEATHER BINDINGS. By Bernard C. Middleton. $39.95. Published by: Oak Knoll Press & The British Library. Information from: Oak Knoll Press, 310 Delaware Street, New Castle, DE 19720, U.S.A. Tel: (302) 328-7232. Fax: 328-7274. Sales Rights: Worldwide except the U.K. Available in the U.K. from The British Library.

VITA SACKVILLE–WEST, A BIBLIOGRAPHY. By Robert Cross & Ann Ravenscroft Hulme. $80.00. Published by: Oak Knoll Press, 310 Delaware Street, New Castle, DE 19720, U.S.A. Tel: (302) 328-7232. Fax: 328-7274. E-Mail: oakknoll@oakknoll.com.

SIR WALTER SCOTT: A BIBLIOGRAPHY 1796 - 1832. By William B. Todd & Ann Bowden. $95.00. Published by: Oak Knoll Press, 310 Delaware Street, New Castle, DE 19720, U.S.A. Tel: (302) 328-7232. Fax: 328-7274. E-Mail: oakknoll@oakknoll.com.

STUDIES IN THE HISTORY OF BOOKBINDING. This book consists of articles on the history of bookbinding and related subjects. Grouped under seven headings ranging from general topics such as bookbinding as a subject for study and the need to preserve the book, to more detailed descriptions of individual bindings from the fifteenth to the twentieth century. £80.00. Published by: Ashgate Publishing Ltd., Gower House, Croft Road, Aldershot, Hampshire GU11 3HR. Distributed by Bookpoint. Tel: (01235) 827730. Fax: 400454.

JULIAN SYMONS, A BIBLIOGRAPHY. By John J. Walsdor, Bonnie J. Allen, and Julian Symons. $85.00. Published by: Oak Knoll Press, 310 Delaware Street, New Castle, DE 19720, U.S.A. Tel: (302) 328-7232. Fax: 328-7274.

THE TARTARUS PRESS GUIDE TO FIRST EDITION PRICES 200/5. Edited by: R.B. Russell. £17.99 inc. p&p. Published by: Tartarus Press, Coverley House, Carlton-in-Coverdale, Leyburn, North Yorks DL8 4AY. Tel: & Fax: (01969) 640399. E-Mail: tartarus@pavilion.co.uk.

J.R.R. TOLKIEN, A DESCRIPTIVE BIBLIOGRAPHY. By Wayne G. Hammond. $94.00. Published by: Oak Knoll Press, 310 Delaware Street, New Castle, DE 19720, U.S.A. Tel: (302) 328-7232. Fax: 328-7274. E-Mail: oakknoll@oakknoll.com.

TASHA TUDOR: THE DIRECTION OF HER DREAMS. By William John & Priscilla T. Hare. $85.00. A definitive bibliography; collector's guide. Published by: Oak Knoll Press, 310 Delaware Street, New Castle, DE 19720, U.S.A. Tel: (302) 328-7232. Fax: 328-7274.

TRUE TO TYPE. By Ruari McLean. A Typographical Autobiography. £25.00. Published by Werner Shaw Ltd and distributed by Alacrity, Eastern Wing, Banwell Castle, Banwell, Weston-Super-Mare, Somerset BS29 6NX. Tel: (01934) 820644, or 820478. Fax: (01934) 820682. E-mail: alacrity@dial.pipex.com

LEONARD WOOLF, A BIBLIOGRAPHY. By Leila Luedeking & Michael Edmonds. $78.00. Published by: Oak Knoll Press, 310 Delaware Street, New Castle, DE 19720, U.S.A. Tel: (302) 328-7232. Fax: 328-7274. E-Mail: oakknoll@oakknoll.com

SUPPLIES AND SERVICES

BOOK AUCTIONEERS

ACORN AUCTIONS, P.O. Box 152, Salford, Manchester M17 1BP. Tel: (0161) 877 8818. Fax: (0161) 877 8819. Web Site: www.invaluable.co.uk/acorn. *Regular Public Auctions of books, autographs, ephemera, postcards and cigarette cards at our premises in Trafford Park, Manchester.* Specimen catalogues and vendors' terms available. Contact: George Wewiora.

BLOOMSBURY BOOK AUCTIONS, Bloomsbury House, 24 Maddox Street, London W1S 1PP. Tel: (020) 7495-9494. Fax: 7495-9499. E-Mail: info@bloomsburybookauctions.com. Web site: www.bloomsburybookauctions.com.

BONHAMS, 101 New Bond Street, London W1S 1SR Tel: (020) 7468-8351. Fax: 7465-0224. E-Mail: books@bonhams.com. View our catalogues on-line at www.bonhams.com. *At least 10 sales each season on books, maps, photographs, autographs and historical manuscripts.*

CAPES DUNN & CO., 38 Charles Street, Manchester M1 7DB. Tel: (0161) 273-1911. Fax: 273-3474. *Three to four sales per year. Catalogues can be accessed on* – www.ukauctioneers.com.

DOMINIC WINTER BOOK AUCTIONS, The Old School, Maxwell Street, Swindon, Wiltshire SN1 5DR. Tel: (01793) 611340. Fax: 491727. E-Mail: info@dominicwinter.co.uk. Web Site: www.dominic winter.co.uk.

FINAN & CO., The Square, Mere, Wiltshire BA12 6DJ. Tel: (01747) 861411. Fax: 861944. E-Mail: post@finanandco.co.uk. Web Site: www.finanandco.co.uk. 3 auctions annually, including specialist books, manuscripts, photographs and ephemera. Enquireis to Julia Finan

GEORGE KIDNER, The Old School, The Square, Pennington, Lymington, Hampshire SO41 8GN. Tel: (01590) 670070. Fax: 675167. E-Mail: info@georgekidner.co.uk. Web Site: www.georgekidner.co.uk. *3 sales a year, 200-300 lots per sale. Catalogues on subscription - £7 a year.* Enquiries to: Andrew Reeves.

GOLDING YOUNG & CO, Old Wharf Road, Grantham, Lincolnshire NG31 7AA. Tel: (01476) 565118. Fax: (01476) 561475. E-mail: enquiries@goldingyoung.com. Web Site: www.goldingyoung.com. Contact: Colin Young. *Established in 1900, Goldings currently hold 6 Fine Art sales per annum. Each sale has a dedicated book section. For vendors a Trade Rate Card is available upon request including some 0% commissions.*

HAMPTON & LITTLEWOOD AUCTIONEERS, The Auction Rooms, Alphin Brook Road, Alphington, Exeter, Devon EX2 8TH. Tel: (01392) 413100. Fax: (01392) 413110. E-Mail: enquiries@hampton andlittlewood.co.uk. Web Site: www.hamptonandlittlewood.co.uk.

KEYS AUCTIONEERS, 8 Market Place, Aylsham, Norwich, Norfolk NR11 6EH. Tel: (01263) 733195. Fax: (01263) 732140. E-mail: mail@aylshamsalerooms.co.uk. Web Site: www.aylshamsalerooms.co.uk.

LAMBRAYS, Polmorla Walk Galleries, The Platt, Wadebridge, Cornwall PL27 7AE. Tel: (01208) 813593. Fax: 814986. E-mail: lambrays@feeuk.com. *Book auctions held as part of quarterly fine art auctions.* Enquiries to: Mr. R. Hamm.

DAVID LAY, F.R.I.C.S., The Penzance Auction House, Alverton, Penzance, Cornwall TR18 4RE. Tel: (01736) 361414. Fax: 360035. E-Mail: david.lays@btopenworld.com. Web Site: www.invaluable.com. *2 book auctions a year in August & December.* Enquiries to: Mr. John Floyd.

MEALY'S LTD, Chatsworth Street, Castlecomer, County Kilkenny, Ireland. Tel: (056) 444-1229. Fax: (056) 444-1627. E-mail: info@mealys.com. Web Site: www.mealys.com. Irelands leading auctioneers of rare, interesting and valuable books. Contact: Fonsie Mealy.

D.M. NESBIT & CO., 7 Clarendon Road, Southsea, Hampshire PO5 2ED. Tel: (023) 9286-4321. Fax: 9229-5522. Web Site: www.nesbits.co.uk. Web Site: www.nesbit.co.uk. Contact: Mr John Cameron.

OUTHWAITE & LITHERLAND, Kingsway Galleries, Fontenoy Street, Liverpool L3 2BE. Tel: (0151) 236-6561. Fax: 236-1070. E-mail: auction@lots.uk.com. Web Site: www.lots.uk.com.

SCARBOROUGH PERRY FINE ARTS, Hove Auction Rooms, Hove Street, Hove, East Sussex BN3 2GL. Tel: (01273) 735266. Fax: 723813.

STRIDE & SON AUCTIONEERS, Southdown House, St. John's Street, Chichester, West Sussex PO19 1XQ. Tel: (01243) 780207. Fax: 786713. E-Mail: enquiries@stridesauctions.co.uk. Web Site: www.stridesauctions.co.uk or www.catmaker.co.uk. Appointment necessary for consultations. Book dept open Wednesdays 9am – 12.30pm for appointments. Buyers premium 15% + VAT. *3 auctions a year covering books, documents, ephemera, stamps & postcards.* Enquiries to: Derek White (ephemera) or Adriaan Van Noorden (books).

LAWRENCES AUCTIONEERS, The Linen Yard, South Street, Crewkerne, Somerset TA18 8AB. E-Mail: enquiries@lawrences.co.uk. Specialist book sales in January and July. *Details of dates and Also, Fine Art, Silver and Pictures. Sporting. Toys, Collectors and Militaria.*

THOMSON, RODDICK & MEDCALF, Coleridge House, Shaddongate, Carlisle CA2 5TU. Tel: (01228) 528939.

P.F. WINDIBANK, The Dorking Halls, Reigate Road, Dorking, Surrey RH4 1SG. Tel: (01306) 884556/ 876280. Fax: 884669. E-Mail: sjw@windibank.co.uk. Web Site: www.windibank.co.uk.

WOOLLEY & WALLIS, Book Dept. at 51-61 Castle Street, Salisbury, Wiltshire SP1 3SU. Head of Dept: Paul Viney. Direct Line (01722) 424500. Direct Fax: (01722) 424508.

BOOK DISPLAY AND STORAGE EQUIPMENT, ETC

D AND M PACKAGING, 5a Knowl Road, Mirfield, West Yorkshire WF14 8DG. Tel: (01924) 495768. Fax: (01924) 491267. E-mail: packaging@dandmbooks.com. Web Site: www.bookcovers.co.uk. Contact: Daniel Hanson. *Suppliers of all types of covers for hardbacks, paperbacks and dust jackets. Also comprehensive range of packaging and book-care materials, adhesives, book cleaners, tapes, etc. Free catalogue on request. We supply both trade and private customers and have no minimum order.*

P.B.F.A., The Old Coach House, 16 Melbourn Street, Royston, Hertfordshire SG8 7BZ. Tel: (01763) 248400. Fax: 248921. *Folding bookshelves in natural beech and new books on book collecting and software for booksellers.*

POINT EIGHT LTD., Unit 14, Narrowboat Way, Blackbrook Valley Industrial Estate, Dudley, West Midlands DY2 0EZ. Tel: (01384) 238282. Fax: 455746. Web Site: www.pointeight.co.uk. *Bookshop and P.O.S. display equipment designer and manufacturer in wood, metal, plastic etc..*

SEALINE BUSINESS PRODUCTS LIMITED, Media House, 27 Postwood Green, Hertford Heath, Herts., SG13 7QJ. Tel: (01992) 558001. Fax: (01992) 304569. E-mail: sales@sealinemediastorage.com. Web Site: www.sealinemediastorage.com. Contact: Sarah White. *Crown Media – An attractive ramge of multi purpose cabinets designed to house a variety, or mix, of media types including CD, DVD, Video, Microfilm, DAT Tapes, Cassettes, Index Cards and much more. Complete with lock and anti-tilt in a choice of colour finishes. Shelving, mobile solutions and fire resistant storage compliment the range. Please visit our web site for full details.*

SIMPLEX, High Street, Oldland Common, Bristol BS30 9TA. Tel: (0117) 932-2279. Fax: 932-8800. *Wooden shelving storing units, bookcases and hi-fi units.*

BOOK-FAIR ORGANISERS

ANTIQUARIAN BOOKSELLERS ASSOCIATION. Est: 1906. International Book Fair held annually in London, in June, also in Chelsea (UK dealers only) in Autumn and, occasional book fairs elsewhere. *For complimentary tickts or handbook of members, please contact:* Antiquarian Booksellers' Association, Sackville House, 40 Piccadilly, London W1J 0DR. Tel: (020) 7439-3118. Fax: 7439-3119. E-Mail: admin@aba.org.uk. Web Site: www.abainternational.com.

BOOK COLLECTORS PARADISE. Est: 1986. *Enquiries to:* Trudy Ashford. Tel: (01442) 824440. Book fairs organiser for Buckinghamshire, Milton Keynes (and Wing Book Fair, 1st Sunday) each month – 10–4pm.

BUXTON BOOK FAIRS, 75 Chestergate, Macclesfield, Cheshire SK11 6DG. Tel: (01625) 425352. *Enquiries to*: Sally Laithwaite. 10 fairs a year, held at Pavilion Gardens.

CIANA LTD., 24 Langroyd Road, London SW17 7PL. Tel: (020) 8682 1969. Fax: 8682 1997. E-mail: enquiries@ciana.co.uk. Organisers of remainder and promotional book fairs, held in London in September, Brighton in January, and Bristol in June.

CLENT BOOKS OF BEWDLEY, Rose Cottage, Habberley Road, Wribbenhall, Bewdley, Worcs. DY12 1JA. Tel: (01299) 401090. E-mail: clent.books@btinternet.com. Web Site: www.clentbooks.co.uk. Co-organiser of Waverley Book Fair (Est. 1981). Third Sunday of each month at Kinver, Nr. Kidderminster. Contact: Ivor Simpson. (Member of P.B.F.A. and Francis Brett Young Soc.).

THE EXHIBITION TEAM LTD (HD Fairs). Independent organisers for over 20 years, running the largest UK monthly Book Fairs in London – 140 plus exhibitors. Fairs in Farnham, Surrey and Kempton Park Racecourse – widest choice of books both Antiquarian and modern, as well as printed collectables. Pay us a visit! Free diary of events available on request; new exhibitors always welcome. Phone, fax or write to HD Fairs Ltd: Wendy Collyer or Peter Sheridan, 38 Fleetside, West Molesey, Surrey KT8 2NF. Tel: (020) 8224-3609 Fax: (020) 8224 3576.

FOREST BOOKS, 7 High Street West, Uppingham, Rutland LE15 9QB. Tel: & Fax: (01572) 821173. E-Mail: forestbooks@rutlanduk.fsnet.co.uk. Web Site: http://homepages.primex.co.uk/~Forest. *6 Book Fairs organised annually: 4 at Farndon Memorial Hall, near Newark, Nottinghamshire and 2 at Uppingham School, Rutland.* Please phone or e-mail for booking details. Maps & photos on our web site.

GERRARDS CROSS BOOK FAIR. Est: 1974. Fairs held at the Memorial Centre, East Common, Gerrards Cross, Bucks. Dates for 2005: 16 April, 14 May; 9 July; 10 September; 8 October; 12 November and 10 December. *Enquiries to:* Patty Lafferty on (01297) 21761. E-mail: patty@gxbooks .freeserve.co.uk

MISSING BOOK FAIRS. Est: 1994. Book fairs Cambridge (12 a year), Peterborough (6 a year), Orford (3 a year), Rayleigh (4 a year), Hatfield House (3 a year) and Dedham (1 a year). *Enquiries to:* Chris Missing,

'Coppers', Main Road, Great Leighs, Essex CM3 1NR. Tel: (01245) 361609. E-mail: missingbooks@ madasafish.com

NORTHWEST BOOK FAIRS. Many different venues throughout the year. *Enquiries to:* Greg Finn, 6 Knowsley View, Rainford, St Helens WA11 8SN. Tel: & Fax: (01744) 883780. E-mail: nwbookfairs@aol.co.uk. Also: V & C Finn; Specialists in Folio Society books, 1200 volumes, 3 catalogues a year. View by appointment; private premises.

PROVINCIAL BOOKSELLERS' FAIRS ASSOCIATION. Est: 1974. Fairs held in Central London (monthly) and in more than 100 other towns in Great Britain. *Enquiries to:* Gina Dolan (Administrator), Provincial Booksellers' Fairs Association, The Old Coach House, 16 Melbourn Street, Royston, Herts, SG8 7BZ. Tel: (01763) 248400. Fax: 248921. Fairs Information Service: (24 hrs) (01763) 249212. E-Mail: info@pbfa.org. Web Site: www.pbfa.org. (See display advertisement).

RYELAND BOOKS, 18 St. George's Place, Northampton. Tel: (01604) 716901. E-mail: amriley@ryeland. demon.co.uk. *Four fairs per year, fourteen dealers with select and changing stock. Held at St. Matthew's Parish Centre, Kettering Road, Northampton.* Contact: A & J Riley. P.B.F.A.

SOUTHHAMPTON BOOK FAIRS. Organisor: Bill Jackson. Tel: (023) 8081 2624. E-mail: bill@ bilberry.ndo.co.uk

SUFFOLK BOOK MARKET at Long Melford. *10 Book Markets are held each year at the Village Memorial Hall with around 30 book and ephemera dealers in attendance.* Exhibitor enquiries, dates etc. from the organisers: K. McLeod, Boxford Books and Fairs, 3 Firs Farm Cottage, Boxford, Sudbury, Suffolk CO10 5NU. Tel: (01787) 210810. Fax: (01473) 823187.

TITLE PAGE BOOK FAIRS, 176 Elmbridge Avenue, Surbiton, Surrey KT5 9HF. Tel: & Fax: (020) 8399 8168. Mobile (07966) 162758. *Fairs in Surrey: Dorking 6 a year, Cobham 4 a year, Banstead 4 a year. Fairs in Kent: Bromley 4 a year. All fairs open 10-15:30 except Banstead 9.15-15:30.* Contact Keith Alexander.

WAVERLEY FAIRS, 9 Hayley Park Road, Halesowen B63 1EJ. Tel: (0121) 550-4123. Kinver Book Fair established 1981. 3rd Sunday of every month. Also at Powick and Callow End Village Hall, Worcestershire. (2nd Sunday)

WINCHESTER BOOK FAIRS, For details contact either Bill Jackson (02380) 812640, or Roly Hann (01962) 713929. E-mail: bill@bilberry.ndo.co.ukWORLD WAR BOOKFAIRS, Oaklands, Camden Park, Tunbridge Wells, Kent TN2 5AE. Tel: & Fax: (01892) 538465. E-Mail: wwarbooks@btinternet.com. Contact: Tim Harper. *Specialist military, aviation and naval bookfairs organised in London, Tunbridge Wells, Marlborough, Chatham and other locations from time to time.* Established in 1990, these are high quality fairs attracting some of the best specialist dealers in the UK.

CATALOGUE PRINTERS

ADVANCE BOOK PRINTING, Unit 9 Northmoor Park, Church Road, Northmoor, Oxfordshire OX29 5UH. Tel: (01865) 301737. E-mail: Advancebp@aol.com. Contact: L Simister. *Catalogues, booklets and short run books.*

THE DOLPHIN PRESS, 96 Whitehill Road, Whitehill Industrial Estate, Glenrothes, Fife. Tel: (01592) 771652. Fax: 630913. E-Mail: liz@dolphinpress.co.uk. Web Site: www.dolphinpress.co.uk *Catalogues and booklets printed.*

HOOVEY'S BOOKS, P.O. Box 27, St. Leonards-on-Sea, East Sussex TN37 6TZ. Tel & Fax: (01424) 753407. E-mail: hooveys@lineone.net. Web Site: www.hooveys.co.uk. We offer a budget-priced, 24 hour turnaround Catalogue Printing Service for book dealers – ask us to quote for your next catalogue – we aim to save you money. We are also suppliers of CoverClean the Trade cleaner for cloth covers, paperbacks and dust jackets (£5.95 inc. p&p), and LeatherBrite for cleaning/restoring leather bindings (£6.50 inc. p&p). Contact: Romney Hoovey.

JOSHUA HORGAN PRINT PARTNERSHIP, 246 Marston Road, Oxford OX3 0EL. Tel: (01865) 246762. Fax: (01865) 250555. E-mail: print@joshuahorgan.co.uk

PARCHMENT PRINTERS, Printworks, Crescent Road, Cowley, Oxford OX4 2PB. Tel: (01865) 747547. Fax: 747551. E-mail: print@ParchmentUK.com. Web Site: www.PrintUK.comSpecialist in short run production. Contact Ian Kinch.

CRAFT BOOKBINDERS

ROBERT ALLERTON BOOKBINDING, 45 Churchill Road, Shenstone, Lichfield, Staffordshire WS14 0LR. Tel & Fax: (01543) 480140. E-mail: robertallerton@clara.co.uk.

JOSEPHINE BACON, 179 Kings Cross Road, London WC1X 9BZ. Tel: (020) 7278 9490. Fax: 7278 2447. E-mail: bacon@americanization.com. *Specialist in foreign language material, judaica and cookery.*

GEORGE BAYNTUN, incorporating Robert Riviere, Manvers Street, Bath BA1 1JW. Tel: (01225) 466000. Fax: 482122. E-mail: ebc@georgebayntun.com. Web Site: www.georgebayntun.com. *Fine binding in leather, restoration and case-making since 1894 (and Robert Riviere since 1829).*

CLIVE BOVILL, "Greenburn" River Lane, East Bilney, Dereham NR20 4HS. Tel: (01362) 860174. *Letterpress fine bindings, gold tooling and design. Special interest in conservation of 17th to 19th century books.*

BRADY BOOKBINDERS, Library Building, Library Avenue, Lancaster University LA1 4YH. Tel: (01524) 592512. E-mail: dot_@yahoo.co.uk. Contact: Gerard Brady. *Craft binding, thesis and book restoration.*

BRISTOL BOUND BOOKBINDING, 300 North Street, Ashton Gate, Bristol BS3 1JU. Tel & Fax: (0117) 9663300. E-mail: information@bristolbound.couk. Web Site: www.bristolbound.co.uk. Rachel and Richard James. *We are a husband and wife team first established in 1986 when Rachel gained distinctions in bookbinding from Brunel Technical College, Bristol. We aim to offer a professional, yet friendly service to our customers, whilst maintaining a high standard of workmanship. We undertake new and restoration binding, thesis and dissertation binding, limited editions, corporate presentation binding, binding of newspapers, journals, magazines, personal memoirs, visitors books, photograph albums, wedding albums and much more.*

PHILIP N. BROOK (BOOKBINDER AND BOOK RESTORER), Bell Hill Farm, Lindale in Cartmel, Grange over Sands, Cumbria LA11 6LD. Tel: (01539) 534241. *Bookbinding, book restoration and conservation. To include single volume restorations, fine binding, short run (up to 1,000) publishers. Case work. All aspects of bookbinding work considered. Serving collectors, libraries and dealers for over twenty years.*

FRANCIS BROWN CRAFT BOOKBINDER, 24 Camden Way, Dorchester, Dorset DT1 2RA. Tel: (01305) 266039. *Francis Brown is a journeyman bookbinder who undertakes all kinds of binding work, ranging from simple repairs to the restoration of antiquarian volumes, fine limited editions or designed bindings. He has recently restored books for Balliol College, Wimborne Minster chained library and the Thomas Hardy Memorial Collection in the County Museum in Dorchester.*

FIONA CAMPBELL, 158 Lambeth Road, London SE1 7DF. Tel: & Fax: (020) 7928-1633. E-mail: fcampbell@britishlibrary.net. *Fine bookbinding. CHALFONT BOOKBINDERS, Chesham Lane, Chalfont St Peter, Buckinghamshire SL9 0RJ. Tel: (01494) 601423. Fax: (01494) 874061. E-mail: bookbinding@epilepsynse.org.uk. Quality binding and restoration by a team of very experienced craftsmen. Chalfont Bookbinding & Printing is a registered charity.*

CHIVERS-PERIOD, Aintree Avenue, White Horse Business Park, Trowbridge, Wiltshire BA14 0XB. Tel: (01225) 752888. Fax: (01225) 752666. E-mail: info@chivers-period.co.uk. Web Site: www. chivers-period.co.uk. Contact: Russell Pocock. *Binding, rebinding and repairing books since 1878. Conserving paper for a quarter of a century.*

CYRIL FORMBY BOOK CONSERVATOR, 19-21 Market Place, Ramsbottom, Lancashire BL0 0AJ. Tel: and Fax: (01706) 825771. E-mail: formbys@tiscali.co.uk. Web Site: www.artisanbooks.co.uk. *Craft Bookbinding and book restoration.*

CHRIS HICKS BOOKBINDER, 64 Merewood Avenue, Sandhills, Oxford OX3 8EF. Tel: (01865) 769346. E-Mail: chrishicksbookbinder@btinternet.com. Web Site: www.book-binder.co.uk. *Binding, rebinding, repairs, theses, slipcases, solander cases, fine bindings, short-run edition binding, blank books etc.*

FELICITY HUTTON, Langore House, Langore, Launceston, Cornwall PL15 8LD. Tel: (01566) 773831. E-Mail: pandfhutton@hotmail.com. *Bookbinding and restoration.*

IPSLEY BINDERY, 10 Driffield Close, Ipsley, Redditch, Worcs. B98 0TH. Prop: Ray Beech. Tel: (01527) 521069. E-Mail: ipsleybind@aol.com. *Antiquarian & traditional craft bookbinding and restoration. Periodicals, theses, slipcases and book boxes.* Prompt Service. Telephone anytime.

KINGSWOOD BOOKS, 17 Wick Road, Milborne Port, Sherborne, Dorset DT9 5BT. Tel: & Fax: (01963) 250280. E-mail: kingswoodbooks@btinternet.com. *Web Site: www.kingswoodbooks .btinternet.co.uk. Bookbinding & conservation.* Enquiries to A.J. Dollery.

D SANDERSON, Primrose Mill, London Road, Preston, Lancashire. Tel: (01772) 253594. Fax: (01772) 253592. E-mail: sanderson2003@aol.com. Contact: D. Sanderson. *Book restoration and print finishers.*

SALISBURY BOOKBINDERS, Woolstone Park, Backe, St Clears, Carmarthenshire, South Wales SA33 4EU. Tel: (01994) 230503. E-mail: salisburybinders@onetel.com. Web Site: www.salisburybookbinders .co.uk. Contact: Nancy Winfield. Established in 1840. *Specialists in fine bindings, book repair and conservation, edge gilding using genuine gold leaf. Also bind small runs up to 1,000 copies.*

CHARLES SYMINGTON, 145 Bishopthorpe Road, York YO23 1NZ. Tel: (01904) 633995. *Bookbinding and restoration.*

JAYNE TANDY (CRAFT BOOKBINDING AND RESTORATION), Bowhayes Cross, Williton, Somerset TA4 4NL. Tel: (01984) 632293. *Bookbinding, book restoration, conservation and repair.*

COLIN TATMAN, Corner House, 121A Lairgate, Beverley, East Yorskire HU17 8JG. Tel: (01482) 880611 (day) and 882153 (evening). *Traditional craft bookbinding; paper repair; slipcases and book boxes; restoration and conservation.*

TEASDALE BOOKBINDERS, Caxton House, Corwen, Dengighshire LL21 0AA. Tel: (01490) 412 713.Fax: (0151) 420 7316. E-Mail: catherinehore@bookbinders.fslife.co.uk. *Hand bookbinding and restoration. Prop: Catherine Hore.*

TEMPLE BOOKBINDERS, 10 Quarry Road, Headington, Oxford OX3 8NU. Tel: (01865) 451940. E-Mail: enquiries@templebookbinders.co.uk. Web Site: www.templebookbinders.co.uk. Mr. Ian Barnes. *Hand bookbinder in fine leathers, vellum, linens, cloth & buckrams. Quality restorer of antiquarian books.*

TRADITIONAL BOOKCRAFTS, 28 Drayton Mill Court, Cheshire Street, Market Drayton, Shropshire TF9 1EF. Tel: (01630) 654410. *Craft bookbinder, antique and modern book repair and restoration, boxes, slipcases, gold tooling, handmade and scribed books. Established: 1983. Limited edition bindings. Prices on request. Prop: Monica Thornton.*

TUDOR BOOKBINDING LTD., 3 Lyon Close, Wigston, Leicestershire LE18 2BJ Tel: (0116) 2883988. Fax: (0116) 2884878. E-mail: sales@tudor-bookbinding.co.uk. Antique and modern book restoration, repair and rebinding; gold tooling; single copy restorations work undertaken.

PERIOD FINE BINDINGS, Yew Tree Farm, Stratford Road, Wootton Wawen, Warwickshire B95 6BY. Tel: (01564) 793800. E-mail: periodfinebindings@tiscali.co.uk. Web Site: www.periodfinebindings .typepad.com/royal_bindings. *Restorer of antiquarian books using ancient formulae and hand-made materials. Fox marks, inkstains etc removed. Rare books bought, sold and valued.*

LIZ YOUNG – BOOKBINDER, The Old Rectory, Buckland, Nr. Aylesbury, Buckinghamshire HP22 5HU. Tel: & Fax: (01296) 630461. E-mail: young.buckland@virgin.net. *Traditional craft bookbinding, restoration and photograph albums.*

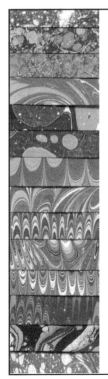

PACKING MATERIALS SUPPLIERS

MACFARLANE GROUP PLC., **Group Head Office:** 21 Newton Place, Glasgow, Scotland G3 7PY. Tel: (0141) 333 9666. Fax: (0141) 333 1988. Web Site: www.macfarlanegroup.net

PACKING CASE MANUFACTURERS: **Grantham Branch:** PO Box 16, Alma Park Industrial Estate, Grantham, Lincolnshire NG31 9SF. Tel: (01476) 574747. Fax: (01476) 577444. **Westbury Branch:** Quartermaster Road, West Wilts Trading Estate, Westbury, Wiltshire BA13 4JT. Tel: (01373) 858588. Fax: (01373) 858999.

PACKAGING DISTRIBUTION: **Bristol Branch:** Western Approach Distribution Park, Severn Beach, Bristol BS35 4GG. Tel: (0870) 850 0542. Fax: (0870) 850 0543. **Exeter Branch:** Windsor Court, Manaton Close, Matford Business Park, Exeter, Devon EX2 8PF, Tel: (0870) 608 6110. Fax: (0870) 608 6111. **Coventry Branch:** Siskin Parkway East, Middlemarch Business Park, Coventry, West Midlands CV3 4PE. Tel: (0870) 608 6205. Fax: (0870) 608 6206. **Enfield Branch:** Unit 5, Delta Park, Millmarsh Lane, Enfield, EN3 7QJ. Tel: (0870) 850 0116. Fax: (0870) 850 0117. **Fareham Branch:** Unit 1, Stephenson Road, Midpoint 27, Segensworth, Fareham, Hampshire PO15 5RZ. Tel: (0870) 608 6160. Fax: (0870) 608 6161. **Glasgow Branch:** Unit 1 Linwood Industrial Estate, Burnbrae Road, Linwood, Paisley PA3 3BD. Tel: (0870) 150 4508. Fax: (0870) 150 4509. **Horsham Branch:** Oakhurst Business Park, Wilberforce Way, Southwater, West Sussex RH13 7NW. Tel: (0870) 608 6150. Fax: (0870) 608 6151. **Manchester Branch:** Empire Court, Trafford Park, Manchester M17 1TN. Tel: (0870) 150 4500. Fax: (0870) 150 4501. **Milton Keynes Branch:** Kingston Gateway, Whitehall Avenue, Milton Keynes, Buckinghamshire MK10 0BU. Tel: (0870) 150 4502. Fax: (0870) 150 4503. **Tyne & Wear Branch:** The Waterfront, Kingfisher Boulevard, Newburn Riverside, Tyne & Wear NE15 8NZ. Tel: (0870) 608 6100. Fax: (0870) 608 6101. **Sudbury Branch:** Windham Road, Chilton Industrial Estate, Sudbury, Suffolk CO10 2XD. Tel: (0870) 608 6140. Fax: (0870) 608 6141. **Telford Branch:** Unit D2, Horton Park Industrial Estate, Hortonwood 7, Telford, Shropshire TF7 4AP. Tel: (0870) 608 6120. Fax: (0870) 608 6121. **Wakefield Branch:** Unit H, Brunel Road, Wakefield 41 Industrial Estate, Wakefield WF2 0XG. Tel: (0870) 850 0118. Fax: (0870) 850 0119. **Wigan Branch:** Northgate Distribution Centre, Caxton Close, Wheatlea Park Industrial Estate, Wigan WN3 6XU. Tel: (0870) 150 4512. Fax: (0870) 150 4513.

Macfarlane Packaging provides a complete range of packaging materials, including New Book Pack and Super Book Pack, Postal bags and Easywrap.

D AND M PACKAGING, 5a Knowl Road, Mirfield, West Yorkshire WF14 8DG. Tel: (01924) 495768. Fax: (01924) 491267. E-mail: packaging@dandmbooks.com. Web Site: www.bookcovers.co.uk. Contact: Daniel Hanson. *Suppliers of all types of covers for hardbacks, paperbacks and dust jackets. Also comprehensive range of packaging and book-care materials, adhesives, book cleaners, tapes, etc. Free catalogue on request. We supply both trade and private customers and have no minimum order.*

PLASPAK, Piperell Way, Haverhill, Suffolk CB9 8QW (A Division of Marchant Manufacturing). Tel: (01440) 765300. Fax: 765302. E-mail: plaspak@marchant.co.uk. Web Site: www.plaspak.co.uk *Polythene manufacturer and specialist packaging.*

REMAINDER MERCHANTS

AWARD PUBLICATIONS LTD., 1st Floor, 27 Longford Street, London NW1 3DZ. Tel: (020) 7388-7800. Fax: 7388-7887. *E-mail: anna@awardpublications.co.uk Genuine remainders for adults and children.*

BOOKMARK REMAINDERS LTD., Rivendell, Illand, Launceston, Cornwall PL15 7LS. Tel: (01566) 782 728. Fax: (01566) 782 059. E-mail: info@book-bargains.co.uk. WebSite: www.book-bargains.co.uk. Range of genuine remainders and bargain books. Check out our website for the latest stocks.

BLAKETON HALL LTD., Unit 1, 26 Marsh Green Road, Marsh Barton, Exeter EX2 8PN. Tel: (01392) 210602. Fax: 421165. E-Mail: sales@blaketonhall.co.uk. *Remainders and overstocks, including scientific, technical, academic, gardening, crafts & children's.* Enquiries to: Martin Shillingford.

FANSHAW BOOKS, Fanshaw House, 3/9 Fanshaw Street, London N1 6HX. Tel: (020) 7729-5373. Fax: 7729-7950. E-Mail: info@roybloom.com. www.roybloom.com. *General remainders. Exhibits at all major book fairs. Note: moving in June - please see web site for new details.*

GRANGE BOOKS PLC., The Grange, Units 1–6 Kingsnorth Industrial Estate, Hoo, Nr. Rochester, Kent ME3 9ND. Tel: (01634) 256000. Fax: 255500. E-Mail: sales@grangebooks.co.uk. Web Site: www.grangebooks.co.uk. *Distributors of remainders, and publisher of promotional books and reprints to the adult illustrated non-fiction and children's market.*

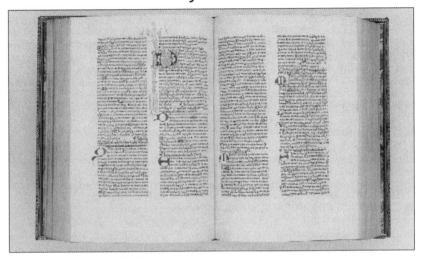

DONALD MURRAY BOOKS LTD., 40 Dunford Road, London N7 6EL. Tel: (020) 7609-1077. E-mail: murrayhind@btconnect.com. *Remainders in a broad range of subjects, literature, art, fiction, non-fiction, children's books, and illustrated titles.*

JIM OLDROYD BOOKS, 14/18 London Road, Sevenoaks, Kent TN13 1AJ. Tel: (01732) 463356. Fax: 464486. E-Mail: paula@oldroyd.co.uk. Web site: www.oldroyd.co.uk. *Adult and children's remainders.*

SANDPIPER BOOKS LTD., Offices and Showroom, 24 Langroyd Road, London SW17 7PL. Tel: (020) 8767-7421. Fax: 8682-0280. E-Mail: enquiries@sandpiper.co.uk. *Scholarly and literary remainders, academic reprints and mail order.*

SUPPLIERS OF MATERIALS AND TOOLS FOR BINDING AND RESTORING BOOKS, ETC.

FALKINER FINE PAPERS, 76 Southampton Row, London WC1B 4AR. Tel: (020) 7831-1151. Fax: 7430-1248. *E-mail: falkiner@ic24.net. PAPERS. Wide selection of papers for repairs, marbled papers and coloured end papers. LEATHERS AND BOOKCLOTHS for repairs and bindings. BOOKS in print on bookbinding, calligraphy, typography, papermaking and printing history. All items can be supplied by post. Price lists.*

FINE CUT GRAPHIC IMAGING LTD., Marlborough Road, Lancing Business Park, Lancing, West Sussex BN15 8UF. Tel: (01903) 751666. Fax: 750462. E-Mail: info@finecut.co.uk. Web Site: www.finecut.co.uk. *Manufacturers of bookbinders' finishing tools and accessories. 80 page catalogue available (also available on-line) showing brass type, handle letters, hand tools and brass rolls. Special designs to order.*

HARMATAN LEATHER LTD, Westfield Avenue, Higham Ferrers, Northamptonshire NN10 8AX. Tel: (01933) 412151. Fax: (01933) 412242. E-mail: marc@harmatan.co.uk. Web Site: www.harmatan.co.uk. Contact: Marc Lamb.

J. HEWIT AND SONS LIMITED, Kinauld Leather Works, Currie, Edinburgh, Scotland EH14 5RS. Tel: (0131) 449-2206. Fax: (0131) 451-5081. E-Mail: sales@hewit.com. Web Site: www.hewit.com. BOOKBINDERS' TOOLS AND SUPPLIES, adhesive (paste, glue, P.V.A.), bone folders, brass type and type holders, brushes, knives, papers (marbled, etc.), presses, tapes, threads. BINDING LEATHERS, in a wide range of colours. BOOKCLOTHS, buckram, linen, cloth, mull, etc. BOOKBINDERS STARTER PACKS, basic tools to get you started.

HOOVEY'S BOOKS, P.O. Box 27, St. Leonards-on-Sea, East Sussex TN37 6TZ. Tel & Fax: (01424) 753407. E-mail: hooveys@lineone.net. Web Site: www.hooveys.co.uk. Suppliers of CoverClean the Trade cleaner for cloth covers, paperbacks and dust jackets (£5.95 inc. p&p), and LeatherBrite for cleaning/restoring leather bindings (£6.50 inc. p&p). We also offer a budget-priced, 24 hour turnaround Catalogue Printing Service for book dealers – ask us to quote for your next catalogue – we aim to save you money. Contact: Romney Hoovey.

ANN MUIR MARBLING, 1 St. Algar's Yard, West Woodlands, Frome, Somerset BA11 5ER. Tel: & Fax: (01985) 844786. E-mail: annmuir@marbling.freeserve.co.uk. *Web Site: www.annmuirmarbling.co.uk. Marbled paper in both modern and traditional patterns and colourways. Matching service fot old papers in restoration work. New papers designed for individual projects. Send for catalogue of samples and pricelist.*

PAPERSAFE, 2 Green Bank, Adderley, Market Drayton TF9 3TH. Tel: (01630) 652217. E-Mail: philip@papersafe.demon.co.uk. Web Site: www.papersafe.demon.co.uk. *Suppliers of archival quality repair materials for book and paper collectors.*

PICREATOR ENTERPRISES LIMITED, 44 Park View Gardens, Hendon, London NW4 2PN. Tel: (020) 8202-8972. Fax: (020) 8282-3435. Web Site: www.info@picreator.co.uk. *Fine–art conservation and restoration materials. Manufacturers of Renaissance wax polish, Vulpex liquid soap and Groom/stick non–abrasive document dry cleaner. Bookdealers are increasingly undertaking basic cleaning and restorative treatment of books and paper. Picreator Enterprises supply professional products which are simple to use and advice is given on their application. The Company has held a Royal warrant of appointment to H.M. The Queen since 1984 as suppliers of products for (fine-art) restoration and conservation.*

RUSSELL BOOKCRAFTS, Unit 1, Bluntswood Hall, Throcking, Buntingford, Hertfordshire SG9 9RN. Tel: (01763) 281430. Fax: (01763) 281431. E-Mail: office@russels.com. Web Site: www.russels.com. *Major supplier of very fine leathers. Range includes the world renowned, and only genuine "OASIS" goatskin, calf and sheepskin skivers – handmade bookbinders' equipment includes, specially designed work benches, nipping presses, lying presses, ploughs, sewing frames and Digby Stuart presses. We offer a fine colour range of Buckrams and bookcloths, mulls, Jaconette, tapes, threads and headbands; a large selection of specialised papers, marbled end papers, & millboards. Tools include: paring knives, bridled glue brushes, decorative hand tools and brass letters. Backing hammers, bone folders, burnishing agates and all types of bookbinders adhesives.*

USEFUL WEB SITES

Please note that in this selection the details are correct when going to press but changes and new ones may appear during the year. Those in bold are multi-search sites. Some trade associations also offer book searching facilities, see pages 20–23.

FOR SEARCHING TITLES

ABooksearch .... www.abooksearch.com
Addall ....**www.addall.com**
Advanced Book Exchange.. www.abebooks.com
Abebooks Europe GmbH...www.abebooks.co.uk
ABookCoOp, Inc .... www.tomfolio.com
Alibris..www.alibris.com
AllSearch Engines... **www.allsearchengines.com/books**
Amazon.. www.amazon.com
Antiqbook (The Netherlands).. www.antiqbook.com
Antiquarian Booksellers Association of America (ABAA) .... www.abaa.org
Barnes & Noble .... www.bn.com
ANZAAB (Australia & New Zealand)...www.anzaab.com.au/anzaab
BiblioDirect (Bibliophile Books Inc.,) .... www.bibliodirect.com
Bibliology...www.bibliology.com
Biblion ....www.biblion.uk
Bibliophile .... www.bibliophile.net
Bibliopoly (England) ....www.bibliopoly.com
BiblioQuest International (Australia)... www.biblioz.com
Bookavenue (New York)... www.bookavenue.com
Books and Collectables (Australia) .... www.booksandcollectables.com.au
Bookfinder.com .... **www.bookfinder.com**
Elephant Books .... www.elephantbooks.com
Independent Booksellers Network (England)..www.ibooknet.co.uk
Internatioanl League of Booksellers (ILAB)... www.ilab-lila.com
Maremagnum (Italy)... www.maremagnum
Odd Volumes.com (England) ....www.oddcolumes.co.uk
Powell's Books .... www.powells.com
Provincial Book Fairs Association (PBFA)..www.booksatpbfa.com
Strand Books (USA)...www.strandbooks.com
UKBookWorld .... www.ukbookworld.com
Used Books Central (USA) ....www.usedbookcentral.com
Zentrales Verzeichnis Antiquarischer Bücher (ZVAB, Germany) .... www.zvab.com

FOR SEARCHING DEALERS

Advanced Book Exchange.. www.abebooks.com
Sheppard's World.. www.sheppardsworld.co.uk

GENERAL SEARCH SITES

Ask Jeeves.. www.askjeeves.com
EBay... www.ebay.co.uk
Google .... www.google.co.uk
Dog Pile .... **www.dogpile.com**

INDEX OF CITIES AND TOWNS

Dealer locations listed alphabetically by country, city, town and village, as shown in the Geographical section.

USE OF THE DIRECTORY

This directory is divided into four sections. The first is the *Geographical Directory of Dealers*, in which full details, where supplied, are given for each business or private dealer. These are listed alphabetically by town in which the shop or business premises are located. The details, as supplied by dealers, are presented in the following manner:

Name of business.	As provided. ■ Indicates that the type of premises is a Shop.
Postal address.	(∗) Indicates the dealer's preference for indexing or where we have imposed current county boundaries.
Prop:	Name of proprietor(s).
Web Site:	Web Site address. Users should ignore the full point at the end of the entry.
Tel:	Telephone number(s), together with the new codes followed by fax and/or mobile number. NOTE: If the code for the fax number is the same as for the telephone, it has sometimes been omitted.
E-Mail:	Electronic mail address. Users should ignore the full point at the end of the entry.
Est:	Date at which business was established.
Type of premises occupied:	Shop, private, mail order/internet, market stall or storeroom.
Opening times:	Of shop, or if premises are private, whether appointments to view stock may be made, or if postal business only.
Normal level of total stock:	Very small (less than 2,000), small (2,000–5,000), medium (5,000–10,000), large (10,000–20,000) or very large (more than 20,000).
Spec:	Subjects in which dealer specialises.
PR:	Price range of stock. This is intended as a guideline only.
CC:	Selection of Credit & Debit Cards eg. AE – American Express, DC – Diners Club, DI – Discovery, EC – Eurocard, JCB – Japanese Credit Bureau, MC – Mastercard, SO – Solo, SW – Switch, V – VISA.
Important lines of business:	Other than secondhand antiquarian books.
Cata:	Frequency and subject of catalogues, if issued.
Corresp:	Languages, other than English, in which correspondence may be conducted.
Mem:	Membership of book trade organisations, eg. A.B.A. – Antiquarian Booksellers' Association B.A. – Booksellers Association of Great Britain & Ireland P.A. – Publishers Association P.B.F.A. – Provincial Booksellers' Fairs Association

The next section is an alphabetical *Index of Businesses*, giving full name and county with the page on which their full entry is to be found.

There is then a new section, the *Index of Web Sites,* which lists dealers alphabetically with their page reference and web site.

This is followed by an alphabetical *Index of Proprietors*, giving their name and trading name followed by their page reference.

The fourth section is the *Speciality Index*. This is presented in alphabetical order by subject heading, giving the dealer's name, county and page on which their details may be found

BEDFORDSHIRE

BEDFORD

Books With Care, 7 Barford Road, Willington, Bedford, MK44 3QP. Prop: Gerald Ford. Tel: (01234) 831288. Fax: (01234) 831288. Website: www.bookswithcare.com. E-mail: gfbooks@ bookswithcare.com. Est: 1996. Private Premises. Postal business only. Appointment necessary. Small general stock. PR: £1–200. CC: MC; V; Paypal. [Updated]

Bunyan Books, 57 Purbeck Close, Goldington, Bedford, MK41 9LX. Prop: R.G Sancto. Tel: (01234) 345518. E-mail: roderick@sanctofamily.fsnet.co.uk. Est: 2002. Private Premises. Appointment necessary. Large general stock. Advertises regularly in Bookdealer. Also, restoration, repair and binding. [Updated]

The Eagle Bookshop, ■ 101 - 103 Castle Road, Bedford, MK40 3QP. Prop: Peter Budek. Tel: (01234) 269295. Fax: (01234) 290920. Website: www.eaglebookshop.co.uk. E-mail: info@eaglebookshop.co.uk. Est: 1991. Shop; Internet and postal. Open: **M:** 10:00–17:30; **T:** 10:00–17:30; **Th:** 10:00–17:30; **F:** 10:00–17:30; **S:** 09:30–17:00. Very large general stock. Spec: Academic/Scholarly; Antiquarian; History - General; History of Ideas; Mathematics; Physics; Science - General; Technology. PR: £1– 2,000. CC: MC; V; SW. Cata: 1 a year. Mem: PBFA. [Updated]

CHICKSANDS

Leslie H. Bolland Books, 1 Warren Court, Chicksands, SG17 5QB. Prop: Les & Anne Bolland. Tel: (01462) 815174. Fax: (01462) 814738. Website: www.bollandbooks.com. E-mail: lesbolland@aol.com. Est: 1997. Office &/or bookroom; Internet and postal. Appointment necessary for viewing by appointment only. Large stock. Spec: Academic/Scholarly; Advertising; Assassinations; Author - Buckeridge, A.; Crime (True); Criminology; Police Force Histories; Sport - Angling/Fishing. PR: £2– 500. CC: MC; V; SW. Also, a booksearch service. Cata: 4 a year. Mem: PBFA. VAT No: GB 806 1492 42. [Updated]

DUNSTABLE

Adrian Walker, 107 Great Northern Road, Dunstable, LU5 4BW. Tel: (01582) 605824. E-mail: adrian-walker@supanet.com. Est: 1965. Private premises; Postal business only. Telephone first. Stock: Very small. Spec: Sport - Falconry. PR: £1–250. [Updated]

The Book Castle, ■ 12 Church St., Dunstable, Bedfordshire, LU5 4RU. Tel: (01582) 605670. Website: www.book-castle.co.uk. E-mail: bc@book-castle.co.uk. Shop; open: **M:** 09:00–17:00; **T:** 09:00–17:00; **W:** 09:00–17:00; **Th:** 08:00–17:00; **F:** 09:00–17:00; **S:** 09:00–17:00. CC: AE; MC; V; Solo. Mem: PBFA. [Updated]

EGGINGTON

Robert Kirkman Ltd., Kings Cottage, Eggington, LU7 9PG. Tel: (01525) 210647. Fax: (01525) 211184. Website: www.robertkirkman.co.uk. E-mail: robertkirkmanltd@btinternet.com. Est: 1987. Private premises. Internet and postal. Appointment necessary. Small stock. Spec: Antiquarian; Author - Bunyan, John; Author - Churchill, Sir Winston; Autographs; Bibles; Bindings; First Editions; Fore-Edge Paintings; Limited Editions; Literature; Sets of Books; Signed Editions. PR: £20–100. CC: MC; V. Literary relics. Cata: occasionally. Mem: ABA; PBFA; ILAB. [Updated]

SANDY

H.J. Morgan, 47 Bedford Road, Sandy, SG19 1ES. Tel: (01767) 691383. E-mail: hedleymorgan@ ntlworld.com. Est: 1980. Private premises. Postal business only and at book fairs. Small stock. Spec: Academic/Scholarly; History - General; Literature; Travel - General. Mem: PBFA. VAT No: GB 467 3823 19. [Updated]

SHARNBROOK

Ouse Valley Books, 16 Home Close, Sharnbrook, Bedford, MK44 1PQ. Prop: Barrie Farnsworth. Tel: (01234) 782411. Fax: (01234) 782411. Website: www.abebooks.com/home/ousevalleybooks. E-mail: ousevalleybooks@btinternet.com. Est: 1990. Private premises. Internet and bookfairs. Appointment necessary. Very small stock. Spec: Academic/Scholarly; Art; History - British; Sport - Cycling; Topography - General; Topography - Local. PR: £5–500. CC: MC; V. Cata: Lists as required. Mem: PBFA. [Updated]

BERKSHIRE

ASCOT

Ian Cross, 83 Gainsborough Drive, Ascot, SL5 8TA. Tel: (01344) 872100. Fax: (01344) 872544. E-mail: ccross@btconnect.com. Est: 1972. Small stock. Spec: Art. PR: £25–1,500. Corresp: Italian. [Updated]

BRACKNELL

Bookzone, 5 Flintgrove, Bracknell, RG12 2JN. Tel: (01344) 421770. E-mail: johnbacon@screaming.net. Est: 1990. Private premises. Appointment necessary. Small general stock. Spec: Sport - Athletics; Sport - Boxing; Sport - Cricket; Sport - Football (Soccer); Sport - Golf; Sport - Horse Racing (all aspects); Sport - Rugby; Sport - Tennis. PR: £5–50. CC: MC; V; PayPal. Also, exhibits at bookfairs. Alternative Tel. No. (01355) 488825. [Updated]

CAVERSHAM

Caversham Emporium, ■ 10, Bridge Street, Caversham, Reading, RG4 8AA. Prop: R.J. & E.M. Maggs, and S. Daniels. Tel: (0118) 946 2175. Est: 1983. Also at: Fosseway Cottage, Stratton-on-the-Fosse, Bath, Somerset, BA3 4RG. Medium stock. PR: £1–500. Mem: PBFA. [23/08/2003]

CROWTHORNE

Malcolm Applin, 21 Larkswood Drive, Crowthorne, RG45 6RH. Tel: (01344) 776881. Est: 1993. Private premises. Postal business only. Small stock. Spec: Biography; Fiction - General; Fiction - Women; Literary Criticism; Poetry. PR: £5–250. Cata: 6 a year. [Updated]

HURLEY

Russell Jones Books, The Coach House, High Street, Hurley, SL6 5NB. Prop: Russell Jones. Tel: (01628) 824237. Est: 1958. Spec: Crafts; Engineering; Military; Mining; Railways; Rural Life; Steam Engines; Traction Engines; Vintage Cars. Also, booksearch. PR: £15–14,800. [30/08/2003]

HURST

Christopher Edwards, Hatch Gate Farmhouse, Lines Road, Hurst, RG10 0SP. Prop: Christopher Edwards & Margaret Erskine. Tel: (0118) 934 0531. Fax: (0118) 934 0539. E-mail: chr.edwards@which.net. Est: 1992. Private premises. Internet. Appointment necessary. Small stock. Spec: Early Imprints; History - General; Literature. CC: MC; V. Cata: 2 a year. Corresp: French. Mem: ABA; ILAB. [Updated]

KINGSCLERE

Wyseby House Books, ■ Kingsclere Old Bookshop, 2a George Street, Kingsclere, Nr. Newbury, RG20 5NQ. Prop: Dr. T. Oldham. Tel: (01635) 297995. Fax: (01635) 297677. Website: www.wyseby.co.uk. E-mail: info@wyseby.co.uk. Est: 1978. Internet and postal. Shop open: **M:** 09:00–17:00; **T:** 09:00–17:00; **W:** 09:00–17:00; **Th:** 09:00–17:00; **F:** 09:00–17:00; **S:** 09:00–17:00. Very large stock. Spec: Applied Art; Architecture; Art; Art - History; Art - Reference; Artists; Arts, The; Biology; Botany; Decorative Art; Ecology; Fine Art; Gardening; Natural History; Natural Sciences; Ornithology; Science - History of; Zoology. PR: £1–1,000. CC: AE; JCB; MC. Cata: 12 a year on art, architecture, natural history, garden and science. Mem: PBFA. VAT No: GB 295 3261 54. [Updated]

MAIDENHEAD

Derek Hayles Military Books, 35 St Marks Road, Maidenhead, SL6 6DJ. Tel: (01628) 639535. Fax: (01628) 788377. Est: 1982. Private premises. Appointment necessary. Open: **M:** 09:00–21:00; **T:** 09:00–21:00; **W:** 09:00–21:00; **Th:** 09:00–21:00; **F:** 09:00–21:00; **S:** 09:00–21:00. Medium stock. Spec: Aviation; Biography; Military; Military History; Naval; War - General. PR: £10–500. CC: E; JCB; MC; V. Publishers of 'Blue List' listing 46 military specialists. Cata: 8 a year. VAT No: GB 491 8512 12. [01/07/2003]

Valerie Peel, t/a Kiandra Associates Ltd., 40 Culley Way, Cox Green, Maidenhead, SL6 3PX. Tel: (01628) 822439. Fax: (01628) 826118. E-mail: valerie_peel@dogbooks.freeserve.co.uk. Est: 1985. Private premises. Internet and postal. Contactable. Small stock. Spec: Dogs. Also, booksearch. PR: £4–750. Also, free booksearch. Cata: 6-monthly. [Updated]

No

NEWBURY

Eastleach Books, Unit 53, Unity House, New Greenham Park, Newbury, RG19 6HU. Prop: Daniel Unwin. Tel: +44 (0)1635 817377. Fax: +44 (0)1635 817375. Website: www.eastleach-book.co.uk. E-mail: dan@bookville.freeserve.co.uk. Est: 1997. Warehouse. Internet and postal. Telephone first. Open: **M:** 09:00–18:00; **T:** 09:00–18:00; **W:** 09:00–18:00; **Th:** 09:00–18:00; **F:** 09:00–18:00; **S:** 09:00–18:00. Large stock. Spec: Academic/Scholarly; Alpinism/Mountaineering; Antiquarian; Applied Art; Art; Biography; History - General. PR: £2–4,500. CC: E; JCB; MC; V. Corresp: French (a little). Mem: PBFA. [Updated]

Invicta Bookshop, ■ 8 Cromwell Place, Northbrook Street, Newbury, RG14 1AF. Prop: Simon & Tina Hall. Tel: (01635) 31176. Est: 1969. Shop open: **M:** 10:30–17:30; **T:** 10:30–17:30; **Th:** 10:30–17:30; **F:** 10:30–17:30; **S:** 10:30–17:30. Large general stock. Spec: Aviation; Cookery/Gastronomy; Military; Sport - Cricket; Topography - Local. PR: £1–200. CC: MC; V. Mem: PBFA. Also at: Hungerford Arcade Antiquess Centre. [Updated]

Railway Book and Magazine Search, The Warren, Curridge, Newbury, RG18 9DN. Prop: N.J. Bridger. Tel: (01635) 200507. Website: www.nevis-railway-bookshops.co.uk. Est: 1981. Private premises. Postal business only. Very small general stock. Spec: Railways. PR: £1–200. Also at: Nevis Railway Bookshop, Goring-on-Thames, Oxon (q.v.) and Nevis Railway Bookshop, Marlborough, Wiltshire (q.v.). [Updated]

READING

Books & Bygones, ■ 40 Hollow Lane, Shinfield, Reading, RG2 9BT. Prop: John Lilly & Pamela Pither. Tel: (0118) 988-4346. Website: www.booksbygones.com. E-mail: booksbygones@btinternet.com. Est: 1992. Shop at: Lane End Farm, Shinfield, RG2 9BE. Very large general stock. Spec: Animals and Birds; Architecture; Artists; Arts, The; Astrology; Autobiography; Children's - General; Cookery/Gastronomy; Crafts; Fiction - Romantic; Fiction - Science Fiction; Fiction - Westerns; Firearms/Guns; First Editions; Food & Drink; Gardening PR: £1–100. CC: MC; V; Switch. Mem: Ibooknet. [16/04/2003]

K.C. Brown, 11 Easington Drive, Lower Earley, Reading, RG6 3XN. Tel: (0118) 966-7013. Fax: (0118) 966-7013. Est: 1991. Private premises. Appointment necessary. Small general stock. [Updated]

Mary Butts Books, 219 Church Road, Earley, Reading, RG6 1HW. Prop: Mary Butts. Tel: (0118) 926-1793. E-mail: mary@mbutts.fsnet.co.uk. Est: 1985. Private premises. Internet and postal. Appointment necessary. Open: **M:** 09:00–17:00; **T:** 09:00–17:00; **W:** 09:00–17:00; **Th:** 09:00–17:00; **F:** 09:00–17:00; **S:** 09:00–17:00. Medium stock. Spec: Applied Art; Architecture; Art; Art - History; Art - Reference; Artists; Children's - General; Decorative Art; Illustrated; Literature; Painting; also, booksearch. PR: £2–50. Corresp: French. [Updated]

Footballana, 275 Overdown Road, Tilehurst, Reading, RG31 6NX. Prop: Bryan Horsnell. Tel: (0118) 942 4448. Fax: (0118) 942 4448. Private premises. Postal business only. Very small stock. Spec: Sport - Football (Soccer). PR: £5–100. Also, pre-1950 football programmes, postcards and ephemera wanted. Cata: occasionally. [Updated]

Forbury Fine Books, 46 Tredegar Road, Reading, RG4 8QF. Stephen Gardner. Tel: (0870) 063 8680. Fax: 0870 286 6874. Website: www.forburyfinebooks.co.uk. E-mail: mail@forburyfinebooks.co.uk. Est: 2004. Private premises. Internet and postal. Appointment necessary. Open: **M:** 09:00–18:00; **T:** 09:00–18:00; **W:** 09:00–18:00; **Th:** 09:00–18:00; **F:** 09:00–18:00. Small general stock. PR: £2–1,000. Also, book Search. [Updated]

J.B. Books, 3 Wenlock Edge, Charvil, Reading, RG10 9QG. Prop: John A. Baker. Tel: (0118) 934-0679. Website: www.balloonbooks.co.uk. E-mail: jb.books@btopenworld.com. Est: 1978. Private premises. Postal business only. Telephone first. Small stock. Spec: Aviation; Sport - Ballooning. PR: £1–250. Corresp: French. [Updated]

Keegan's Bookshop, ■ Merchant's Place, (off Friar Street), Reading, RG1 1DT. Prop: John & Judith Keegan. Tel: (0118) 958-7253. Fax: (0118) 958-5220. Est: 1979. Shop; open: **M:** 09:00–17:30; **T:** 09:00–17:30; **W:** 09:00–17:30; **Th:** 09:00–17:30; **F:** 09:00–17:30; **S:** 09:00–17:30. Medium stock. Spec: Military; Railways; Topography - General. PR: £1–100. CC: MC; V; SW. Corresp: Italian. [Updated]

Veronica Mayhew, Trewena, Behoes Lane, Woodcote, Reading, RG8 0PP. Tel: (01491) 680743. E-mail: veronica.mayhew@virgin.net. Est: 1972. Private premises. Appointment necessary. Small stock. Spec: Animals and Birds; Apiculture; Cats; Farming & Livestock; Ornithology. PR: £1–500. Cata: 1 each on poultry, pigeons, cagebirds, farm livestock. VAT No: GB 537 6954 02. [Updated]

WINDSOR

Brian Billing, 28 Athlone Square, Ward Royal, Windsor, SL4 1SS. Tel: (01753) 851343. Est: 1965. Private premises. Postal business only. Small stock. Spec: Economics; Natural History; Travel - General. PR: £2–250. Cata: occasionally. [Updated]

Eton Antique Bookshop, ■ 88 High Street, Eton, Windsor, SL4 6AF. Prop: Maurice Bastians. Tel: (01753) 855534. Est: 1975. Shop open: **M:** 11:00–18:00; **T:** 11:00–18:00; **W:** 11:00–18:00; **Th:** 11:00–18:00; **F:** 11:00–18:00; **S:** 11:00–18:00; **Su:** 12:00–17:00. Medium stock. Spec: Antiquarian; Antiques; Bindings; History - General; Literature; Military; Poetry; Sets of Books; Sport - General; Topography - General. PR: £3–2,000. CC: E; MC; V and others. Also, bookserach, old prints and maps, bookbinding and repairs. Often open early and late - call first. Corresp: Spanish. Mem: Eton Traders Assoc. VAT No: GB 787 1877 65. [Updated]

WOKINGHAM

John Townsend, 33 Bishop's Drive, Wokingham, RG40 1WA. Tel: (0118) 978-5463. Fax: (0118) 978-5463. Website: www.johntownsend.demon.co.uk. E-mail: john@johntownsend.demon.co.uk. Est: 1991. Private premises. Internet and postal. Appointment necessary. Medium stock. Spec: Genealogy; Heraldry; History - General; Manuscripts; Parish Registers; School Registers/Rolls of Honour; Topography - General; Topography - Local. PR: £10–200. Cata: 6 a year on Genealogy, Heraldry, British Local History. Corresp: French, German. VAT No: GB 591 8061 25. [Updated]

BRISTOL

Ambra Books, 22 West Shrubbery, Redland, Bristol, BS6 6TA. Prop: Ivor Cornish. Tel: (0117) 907-6899. Fax: (0117) 974-1962. Website: www.localhistory.co.uk/ambra. E-mail: ambra@localhistory.co.uk. Est: 1972. Private premises. Internet and postal. Appointment necessary. Open: **M:** 09:00–17:00; **T:** 09:00–17:00; **W:** 09:00–17:00; **Th:** 09:00–17:17; **F:** 09:00–00:00; **S:** 09:00–12:00. Small stock. Spec: Genealogy; History - Local; Topography - Local. PR: £10–3,000. CC: MC; V; SW. Cata: 6 a year on West Country topography. Corresp: French, Italian. [05/09/2003]

Avon Books, ■ 4 Waterloo Street, Clifton, Bristol, BS8 4BT. Prop: John Ray. Tel: (0117) 973-9848. E-mail: sales@avonbook.co.uk. Est: 1991. Shop open: **M:** 11:00–18:00; **T:** 11:00–18:00; **W:** 11:00–18:00; **Th:** 11:00–17:00; **F:** 11:00–18:00; **S:** 11:00–18:00. Medium stock. Spec: PR: £2–200. CC: MC; V. [19/08/2003]

Beware of The Leopard Books, 66–69 & 77 The Covered Market, St. Nicholas Market, St Nicholas Street, Bristol, BS1 1LJ. Prop: David Jackson. Tel: (0117) 925-7277. E-mail: bewareoftheleopard@hotmail.com. Est: 1991. Market stand/stall; open: **M:** 10:00–17:00; **T:** 10:00–17:00; **W:** 10:00–17:00; **Th:** 10:00–17:00; **F:** 10:00–17:00; **S:** 10:00–17:00. Very large general stock. Spec: Academic/Scholarly; Art; Biography; Chemistry; Computing; Economics; Fairgrounds; Fiction - General; First Editions; History - General; Humanities; Languages - Foreign; Law; Literature; Mathematics; Medicine; Music - General; Poetry; Politics and more. PR: £1–75. CC: JCB; MC; V. VAT No: GB 520 0870 87. [Updated]

Bishopston Books, ■ 259, Gloucester Rd, Bishopston, Bristol, BS7 8NY. Prop: Bill Singleton. Tel: (0117) 944-5303. E-mail: bishopstonbooks@btinternet.com. Est: 1995. Shop open: **T:** 10:00–17:00; **W:** 10:00–17:30; **Th:** 10:00–17:30; **F:** 10:00–17:30; **S:** 09:30–16:30. Medium stock. Spec: PR: £1–200. CC: JCB; V. [Updated]

James Burmester, Pipley Old Farm, Upton Cheyney, Bristol, BS30 6NG. Prop: James & Rosamund Burmester. Tel: (0117) 932-7265. Fax: (0117) 932-7667. E-mail: james.burmester@btconnect.com. Est: 1985. Private premises. Appointment necessary. Small stock. Spec: Agriculture. PR: £50–10,000. CC: MC; V. Cata: 3 a year. Mem: PBFA. VAT No: GB 404 6808 60. [Updated]

Byass Rare Books, ■ 14 Clifton Arcade, Boyces Avenue, Clifton, BS8 4AA. Prop: Dean Byass. Tel: 0117 974 2555. E-mail: byass@btopenworld.com. Est: 1994. Shop. Telephone first. Spec: Antiquarian; Fine & Rare; History of Ideas; Law; Literature; Philosophy; Science - History of. PR: £50–10,000. CC: AE; MC; V. VAT No: GB 799 9334 44. [Updated]

Court Hay Books, Court Hay, 26 Church Road, Easton-in-Gordano, Bristol, BS20 0PQ. (*) Prop: Howard and Gilian Walters. Tel: (01275) 372751. Website: www.courthaybooks.co.uk. E-mail: courthaybooks@btconnect.com. Est: 1990. Private premises. Internet and postal. Appointment necessary. Small stock. Spec: Flower Arranging; Gardening. PR: £10–2,000. CC: AE; JCB; MC; V. [Updated]

Deverell Books, 86a Memorial Road, Hanham, Bristol, BS15 3LA. Prop: Paul Deverell Hughes. Tel: (0117) 961-6234. Fax: (0117) 373-8786. E-mail: pdhbooks@hotmail.com. Est: 2001. Private premises. Appointment necessary. Very small stock. Spec: Books about Books; Children's - General; Illustrated. PR: £10–2,000. Cata: 1 annually. Mem: PBFA. [Updated]

R.A. Gilbert, 4 Julius Road, Bishopston, Bristol, BS7 8EU. Tel: (0117) 924-6936. Fax: (0117) 924-4937. Est: 1963. Private premises. Appointment necessary. Small stock. Spec: Alchemy; Folklore; Freemasonry & Anti-Masonry; Gnostics; Occult; Psychic; Religion - General; Theology; Witchcraft. PR: £5–1,000. Cata: 1 on specialities and occasionally. Corresp: French. Mem: PBFA. VAT No: GB 138 9728 22. [Updated]

Looking for a book dealer overseas? Then search Sheppard's on-line directories at:

www.sheppardsworld.co.uk

For overseas bookdealers

Harlequin Books,■ 122 High Street, Staple Hill, Bristol, BS16 5HH. Prop: Brian W. Ball. Tel: (0117) 970-1801. Fax: (0117) 970-1801. Website: www.harlequinbooks.co.uk. E-mail: harlequin.books@ virgin.net. Est: 1984. Shop. Internet and postal. Open: **M:** 09:30–16:30; **T:** 09:30–16:30; **W:** 09:30–16:30; **Th:** 09:30–16:30; **F:** 09:30–16:30; **S:** 09:30–16:30. Medium stock. Spec: Aviation; Military; Motoring; Railways; Topography - Local. PR: £2–200. CC: AE; JCB; MC; V. [Updated]

James Hawkes, 18 Caledonia Place, Bristol, BS8 4DJ. Tel: (0117) 317 9268. Website: www.abebooks. com/home/JAMESHAWKES/. E-mail: jameshawkes1977@yahoo.com. Private premises. Internet and postal. Appointment necessary. Mail to: James Hawkes, P.O. Box 2341, Bristol, BS8 9ZY, United Kingdom. Small stock. Spec: Academic/Scholarly; Literary Criticism; Literature. PR: £20–950. CC: MC; V; Maestro SW. Cata: occasionally. [Updated]

A.R. Heath, 62 Pembroke Road, Clifton, Bristol, BS8 3DX. Tel: (0117) 974-1183. Fax: (0117) 973-2901. Website: www.heathrarebooks.co.uk. E-mail: heath.rare-books@dsl.pipex.com. Est: 1964. Spec: Fine & Rare; Manuscripts. PR: £50–10,000. [updated]

Hinchliffe Books, Clematis Cottage, 15 Castle Street, Thornbury, Bristol, BS35 1HA. Prop: Geoffrey Hinchliffe. Tel: (01454) 415177. E-mail: geoff@sumbooks.co.uk. Est: 1972. Private premises. Appointment necessary. Medium stock. Spec: Countries - Melanesia; Homeopathy; Industry; Mathematics; Physics; Science - General; Technology; Topography - General. PR: £2–200. Cata: 2 – mathematics; occasionally other specialities. VAT No: GB 520 4690 69. [Updated]

Arthur Hook, 54 Egerton Road, Bristol, BS7 8HL. Tel: (0117) 9144673. E-mail: hooksbooks@ blueyonder.co.uk. Est: 1997. Private premises. Postal business only. Very small stock. Spec: Naval; Railways; Topography - General. Cata: 6 occasionally. [Updated]

A.J. Kitley, 31 Perrys Lea, Bradley Stoke, Bristol, BS32 0EE. Tel: (01454) 615261. Est: 1986. Private premises. Postal business only. Very small stock. Spec: Musical Instruments. PR: £1–150. Cata: – occasionally. [Updated]

Rachel Lee Rare Books, The Old Bakery, 30 Poplar Road, Warmley, Bristol, BS30 5JU. Prop: Rachel Lee. Tel: (0117) 960-6891. Fax: (0117) 960-6935. Website: www.rleerarebooks.co.uk. E-mail: rachellee. books@virgin.net. Est: 1979. Private premises. Internet and postal. Appointment necessary. Small stock. Spec: Academic/Scholarly; Economics; History of Ideas; Humanities; Philosophy. PR: £30–20,000. CC: AE; MC; V. Also, a booksearch service for philosophy only. Cata: 3 a year. Mem: ABA; ILAB. VAT No: GB 783 5078 02. [Updated]

Paperbacks Plus, ■ Regent Street Shopping Arcade, 98 Regent Street, Kingswood, Bristol, BS15 8HP. Prop: Mr. T. Nicholls. Tel: (0117) 9566232. Website: www.pbbooks.freeserve.co.uk. E-mail: books@ pbplus.freeserve.co.uk. Est: 1994. Shop open: **M:** 09:00–17:00; **T:** 09:00–17:00; **W:** 09:00–17:00; **Th:** 09:00–17:00; **F:** 09:00–17:00; **S:** 09:00–17:00. Spec: Biography; Children's - General; Fiction - General; Fiction - Crime, Detective, Spy, Thrillers; Fiction - Fantasy, Horror; Fiction - Science Fiction; Fiction - Women; Military History. PR: £1–20. [Updated]

S.P.C.K., ■ 79 Park Street, Bristol, BS1 5PF. Tel: (0117) 9273461. Fax: (0117) 9293525. Website: www.spck.org.uk. E-mail: bristol@spck.org.uk. Est: 1698. Shop open: **M:** 09:00–17:30; **T:** 09:00–17:30; **W:** 09:30–17:30; **Th:** 09:00–17:30; **F:** 09:00–17:30; **S:** 09:00–17:30. Large stock. Spec: Prayer Books; Religion - Christian; Theology. PR: £1–200. CC: MC; V. VAT No: GB 232 8071 82. [Updated]

Morris & Juliet Venables, 270 Henbury Road, Bristol, BS10 7QR. Morris & Juliet Venables. Tel: (0117) 950-7362. Fax: (0117) 959-2361. E-mail: morris.venables@ukgateway.net. Est: 1970. Private premises. Appointment necessary. Medium stock. Spec: Academic/Scholarly; Antiquarian; Art; Fine & Rare; Literary Criticism; Literature; Music - General; Music - Classical; Music - Composers; Poetry; Stained Glass. PR: £5–1,000. CC: MC; V. Cata: 2 on Stained glass; literature. Mem: PBFA. VAT No: GB 397 3454 11. [Updated]

The Wise Owl Bookshop, 4 Julius Road, Bishopston, Bristol, BS7 8EN. Mrs. Patricia Gilbert. Tel: (0117) 924-6936. Fax: (0117) 949-4937. Est: 1968. Private premises. Appointment necessary. Small stock. Spec: Cats; Children's - General; Music - General. PR: £1–100. Cata: 1 on each on children's and cats. Corresp: French. [17/08/2003]

Gerald Baker, 28 Beaconsfield Road, Clifton, BS8 2TS. Tel: (0117) 974-4319. Website: www.gwrpublicity. co.uk. E-mail: gwrpublicity@btinternet.com. Postal business only. Very small stock. Spec: Railways. PR: £5–200. Cata: every 3 months. [Updated]

BUCKINGHAMSHIRE

AMERSHAM

Gill Bilski, 4 Sheepfold Lane, Amersham, HP7 9EL. Gill Bilski. Tel: (01494) 433895. Website: www.gillbilski.com. E-mail: gill@bilski.freeserve.co.uk. Est: 1983. Private premises. Postal business only. Very small stock. Spec: Author - Brent-Dyer, Elinor M.; Author - Fairlie–Bruce, D.; Author - Oxenham, Elsie; Children's - General. PR: £1–200. CC: via Paypal. Also, a booksearch service. Cata: 4 or 5 per annum. Corresp: French. [Updated]

AYLESBURY

Bernwode Books, 48 Worminghall Road, Oakley, Aylesbury, HP18 9QY. Prop: Dr. S.R.J. Woodell. Tel: (01844) 238399. Est: 1984. Private premises. Appointment necessary. Small stock. Spec: Botany; Evolution; Natural History; Science - General; Travel - General. PR: £2–400. Cata: occasionally. Corresp: French. [17/08/2003]

BEACONSFIELD

Barn Books, Old Hay Barn, Holtspur Top Lane, Beaconsfield, HP9 1BS. Prop: Elisabeth & Wolfgang Ansorge. Tel: (01494) 671122. Fax: (01494) 671122. E-mail: barnbooks@supanet.com. Est: 1991. Private premises. Appointment necessary. Small stock. Spec: Archaeology; Art; Cinema/Film; Collecting; Crafts; History - General; Military; Natural History; Politics; Royalty - General; Voyages & Discovery. PR: £5–3,000. Corresp: German. Also, booksearch. VAT No: GB 578 4204 21. [Updated]

BUCKINGHAM

Corvus Books, 11 Parsons Close, Winslow, Buckingham, MK18 3BX. Prop: Chris Corbett. Tel: (01296) 713393. Fax: (01296) 713393. E-mail: corvusbooks@btinternet.com. Est: 1990. Private premises. Internet and postal. Appointment necessary. Very small stock. Spec: Atlases; Colour-Plate; Natural History; Travel - General. PR: £50–5,000. CC: Pay Pal. Also attends 11 fairs a year at the Hotel Russell, London. Mem: PBFA. [Updated]

Peter Eaton (Booksellers) Ltd, 1 Sandhill House, Middle Claydon, Buckingham, MK18 2LD. Prop: M. Eaton. Tel: (01296) 738888. E-mail: margaret@peaton.plus.com. Est: 1944. Private premises. Postal business only. Medium stock. Spec: Antiquarian. PR: £25–10,000. CC: V. Corresp: French. Mem: ABA; ILAB. VAT No: GB 238 7381 36. [Updated]

E. & J. Shelley, Quakers Orchard, 12 Moreton Road, Buckingham, MK18 1LA. Prop: Jennifer Shelley. Tel: (01280) 812307. E-mail: shellbooks@btinternet.com. Est: 1996. Private premises. Postal business only. Telephone first. Large stock. Spec: Children's - General; First Editions; Illustrated; Literature; Poetry. PR: £10–1,000. [Updated]

CHESHAM

David Mundy at Nooks and Crannies, ■ 9 Market Square, Chesham, HP5 1HG. Tel: (020) 7482 7087. Est: 2000. Shop open: **M:** 09:30–17:30; **T:** 09:30–17:30; **W:** 09:30–17:30; **Th:** 09:30–17:30; **F:** 09:30–17:30; **S:** 09:30–17:30; **Su:** 11:00–16:30. Very small stock. Spec: Antiques; Art; History - General; Topography - General; Travel - General. PR: £1–50. CC: MC; V. Also at: David Mundy at Heritage Antiques, Berkhamstead (q.v.). [Updated]

Omniphil Prints, Germain's Lodge, Fullers Hill, Chesham, HP5 1LR. Tel: (01494) 771851. E-mail: omniphil@talk21.com. Private premises. Appointment necessary. Spec: Periodicals & Magazines. Specialist stocks of Illustrated London News. [03/03/2003]

GREAT MISSENDEN

Martin Blackman, 6 Wychwood Rise, Great Missenden, HP16 0HB. Tel: (01494) 890839. Fax: (01494) 890839. E-mail: blackmanbooks@yahoo.co.uk. Est: 1993. PR: £5–200. [Updated]

HIGH WYCOMBE

Rivendale Press Ltd, P O Box 85, High Wycombe, HP14 4WZ. Tel: (01494) 562266. Fax: (01494) 565533. Website: www.rivendalepress.com. E-mail: sales@rivendalepress.com. Est: 1999. Private premises. Internet and postal. Small stock. Spec: Bibliography; Biography; Literature - Victorian; Poetry. PR: £10–1,000. Mem: PBFA. [Updated]

IVER

Pemberley Books, ■ 18 Bathurst Walk, Richings Park, Iver, SL0 9AZ. Prop: Ian A. Johnson. Tel: (01753) 631114. Fax: (01753) 631115. Website: www.pembooks.demon.co.uk. E-mail: ij@pembooks. demon.co.uk. Est: 1985. Internet and postal. Shop open but telephone first. Open: **M:** 10:00–17:30; **T:** 10:00–17:30; **W:** 10:00–17:30; **Th:** 10:00–17:30; **F:** 10:00–17:30; **S:** 10:00–17:00. Medium stock. Spec: Antiquarian; Botany; Entomology; Herpetology; Lepidopterology / Lepidoptery; Natural History; New Naturalist; Ornithology; Palaeontology; Zoology. PR: £5–8,000. CC: AE; E; JCB; MC; V. Also, new books on specialities. Cata: 2 a year. Corresp: German. Mem: PBFA. VAT No: GB 646 2266 34. [Updated]

MILTON KEYNES

Andromeda Books, 4 Glovers Lane, Heelands, Milton Keynes, MK13 8LW. Prop: Annie & Mike Eynon. Tel: (01908) 312046. Fax: (01908) 312046. Website: www.m31books.co.uk. E-mail: andromedabooks @btopenworld.com. Est: 1998. Private premises. Postal business only. Small stock. Spec: Art; Astronomy; Decorative Art. PR: £2–100. CC: AE; JCB; MC; V; Switch. Cata: quarterly. Mem: FSB. [Updated]

Daeron's Books, ■ 13 Market Square, Stony Stratford, Milton Keynes, MK11 1BE. Prop: Angela Gardner. Tel: (01908) 568989. Fax: (01908) 266092. Website: www.daerons.co.uk. E-mail: books@daerons.co.uk. Est: 1992. Internet and postal. Shop open at: The Office: 69 Malletts Close, Stony Stratford MK11 1DG. Open: **M:** 09:30–17:30; **T:** 09:30–17:30; **W:** 09:30–17:30; **Th:** 09:30–17:30; **F:** 09:30–17:30; **S:** 09:00–17:00. Medium stock. Spec: Antiquarian; Arthurian; Author - Chesterton, G.K.; Author - Inklings, The; Author - Kipling, Rudyard; Author - Lewis, C.S.; Author - MacDonald, George; Author - Pratchett, Terry; Author - Tolkien, J.R.; Fiction - Fantasy, Horror; Fiction - Science Fiction. PR: £1–500. CC: AE; D; E; JCB; MC; V. Mem: FSB, SSBA. VAT No: GB 776 7066 85. [Updated]

Janian Comics / Computer Manuals, Chelworth House, 14 Chillery Leys, Willen, Milton Keynes, MK15 9LZ. Prop: Ian Kiddley. Tel: (07974) 155379. Website: www.janiancomics.com & www.janian.co.uk. E-mail: ian@janian.plus.com. Est: 1994. Private premises. Internet and postal. Appointment necessary. Very large stock. Spec: Comics; Computing. PR: £1–1,500. CC: AE; MC; V; SW. Organiser of Milton Keynes Book Festival. VAT No: GB 639 9941 73. [Updated]

Periplus Books, ■ 2 Timor Court, Stony Stratford, Milton Keynes, MK11 1EJ. Prop: John Phillips. Tel: (01908) 263300. Fax: (01908) 663579. Website: www.periplusbooks.co.uk. E-mail: info@ periplusbooks.co.uk. Est: 1997. Shop open: **M:** 10:30–17:00; **T:** 10:30–17:00; **W:** 10:30–17:00; **Th:** 10:30–17:00; **F:** 10:30–17:00; **S:** 10:30–17:00. Medium stock. Spec: Geology; Marine Sciences; Meteorology. PR: £1–500. Specialist subjects by post only. [Updated]

NEWPORT PAGNELL

Ken's Paper Collectables, 29 High Street, Newport Pagnell, MK16 8AR. Prop: Ken Graham. Tel: (01908) 610003. Fax: (01908) 610003. Website: www.kens.co.uk. E-mail: ken@kens.co.uk. Est: 1983. Open: **M:** 09:30–17:00; **T:** 09:30–17:00; **W:** 09:30–17:00; **F:** 09:30–17:00; **S:** 09:30–16:00. Large general stock. Spec: Autographs; Comics; Manuscripts; Newspapers - General; Paper Collectables; Periodicals & Magazines. PR: £1–400. CC: MC; V. Mem: Ephemera Society. [Updated]

PENN

Penn Barn Bookshop, ■ By the Pond, Elm Road, Penn, HP10 8LB. Prop: P.J.M. Hunnings. Tel: (01494) 815691. Est: 1968. Shop open: **T:** 10:30–16:00; **W:** 10:30–16:00; **Th:** 10:30–16:00; **F:** 10:30–16:00; **S:** 10:30–16:00. Small stock. Spec: Antiquarian; Art; Bindings; Illustrated; Topography - General. PR: £2–300. CC: MC; V. Also, picture dealer. [Updated]

STOKE GOLDINGTON

Fireside Books, Harebell Cottage, 14 Mount Pleasant, Stoke Goldington, MK13 7EP. Prop: John and Catherine Coppock. Tel: (01908) 551199. Fax: (0870) 1617621. Website: www.firesidebooks.demon. co.uk. E-mail: john@firesidebooks.demon.co.uk. Est: 1998. Private premises. Postal business only. Very small stock. Spec: Author - Morton, H.V.; History - General; Rural Life; Topography - General; Topography - Local; Travel - General. PR: £2–300. Also, booksearch. [Updated]

WING

Book Collectors Paradise, 38 Windmill Way, Tring, HP23 4HH. Prop: Trudy Ashford. Tel: (01442) 824440. Est: 1985. Book fairs only at Wing Village Hall, Buckinghamshire. **Su:** 10:00–16:00. PR: £1–100. Also at: At Milton Keynes Shopping Centre. [17/05/2003]

CAMBRIDGESHIRE

BLUNTISHAM

Bluntisham Books, Oak House, 4 East Street, Bluntisham, Huntingdon, PE28 3LS. Prop: D.W.H. & S. Walton. Tel: (01487) 840449. Fax: (01487) 840894. Website: www.bluntishambooks.co.uk. E-mail: contact@bluntishambooks.co.uk. Est: 1976. Private premises. Postal business only. Small stock. Spec: Countries - Antarctic, The; Countries - Arctic, The; Countries - Greenland; Countries - Polar; Travel - Polar; Whaling. PR: £5–2,000. CC: MC; V. Also, publishers of Antarctic book, inc. reprints of classics. Cata: 3 a year. VAT No: GB 344 2959 39. [Updated]

CAMBRIDGE

Adab Books, 11 Causewayside, Cambridge, CB3 9HD. Prop: Daphne Roper. Tel: (01223) 323047. Fax: (01223) 367190. E-mail: adab@adabbooks.co.uk. Est: 1993. Private premises. Postal business only. Appointment necessary. Very small stock. Spec: Antiquarian. PR: £20–2,500. CC: AE; D; MC; V. Cata: 5 a year. Mem: ABA. VAT No: GB 532 2307 85. [Updated]

Book Barrow, 93 Cam Causeway, Chesterton, Cambridge, CB4 1TL. Tel: (01223) 424 429. E-mail: bookbarrow@ntlworld.com. Market stand/stall. Internet and postal. Spec: Academic/Scholarly; Africana; American Indians; Esoteric; First Editions; Modern First Editions; Signed Editions. [Updated]

Books & Collectables Ltd.,■ Unit 7/8, Railway Arches, Coldhams Road, Cambridge, CB1 3EW. Prop: A. Doyle, J. Cross, D.B. & M. Doyle & P. Brown. Tel: (01223) 412845. Website: www. booksandcollectables .com. E-mail: ask@booksandcollectables.com. Est: 1993. Shop; Internet and postal. Open: **M:** 10:00–17:00; **T:** 10:00–17:00; **W:** 10:00–17:00; **Th:** 10:00–17:00; **F:** 10:00–17:00; **S:** 10:00–17:00; **Su:** 10:00–16:00. Very large general stock. Spec: Antiques; Art; Children's - General; Cinema/Film; Comic Books & Annuals; Comics; Cookery/Gastronomy; Fiction - General; First Editions; Gardening; History - General; Literature; Military; Motoring; Music - General; Natural History; Periodicals & Magazines. PR: £1–300. [Updated]

Books of Note, 19 Howard Close, Cambridge, CB5 8QU. Prop: Mark Richardson. Tel: (01223) 292280. Fax: (01223) 292280. Website: www.booksofnote.co.uk. E-mail: markcamb@gxn.co.uk. Est: 1996. Private premises. Postal business only. Spec: Music - Folk & Irish Folk; Music - Popular. PR: £5–30. [17/06/2003]

The Bookshop,■ , 24 Magdalene Street, Cambridge, CB3 0AF. Prop: Peter Bright & Hugh Hardinge. Tel: (01223) 362457. E-mail: hardinge@ntlworld.com. Est: 1996. Shop open: **M:** 10:30–17:30; **T:** 10:30–17:30; **W:** 10:30–17:30; **Th:** 10:30–17:30; **F:** 10:30–17:30; **S:** 10:30–17:30. Medium stock. Spec: Academic/Scholarly; Art; Children's - General; Literature; Poetry; Sport - Cricket; Topography - General. PR: £3–250. Also at: P.G. Bright, 11 Ravens Court, Ely (q.v.) and Hugh Hardinge, Cambridge Market Square, Tues & Thurs. [20/08/2003]

Bracton Books, 25 Lode Road, Lode, Cambridge, CB5 9ER. Prop: Mrs S.J. Harrison. Tel: (01223) 811976. Website: www.bractonbooks.co.uk. E-mail: bractonbooks@uk2.net. Est: 1981. Private premises. Postal business only. Appointment necessary. Large stock. Spec: Academic/Scholarly; American Indians; Anthropology; Archaeology; Biology; Books about Books; Countries - Africa; Countries - Americas, The; Countries - Asia; Countries - Melanesia; Countries - Polynesia; Ethnography; Evolution; Folklore; History - General. PR: £2–100. Cata: occasionally. Computer listings on request. [Updated]

J. & J. Burgess Booksellers, 2 St Thomas's Road, Cambridge, CB1 3TF. Prop: John Burgess. Tel: (01223) 249037. E-mail: jandjburgess2@ntlworld.com. Est: 1997. Private premises. Postal business only. Appointment necessary. Medium stock. Spec: Academic/Scholarly; Animals and Birds; Arms & Armour; Astrology; Author - General; Aviation; Buses/Trams; Children's - General; Maritime/Nautical; Medicine; Military; Natural History; New Age; Politics; Science - General; Witchcraft. PR: £4–150. [Updated]

G. David, ■ 16 St. Edward's Passage, Cambridge, CB2 3PJ. Prop: D.C. Asplin, N.T. Adams & B.L. Collings. Tel: (01223) 354619. Fax: (01223) 324663. E-mail: gdavid.books@btinternet.com. Est: 1896. Shop open: **M:** 09:00–17:00; **T:** 09:00–17:00; **W:** 09:00–17:00; **Th:** 09:00–17:00; **F:** 09:00–17:00; **S:** 09:00–17:00. Medium stock. Spec: Academic/Scholarly; Antiquarian; Bindings; Children's - General; Early Imprints; Fine & Rare; Illustrated; Literature; Natural History; Travel - General. PR: £1–10,000. CC: JCB; MC; V. Large selection of remainders & publishers' returns. Corresp: Japanese, Swedish. Mem: ABA; PBFA. VAT No: GB 599 5999 44. [Updated]

de Visser Books, 309 Milton Road, Cambridge, CB4 1XQ. Prop: Erik de Visser. Tel: (01223) 500909. Fax: (01223) 500909. Website: devisserbooks@hotmail.com. E-mail: devisserbooks@hotmail.com. Est: 1988. Private premises. Internet and postal. Appointment necessary. Small stock. Spec: Academic/Scholarly; Countries - Albania; Countries - Austria; Countries - Balkans, The; Countries - Baltic States; Countries - East Europe; Countries - Germany; Countries - Hungary; History - European; Royalty - European; Travel - Europe. PR: £10–750. CC: E; JCB; MC; V; Delta. Cata: 5 a year on Central & East Europe only. Corresp: German French Dutch. VAT No: GB 493 3891 05. [Updated]

Galloway & Porter Limited, ■ 30 Sidney Street, Cambridge, CB2 3HS. Tel: (01223) 367876. Fax: (01223) 360705. E-mail: galpor1@aol.com. Est: 1900. Shop open: **M:** 08:45–17:00; **T:** 08:45–17:00; **W:** 08:45–17:00; **Th:** 08:45–17:00; **F:** 08:45–17:00; **S:** 09:00–17:15. Large stock. Spec: Academic/Scholarly; Mythology. PR: £1–2,000. Also, remainders and bargain books. Mem: ABA; PBFA; BA; BT. VAT No: GB 213 4374 92. [16/07/2003]

K.P. Hunter, Bookseller, 13, St. Margaret's Road, Girton, Cambridge, CB3 0LT. Tel: (01223) 529295. Website: www.abebooks.com. E-mail: kate.hunter1@ntlworld.com. Est: 1995. Private premises. Book fairs only. Very small stock. Spec: Academic/Scholarly; Author - 20th Century; Author - Lawrence, T.E.; Authors - Women; Bibliography; First Editions; Fishes; Gardening; Literature. PR: £5–500. Corresp: French. Mem: PBFA. [04/06/2003]

Sarah Key Books, ■ The Haunted Bookshop, 9 St. Edward's Passage, Cambridge, CB2 3PJ. Prop: Sarah Key & Phil Salin. Tel: (01223) 312913. Fax: 0870 056 9392. E-mail: sarahkey@hauntedbooks. demon.co.uk. Est: 1985. Shop open: **M:** 10:00–17:00; **T:** 10:00–17:00; **W:** 10:00–17:00; **Th:** 10:00–17:00; **F:** 10:00–17:00; **S:** 10:00–17:00. Medium stock. Spec: Academic/Scholarly; Aeronautics; Annuals; Author - Ardizzone, Edward; Author - Barker, Cecily M.; Author - Blyton, Enid; Author - Brent-Dyer, Elinor M.; Author - Buckeridge, A.; Author - Carroll, Lewis; Author - Crompton, Richmal; Author - Dahl, Roal. PR: £1–2,000. CC: AE; JCB; MC. Also, local interest items & a booksearch service. Cata: 1 on children's & illustrated. Corresp: French. Mem: PBFA. VAT No: GB 572 9680 04. [Updated]

Paul Kunkler Books, 6 Hardwick Street, Cambridge, CB3 9JA. Tel: (01223) 321419. Fax: (01223) 321419. Private premises. Appointment necessary. Very small stock. Spec: Art - History; Manuscripts. [30/04/2003]

Lund Theological Books, 1 Arbury Road, Cambridge, CB4 2JB. Prop: Philip Lund. Tel: (01223) 565303. Website: www.lundbooks.co.uk. E-mail: sales@lundbooks.co.uk. Est: 1983. Private premises. Internet and postal. Medium stock. Spec: Bibles; Ecclesiastical History & Architecture; History - Byzantine; History - Middle Ages; Medieval; Mysticism; Philosophy; Prayer Books; Religion - Buddhism; Religion - Christian; Religion - Islam; Religion - Jewish; Theology; Vatican and Papal History. PR: £5–300. CC: MC; V. Cata: on specialities. Also on IBooknet. VAT No: GB 386 0602 50. [Updated]

Adam Mills Rare Books, 328 High Street, Cottenham, Cambridge, CB4 8TX. Tel: (01954) 250106. Fax: (01954) 250106. Website: www.abebooks.com. E-mail: adam@millsrb.freeserve.co.uk. Est: 1981. Private premises. Internet and postal. Contactable. Small stock. Spec: Bibliography; Books about Books; Fine Printing; Illustrated; Literature; Private Press; Typography. CC: MC; V. Cata: 4 regularly. Corresp: French, Italian. Mem: PBFA. [Updated]

Peter Moore, P.O. Box 66, 200a Perne Road, Cambridge, CB1 3PD. Prop: Peter Moore. Tel: (01223) 411177. Fax: (01223) 240559. Website: www.aus-pacbooks.co.uk. E-mail: aus-pacbooks@lineone.net. Est: 1970. Office &/or bookroom. Internet and postal. Appointment necessary. Small stock. Spec: Countries - Australia; Countries - Pacific, The; Countries - Papua New Guinea; Travel - Australasia/Australia. PR: £1–500. CC: MC; V. Cata: 2 – occasionally. Mem: PBFA; BCSA. VAT No: GB 215 3610 02. [Updated]

Mike Parker Books, 2 Mill Lane, Duxford, Cambridge, CB2 4PT. (*). Tel: (01223) 835935. Fax: (01223) 839737. E-mail: mjp@lineone.net. Est: 1995. Private premises. Internet and postal. Appointment necessary. Small stock. Spec: Academic/Scholarly; Advertising; Modern First Editions. PR: £5–500. [Updated]

Plurabelle Books, 77 Garden Walk, Cambridge, CB4 3EW. Prop: Dr. Michael Cahn. Tel: (01223) 571105. Website: www.plurabelle.co.uk. E-mail: books@plurabelle.co.uk. Est: 1993. Warehouse; Postal business only. Telephone first. Very large stock. Spec: Academic/Scholarly; Computing; Foreign Texts; Humanities; Linguistics; Literary Criticism; Literature; Philology; Philosophy; Science - History of. PR: £8–200. CC: MC; V. Corresp: German, Italian. Also on Tom Folio and IBookNnet. VAT No: GB 636 8493 00. [updated]

Quest Booksearch, 24 Hawthorne Road, Stapleford, Cambridge, CB2 5DU. Prop: Dr. Rosemary Scott. Tel: (01223) 844080. Fax: (01223) 844080. E-mail: qbs2@lineone.net. Est: 1997. Private premises. Postal business only. Very small stock. Spec: Literature; Poetry, also booksearch. PR: £1–1,000. [Updated]

Rupert Books, 58/59 Stonefield, Bar Hill, Cambridge, CB3 8TE. Prop: Paulina M. & R. Dixon Smith. Tel: (01954) 781861. Website: www.rupert-books.co.uk. E-mail: sales@rupert-books.co.uk. Est: 1984. Spec: Author - Conan Doyle, Sir Arthur; Crime (True); Sherlockiana. PR: £3–1,000. [Updated]

Frances Wetherell, 8 Highworth Avenue, Cambridge, CB4 2BG.Tel: (01223) 363537. E-mail: frances. wetherell@talk21.com. Est: 1988. Private premises. Postal business only. Very small general stock. Spec: Art; Economics; Literature; Social History; also Booksearch. PR: £10–100. Also, a booksearch service. [Updated]

David White, The Old Guildhall, 4 Church Lane, Linton, Cambridge, CB1 6JX. Prop: David White. Tel: (01223) 894447. Fax: (01223) 894449. Website: www.davidwhitebooks.co.uk. E-mail: david.white23@ virgin.net. Est: 1987. Private premises. Internet and postal. Appointment necessary. Very small stock. Spec: Medicine; Medicine - History of; Pharmacy/Pharmacology. PR: £10–2,000. CC: MC; V. Cata: 1 a year. [Updated]

Peter Wood, 20 Stonehill Road, Great Shelford, Cambridge, CB2 5JL. Tel: (01223) 842419. Website: www.booksatpbfa.com. E-mail: peterwoodbooks@waitrose.com. Est: 1973. Private premises. Appointment necessary. Small stock. Spec: Art; Biography; Broadcasting; Cinema/Film; Entertainment - General; Music - General; Performing Arts; Theatre. PR: £10–500. CC: MC; V. Cata: 4 a year. Mem: PBFA. VAT No: GB 214 4339 88. [Updated]

CASTLE CAMPS

Harry Brett, Pepperpot Cottage, Bartlow Road, Castle Camps, Cambridge, CB1 6SX. Tel: (01799) 584515. Est: 1968. Private premises. Postal business only. Small stock. PR: £2–500. [Updated]

CHATTERIS

Joan Stevens, Books, ■ 3 High Street, Chatteris, PE16 6BE. Tel: (01354) 696874. Fax: (01354) 696874. Est: 1962. Shop and market stand. Small stock. Spec: Art - History; Art - Reference; Artists; Arts, The; Black Studies; Feminism; Fiction - General; Illustrated; Literary Criticism; Literature; Literature in Translation; Music - General; Poetry; Politics; Social History; War - General; Women. PR: £1–500. Open at other times by appointment. Cata: 3 a year on literature, poetry, black studies. [Updated]

ELY

P.G. Bright, 11 Ravens Court, Ely, CB6 3ED. Tel: (01353) 661727. E-mail: peter.bright@care4free.net. Est: 1982. Private premises. Appointment necessary. Medium stock. Spec: Children's - General; Illustrated; Literature; Sport - Cricket. PR: £1–500. Mem: PBFA. Also at: The Bookshop, 24 Magdalene Street, Cambridge (q.v.). [Updated]

Ely Books, 24 Downham Road, Ely, CB6 1AF. Prop: Michael G. Kousah. Tel: (01353) 661824. Website: http://www.elybooks.com. E-mail: elybooks@ntlworld.com. Est: 1986. Private premises. Internet. Appointment necessary. Very small stock. Spec: Americana; Antiquarian; Bindings; Illustrated; Travel - General. PR: £5–2,000. Mem: PBFA.VAT No: GB 572 9042 32. [Updated]

New dealers in the British Isles can register their business on
www.sheppardsdirectories.com

Hereward Books,■17 High Street, Haddenham, Ely, CB6 3XA. Prop: Roger J. Pratt. Tel: (01353) 740821. Fax: (01353) 741721. Website: www.herewardbooks.co.uk. E-mail: sales@herewardbooks. co.uk. Est: 1985. Shop, Internet and postal. Telephone first. Medium stock. Spec: Bindings; Illustrated; Natural History; Sport - Angling/Fishing; Sport - Falconry; Sport - Field Sports; Travel - General. PR: £15–1,000. CC: JCB; MC; V; Debit. Cata: 2 on field sports. Mem: PBFA. VAT No: GB 382 3886 03. [Updated]

Octagon Books,■ 14 Pilgrims Way, Ely, CB6 3DL. Prop: John & Jacqueline Williams. Tel: (01353) 610244. Website: www.cloistersantiques.co.uk/octagon. E-mail: octagonbooks@aol.com. Est: 1982. Shop at Cloister's Antique Shop, 1A Lynn Road, Ely. Open: **M:** 10:00–16:30; **W:** 10:00–16:30; **Th:** 10:00–16:30; **F:** 10:00–16:30; **S:** 10:00–16:30; **Su:** 12:30–16:30. Small stock. Spec: Architecture; Art. Mem: PBFA. VAT No: GB 393 2186 39. [28/07/2003]

GODMANCHESTER

Godmanchester Books, Staughton House, 11 Post Street, Godmanchester, PE29 2BA. Prop: Doreen Lewis. Tel: (01480) 455020. Est: 1974. Private premises. Appointment necessary. Small stock. Spec: History - Local; Topography - Local; also, booksearch. PR: £1–100. [20/05/2003]

HADDENHAM

John Lewcock, 6 Chewells Lane, Haddenham, Ely, CB6 3SS. Prop: John Lewcock. Tel: (01353) 741960. Fax: (01353) 741710. Website: www.abebooks.com/home/maritime. E-mail: lewcock@maritime-bookseller.com. Est: 1984. Office &/or bookroom. Internet and postal. Telephone first. Medium stock. Spec: Academic/Scholarly; Deep Sea Diving; Manuals - Seamanship; Maritime/Nautical; Naval; Navigation; Shipbuilding; Sport - Yachting; Voyages & Discovery. PR: £5–1,500. CC: AE; E; JCB; MC; V; SW. Also, insurance & probate valuations. Cata: Quartely. Mem: ABA; PBFA; ILAB; CEng/IEE. VAT No: GB 410 5334 04. [Updated]

HUNTINGTON

The Curiosity Shop, ■ 7 High Street, Huntingdon, PE29 3TE. Prop: D. Fletcher & A. Bowers. Tel: (01480) 411605. Est: 1982. Shop open: **M:** 10:00–16:00; **T:** 10:00–16:00; **W:** 10:00–16:00; **Th:** 10:00–16:00; **F:** 10:00–16:00; **S:** 10:00–16:00. Small stock. Spec: Topography - General; Travel - General. PR: £1–75. [01/07/2003]

Roger Gaskell Rare Books, 17 Ramsey Road, Warboys, Huntingdon, PE28 2RW. Tel: (01487) 823059. Fax: (01487) 823070. Website: www.RogerGaskell.com. E-mail: roger@rogergaskell.com. Est: 1989. Private premises. Postal business only. Appointment necessary. Very small stock. Spec: Medicine; Science - General; Technology. PR: £100–10,000. Cata: 2 a year. Mem: ABA; ILAB. VAT No: GB 550 6050 74. [16/07/2003]

MK Book Services, 7 East Street, Huntingdon, PE29 1WZ. Prop: Melvyn R King. Tel: (01480) 353710. Fax: (01480) 431703. E-mail: mkbooks@tiscali.co.uk. Est: 1983. Private premises. Postal business only. Appointment necessary. Very small general stock. Spec: Authors - Local; Countries - Baltic States; Countries - South Atlantic Islands; Religion - Methodism; Sport - Horse Racing (all aspects); also, booksearch. PR: £1–50. CC: E; MC; V; Maestro. Mem: BA. VAT No: GB 958 0474 91. [Updated]

John Robertshaw, 5 Fellowes Drive, Ramsey, Huntingdon, PE26 1BE. Tel: (01487) 813330. Fax: (01487) 711901. E-mail: robertshaw.books@virgin.net. Est: 1983. Office &/or bookroom. Appointment necessary. Shop at: 24G Great Whyte Ramsey, Huntingdon, Cambridgeshire, PE26 1HA. Small general stock. Spec: Antiquarian; Foreign Texts; Languages - Foreign. Cata: 4 a year. Corresp: French, German. Mem: PBFA. VAT No: GB 360 1311 09. [Updated]

Ken Trotman, P.O.Box 505, Huntingdon, PE29 2XW. Prop: Richard & Roz Brown. Tel: (01480 454292. Fax: (01480 384651. Website: www.kentrotman.com. E-mail: rlbtrotman@aol.com. Est: 1949. Storeroom. Postal business only. Appointment necessary. Spec: Military. PR: £5–1,500. CC: MC; V. Cata: quarterly. Corresp: French. Mem: PBFA. VAT No: GB 386 4614 23. [Updated]

PETERBOROUGH

Francis Bowers Chess Suppliers, 1 Marriott Road, Oxney Road, Peterbough, PE1 5NQ. Tel: (01733) 897119. E-mail: chessbower@aol.com. Est: 1991. Private premises. Spec: Chess. PR: £1–1,000. [Updated]

Broadway Books, 144 Broadway, Peterborough, PE1 4DG. Prop: Alan & Marion Peasgood. Tel: (01733) 565055. Est: 1997. Private premises. Postal business only. Small general stock. Spec: PR: £1–25. Also at: Gildenbergh Gallery, Broadway, Peterborough. [Updated]

Brian Cocks Books, 18 Woodgate, Helpston, Peterborough, PE6 7ED. Brian Cocks. Tel: (01733) 252791. Fax: (01733) 252791. E-mail: brianc@uku.co.uk. Est: 1982. Private premises. Postal business only. Appointment necessary. Small stock. Spec: Aviation; also, booksearch. PR: £3–800. Cata: 2 on Aviation only. Corresp: French, German, Spanish. Mem: PBFA. VAT No: GB 513 933 431. [Updated]

T.V. Coles, ■ 981 Lincoln Road, Peterborough, PE4 6AH. Tel: (01733) 577268. Est: 1982. Shop open: **M:** 09:30–15:30; **T:** 09:30–15:30; **W:** 09:30–15:30; **Th:** 09:30–15:30; **F:** 09:30–15:30; **S:** 09:30–15:30. Small stock. Spec: Aviation; Military; Military History; Naval; Topography - General. PR: £1–200. [Updated]

DoublePlusBooks, 25 Princes Gardens, Peterborough, PE1 4DP. Prop: Richard Mankiewicz. Tel: (07092) 121 393. Fax: (07092) 121 393. Website: www.doubleplusbooks.com. E-mail: doubleplusbooks@ ntlworld.com. Est: 2002. Private premises. Internet and postal. Appointment necessary. Small stock. Spec: Antiquarian; Antiques; Applied Art; Architecture; Arms & Armour; Art; Art - History; Art - Reference; Author - General; Catalogues Raisonnes; Ceramics; Collecting; Crafts; Decorative Art; Design; Fiction - General; Fine & Rare; Firearms/Guns. PR: £3–500. CC: Paypal. Free Booksearch, Books Bought or Sold on Commission. Corresp: Italian. Also at: Leicester Antiques Warehouse and Olney Antiques Centre. [20/08/2003]

Paul Green, 83b London Road, Peterborough, PE2 9BS. Tel: Withheld. Est: 1998. Private premises. Postal business only. Very small stock. Spec: Naturism; Poetry. PR: £2–50. Cata: 2 on naturism and poetry. [Updated]

Peakirk Books, ■ Railway Cottage, 15 St Pegas Road, Peterborough, PE6 7NF. Prop: Heather and Jeff Lawrence. Tel: (01733) 253182. Website: www.peakirkbooks.com. E-mail: peakirkbooks@ btinternet.com. Est: 1997. Internet and postal. Shop open: **W:** 14:00–17:00; **Th:** 09:30–17:00; **F:** 09:30–17:30; **S:** 09:30–17:00; **Su:** 12:00–16:00. Large stock. Spec: Academic/Scholarly; Annuals; Author - General; Children's - General; Fiction - General; Illustrated; Military; Natural History; Poetry; Publishers - Penguin; Railways; Topography - Local; War - General; also, booksearch. PR: £1–500. CC: AE; MC; V; Debit card. Available on internet/telephone every day except Tuesday. [updated]

Frank T. Popeley, 27 Westbrook Park Road, Woodston, Peterborough, PE2 9JG. Tel: (01733) 562386. Private premises. Postal business only. Small stock. Spec: Animals and Birds; Countries - Africa; Countries - Kenya; Countries - Tanzania; Countries - Uganda; Sport - Big Game Hunting; Tribal. PR: £1–1,000. Books on early administration in Uganda. Cata: 2 general. [Updated]

Wizard Books, 106 Church Street, Deeping St. James, Peterborough, PE6 8HB. Prop: Stephen Blessett. Tel: (01778) 343175. Fax: (01778) 380538. E-mail: wizardbooks@aol.com. Private premises. Internet and postal. Small general stock. Spec: Arms & Armour; Arthurian; Cryptozoology; Divining; Ghosts; Magic & Conjuring; Military; Military History; Mysteries; Mysticism; Mythology; Occult; Psychic; Psychology/Psychiatry; Religion - General; Spiritualism; U.F.O.s; Witchcraft. PR: £5–100. CC: JCB; MC; V. [Updated]

SAINT IVES

Brunner Books,■, 1 White Hart Court, St. Ives, PE27 5EA. Prop: Chris & Barbara Frances Coupland. Tel: (01480) 300032. Fax: (01480) 300032. Est: 1999. Shop open: **M:** 09:30–17:00; **T:** 09:30–17:00; **W:** 09:30–17:00; **Th:** 09:30–12:30; **F:** 09:30–17:00; **S:** 09:00–17:00. Closed for lunch: 12:30–14:00. Spec: Fiction - General; Fiction - Crime, Detective, Spy, Thrillers; Fiction - Science Fiction; First Editions; Proof Copies. PR: £1–250. Also, new books. Cata: occasionally, on modern first editions. Mem: BA; VAT No: GB 716 6471 26. [Updated]

SAINT NEOTS

Target Books, 200 Cambridge Street, St. Neots, PE19 1PX. Prop: Michael Gaadt. Tel: (01480) 351832. E-mail: m.gaadt@ntlworld.com. Est: 1982. Private premises. Postal business only. Small stock. Spec: Biography; Health; History - General; Sport - Field Sports; Sport - Horse Racing (all aspects). PR: £1–300. [01/08/2003]

WISBECH

Oasis Booksearch,■, 88 Norfolk Street, Wisbech, PE13 2LF. Prop: R.G.M. & M.E. Welford. Tel: (01945) 420438. Fax: (01945) 465187. Website: www.ukbookworld.com/members/welford. E-mail: rwelford@onetel.com. Est: 1998. Internet and postal. Shop open: **T:** 09:00–17:00; **W:** 09:00–17:30; **Th:** 09:00–17:30; **F:** 09:00–17:30; **S:** 09:00–16:00. Small stock. Spec: Author - Ballantyne, Robert M.; Author - Lewis, C.S.; Author - Morton, H.V.; Bibles; Mind, Body & Spirit; Prayer Books; Religion - Christian; Religion - Methodism; Religion - Roman Catholic; Theology. PR: £1–25. CC: AE; JCB; MC; V. Mem: PBFA. [Updated]

CHESHIRE

CHEADLE (SEE ALSO UNDER GREATER MANCHESTER)

Geoff Booth (Booksearch Service), 2 Hastings Close, Cheadle Hulme, Cheadle, SK8 7BE. Tel: (0161) 485-4246. E-mail: geoff.booth131@btopenworld.com. Est: 1981. Private premises. Internet and postal. Appointment necessary. Open: **M:** 09:00–17:00; **T:** 09:00–17:00; **W:** 09:00–17:00; **Th:** 09:00–17:00; **F:** 09:00–17:00. Small stock. Spec: Art; Autobiography; Aviation; Biography; Colour-Plate; Crime (True); Fiction - General; Magic & Conjuring; Modern First Editions; Natural History; Proof Copies; Topography - General; also, booksearch. PR: £1–150. CC: Paypal. Cata: irregularly on specialities. [Updated]

A. Browne, 8 Lincoln Avenue, Heald Green, Cheadle, SK8 3LJ. Tel: withheld. E-mail: abrowne@talk21.com. Est: 1998. Private premises. Postal business only. Small stock. Spec: Geology; Mineralogy; Mining; Palaeontology. Cata: quarterly. [14/04/2003]

Tennis Collectables, 31 Syddall Avenue, Cheadle, SK8 3AA. Prop: Fiona & John Partington. Tel: (0161) 718-5378. Fax: (0161) 718-5378. E-mail: john@partbook.demon.co.uk. Private premises. Postal business only. Very small stock. Spec: Periodicals & Magazines; Sport - Tennis; also Booksearch. PR: £2–200. CC: AE; JCB; MC; V. Cata: 3 a year. VAT No: GB 748 5252 10. [Updated]

CHESTER

A. Grieveson, 34 Pickmere Drive, Eastham, Chester, Wirral, CH62 9EW. Prop: Andrea Grieveson. Tel: (0151) 3280172. Website: www.alibris.com. E-mail: golden.frog@lineone.net. Est: 1988. Spec: Alternative Medicine; Astrology; Ghosts; Parapsychology; Philosophy; Psychic; Supernatural. PR: £3–100. [05/09/2003]

Richard Nicholson of Chester, Stoneydale, Pepper Street, Christleton, Chester, CH3 7AG. Tel: (01244) 336004. Fax: (01244) 336138. Website: www.antiquemaps.com. Est: 1961. Postal business only. Very small stock. Spec: Atlases. PR: £10–3,000. CC: MC; V. [05/06/2003]

Stothert Old Books, ■ 4 Nicholas Street, Chester, CH1 2NX. Prop: Alan Checkley. Tel: (01244) 340756. Fax: (01829) 770628. E-mail: alancheckley@yahoo.com. Est: 1978. Shop open: **M:** 10:00–17:00; **T:** 10:00–17:00; **W:** 10:00–17:00; **Th:** 10:00–17:00; **F:** 10:00–17:00; **S:** 10:00–17:00. Medium stock. Spec: Antiquarian; Bindings; Children's - General; Fine & Rare; Literature; Private Press; Topography - General; Topography - Local; Transport; Travel - General; War - General. PR: £1–1,000. CC: JCB; MC; V. Corresp: French. VAT No: GB 691 9276 88. [Updated]

Words & Music, 2 City Walls, Northgate, Chester, CH1 2JG. Prop: Mr. S.M. Whitaker. Tel: (01244) 311910. Est: 1991. Spec: Art; Arts, The; Children's - General; Countries - Melanesia; Drama; First Editions; Food & Drink; History - General; Literature; Music - Composers; Music - Jazz; Music - Opera. PR: £1–100. [17/08/2003]

CREWE

Copnal Books, ■ 18 Meredith Street, Crewe. Prop: P.E. Ollerhead. Tel: (01270) 580470. E-mail: copnalbooks@yahoo.co.uk. Est: 1980. Shop open: **M:** 09:30–16:30; **T:** 09:30–16:30; **W:** 09:30–16:30; **Th:** 09:30–16:30; **F:** 09:30–16:30; **S:** 09:30–16:30. Large general stock. PR: £1–50. Open other times by appointment. Corresp: French. [Updated]

HOYLAKE

Marine and Cannon Books, Naval & Maritime Dept., 'Nilcoptra', 3 Marine Road, Hoylake, Wirral, CH47 2AS. Prop: Michael & Vivienne Nash and Diane Churchill-Evans. Tel: (0151) 632-5365. Fax: (0151) 632-6472. E-mail: michael@marinecannon.com. Est: 1983. Private premises. Internet and postal. Appointment necessary. Open: **M:** 09:00–18:00; **T:** 09:00–18:00; **W:** 09:00–18:00; **Th:** 09:00–18:00; **F:** 09:00–18:00; **S:** 09:00–17:00. Closed for lunch: 13:00–13:30. Medium stock. Spec: Antiquarian; Aviation; History - General; Manuscripts; Maritime/Nautical; Military; Military History; Naval; Shipbuilding; Transport; Voyages & Discovery; War - General; Whaling; also Booksearch. PR: £10–20,000. CC: JCB; MC; V; Maestro. Cata: One every 3 months. Mem: ABA; PBFA; ILAB. Also at: Military & Aviation Dept., Outlets at RN Museum Portsmouth; Albert Dock Liverpool. VAT No: GB 539 4137 32. [Updated]

HYDE

J.A. Heacock (Antiques and Books), ■ 155 Market Street, Hyde, SK14 1HG. Prop: Joseph Anthony Heacock. Tel: (0161) 366 5098. Est: 2000. Shop. Medium stock. Spec: History - General; Literature; Natural History; Topography - General; Travel - General. [03/09/2003]

KNUTSFORD

BC Books, 12 Mallard Close, Knutsford, WA16 8ES. Prop: Brian Corrigan. Tel: (01565) 654014. E-mail: brian@corrigan.demon.co.uk. Est: 1993. Private premises. Postal business only. Small general stock. Spec: First Editions; History - Ancient; History - British; Humour; Literature. PR: £1–250. Corresp: French. [Updated]

Fiction First, The Old Chapel, Knolls Green Village, Knutsford, WA16 7BW. Tel: (01565) 872634. Website: www.abebooks.com. E-mail: richard.offer@virgin.net. Est: 1992. Private premises. Internet and postal. Appointment necessary. Medium stock. Spec: Fiction - General; Fiction - Crime, Detective, Spy, Thrillers; Fiction - Fantasy, Horror; Fiction - Science Fiction; First Editions. PR: £10–2,000. CC: AE; MC; V. [Updated]

LYMM

K Books, 60 Mardale Crescent, Lymm, WA13 9PJ. Prop: Jef & Janet Kay. Tel: (01925) 755736. E-mail: jefkay@supanet.com. Est: 1994. Private premises. Appointment necessary. Small general stock. Spec: Astronautics; Author - Blyton, Enid; Author - Charteris, Leslie; Children's - General; Comic Books & Annuals; Fiction - General; Fiction - Science Fiction; First Editions; Juvenile. PR: £1–100. Corresp: German. Mem: Followers of Rupert. [Updated]

MACCLESFIELD

George Longden, 71 Grimshaw Lane, Bollington, Macclesfield, SK10 5LY. Prop: George Longden. Tel: (01625) 572584. Est: 1998. Private premises. Postal business only. Small stock. Spec: Cartoons; Comic Books & Annuals; Comics. PR: £2–200. Exhibits at book fairs in the North and Midlands. Mem: PBFA. [Updated]

Mereside Books, ■ 75 Chestergate, Macclesfield, SK11 6DG. Prop: Sally Laithwaite & Steve Kowalski. Tel: Shop (01625) 425352. Est: 1996. Shop open: **W:** 10:00–17:00; **Th:** 10:00–17:00; **F:** 10:00–17:00; **S:** 10:00–17:00. Small general stock. Spec: Illustrated. PR: £3–500. CC: E; JCB; MC; V. Organisers of Buxton Book Fairs. Mem: PBFA. [Updated]

Roger J. Treglown, Sunderland House, Sunderland Street, Macclesfield, SK11 6JF. Tel: (01625) 618978. Fax: (01625) 618978. Website: www.rogerjtreglown.com. E-mail: roger@rogerjtreglown.com. Est: 1980. Spec: Antiquarian; Chess; Early Imprints; Esoteric; Odd & Unusual. PR: £2–2,000. Also, valuations for probate etc. [01/08/2003]

NANTWICH

Cavern Books, ■ Units 2-4 & 16, Dagfields Antique Centre, Audlem Rd, Walgherton, Nantwich, CW5 7LG. Prop: Harry Madden. Tel: (01270) 841594. Website: www.cavernbooks.co.uk. E-mail: cavernbks@aol.com. Shop open: **M:** 10:00–17:00; **T:** 10:00–17:00; **W:** 10:00–17:00; **Th:** 10:00–17:00; **F:** 10:00–17:00; **S:** 10:00–17:00; **Su:** 10:00–17:00. Small stock. Spec: Entertainment - General; Military; Spiritualism; Topography - General; Transport. PR: £1–250. Also, stamps, CDs, Vinyl, postcards and 35mm slides. Also at: Internet Bookshop, Gloucestershire and and Biblion, London W1. [Updated]

Guildmaster Books, 81 Welsh Row, Nantwich, CW5 5ET. Prop: Guildmaster. Tel: (01270) 629982. Fax: (01270) 629108. E-mail: guild.house@virgin.net. Est: 1986. Office &/or bookroom. Internet and postal. Appointment necessary. Very small stock. Spec: Agriculture; Antiquarian; Churchilliana; Culture - National; Firearms/Guns; Herbalism; History - British; Maritime/Nautical; Military History; Topography - General. PR: £10–500. Cata: 1 on unsold. Corresp: Most major. Mem: On request, US verified. [Updated]

J & D Jones, 2 Butler Way, Nantwich, CW5 7AS. Prop: J & D Jones. Tel: (01270) 583431. Fax: (01270) 623644. Website: jonesthebook.com. E-mail: jdjones@rmplc.co.uk. Est: 1990. Private premises. Internet and postal. Telephone first. Small stock. Spec: Author - Brent-Dyer, Elinor M.; Children's - General; Children's - Illustrated; Illustrated. PR: £5–800. CC: Paypal. Corresp: French, German. [Updated]

Leona Thomas (Books), 84, London Road, Nantwich, CW5 6LT. Prop: Leona Thomas. Tel: (01270) 627779. Website: www.leonathomas.co.uk. E-mail: books@leonathomas.co.uk. Est: 1990. Private premises. Telephone first. Small stock. Spec: Antiquarian; Antiques; Bindings; Books about Books; Folio Society, The; History - General; Poetry; Topography - Local; War - English Civil Wars. PR: £1–500. Corresp: French. Also at: Brewing books at Barleycorns, Welsh Row, Nantwich. [Updated]

NORTHWICH

KSC Books, 48 Chapel Street, Castle, Northwich, CW8 1HD. Prop: K. Stuart Crook. Tel: (01606) 79975. Fax: by prior arrangement. E-mail: kscbooks@btinternet.com. Est: 1995. Private premises. Internet and postal. Telephone first. Small stock. Spec: Author - Laithwaite, Eric; Canals/Inland Waterways; Engineering; History - British; Musical Instruments; Science - General; Technology. PR: £1–100. CC: JCB; MC; V; Maestro. Also, a booksearch service. VAT No: GB 798 2130 04. [Updated]

RUNCORN

Kirk Ruebotham, 16 Beaconsfield Road, Runcorn, WA7 4BX. Tel: (01928) 560540. Website: www.abebooks .com/home/kirk61. E-mail: kirk.ruebotham@ntlworld.com. Est: 1993. Private premises. Postal business only. Small stock. Spec: Agriculture; Crime (True); Fiction - Crime, Detective, Spy, Thrillers; Fiction - Fantasy, Horror; Fiction - Science Fiction; First Editions; Vintage Paperbacks. PR: £2–150. Cata: 4 a year. [Updated]

TARPORLEY

Marine & Cannon Books, Sandowne, Four Lanes End, Tiverton Heath, Tarporley, CW6 9HN. Prop: Mrs Diane Churchill-Evans (Military & Aviation Dept). Tel: (01829) 732524. Fax: (01829) 730710. E-mail: diane@marinecannon.com. Est: 1983. Private premises. Open: **M:** 09:00–18:00; **T:** 09:00–18:00; **W:** 09:00–18:00; **Th:** 09:00–18:00; **F:** 09:00–18:00; **S:** 09:00–17:00; **Su:** 00:00–00:00. Medium stock. Spec: Academic/Scholarly; Antiquarian; Aviation; Military; Military History; Transport; War - General; also Booksearch. PR: £10–20,000. CC: JCB; MC; V; Maestro. Occasional fairs and booksearch. Cata: 4 a year on naval, military & aviation. Mem: ABA; PBFA; ILAB. VAT No: GB 539 4137 32. [Updated]

TARVIN

Henry Wilson Books, 14 Broomheath Lane, Tarvin, Chester, CH3 8HB. Prop: HGE Wilson. Tel: (01829) 740693. Fax: (01829) 749060. Website: www.henrywilsonbooks.co.uk. E-mail: hwrailwaybooks@ aol.com. Est: 1983. Private premises. Internet and postal. Appointment necessary. Shop at: Unit 18 Barrowmore Enterprise Estate, Great Barrow, Chester, CH3 8JA. Large stock. Spec: Author - Rolt, L.T.C.; Buses/Trams; Canals/Inland Waterways; History - Industrial; Railways; Steam Engines; Traction Engines; Transport; also Booksearch. PR: £2–500. CC: JCB; MC; V; Maestro. New books & back issues of railway journals. Cata: 1 a year on railways, transport and industrial history. Corresp: French, German. Mem: PBFA. VAT No: GB 439 7672 03. [Updated]

WARRINGTON

Halson Books, The Oaks, Farnworth Road, Penketh, Warrington, WA5 2TT. Tel: (01925) 726699. Website: www.users.zetnet.co.uk/halsongallery. E-mail: halson.gallery@zetnet.co.uk. Private premises. Internet and postal. Appointment necessary. Large stock. Spec: Colour-Plate; Dogs; Natural History. CC: PayPal. Cata: monthly. [11/05/2003]

Sensawunda Books, 59 Dunnock Grove, Birchwood, Warrington, WA3 6NW. Prop: Grant Flexman–Smith. Tel: (01925) 838501. E-mail: grant@sensawunda.freeserve.co.uk. Est: 1994. Private premises. Postal business only. Small stock. Spec: Fiction - Fantasy, Horror; Fiction - Science Fiction; Signed Editions. PR: £1–100. Cata: 3 a year. [Updated]

Dr. B. Shakeshaft, 15 Marlborough Crescent, Grappenhall, Warrington, WA4 2EE. Prop: B.L. Shakeshaft. Tel: (01925) 264790. E-mail: blsbooks@btopenworld.com. Est: 1999. Private premises. Postal business only. Very small stock. Spec: Americana; Children's - General; Illustrated; Modern First Editions; Natural History. PR: £1–500. Attends Knutsford Book Fair. [08/07/2003]

David M. Shaw, 31 Newlands Drive, Lowton, Warrington, WA3 2RJ. Tel: (01942) 726319. Website: www.antiquemapsuk.com. E-mail: david@antiquemapsuk.com. Est: 1986. Postal business only. Spec: Atlases; Canals/Inland Waterways. PR: £1–1,000. Also, remainders. Mem: PBFA. VAT No: GB 153 1344 96. [17/09/2003]

Naomi Symes Books, 2 Pineways, Appleton Park, Warrington, WA4 5EJ. Prop: Naomi Symes. Tel: 44 (0)1925 602898. Fax: 44 (0)1925 602898. Website: www.naomisymes.com. E-mail: books@naomisymes.com. Est: 1994. Private premises. Postal business only. Contactable. Open: **M:** 10:00–18:00; **T:** 10:00–18:00; **W:** 10:00–18:00; **Th:** 10:00–18:00; **F:** 10:00–18:00; **S:** 10:00–18:00; **Su:** 10:00–18:00. Small stock. Spec: Academic/Scholarly; Authors - Women; Feminism; Fiction - Women; History - General; History - 19th Century; History - British; History - European; History - Industrial; History - Labour/Radical Movements; History - Local; History - Modern. PR: £5–1,000. CC: AE; D; E; JCB; MC; V; Maestro, Solo. Also: History A Level tuition; booksearch service; proof reading; copy editing and history resource centre on-line. Cata: 3 a year. Corresp: French. Mem: PBFA. [Updated]

The Warrington Book Loft, ■ Osnath Works, Lythgoes Lane, Warrington, WA2 7XE. Prop: Mrs Pat Devlin. Tel: (01925) 633907. Est: 1994. Shop open: **M:** 10:30–18:30; **T:** 10:30–18:30; **W:** 10:30–18:30; **Th:** 10:30–18:30; **F:** 10:30–18:30; **S:** 10:00–18:00. Very large general stock. Spec: Academic/Scholarly; Fiction - General; University Texts. PR: £1–50. [Updated]

WIDNES

Iain Campbell, Unit A5, Moor Lane Business Centre, Moor Lane, Widnes, WA8 7AQ. Tel: (0151) 420-5545. Storeroom. Appointment necessary. Small stock. PR: £1–1,000. CC: D; MC; V. Mem: PBFA. VAT No: GB 166 7763 21. [07/09/2003]

WINSFORD

Blackman Books, 46 The Loont, Winsford, CW7 1EU. Prop: Margaret & Roger Blackman. Tel: (01606) 558527. Website: www.abebooks.com/home/rtmb. E-mail: books@blackmanbooks.freeserve.co.uk. Est: 1997. Private premises. Internet and postal. Appointment necessary. Very small stock. Spec: PR: £10–1,000. CC: JCB; MC; V; Da, S. Corresp: French. [Updated]

CORNWALL

BODMIN

Dusty Miller, Bruach, Cassacawn Road, Blisland, Bodmin, PL30 4JF. Tel: (01208) 851220. Fax: (01208) 851554. E-mail: pamdus@aol.com. Spec: Biography; Children's - General; Crafts; Fiction - General. [02/05/2003]

BUDE

David Eastwood Books, Ardoch Poundstock, Bude, EX23 0DF. Tel: (01288) 361847. E-mail: d_eastwood37@hotmail.com. Spec: Antiquianes; Children's - Illustrated; Fine & Rare; Illustrated; Limited Editions; Literature. PR: £10–1,000. Mem: PBFA. [updated]

CALLINGTON

Music By The Score, South Coombe, Downgate, Callington, PL17 8JZ. Prop: Eileen Hooper–Bargery. Tel: (01579) 370053. Fax: (01579) 370053. Website: www.musicbythescore.com. E-mail: musicbythescore@kernowserve.co.uk. Est: 1993. Private premises. Internet and postal. Appointment necessary. Open: **M:** 10:00–20:00; **T:** 10:00–20:00; **W:** 10:00–20:00; **Th:** 10:00–20:00; **F:** 10:00–20:00; **S:** 10:00–20:00; Closed for lunch: 13:00–14:00. Large stock. Spec: Magic & Conjuring; Music - General; Music - Composers; Music - Music Hall; Music - Musicians; Music - Opera; Music - Political Songs & Ballads; Music - Popular; Music - Printed. PR: £4–40. CC: D; MC; V; Switch. [Updated]

CAMBORNE

Humanist Book Services, 15 Basset Street, Camborne, TR14 8SW. Prop: Linnea Timson. Tel: (01209) 716470. Fax: (0870) 125 8049. Website: www.cornwallhumanists.org.uk. E-mail: humbooks@ ukgateway.net. Est: 1964. Spec: Evolution; Free Thought; Humanism; Philosophy. PR: £1–15. [Updated]

CHARLESTOWN

BBNO, 10 Quay Road, Charlestown, PL25 3NX. Prop: J.S. Kinross. Tel: Est: 1971. Private premises. Small stock. Spec: Apiculture; Children's - General; Crafts; Natural History. CC: MC; V. [25/06/2002]

DOWNDERRY

The Book Bungalow, Victoria Villa, Downderry, PL11 3LE. Prop: Simon and Janet Alloway. Tel: (01503) 250388. E-mail: email@bookbungalow.com. Est: 2000. Postal business only. Spec: Author - Cornwell, Bernard; Author - Fleming, Ian; Author - Rowling, J.K.; Biography; Children's - General; Crime (True); Fiction - Science Fiction; Illustrated; Modern First Editions; Signed Editions. PR: £2–1,500. [27/08/2003]

EAST LOOE

Bosco Books, ■ The Old Hall Bookshop, Chapel Court, Shutta Road, East Looe, PL13 1BJ. Prop: Mr. & Mrs. S. Hawes. Tel: (01503) 263700. Fax: (01503) 263700. E-mail: boscobooks@aol.com. Est: 1971. Internet and postal. Shop open: **M:** 10:30–17:00; **T:** 10:30–17:00; **W:** 10:30–17:00; **Th:** 10:30–17:00; **F:** 10:30–17:00; **S:** 10:30–17:00. Very large stock. Spec: Alpinism/Mountaineering; Archaeology; Architecture; Art; Art - History; Art - Reference; Biography; Crafts; Fiction - General; Gardening; Military; Ornithology; Transport; Victoriana. PR: £1–750. CC: MC; V; SW. Winter: closed Mondays and Sundays, please ring to confirm. Corresp: French, Italian. [19/08/2003]

**Dealers need to update their entry
at least once a year. Visit your page on
*www.sheppardsdirectories.com***

FALMOUTH

Browser's Bookshop, ■ 13, 14 & 15, St. George's Arcade, Falmouth, TR11 3DH. John Floyd. Tel: (01326) 313464. Est: 1985. Shop open: **M:** 10:00–17:00; **T:** 10:00–17:00; **W:** 10:00–17:00; **Th:** 10:00–17:00; **F:** 10:00–17:00; **S:** 10:00–17:00. Large stock. Spec: Maritime/Nautical; Odd & Unusual; Railways; Topography - General. PR: £1–200. CC: AE; V. [23/06/2002]

Isabelline Books, 2 Highbury House, 8 Woodlane Crescent, Falmouth, TR11 4QS. Prop: Michael Whetman. Tel: (01326) 210412. Fax: 0870 051 6387. Website: www.beakbook.demon.co.uk. E-mail: mikann@beakbook.demon.co.uk. Est: 1997. Private premises. Internet and postal. Appointment necessary. Very small stock. Spec: Ornithology. PR: £10–2,000. CC: JCB; V. Cata: 3 a year. [Updated]

FOWEY

Bookends of Fowey, ■ South Street, Fowey, PL23 1AR. Tel: (01726) 833361. Website: www. bookendsoffowey.com. E-mail: info@bookendsoffowey.com. Est: 1985. Shop; Internet and postal. Open. Shop at: 4 South Street, Fowey, Cornwall. PL23 1AR. Open: **M:** 10:00–18:00; **T:** 10:00–18:00; **W:** 10:00–18:00; **Th:** 10:00–18:00; **F:** 10:00–18:00; **S:** 10:00–18:00; **Su:** 14:00–18:00; Large stock. Spec: Author - du Maurier, Daphne; Author - Quiller-Couch, Sir A.T.; Naval; Sport - Yachting; Topography - Local; War - World War II; also Booksearch. CC: MC; V. VAT No: GB 813 0114 90. [Updated]

Ronald C. Hicks, Ardwyn, 22 Park Road, Fowey, PL23 1ED. Tel: (01726) 832739. Est: 1964. Private premises. Postal business only. Very small stock. Spec: Architecture; Art; History - Local; also Booksearch. PR: £1–500. Cata: occasionally. [Updated]

Sue Moore, 37 Passage Street, Fowey, PL23 1DE. Prop: Susan M. Moore. Tel: (01726) 832397. Est: 1986. Private premises. Appointment necessary. Small stock. Spec: Modern First Editions; also Booksearch. PR: £2–50. [Updated]

HELSTON

Peter Clay, Heatherbank, North Corner, Coverack, Helston, TR12 6TH. Prop: Peter & Linda Clay. Tel: (01326) 280475. E-mail: pete.clay@virgin.net. Est: 1982. Private premises. Internet and postal. Appointment necessary. Open: **M:** 10:30–17:30; **T:** 10:30–17:30; **W:** 10:30–17:30; **Th:** 10:30–17:30; **F:** 10:30–17:30. Medium stock. Spec: Antiques; History - Local; Topography - Local. PR: £1–100. Corresp: French. [24/11/2003]

The Helston Bookworm, ■ 9 Church Street, Helston, TR13 8TA. Prop: Ann & Malcolm Summers. Tel: (01326) 565079. Website: www.users.dialstart.net/~helstonb. E-mail: helstonb@btopenworld.com. Est: 1994. Internet and postal. Shop open: **M:** 10:00–17:30; **T:** 10:10–17:30; **W:** 10:00–17:30; **Th:** 10:00–17:30; **F:** 10:00–17:30; **S:** 10:00–14:00. Large general stock. Spec: Antiquarian; Topography - Local. PR: £1–300. CC: AE; MC; V. Mem: PBFA. [Updated]

J.T. & P. Lewis, 'Leaway', Tresowes Green, Ashton, Helston, TR13 9SY. Prop: John T. & Pearl Lewis. Tel: (01736) 762406. Website: http://ukbookworld.com/members/JTLANDPL. E-mail: JohnandPearl@aol.com. Est: 1990. Private premises. Internet and postal. Medium stock. Spec: Academic/Scholarly; Fiction - General; History - General; Modern First Editions; Odd & Unusual; Religion - General; Science - General; Theology; Topography - General; Travel - General; War - General. PR: £5–500. CC: Paypal. Payment via Paypal using JohnandPearl@aol.com. VAT No: GB 803 4711 59. [Updated]

LAUNCESTON

Abbey Bookshop, ■ 2 White Hart Arcade, Launceston, PL15 8AA. Prop: Spencer Magill. Tel: (01566) 779113. E-mail: SpencerMagill@aol.com. Est: 1981. Shop open: **M:** 09:00–17:00; **T:** 09:00–17:00; **W:** 09:00–17:00; **Th:** 09:00–17:00; **F:** 09:00–17:00; **S:** 09:00–16:00. Large general stock. Spec: Archaeology; Art; Autobiography; Cinema/Film; Countries - Ireland; Fiction - Crime, Detective, Spy, Thrillers; Fiction - Science Fiction; First Editions; History - General; History - Irish; Irish Interest; Literature; Mind, Body & Spirit; Modern First Editions. PR: £1–200. VAT No: GB 795 7472 66. [Updated]

Charles Cox Rare Books, River House, Treglasta, Launceston, PL15 8PY. Tel: (01840) 261085. Fax: (01840) 261464. Website: www.abebooks.com. E-mail: charlescox@verso.fsnet.co.uk. Est: 1974. Private premises. Internet and postal. Appointment necessary. Small stock. Spec: Antiquarian; Author - Browning, Robert.; Author - Byron, Lord; Author - Hardy, Thomas; Author - Housman, A.E.; Author - Newman, Cardinal; Author - Rossetti, C.; Author - Ruskin, John; Author - Swinburne, A.C.; Author - Tennyson, Lord Alfred. PR: £10–2,500. CC: Paypal. Cata: 3 a year on Literature 1780-1920. VAT No: GB 797 4887 40. [Updated]

R. & B. Graham, ■ 10 Church Street, Launceston, PL15 8AP. Prop: Richard & Beryl Graham. Tel: (01566) 774107. Fax: (01566) 777299. Website: www.cookery-books-online.com. E-mail: thebookshop @eclipse.co.uk. Est: 1984. Internet and postal. Shop open: **M:** 09:30–16:30; **T:** 09:30–16:30; **W:** 09:30–16:30; **Th:** 09:30–16:30; **F:** 09:30–16:30; **S:** 09:30–16:30. Small stock. Spec: Authors - Local; Cookery/ Gastronomy; History - Local; Natural History; Topography - General; Topography - Local. PR: £1–300. CC: AE; E; JCB; MC; V. Mem: BA. VAT No: GB 750 5071 55. [Updated]

Wayfarer Books, 3 Highgrove, Trevadlock Hall, Launceston, PL15 7PW. Prop: Bob & Brenda Brown. Tel: (01566) 782325. Fax: (01566) 782325. Website: www.ukbookworld.com/members/wayfarer. E-mail: beebeebrownwayfarer@eclipse.co.uk. Est: 1985. Private premises. Postal business only. Open: Small stock. Spec: Antiquarian; Aviation; Bindings; History - General; Maritime/Nautical; Military; Puzzles; Topography - General; also Booksearch. PR: £10–1,000. Cata: 3 a year on specialities. Mem: PBFA. [13/03/2003]

LISKEARD

P. & K. Stanton, Trafalgar, Pensilva, Liskeard, PL14 5PH. Prop: Pam and Kent Stanton. Tel: (01579) 362448. Fax: (01579) 363376. E-mail: books@liskeard.demon.co.uk. Est: 1982. Private premises. Appointment necessary. Very small stock. Spec: Author - Churchill, Sir Winston; Poetry. PR: £5–200. Major stocks of poet: Dr Charles Causely. [18/06/2003]

LOOE

A. & R. Booksearch, High Close, Lanreath, Looe, PL13 2PF. Prop: Avis & Robert Ronald. Tel: (01503) 220246. Fax: (01503) 220965. Website: www.musicbooksrus.com. E-mail: sales@ musicbooksrus.com. Est: 1984. Postal business only. Spec: Music - Popular. PR: £1–500. [12/08/2003]

MARAZION

Andrew Stewart, Castledene, Turnpike Hill, Marazion, TR170BZ. Tel: (01736) 794927. Fax: (01736) 719333. E-mail: espaceblue@btopenworld.com. Est: 1978. Private premises. Appointment necessary. Small stock. Spec: Classical Studies; Medieval; Printing; Theology. PR: £20–500. Cata: 3 a year. Corresp: French, German. Mem: PBFA. VAT No: GB 328 0066 78. [03/03/2003]

NEWQUAY

recollectionsbookshop.co.uk, Old Kiddlywink Cottage, Tresean, Newquay, TR8 5HN. Prop: Valerie Frith & Ray Frith. Tel: (01637) 830539. Website: recollectionsbookshop.co.uk. E-mail: railtonfrith@tiscali.co.uk. Est: 1996. Private premises. Internet and postal. Shop at: 8F Cardrew Indusrial Estate, Redruth, Cornwall UK TR15 1SS. Large stock. Spec: Topography - Local. PR: £4–100. CC: MC; V. VAT No: GB 760 4240 56. [Updated]

PENZANCE

Green Meadow Books, 2 Bellair House, Bellair Road, Madron, Penzance, TR20 8SP. Prop: Sue Bell. Tel: (01736) 351708. Fax: (01736) 351708. Website: www.greenmeadowbooks.co.uk. E-mail: sue@ bell83.fsnet.co.uk. Est: 1982. Private premises. Internet and postal. Appointment necessary. Medium stock. Spec: Author - Blyton, Enid; Author - Saville, M.; Children's - General; Children's - Illustrated; Illustrated. PR: £2–2,500. CC: MC; V. Also, toys, games, ephemera & booksearch service. Cata: 5 a year. [Updated]

Mount's Bay Books, 12 Garth Road, Newlyn, Penzance, TR18 5QJ. Prop: Tim Scott. Tel: (01736) 351335. Website: www.mountsbaybooks.co.uk. E-mail: timscott@mountsbaybooks.co.uk. Est: 1994. Private premises. Internet and postal. Appointment necessary. Open: **M:** 10:00–17:00; **T:** 10:00–17:00; **W:** 10:00–17:00; **Th:** 10:00–17:00; **F:** 10:00–17:00; **S:** 10:00–16:00; Very small stock. Spec: Author - Seymour, John; Author - Tangye, D.; Natural History; Rural Life; Topography - Local. PR: £2–150. Cata: 5 – Specialist areas. [Updated]

Newlyn & New Street Books, ■ New Street Bookshop, 4 New Street, Penzance, TR18 2LZ. Prop: Kelvin Hearn. Tel: (1736) 362758. E-mail: eankelvin@yahoo.com. Est: 1992. Internet and postal. Shop open: **M:** 10:00–17:00; **T:** 10:00–17:00; **W:** 10:00–17:00; **Th:** 10:00–17:00; **F:** 10:00–17:00; **S:** 10:00–17:00. Medium stock. Spec: Art; Topography - General; Topography - Local. PR: £1–350. CC: MC; V. [Updated]

REDRUTH

Anne Jones, Bryher, Barncoose Terrace, Redruth, TR15 3EP. Tel: (01209) 211180. Fax: (01209) 211180. E-mail: jones@bryherbooks.fsnet.co.uk. Est: 1989. Private premises. Postal business only. Very small stock. Spec: Architecture; Bridge; Canals/Inland Waterways; Civil Engineering; Company History; Engineering; History - Industrial; Industry; Steam Engines; Technical; Technology; Traction Engines. PR: £5–250. CC: MC; V. Cata: 2 a year. [31/07/2003]

SAINT AUSTELL

Neville Chapman, 24 Caudledown Lane, Stenalees, St. Austell, PL26 8TG. Tel: (01726) 850067. Website: www.abebooks.com/home/chapbooks. E-mail: chapbooks@aol.com. Est: 1992. Private premises. Internet and postal. Appointment necessary. Small stock. Spec: Academic/Scholarly; Advertising; Author - Bellairs, George; Topography - Local. PR: £1–100. [Updated]

SAINT IVES

The Book Gallery, The Old Post Office Garage, Chapel Street, St. Ives, TR26 2LR. Prop: David Wilkinson. Tel: (01736) 793545. Website: www.abebooks.com/home/tinyworld. E-mail: books@book-gallery.co.uk. Est: 1991. Private premises. Internet and postal. Telephone first. Small stock. Spec: Art; Art - History; Art - Reference; First Editions; Topography - Local. PR: £5–2,500. [Updated]

SAINT TEATH

Christopher Holtom, Aaron's, Treburgett, St. Teath, PL30 3LJ. Tel: (01208) 851062. Fax: (01208) 851062. Est: 1972. Private premises. Appointment necessary. Medium stock. Spec: Antiquarian; Children's - General; Education & School; Fables; Folklore; Juvenile; Mathematics. PR: £3–150. Cata: 6 a year on 18th–20thC children's books and school text books. Corresp: French. [Updated]

TRURO

Bonython Bookshop, 16 Kenwyn Street, Truro, TR1 3BU. Prop: R.D. Carpenter. Tel: (01872) 262886. E-mail: bonythonbooks@btconnect.com. Est: 1996. Open: **M:** 10:30–16:30; **T:** 10:30–16:30; **W:** 10:30–16:30; **Th:** 10:30–16:30; **F:** 10:30–16:30; **S:** 10:30–16:30; Medium stock. Spec: Archaeology; Author - du Maurier, Daphne; Author - Tangye, D.; History - Local; Topography - Local; also Booksearch. PR: £1–1,000. CC: D; E; JCB; MC; V. Also, books on Cornwall. Corresp: French. [Updated]

Just Books, ■ 9 Pydar Mews, Truro, TR1 2UX. Prop: Jennifer Wicks. Tel: (01872) 242532. Est: 1987. Shop open: **M:** 09:30–17:00; **T:** 09:30–17:00; **W:** 09:30–17:00; **Th:** 09:30–17:00; **F:** 09:30–17:00; **S:** 09:30–17:00. Medium stock. Spec: History - Local; Topography - Local. PR: £1–200. CC: AE; E; JCB; MC; V. Books on Cornwall. Cata: occasionally. VAT No: GB 789 3503 84. [Updated]

Kenneth Langmaid, Glencairn House, Grampound Road, Truro, TR2 4EE. Tel: (01726) 882280. Est: 1966. Private premises. Appointment necessary. Very large stock. Spec: Arts, The; Author - General; Biography; Countries - France; Countries - Italy; Ecclesiastical History & Architecture; Fiction - General; First Editions; Guide Books; History - General; International Affairs; Law; Literature; Military; Music - General. PR: £1–200. Also, postcards. Cata: occasionally on theology and topography. Corresp: German. [15/08/2003]

Westcountry Old Books, ■ 8, St.Mary's St., Truro, TR12AF. Prop: David Neil. Tel: 01803-322712. Website: www.abebooks.com. E-mail: westcountryoldbooks@btopenworld.com. Est: 1988. Shop open: **M:** 09:30–17:30; **T:** 09:30–17:30; **W:** 09:30–17:30; **Th:** 09:30–17:30; **F:** 09:30–17:30; **S:** 09:30–17:30. Very small stock. Spec: Antiquarian; History - General; Literature. CC: E; JCB; MC; V. Mem: PBFA. Also at: Top Floor, S.P.C.K. Bookshop, 1-2 Catherine St.Exeter, Devon. [Updated]

WADEBRIDGE

Polmorla Books, ■ 1 Polmorla Road, Wadebridge, PL27 7NB. Prop: John Buck. Tel: (01208) 814399. Est: 1990. Shop open: **M:** 10:30–16:00; **T:** 10:30–16:00; **W:** 09:30–16:00; **Th:** 10:30–16:00; **F:** 10:30–16:00; **S:** 10:30–16:00. Large stock. Spec: Art; Art - History; Biography; Classical Studies; Drama; Engineering; Fiction - General; History - General; History - Local; Literature; Military; Music - General; Natural History; Philosophy; Transport. PR: £1–50. Winter hours 10:30–16:30. [Updated]

CUMBRIA

ALSTON

Durham Book Centre, ■ Front Street, Alston, CA9 3HU. Prop: Mrs. A. Dumble. Tel: (01434) 381066. E-mail: ann@absolutely.fsnet.co.uk. Est: 1968. Shop open: **S:** 10:00–17:00; **Su:** 10:00–17:00. Small general stock. PR: £1–50. VAT No: GB 176 3861 34. [Updated]

APPLEBY–IN–WESTMORLAND

Barry McKay Rare Books, Kingstone House, Battlebarrow, Appleby–in–Westmorland, CA16 6XT. Prop: Barry McKay. Tel: (01768) 352282. Fax: (01768) 352946. Website: www.abebooks.com/home/ barrymckayrarebks. E-mail: barry.mckay@britishlibrary.net. Est: 1986. Office &/or bookroom; Internet and postal. Telephone first. Open: **M:** 09:00–17:00; **T:** 09:00–17:00; **W:** 09:00–17:00; **Th:** 09:00–17:00; **F:** 09:00–17:00; **S:** 09:00–17:00. Medium stock. Spec: Antiquarian; Bibliography; Bookbinding; Books about Books; Calligraphy; Fine Printing; Imprints; Palaeography; Papermaking; Printing; Publishing. PR: £5–500. CC: E; JCB; MC; V. Cata: quarterly. Corresp: French. Mem: PBFA. VAT No: GB 448 5469 09. [29/06/2003]

Major John R. McKenzie, Town End Farm, Brampton, Appleby–in–Westmorland, CA16 6JS. Prop: Major J.R. McKenzie & Susana Hunter. Tel: (01768) 351384. E-mail: mckenzie@ militarybooks.freeserve.co.uk. Est: 1993. Private premises. Postal business only. Spec: Military; also Booksearch. PR: £10–1,000. Corresp: Spanish. [29/06/2003]

BARROW–IN–FURNESS

Americanabooksuk, 72 Park Drive, Barrow–in–Furness, LA13 9BB. Prop: Alan R. Beattie. Tel: (01229) 829722. Website: www.americanabooks.co.uk. E-mail: alan.rbeattie@virgin.net. Private premises. Very small stock. Spec: American Indians; Americana; Art; Countries - U.S.A.; Fiction - Westerns; Firearms/Guns; History - American; Literature; Military History; Travel - Americas; Voyages & Discovery; War - American Civil War; also, booksearch. PR: £3–150. Cata: 1 a year [13/04/2003]

BOWNESS–ON–WINDERMERE

Past & Presents, ■ Crag Brow, Bowness–on–Windermere, LA23 3BX. Prop: W.F. & C.R. Johnson. Tel: (01539) 445417. E-mail: billnchris.johnson@btinternet.com. Est: 1995. Shop open: **M:** 09:30–17:30; **T:** 09:30–17:30; **W:** 09:30–17:30; **Th:** 09:30–17:30; **F:** 09:30–17:30; **S:** 09:30–17:30; **Su:** 09:30–17:30; Very small general stock. Spec: Author - Ransome, Arthur. PR: £2–85. CC: AE; D; MC; V. VAT No: GB 652 1595 37. [18/08/2003]

BROUGH

Summerfield Books, ■ Main Street, Brough, CA17 4AX. Prop: Jon & Sue Atkins. Tel: (01768) 341577. Fax: (01768) 341687. Website: www.summerfieldbooks.com. E-mail: info@summerfieldbooks.com. Est: 1983. Internet and postal. Shop open: **M:** 09:30–16:30; **T:** 09:30–16:30; **Th:** 09:30–16:30; **F:** 09:30–16:30. Medium stock. Spec: Botany; Conservation; Ecology; Forestry; Gardening; Herbalism; Horticulture; Natural History; Plant Hunting; also, booksearch. PR: £1–2,000. CC: AE; JCB; MC; V. Open at other times by appointment. Cata: 2 on specialities and natural history. Corresp: French, German. Mem: PBFA. VAT No: GB 442 8165 50. [Updated]

CARLISLE

Maurice Dodd Books, Greenwood House, Thursby, Carlisle, CA5 6NU. Prop: R.J. McRoberts. Tel: (01228) 710456. Fax: (01228)710456. E-mail: doddrarebooks@btconnect.com. Est: 1945. Office &/or bookroom. Telephone first. Shop at: Bookroom at 44 Cecil Street, Carlisle CA1 1NT. Open: Medium stock. Spec: Antiquarian; Bindings; History - General; History - Local; Illustrated; Literature; Science - General; Topography - Local; Travel - General. PR: £5–1,500. Cata: 2 a year. Mem: PBFA. VAT No: GB 256 3359 47. [04/06/2003]

Anne Fitzsimons, 3 Croft Park, Wetheral, Carlisle, CA4 8JH. Tel: (01228) 562184. Fax: (01228) 562184. Est: 1978. Private premises. Postal business only. Small stock. Spec: Cinema/Film; Circus; Dance; Magic & Conjuring; Music - General; Music - Music Hall; Music - Opera; Performing Arts; Puppets & Marionettes; Television; Theatre. Cata: 2 a year. Mem: PBFA. [Updated]

CARTMEL

Peter Bain Smith, ■ Bank Court, Market Square, Cartmel, LA11 6QB. Tel: (01539) 536369. Est: 1972. Shop open: **M:** 13:30–17:00; **T:** 13:30–17:00; **W:** 13:30–17:00; **Th:** 13:30–17:00; **F:** 13:30–17:00; **S:** 13:30–17:00; **Su:** 13:30–17:00. Very large stock. Spec: Children's - General; Classical Studies; Topography - Local. PR: £1–400. CC: E; MC; V; SO. Winter open, Thursday to Sunday 13.30–16.30. [Updated]

GRANGE–OVER–SANDS

Norman Kerr Booksellers, Priory Barn, Cartmel, Grange–over–Sands, LA11 6PX. Prop: H. & J.M. Kerr. Tel: (015395) 36247/32508. Fax: n/a. Website: www.kerrbooks.co.uk. E-mail: enquiries@kerrbooks.co.uk. Est: 1933. Shop &/or showroom; telephone first. Also at: Gatehouse Bookshop, The Square, Cartmel. Medium stock. Spec: Architecture; Arts, The; Engineering; Illustrated; Maritime/Nautical; Motoring; Natural History; Ornithology; Railways; Topography - Local; Transport; Travel - General. PR: £5–1,000. Alternative tel: (015395) 32508. Cata: occasionally. Mem: PBFA. VAT No: GB 312 3475 89. [Updated]

GRASMERE

Yewtree Books, ■ The Lakes Crafts & Antiques Gallery, 3 Oakbank Broadgate, Grasmere, LA22 9TA. Prop: Joe and Sandra Arthy. Tel: (015394) 35037. Fax: (015394) 44234. E-mail: lakescrafts@dsl.pipex.com. Est: 1990. Shop open: **M:** 10:00–17:00; **T:** 10:00–17:00; **W:** 10:00–17:00; **Th:** 10:00–17:00; **F:** 10:00–17:00; **S:** 10:00–17:00; **Su:** 10:00–17:00. Small stock. Spec: Alpinism/Mountaineering; History - General; Railways; Sport - General; Topography - General; Topography - Local; Travel - General. PR: £1–300. CC: JCB; MC; V. [Updated]

KENDAL

Kirkland Books, ■ 68 Kirkland, Kendal, LA9 5AP. Prop: Linden Burke. Tel: (0800) 0112368. Fax: (0800) 0112568. Website: http://www.kirklandbooks.co.uk. E-mail: linden@kirklandbooks.co.uk. Est: 1980. Internet and postal. Shop at: http://www.kirklandbooks.com. Open: **Th:** 10:00–17:00; **F:** 10:00–17:00; **S:** 10:00–17:00. Medium stock. Spec: Railways; Sport - Climbing & Trekking; Topography - Local; Transport. PR: £5–500. CC: AE; D; E; JCB; MC; V. Mem: Also at: Kirkland Books, 68 Kirkland, Kendal, Cumbria, LA9 5AP. [Updated]

Left on The Shelf, Yard 91, Highgate, Kendal, LA9 4ED. Prop: Dave Cope. Tel: (01539) 729599. Website: www.abebooks.com/home/leftontheshelf. E-mail: leftontheshelf@cricketfield.demon.co.uk. Est: 1992. Storeroom; Internet and postal. Telephone first. Large stock. Spec: History - Labour/Radical Movements; Marxism; Pacifism; Radical Issues; Socialism; Trade Unions; War - Spanish Civil War; also Booksearch. PR: £2–150. CC: MC; V. Cata: 4 on Socialism. Corresp: French. Mem: PBFA. [Updated]

The Riverside Bookshop, ■ Yard 39, Highgate, Kendal, LA9 4ED. Prop: Paul & Carole Lee. Tel: (01539) 735173. Fax: (0870) 124-8380. Website: www.riversidebooks.co.uk. E-mail: riversidebooks@aol.com. Est: 1993. Internet and postal. Shop open: **M:** 10:30–16:00; **T:** 10:30–16:00; **W:** 10:30–16:00; **F:** 10:30–16:00; **S:** 10:30–15:00. Medium stock. Spec: Academic/Scholarly; Advertising; Alpinism/ Mountaineering; Children's - General; Fiction - General; First Editions; Railways; Topography - Local. PR: £1–250. CC: JCB; MC; V. Mem: PBFA. [29/06/2003]

KESWICK

Jean Altshuler, 54 St. John Street, Keswick, CA12 5AB. Tel: (01768) 775745. E-mail: books@ jopplety.demon.co.uk. Est: 1996. Private premises. Internet and postal. Appointment necessary. Small general stock. Spec: Children's - General; Fiction - Science Fiction. PR: £5–200. [Updated]

Keswick Bookshop, ■ 4 Station Street, Keswick, CA12 5HT. Prop: Jane & John Kinnaird. Tel: (01228) 528567. Est: 1994. Shop open: **M:** 10:30–17:00; **T:** 10:30–17:00; **W:** 10:30–17:00; **Th:** 10:30–17:00; **F:** 10:30–17:00. **S:** 10:30–17:00. Medium stock. Spec: Antiques; Applied Art; Architecture; Art; Children's - General; Decorative Art; First Editions; Illustrated; Interior Design; Photography. PR: £1–500. CC: JCB; MC; V. Winter opening: Saturday only (Nov-March). Mem: PBFA. VAT No: GB 531 4987 33. [Updated]

KIRKBY STEPHEN

The Book House, Ravenstonedale, Kirkby Stephen, CA17 4NG. Prop: Chris & Mary Irwin. Tel: (01539) 623634. Website: www.thebookhouse.co.uk. E-mail: mail@thebookhouse.co.uk. Est: 1963. Private premises. Open: **M:** 10:00–17:00; **W:** 10:00–17:00; **Th:** 10:00–17:00; **F:** 10:00–17:00; **S:** 09:00–17:00; Large stock. Spec: Children's - General; Engineering; Fiction - General; Gardening; History - Industrial; Industry; Languages - Foreign; Languages - National; Mining; Railways; Technology; Transport; also, booksearch. PR: £1–750. CC: E; MC; V. Cata: 8 a year. Corresp: French, Italian. Mem: PBFA. VAT No: GB 113 8746 69. [Updated]

PENRITH

David A.H. Grayling, Verdun House, Main Street, Shap, Penrith, CA10 3NG. David A H Grayling. Tel: (01931) 716746. Fax: (01931) 716746. Website: www.davidgraylingbooks.co.uk. E-mail: graylingbook@fsbdial.co.uk. Est: 1970. Private premises. Internet and postal. Appointment necessary. Medium stock. Spec: Colour-Plate; Fine & Rare; Natural History; Scottish Interest; Sport - Angling/Fishing; Sport - Big Game Hunting; Sport - Field Sports; Sport - Shooting; Travel - Africa; Travel - Americas; Travel - Asia; Zoology. PR: £20–5,000. CC: AE; MC; V. Publishers of reprints of rare books. Cata: 8 a year on hunting, shooting, fishing, big game, natural history. Corresp: French, German. Mem: PBFA. VAT No: GB 154 6592 46. [Updated]

G.K. Hadfield, Beck Bank, Great Salkeld, Penrith, CA11 9LN. Prop: G.K. & J.V. Hadfield & D.W. & N.R. Hadfield–Tilly. Tel: (01768) 870111. Fax: (01768) 870111. Website: www.gkhadfield-tilly.co.uk. E-mail: gkhadfield@dial.pipex.com. Est: 1974. Shop &/or showroom. Internet and postal. Open: **M:** 09:00–17:00; **T:** 09:00–17:00; **W:** 09:00–17:00; **Th:** 09:00–17:00; **F:** 09:00–17:00; **S:** 09:00–17:00. Very small stock. Spec: Antiques; Astronomy; Bell-Ringing (Campanology); Furniture; Gemmology; Horology; Mathematics; Microscopy; Scientific Instruments. CC: AE; JCB; MC; V; SO, ELEC. Also, a booksearch service, antique clocks & materials for restoring antique clocks. Cata: 2 a year as listed. Corresp: French. Mem: B.H.I. VAT No: GB 114 809 578. [Updated]

Phenotype Books Ltd, 39 Arthur Street, Penrith, CA11 7TT. Prop: J.E. Mattley. Tel: (01768) 863049. Fax: (01768) 890493. Website: www.phenotypebooks.co.uk. E-mail: phenobooks@btconnect.com. Est: 1985. Private premises. Internet and postal. Telephone first. Small stock. Spec: Agriculture; Animals and Birds; Carriages & Driving; Farming & Livestock; Farriers; Humanities; Periodicals & Magazines; Veterinary. PR: £5–1,800. Cata: 6 a year on subjects relating to the farm. Mem: PBFA. VAT No: GB 442 8614 47. [Updated]

SEASCALE

Archie Miles Book Shop, ■ Beck Place, Gosforth, Seascale, CA20 1AT. Prop: Mrs. C. M. Linsley. Tel: (01946) 725792. Est: 1870. Shop open: **T:** 10:00–17:00; **W:** 10:00–17:00; **Th:** 10:00–17:00; **F:** 10:00–17:00; **S:** 10:00–17:00. Medium stock. Spec: Illustrated; Literature; Topography - General; also Booksearch. PR: £1–1,000. Opening hours varied in winter, phone first. [Updated]

SEDBURGH

R.F.G. Hollett and Son, 6 Finkle Street, Sedbergh, LA10 5BZ. Prop: C.G. & R.F.G. Hollett. Tel: (01539) 620298. Fax: (01539) 621396. Website: www.holletts-rarebooks.co.uk. E-mail: hollett@ sedbergh.demon.co.uk. Est: 1959. Shop &/or showroom; Internet and postal. Appointment necessary. Very large stock. Spec: Alpinism/Mountaineering; Antiquarian; Antiques; Biography; Children's - General; Collecting; Colour-Plate; Fine Art; Gardening; Geology; Limited Editions; Literature; Modern First Editions; Natural History; New Naturalist; Plant Hunting; Private Press. PR: £30–50,000. CC: AE; E; JCB; MC; V; Maestro. Valuations. Cata: 15 a year regularly. Mem: ABA. VAT No: GB 343 4391 63. [Updated]

Avril Whittle, Bookseller, Whittle's Warehouse, 7–9 (Rear) Bainbridge Road, Sedbergh, LA10 5AU. Prop: Avril Whittle. Tel: (015396) 21770. Fax: (015396) 21770. E-mail: avrilsbooks@aol.com. Est: 1980. Warehouse. Appointment necessary. Shop at: Sleepy Elephant Books & Artefacts, 16 Back Lane, Sedburgh, LA10 5AQ. Medium stock. Spec: Crafts; Crochet; Decorative Art; Embroidery; Fashion & Costume; Illustrated; Interior Design; Needlework; Rugs; Social History; Tapestry; Textiles; Theatre; Toys; Woodwork. PR: £1–600. CC: MC; V. Cata: 1 a year on art, craft, design, emphasis on textile arts. Corresp: French. VAT No: GB 379 7477 78. [Updated]

ULVERSTON

Bookfare, Lowick Hall, Ulverston, LA12 8ED. Prop: Dr. A.C.I. Naylor. Tel: (01229) 885240. Fax: (01229) 885240. Website: www.bookfare.co.uk. E-mail: ambookfare@aol.com. Est: 1977. Private premises. Postal business only. Small general stock. Spec: PR: £6–300. Corresp: French. [13/04/2003]

WELTON

All Seasons Books, Sebergham Castle Mansion, Welton, Near Carlisle, CA5 7HG. Prop: Frank Grant. Tel: (01697) 476061. Fax: (01697) 476079. E-mail: FGrant7472@aol.com. Est: 1994. Private premises. Postal business only. Appointment necessary. Small stock. Spec: Alpinism/Mountaineering; Geology; Sport - Climbing & Trekking; Topography - Local. PR: £2–500. Also, a booksearch service. Cata: 1 a year on specialities. [Updated]

WHITEHAVEN

Michael Moon's Bookshop, ■ 19 Lowther Street, Whitehaven, CA28 7AL. Prop: Michael Moon. Tel: (01946) 599010. Fax: (09146) 599010. Est: 1970. Shop; Open: **M:** 09:30–17:00; **T:** 09:30–17:00; **W:** 09:30–17:00; **Th:** 09:30–17:00; **F:** 09:30–17:00; **S:** 09:30–17:00. Very large general stock. Spec: Cinema/Film; History - Local; Topography - Local; also Booksearch. PR: £1–1,000. CC: D; JCB; MC. Closed Wed - from Jan to Easter. Publisher on Cumbrian history. Mem: PBFA; SBA. VAT No: GB 288 1073 42. [Updated]

WIGTON

Chelifer Books, Todd Close, Curthwaite, Wigton, CA7 8BE. Prop: Mike Smith & Deryn Walker. Tel: (01228) 711388. Website: www.militarybooks.net. Est: 1985. Private premises. Internet and postal. Appointment necessary. Small stock. Spec: American Indians; Antiquarian; Arms & Armour; Aviation; Military; Military History; War - General; Wargames. PR: £5–1,500. CC: MC; V; Switch. Cata: 6 a year. [12/07/2003]

Rosley Books, Rosley Farmhouse, Rosley, Wigton, CA7 8BZ. Prop: Ian Blakemore. Tel: (016973) 49924. Fax: (016973) 45149. Website: www.rosleybooks.com. Est: 2000. Private premises. Appointment necessary. Open: Medium stock. Spec: Academic/Scholarly; Antiquarian; Author - Belloc, Hilaire; Author - Bunyan, John; Author - Chesterton, G.K.; Author - Eliot, T.S.; Author - Inklings, The; Author - Lewis, C.S.; Author - MacDonald, George; Author - Ruskin, John; Author - Tolkien, J.R PR: £5–5,000. [18/04/2003]

**Dealers need to update their entry
at least once a year. Visit your page on
*www.sheppardsdirectories.com***

WINDERMERE

Fireside Bookshop, ■ 21 Victoria Street, Windermere, LA23 1AB. Prop: Mr R.D. Sheppard. Tel: (015394) 45855. Website: www.firesidebookshop.co.uk. E-mail: firesidebookshop@btconnect.com. Est: 1977. Shop open: **M:** 11:00–17:00; **T:** 11:00–17:00; **W:** 11:00–17:00; **Th:** 11:00–17:00; **F:** 11:00–17:00; **S:** 11:00–17:00; **Su:** 11:00–17:00. Large stock. Spec: Academic/Scholarly; Alpinism/Mountaineering; Antiquarian; Art; Fiction - General; History - General; Humanities; Maritime/Nautical; Medicine - History of; Military; Natural History; Rural Life; Science - History of; Social History; Transport. PR: £1–1,000. CC: AE; JCB; MC; Switch. [Updated]

WITHERSLACK

Rosemary Dooley, Crag House, Witherslack, Grange–over–Sands, LA11 6RW. Prop: R.M.S. Dooley. Tel: (01539) 552286. Fax: (01539) 552013. Website: www.booksonmusic.co.uk. E-mail: rd@booksonmusic.co.uk. Est: 1992. Private premises. Postal business only. Medium stock. Spec: Music - General. PR: £3–400. CC: AE; E; MC; V. Cata: 6 every 2 months. Mem: PBFA. VAT No: GB 393 1979 09. [Updated]

DERBYSHIRE

ALFRETON

John Titford, Yew Tree Farm, Hallfieldgate, Higham, Alfreton, DE55 6AG. (*). Tel: (01773) 520389. Fax: (01773) 833373. E-mail: J.Titford@zen.co.uk. Est: 1987. Private premises. Postal business only. Appointment necessary. Small stock. Spec: Genealogy; History - General; Topography - General; also Booksearch. PR: £2–1,000. Corresp: French. Mem: PBFA. [Updated]

ASHBOURNE

Pamela Elsom - Antiques, ■ 5 Church Street, Ashbourne, DE6 1AT. Tel: (01335) 343468. Est: 1963. Shop open: **Th:** 10:00–17:00; **F:** 10:00–17:00; **S:** 10:00–17:00. Small stock. Spec: PR: £1–50. [23/06/2002]

BAKEWELL

Country Books, Courtyard Cottage, Little Longstone, Bakewell, DE45 1NN. Prop: Richard J.T. Richardson. Tel: (01629) 640670. Fax: (01629) 640670. E-mail: dickrichardson@country-books.co.uk. Est: 1992. Private premises. Book fairs only. Appointment necessary. Small general stock. Spec: Academic/Scholarly; Architecture; Farming & Livestock; Folklore; History - Local; Rural Life. PR: £3–150. CC: V. Cata: 4 A YEAR. [Updated]

BELPER

Green Man Books, 12 The Scotches, Belper, DE56 2UE. Prop: N. Rigby. Tel: (01773) 828503. Est: 1984. Private premises. Postal business only. Small stock. [24/06/2002]

BUXTON

Scrivener's Books & Book Binding, ■, 42 High St., Buxton, SK17 6HB. Prop: Alastair Scrivener. Tel: (01298) 73100. Est: 1990. Shop open: **M:** 09:00–17:00; **T:** 09:00–17:00; **W:** 09:00–17:00; **Th:** 09:00–17:00; **F:** 09:00–17:00; **S:** 09:00–17:00; **Su:** 12:00–16:00. Very large stock. Spec: Academic/Scholarly; Animals and Birds; Antiquarian; Archaeology; Art - Reference; Children's - General; Cinema/Film; Comic Books & Annuals; Countries - Poland; Crafts; Dictionaries; Engineering; Farming & Livestock; Fiction - General; First Editions. PR: £1–2,000. CC: AE; D; E; JCB; MC; V. [02/07/2003]

CASTLETON

Hawkridge Books, ■ The Cruck Barn, Cross Street, Castleton, Hope Valley, S33 8WH. Prop: Dr. J. & Mrs. I. Tierney. Tel: (01433) 621999. Website: www.hawkridge.co.uk. E-mail: books@hawkridge.co.uk. Est: 1995. Shop open: **M:** 10:00–17:30; **T:** 10:00–17:30; **W:** 10:00–17:30; **Th:** 10:00–17:30; **F:** 10:00–17:30; **S:** 10:00–17:30; **Su:** 12:00–17:30. Large general stock. Spec: Natural History; Ornithology. PR: £5–900. CC: AE; JCB; MC; V. Also, barn bed & breakfast. [Updated]

CHESTERFIELD

Ian Briddon, Meynell Close, Chesterfield, S40 3BL. Tel: (01246) 208411. E-mail: Briddianbuks@aol.com. Est: 2004. Private premises. Internet and postal. Very small stock. Spec: Annuals; Antiquarian; Children's - Illustrated; Erotica; Fine & Rare; First Editions; Food & Drink; Homosexuality & Lesbianism; Humour; Signed Editions; Vintage Paperbacks. PR: £3–250. [Updated]

Tilleys Vintage Magazine Shop, ■ 21 Derby Road, Chesterfield, S40 2EF. Prop: Antonius & Albertus Tilley. Tel: (01246) 563868. Website: www.tilleysmagazines.com. E-mail: tilleysoldmags@aol.com. Est: 1978. Shop but telephone first. Very large stock. Spec: Comic Books & Annuals; Glamour; Newspapers - General; Periodicals & Magazines. PR: £1–100. CC: AE; MC; V. Mail order. 2 million + items in stock 1890s to present. Corresp: Dutch. Also at: 281 Shoreham Street, Sheffield (q.v.). [updated]

CROMFORD

Scarthin Books, ■ The Promenade, Scarthin, Cromford, DE4 3QF. Prop: Dr. D.J. Mitchell. Tel: (01629) 823272. Fax: (01629) 825094. Website: www.scarthinbooks.com. E-mail: clare@scarthinbooks.com. Est: 1974. Shop open: **M:** 09:30–18:00; **T:** 09:30–18:00; **W:** 09:30–18:00; **Th:** 09:30–18:00; **F:** 09:30–18:00; **S:** 09:30–18:00; **Su:** 12:00–18:00. Very large stock. Spec: Academic/Scholarly; Alpinism/Mountaineering; American Indians; Animals and Birds; Antiquarian; Architecture; Author - Uttley, Alison; History - Industrial; History - Local; Music - General; Topography - Local; also, booksearch. PR: £1–5,000. CC: MC; V. Also, new books, publishers of local history and walking books. Corresp: French, German. Mem: BA; IPG. VAT No: GB 127 6427 64. [Updated]

FROGGATT

Jarvis Books (incorporating 'Gastons' Books), Valleyside, Malthouse Lane, Froggatt, Hope Valley, S32 3ZA. Grant & Valerie Jarvis. Tel: (01433) 631 951. Website: www.mountainbooks.co.uk. E-mail: jarvis@mountainbooks.co.uk. Est: 1979. Private premises. Internet and postal. Telephone first. Medium stock. Spec: Alpinism/Mountaineering. CC: AE; MC; V. Cata: 5 a year. Mem: PBFA. VAT No: GB 439 5226 36. [Updated]

GLOSSOP

George Books, ■ 14 -16 George Street, Glossop, SK13 8AY. Prop: Andrew Hancock. Tel: (01457) 853413. Fax: (01457) 853413. Website: www.multifuel.com. Est: 1986. Shop open: **W:** 10:00–17:00; **Th:** 10:00–17:00; **F:** 10:00–17:00; **S:** 10:00–17:00. Medium stock. Spec: PR: £1–100. CC: MC; V. [Updated]

MATLOCK

Hunter and Krageloh, Honeybee Cottage, In the Dale, Wensley, Matlock, DE4 2LL. Prop: J.A. Hunter. Tel: (01629) 732845. E-mail: hunterandkrageloh@btinternet.com. Est: 1993. Telephone first. Spec: Alpinism/Mountaineering; Plant Hunting; Sport - Climbing & Trekking; Travel - Asia; Travel - Polar. PR: £1–12,000. Mem: PBFA. [Updated]

John O'Reilly - Mountain Books, Netherlea Barn, Bracken Lane, Holloway, Matlock, DE4 5AS. Tel: (01629) 534773. Fax: (01629) 534773. E-mail: johnoreill@aol.com. Est: 1972. Private premises. Postal business only. Very small stock. Spec: Alpinism/Mountaineering; Sport - Climbing & Trekking; Travel - Asia; Travel - Polar; Voyages & Discovery. PR: £5–500. CC: MC; V. Cata: 1 a year on mountaineering & mountain travel. [Updated]

DEVON

ASHBURTON

Ashburton Books, ■ 44 East Street, Ashburton, TQ13 7AX. Prop: J.C. Tasker. Tel: (01364) 654744. Shop open: **T:** 10:00–18:00; **Th:** 10:00–18:00; **F:** 09:00–18:00; **S:** 10:00–17:00; Small stock. Spec: Biography; Drama; Fiction - General; Music - General; Poetry. [08/07/2003]

The Dartmoor Bookshop, ■ 2 Kingsbridge Lane, Ashburton, TQ13 7DX. Prop: Mr. & Mrs. P.R. Heatley. Tel: (01364) 653356. Shop open: **M:** 09:30–17:30; **T:** 09:30–17:30; **W:** 09:30–17:30; **Th:** 09:30–17:30; **F:** 09:30–17:30; **S:** 09:30–17:30. Very large stock. Spec: Alpinism/Mountaineering; Antiquarian; Architecture; Art; Art - History; Art - Reference; Artists; Fiction - General; Fine & Rare; Gardening; Maritime/Nautical; Military; Military History; Natural History; Occult; Topography - General; Topography. PR: £1–250. CC: AE; JCB; MC; V. Mem: PBFA. VAT No: GB 365 7662 17. [Updated]

AXIMINSTER

Bookquest, High Grange, Dalwood, Axminster, EX13 7ES. Prop: E.M. Chapman. Tel: (01404) 831317. Est: 1968. Private premises. Postal business only. Also, booksearch. [Updated]

W.C. Cousens, 'The Leat', Lyme Road, Axminster, EX13 5BL. Prop: William Clifford Cousens. Tel: (01297) 32921. Est: 1988. Private premises. Appointment necessary. Small stock. Spec: Gardening; Topography - Local; also Booksearch. PR: £1–200. Cata: 3 a year. Mem: PBFA. [Updated]

BARNSTAPLE

B. Butler – Books, 68 Gould Road, Barnstaple, EX32 8ET. Prop: Brian Butler. Tel: (01271) 371794. Fax: (01271) 343211. Est: 1982. Private premises. Postal business only. Very small stock. Spec: Author - Byron, Lord. PR: £5–5,000. Cata: rarely. [05/07/2002]

Tarka Books, ■ 5 Bear Street, Barnstaple, North Devon, EX32 7BU. Prop: Fiona Broster. Tel: (01271) 374997. Website: www.tarkabooks.co.uk. E-mail: books@tarkabooks.co.uk. Est: 1988. Shop open: **M:** 09:45–17:00; **T:** 09:45–17:00; **W:** 09:45–17:00; **Th:** 09:45–17:00; **F:** 09:45–17:00; **S:** 09:45–17:00; Very large general stock. Spec: Author - Williamson, Henry; also Booksearch. PR: £1–100. CC: D; MC; V. Mem: BA; FSB. [checked]

BERE ALSTON

The Victoria Bookshop, ■ 9 Fore Street, Bere Alston, PL20 7AA. Prop: Peter Churcher. Tel: (01822) 841638. Website: www.victoriabookshop.co.uk. E-mail: victoria_bookshop@btopenworld.com. Est: 2000. Shop open: **T:** 10:30–16:30; **W:** 10:30–16:30; **Th:** 10:29–16:30; **F:** 10:30–16:30; **S:** 10:30–16:30; **Su:** 10:30–16:30. Very large stock. Spec: Academic/Scholarly; Occult; Psychology/Psychiatry. PR: £3–600. CC: AE; MC; V; SW. [19/03/2003]

BIDEFORD

Allhalland Books, ■ 7 Allhalland St., Bideford, EX39 2JD. Prop: J.P. Simpson O'Gara and S. Sutherland. Tel: (01237) 479301. Est: 1997. Shop open: **M:** 09:00–17:00; **T:** 09:00–17:00; **W:** 09:00–17:00; **Th:** 09:00–17:00; **F:** 09:00–17:00; **S:** 09:00–17:00. Small stock. Spec: Natural History; Topography - General. PR: £2–500. Also, bookbinding. [Updated]

C. & D. Davis, 9 Great Burrow Rise, Northam, Bideford, EX39 1TB. Prop: Carol & Dennis Davis. Tel: (01237) 475165. E-mail: dddesigns@mailcity.com. Est: 1994. Private premises. Postal business only. Spec: Sport - Canoeing/Kayaks. PR: £1–100. [Updated]

Discovery, ■ 8a Grenville Street, Bideford, EX39. Prop: Peter Christie. Tel: (01237) 473577. E-mail: pchristi@ndevon.ac.uk. Est: 1978. Shop open: **M:** 10:00–04:00; **T:** 10:00–04:00; **W:** 10:00–04:00; **Th:** 10:00–04:00; **F:** 10:00–04:00; **S:** 09:00–05:00. Small general stock. PR: £1–50. Also, secondhand records, tapes, compact discs, videos & comics. [29/06/2003]

Peter Hames, Old Bridge Antiques Centre, 19 Market Place, Bideford, EX39 1HG. Prop: Old Bridges Antiques Centre. Tel: (01237) 421065. Fax: (01237) 421065. E-mail: peterhames@hotmail.com. Est: 1980. Spec: Topography - Local. PR: £5–50. [31/07/2003]

BRIXHAM

Kate Armitage (Booksearch), 5 Park Court, Heath Road, Brixham, TQ5 9AX. Tel: (01803) 850277. E-mail: katesbooks@tinyonline.co.uk. Postal business only. Spec: Children's - General; Maritime/Nautical; Military History; Modern First Editions. PR: £1–20. [Updated]

Book Warren, ■ 9a Bolton Street, Brixham, TQ5 9BZ. Prop: Mrs. E.M. Dare. Tel: (01803) 858531. Est: 1987. Shop open: **M:** 10:00–16:30; **T:** 10:00–16:30; **W:** 10:00–16:30; **Th:** 10:00–16:30; **F:** 10:00–16:30; **S:** 10:00–16:30. Very large general stock. Spec: Autobiography; Children's - General; Cookery/ Gastronomy; Criminology; Fiction - General; Fiction - Crime, Detective, Spy, Thrillers; History - General; Music - General; Natural History; Navigation; Sport - General; Topography - General. PR: £1–100. Also, October to May, closed Wednesday & 1st Monday and Tuesday of each month. [27/04/2003]

COLYTON

Island Books, Shutes Farm, Northleigh, Colyton, EX24 6BL. Tel: (01404) 871600. Fax: (01404) 871601. E-mail: island@swauk.freeserve.co.uk. Est: 1974. Private premises. Internet and postal. Appointment necessary. Medium stock. Spec: Academic/Scholarly; Aeronautics; Agriculture; Animals and Birds; Antiquarian; Applied Art; Archaeology; Architecture; Author - 20th Century; Author - Austen, Jane; Author - Baring-Gould, S.; Author - Belloc, Hilaire; Author - Betjeman, Sir John. PR: £10–10,000. CC: AE; JCB; MC; V. [Updated]

COMBE MARTIN

Golden Books Group, Blurridge, Ridge Hill, Combe Martin, EX34 0NR. Tel: (01271) 883204. Website: www.abook4all.com. E-mail: ivan@abook4all.com. Est: 1991. Private premises. Internet. Appointment necessary. Open: **M:** 09:00–18:00; **T:** 09:00–18:00; **W:** 09:00–18:00; **Th:** 09:00–18:00; **F:** 09:00–18:00; **S:** 09:00–18:00; **Su:** 09:00–18:00. Large stock. Spec: Antiquarian; Bindings. CC: MC; V; Switch. Mem: PBFA; LAPADA, CINOA. VAT No: GB 822 1619 54. [Updated]

DARTMOUTH

Chantry Bookshop & Gallery, ■ 11 Higher Street, Dartmouth, TQ6 9RB. Prop: M.P. Merkel. Tel: (01803) 832796. Est: 1948. Shop open: **M:** 10:30–17:00; **T:** 10:30–17:00; **W:** 10:30–17:00; **Th:** 10:30–17:00; **F:** 10:30–17:00. Medium stock. Spec: Antiquarian; Author - Dickens, Charles; Fine & Rare; First Editions. CC: AE; MC; V. Alternative Tel: (01803) 834208. Also, antique prints, pencil drawings and aquatints. [08/07/2003]

DAWLISH

Dawlish Books, ■ White Court, Beach Street, Dawlish, EX7 9PN. Prop: S. French. Tel: (01626) 866882. E-mail: frenchatavalon@aol.com. Est: 2000. Shop open: **M:** 10:30–16:30; **T:** 10:30–16:30; **Th:** 10:30–16:30; **F:** 10:30–16:30; **S:** 10:30–16:30. Medium stock. Spec: Comic Books & Annuals; Esoteric; New Age; Occult; Psychic; Spiritualism; U.F.O.s; Unexplained, The. PR: £1–150. Open 10:30–16:00 in summer. [Updated]

EXETER

Mrs. Muriel J. Bryant, 5 Clipper Quay, The Quay, Exeter, EX2 4AP. Tel: (01392) 434674. Est: 1993. Private premises. Appointment necessary. Small stock. Booksearch. PR: £2–20. [18/06/2003]

Lisa Cox Music, The Coach House, Colleton Crescent, Exeter, EX 2 4DG. Prop: Ms. L. Cox. Tel: (01392) 490290. Fax: (01392) 277336. Website: www.lisacoxmusic.co.uk. E-mail: music@ lisacoxmusic.co.uk. Est: 1984. Private premises. Internet and postal. Appointment necessary. Open: **M:** 10:00–17:00; **T:** 10:00–17:00; **W:** 10:00–17:00; **Th:** 10:00–17:00; **F:** 10:00–12:00. Medium stock. Spec: Autographs; Manuscripts; Music - Printed. PR: £100–50,000. CC: MC; V. Cata: 3 a year. Corresp: French. Mem: ABA. VAT No: GB 631 4239 64. [04/08/2003]

Exeter Rare Books, ■ 13a, Guildhall Shopping Centre, Exeter, EX8 5AX. R.C. Parry M.A. Tel: (01392) 436021. Est: 1977. Shop open: **M:** 10:00–17:00; **T:** 10:00–17:00; **W:** 11:00–17:00; **Th:** 10:00–17:00; **F:** 10:00–17:00; **S:** 10:00–17:00; closed for lunch: 13:00–14:00. Medium stock. Spec: Topography - Local. PR: £2–500. CC: MC; V. Corresp: German. Mem: ABA; PBFA. VAT No: GB 142 3267 91. [Updated]

John S. Hill, 78 Pinhoe Road, Exeter, EX4 7HL. Tel: (01392) 439753. Fax: (01392) 439753. E-mail: john@hill6383.fsnet.co.uk. Est: 1988. Private premises. Internet and postal. Appointment necessary. Small stock. Spec: Fiction - Crime, Detective, Spy, Thrillers; Fiction - Science Fiction; First Editions; Military; also, booksearch. PR: £5–1,500. Cata: 1 – variable. [Updated]

Joel Segal Books, ■ 27 Fore Street, Topsham, Exeter, EX3 0HD. Joel Segal & Lily Neal. Tel: (01392) 877895. Website: www.joelsegalbooks.eclipse.co.uk. E-mail: lily@segalbooks.com. Est: 1993. Shop open: **M:** 10:30–17:00; **T:** 10:30–17:00; **W:** 10:30–17:00; **Th:** 10:30–17:00; **F:** 10:30–17:00; **S:** 10:30–17:00; Closed for lunch: 13:00–14:00. Very large stock. Spec: Arts, The; Literature; Natural History; Social History; Topography - General; Topography - Local; Transport. PR: £1–200. CC: MC; V. Also, valuation service, and ephemera. Corresp: French. [Updated]

Westcountry Oldbooks, ■ S.P.C.K. Bookshop, 1-2 Catherine St., Exeter, EX11EX. Prop: David Neil. Tel: (01803) 322712. Website: www.abebooks.com. E-mail: westcountryoldbooks@btopenworld.com. Est: 1988. Shop open: **M:** 09:00–17:30; **T:** 09:00–17:30; **W:** 09:00–17:30; **Th:** 09:00–17:30; **F:** 09:00–17:30; **S:** 09:00–17:30. Small stock. Spec: Antiquarian; Literature; Theology; Topography - General. CC: AE; D; JCB; MC; V. Mem: PBFA. [Updated]

HONITON

Ænigma Designs (Books), Whites Plot, Luppitt, Honiton, EX14 4RZ. Tel: (01404) 891560. Fax: (01404) 891560. Website: www.puzzlemuseum.com. E-mail: books@puzzlemuseum.com. Est: 1973. Private premises. Internet and postal. Appointment necessary. Very small stock. Spec: Mathematics; Puzzles; Science - General. PR: £5–200. CC: PayPal. Cata: 1 a year. [Updated]

High Street Books, ■ 150 High Street, Honiton, EX14 8JX. Prop: Geoff Tyson. Tel: (01404) 45570. Fax: (01404) 45570. Est: 1992. Shop open: **M:** 10:00–17:00; **T:** 10:00–17:00; **W:** 10:00–17:00; **Th:** 10:00–17:00; **F:** 10:00–17:00; **S:** 10:00–17:00. Large stock. Spec: Applied Art; Erotica; Maritime/Nautical; Military; Topography - General; Topography - Local; Travel - General. PR: £1–600. [Updated]

Roger Collicot Books, Felix House, 51 High Street, Honiton, EX14 1PW. Prop: Roger & Adela Collicott. Tel: (01404) 47180. E-mail: honitonoldbooks@btinternet.co.uk. Est: 1978. Storeroom: open: **M:** 10:00–17:00; **T:** 10:00–17:00; **W:** 10:00–17:00; **Th:** 10:00–17:00; **F:** 10:00–17:00; **S:** 10:00–17:00. Small stock. Spec: Antiquarian; Bindings; Geology; History of Ideas; Natural History; Natural Sciences; New Naturalist; Topography - Local. PR: £20–100. CC: MC; V. Cata: 4 a year on British topography & early printed books. Mem: ABA; PBFA. VAT No: GB 568 9200 11. [Updated]

KINGSBRIDGE

Booktrace International, The Hald, Kernborough, Kingsbridge, TQ7 2LL. Prop: Richard Newbold. Tel: (01548) 511366. E-mail: booktrace@aol.com. Est: 1995. Private premises. Postal business only. Very small stock. Spec: booksearch. PR: £5–200. Booksearch service is main line of business. [Updated]

LYMPSTONE

Reaveley Books, 1 Church Road, Lympstone, Nr Exmouth, EX8 5JU. Prop: Jane Johnson. Tel: (01395) 225462. Website: www.reaveleybooks.com. E-mail: jane@johnsgrj.demon.co.uk. Est: 1998. Private premises. Internet and postal. Telephone first. Small stock. Spec: Author - Murdoch, I.; Modern First Editions. PR: £5–500. CC: Paypal. Monthly newsletter sent on request - see www. reaveleybooks.co.uk. Mem: FSB. [Updated]

MODBURY

Lamb's Tales Books, 63 Brownston Street, Modbury, Ivybridge, PL21 0RQ. Prop: James & Elizabeth Lamb. Tel: (01548) 830317. Website: www.lambstales.co.uk. E-mail: books@lambstales.co.uk. Est: 1988. Private premises. Internet and postal. Contactable. Small general stock. PR: £5–150. VAT No: GB 768 6509 77. [Updated]

MORETONHAMPSTEAD

Moreton Books, ■ 3a The Square, Moretonhampstead, TQ13 8NF. Tel: (01647) 441176. E-mail: davejelfs@moretonbooks.co.uk. Website: www.moretonbooks.co.uk. Est: 1994. Shop open: **M:** 10:00–17:00; **T:** 10:00–17:00; **W:** 10:00–17:00; **Th:** 10:00–17:00; **F:** 10:00–17:00; **S:** 10:00–17:00. Medium stock. Spec: Antiquarian; Art - History; Art - Reference; Autobiography; Literature; Modern First Editions; Natural History; Poetry; Railways; Topography - Local; Travel - General. PR: £1–500. CC: E; MC; V; SO, SW. Viewing times may vary in winter. Stock include Dartmoor and West Country topography. Mem: PBFA. [Updated]

OTTERTON

The Book Shelf, Butterfly Cottage, Behind Hayes, Otterton, EX9 7JQ. Prop: Sandra George. Tel: (01395) 567565. Website: www.bookshelfuk.com. E-mail: sales@bookshelfuk.com. Est: 1994. Private premises. Internet and postal. Telephone first. Open: **M:** 08:00–18:00; **T:** 08:00–18:00; **W:** 08:00–18:00; **Th:** 08:00–18:00; **F:** 08:00–18:00; **S:** 08:00–14:00. Medium stock. Spec: Illustrated; Modern First Editions; Poetry; Victoriana. **PR:** £5–1,200. CC: AE; MC; V; PayPal. Cata: On request. Mem: PBFA. VAT No: GB 631 2242 85. [Updated]

PAIGNTON

David Way Angling Books, 10 Cedar Road, Preston, Paignton, TQ3 2DD. Prop: David Way. Tel: (01803) 390824. Est: 1990. Private premises. Appointment necessary. Small stock. Spec: Sport - Angling/ Fishing. **PR:** £1–120. Stock majors in books on carp, barbel, pike, and bass. Cata: 3 on specialities and carp. [Updated]

The Old Celtic Bookshop, ■ 43 Hyde Road, Paignton, TQ4 5BP. Prop: Michael Sutton. Tel: (01803) 558709. E-mail: michael.sutton2@virgin.net. Est: 1989. Shop open: **M:** 09:00–18:00; **T:** 09:00–18:00; **W:** 09:00–18:00; **Th:** 09:00–18:00; **F:** 09:00–18:00; **S:** 09:00–18:00; **Su:** 09:00–18:00. Large stock. **PR:** £1–50. Extended opening until 21:30 June to September. [12/08/2003]

The Pocket Bookshop, ■ 159 Winner Street, Paignton, TQ3 3BP. Prop: Leon Corrall. Tel: (01803) 529804. Est: 1985. Shop open: **T:** 10:30–17:30; **W:** 10:30–17:30; **Th:** 10:30–17:30; **F:** 10:30–17:30; **S:** 10:30–17:30. **PR:** £1–50. Open Mondays in from July to September. [12/08/2003]

PLYMOUTH

Anne Harris Books & Bags Books, 38 Burleigh Park Road, Peverell, Plymouth, PL3 4QH. Tel: (01752) 775853. E-mail: anne.harris1@virgin.net. Est: 2000. Private premises. Postal business only. Appointment necessary. Very small stock. Spec: Architecture; Art; Plant Hunting; Travel - General. **PR:** £1–500. [Updated]

Barbican Booksearch, ■ Old Customs House, 18 The Parade, Barbican, Plymouth, PL1 2JW. Tel: (01752) 226311. Fax: (08701) 698629. E-mail: barbbook@globalnet.co.uk. Shop open: **M:** 10:30–16:30; **T:** 10:30–16:30; **W:** 10:30–16:30; **Th:** 10:30–16:30; **F:** 10:30–16:30; **S:** 10:30–16:30; **Su:** 10:30–16:30. Very large general stock. CC: AE; D; E; JCB; MC; V. [Updated]

Cornerstone Books, New Street Antiques Centre, 27 New Street, The Barbican, Plymouth, PL1 2NB. Prop: Mark Treece. Tel: (01752) 661165. Website: mark@streece.freeserve.co.uk. E-mail: mark@streece.freeserve.co.uk. Est: 1986. Market stand/stall; Internet and postal. Shop at: 11 Inverdene Peverell Plymouth Devon. PL3 4LE (postal only). Open: **M:** 09:00–17:00; **T:** 09:00–17:00; **W:** 09:00–17:00; **Th:** 09:00–17:00; **F:** 09:00–17:00; **S:** 09:00–17:00. Large general stock. [05/09/2003]

Rods Books, ■ 20–21 Southside Street, Barbican, Plymouth, PL1 2LD. Prop: R.P. Murphy. Tel: (01752) 253546. E-mail: rmurphy980@aol.com. Est: 1996. Shop; Internet and postal. Spec: Deep Sea Diving; Fiction - Science Fiction; Fiction - Westerns; History - General; History - Ancient; History - British; History - Local; Maritime/Nautical; Military; Military History; Naval; Navigation; Rural Life; Shipbuilding; Transport; War - general. **PR:** £2–40. [Updated]

The Sea Chest Nautical Booksho, ■ Queen Anne's Battery Marina, Coxside, Plymouth, PL4 0LP. Prop: R.A. Dearn. Tel: (01752) 222012. Fax: (01752) 252679. Website: www.seachest.co.uk. E-mail: sales@seachest.co.uk. Est: 1987. Shop open: **M:** 09:00–17:00; **T:** 09:00–17:00; **W:** 09:00–17:00; **Th:** 09:00–16:00; **F:** 09:00–17:00; **S:** 09:00–17:00. Small stock. Spec: Maritime/Nautical; Navigation; Sport - Yachting; also, booksearch. **PR:** £2–750. CC: AE; MC; V. Also, new nautical books, pilots & charts, & British Admiralty chart agent. Mem: BA. VAT No: GB 501 5928 65. [Updated]

SEATON

Hill House Books, Hill House, Highcliffe Crescent, Seaton, EX12 2PS. Prop: Phil Beard. Tel: (01297) 20377. E-mail: jphil.beard@lineone.net. Est: 1982. Private premises. Appointment necessary. Very small stock. Spec: Advertising; Art; Art - History; Photography. **PR:** £1–500. [Updated]

Tantalus Antiques & Books, Holly Cottage, Watercombe, Branscombe, Seaton, EX12 3BT. Prop: A. & B. Dustan-Smith. Tel: (0129) 680457. E-mail: tonydustansmith@onetel.net.uk. Est: 1971. Private premises. Small general stock. Spec: Antiques; Biography. **PR:** £3–150. CC: JCB; V. Mem: PBFA. [04/09/2003]

SIDMOUTH

Books Plus, ■ 91 High Street, Sidmouth, EX10 8DL. Prop: Robert Starling. Tel: (01395) 578199. Est: 1999. Shop open: **M:** 09:00–17:00; **T:** 09:00–17:00; **W:** 09:00–17:00; **Th:** 09:00–17:00; **F:** 09:00–17:00; **S:** 09:00–17:00. Small general stock. Spec: Cinema/Film; Military; Music - Jazz. PR: £1–30. Also, videos & CDs. [12/08/2003]

SOUTH BRENT

P.M. Pollak, Moorview, Plymouth Road, South Brent, TQ10 9HT. Tel: (01364) 73457. Fax: (01364) 649126. Website: www.rarevols.co.uk. E-mail: patrick@rarevols.co.uk. Est: 1973. Private premises. Internet and postal. Telephone first. Small stock. Spec: Academic/Scholarly; Economics; Medicine; Natural Sciences; Photography; Science - General; Science - History of; Scientific Instruments; Social History; Technology. PR: £30–5,000. CC: AE; JCB; MC; V. Cata: 6 on history of medicine & science. Corresp: German, French. Mem: ABA; ILAB. VAT No: GB 267 5364 31. [Updated]

Rosemary Stansbury, 25 Church Street, South Brent, TQ10 9AB. Tel: (01364) 72465. Est: 1985. Private premises. Appointment necessary. Small stock. Spec: Children's - General. PR: £1–100. Children's titles only. Cata: 2 a year. [Updated]

TAVISTOCK

Bookworm Alley, 36 Brook Street, Tavistock, PL19 0HE. Prop: Joan Williams. Tel: (01822) 617740. E-mail: bookworm-alley@freenet.co.uk. Est: 2000. Private premises. Appointment necessary. Small stock. Spec: Religion - Christian. PR: £1–50. [27/08/2003]

Lee Furneaux Books, 6 Lopes Road, Dousland, Yelverton, Tavistock, PL20 6NX. Tel: (01822) 853243. Website: www.abebooks.com/home/madeleine. E-mail: lee@furneauxbooks.freeserve.co.uk. Est: 1987. Market stand/stall; Internet and postal. Telephone first. Shop at: Tavistock Pannier Market, Tavistock, Devon. Open: **T:** 08:30–16:00; **Th:** 08:30–16:00; **F:** 08:30–16:00; **S:** 08:30–16:00; Small stock. Spec: Art; Children's - General; Crafts; Gardening; History - General; Literature; Mind, Body & Spirit; Music - Popular; Music - Rock; Mysteries; Rural Life; Topography - Local; Travel - General. PR: £1–100. [26/06/2003]

TEIGNMOUTH

IKON, Magnolia House, New Road, Teignmouth, TQ14 8UD. Prop: Dr. Nicholas & Clare Goodrick–Clarke. Tel: (01626) 776528. Fax: (01626) 776528. E-mail: ikon@globalnet.co.uk. Est: 1982. Postal business only. Spec: Alchemy; Esoteric; Herbalism; History - European; Literature in Translation; Natural Health; New Age. PR: £10–75. [09/07/2003]

Quayside Bookshop, ■ 43 Northumberland Place, Teignmouth, TQ14 8DE. Prop: V.K. & E.C. Marston. Tel: (01626) 775436. Fax: (01626) 777023. Website: www.milestonebooks.co.uk. E-mail: quaybook@ aol.com. Est: 1982. Internet and postal. Shop open: **M:** 09:30–17:30; **T:** 09:30–17:30; **W:** 09:30–17:30; **F:** 09:30–17:30; **S:** 09:30–17:30; Closed for lunch: 13:30–14:00. Medium stock. Spec: Aviation; Buses/Trams; Maritime/Nautical; Naval; Navigation; Railways; Ship Modelling; Shipbuilding; Steam Engines; Transport; Voyages & Discovery. PR: £2–800. CC: AE; D; MC; V; SW. Also, new books on specialities. Cata: 2 on maritime and aviation. Mem: BA. VAT No: GB 585 7083 03. [13/03/2003]

TIVERTON

Heartland Old Books, ■, 12–14 Newport Street, Tiverton, EX16 6NL. Prop: Jeremy Whitehorn. Tel: (01884) 254488. Website: www.heartlandoldbooks.co.uk. E-mail: jwhitehorn@ heartlandoldbooks.co.uk. Est: 2001. Shop open: **M:** 10:00–17:00; **T:** 10:00–17:00; **W:** 10:00–17:00; **Th:** 10:00–17:00; **F:** 10:00–17:00; **S:** 10:00–17:00. Medium stock. Spec: Art; Cookery/Gastronomy; Military; Sport - Field Sports; Topography - Local; Travel - General. PR: £1–750. Easy parking in Pannier Market opposite. Mem: PBFA. [09/01/2003]

Kelly Books Limited, 6 Redlands, Tiverton, EX16 4DH. Props: Len & Lynda Kelly. Tel: (01884) 256170. Fax: (01884) 251063. Website: www.kellybooks.co.uk. E-mail: len@kellybooks.co.uk. Est: 1972. Private premises. Internet and postal. Appointment necessary. Open: **M:** 09:00–18:00; **T:** 09:00–18:00; **W:** 09:00–18:00; **Th:** 09:00–18:00; **F:** 09:00–18:00; **S:** 09:00–18:00. Medium stock. Spec: Advertising; Aeronautics; Broadcasting; Cinema/Film; Journalism; Media; Radio/Wireless; Television. PR: £5–600. CC: AE; MC; V; SW. Also, supply of back numbers of Radio Times, The Listener, and other radio magazines. Cata: 2 a year. VAT No: GB 799 7192 48. [Updated]

TORQUAY

Colin Baker - Books for the Collector, 66 Marldon Road, Shiphay, Torquay, TQ2 7EH. Tel: (01803) 613356. Fax: (01803) 613356. E-mail: colnbakerbooks@ukonline.co.uk. Est: 1994. Private premises. Postal business only. Appointment necessary. Small general stock. Spec: Author - Betjeman, Sir John; Author - Read, Miss; Author - Tangye, D.; Children's - General; Children's - Illustrated; Illustrated; Topography - General; Topography - Local. PR: £5–500. [Updated]

Duncan's Books, ■ 176 Union Street, Torquay, TQ2 5QP. Prop: Duncan Campbell. Tel: (01803) 294081. Est: 1996. Shop open: **M:** 09:30–17:00; **T:** 09:30–17:00; **W:** 09:30–17:00; **Th:** 09:30–17:00; **F:** 09:30–17:00; **S:** 09:30–17:00. Small general stock. Spec: Music - General; Theology; Travel - General. PR: £1–20. Also, sheet music & memorabilia. [Updated]

TORRINGTON

The Archivist, Priory Cottage, Frithelstock, Torrington, EX38 8JH. Tel: (01805) 625750. Fax: (01805) 625376. E-mail: admin@sheppardsworld.eclipse.co.uk. Est: 1990. Private premises. Internet and postal. Appointment necessary. Very small stock. Spec: Cats; Journalism; Literature; Publishers - Joseph Ltd., Michael. PR: £1–1,000. CC: JCB; MC. [Updated]

Books Antiques & Collectables, ■ 3 Well Street, Torrington, EX38 8EP. Tel: (01805) 625624. E-mail: joannaford8@hotmail.com. Shop open: **T:** 10:30–16:00; **W:** 10:30–16:00; **Th:** 10:00–16:00; **F:** 10:00–16:00; Closed for lunch: 13:00–14:00. Very small stock. Spec: Art; Biography; Children's - General; Fiction - General; History - General; Philosophy; Plays; Poetry. PR: £1–25. [Updated]

River Reads Bookshop, ■ 21 South Street, Torrington, EX38 8AA. Tel: (01805) 625888. Fax: (01805) 622064. E-mail: keitarmshw@aol.com. Est: 2002. Shop open: **M:** 10:00–16:00; **T:** 10:00–16:00; **W:** 10:00–13:00; **Th:** 10:00–16:00; **F:** 10:00–16:00; **S:** 10:00–16:00. Large stock. Spec: Art; Children's - General; Cookery/Gastronomy; Fishes; Gardening; Health; Hobbies; Natural History; Sport - Angling/Fishing. PR: £2–200. Also, vintage fishing tackle, fishing prints. [Updated]

TOTNES

Collards Bookshop, ■ 4 Castle Street, Totnes, TQ9 5NU. Prop: Belle Collard. Tel: (01548) 550246. Est: 1970. Shop open: **M:** 10:30–17:00; **T:** 10:30–17:00; **W:** 10:30–17:00; **Th:** 09:30–17:00; **F:** 10:30–17:00; **S:** 10:30–17:00. Small general stock. Spec: PR: £1–300. Hours vary midweek January to March. [Updated]

Geoff Cox, Lower West Wing, Tristford House, Harberton, Totnes, TQ9 7RZ. Tel: (01803) 866181. Fax: (01803) 866181. E-mail: geoffcox46@hotmail.com. Est: 1978. Private premises. Appointment necessary. Medium stock. Spec: Aviation; Canals/Inland Waterways; History - Industrial; Maritime/Nautical; Mining; Motoring; Railways; Social History; Steam Engines; Traction Engines; Vintage Cars. PR: £1–500. [13/08/2003]

Harlequin, ■ 41 High Street, Totnes, TQ9 5NP. Prop: Paul Wesley. Tel: (01803) 865794. Est: 1983. Shop open: **M:** 10:00–17:30; **T:** 09:00–17:30; **W:** 10:00–17:30; **Th:** 10:00–17:30; **F:** 10:00–17:30; **S:** 10:00–17:30. Medium stock. PR: £1–50. [Updated]

Pedlar's Pack Books, ■ 4 The Plains, Totnes, TQ9 5DR. Prop: Peter & Angela Elliott. Tel: (01803) 866423. E-mail: pedlar@aol.com. Est: 1981. Internet and postal. Shop open: **M:** 09:00–17:00; **T:** 09:00–17:00; **W:** 09:00–17:00; **Th:** 09:00–17:00; **F:** 09:00–17:00; **S:** 09:00–17:00. Large stock. Also, booksearch. PR: £1–500. CC: AE; JCB; V; Switch. Mem: PBFA. [15/07/2003]

UMBERLEIGH

D. & D.H.W. Morgan, Whitmore, Chittlehamholt, Umberleigh, EX7 9HB. Tel: Website: www.birdjournals.com. E-mail: stjamestree@btopenworld.com. Est: 1978. Private premises. Postal business only. Appointment necessary. Medium stock. Spec: Botany; Gardening; Natural History; Ornithology; Periodicals & Magazines. PR: £1–100. Also, ornithological periodicals. Cata: 1 a year. Corresp: French. [Updated]

YEALMPTON

Lesley Evans Booksearch, The Old School House, 3 Chapel Road, Yealmpton, PL8 2LZ. Prop: Lesley Evans. Tel: (01752) 880386. E-mail: yealmptonbooks@aol.com. Est: 1996. Spec: Maritime/Nautical; Military History; Naval; Topography - Local; also Booksearch. PR: £1–250. [19/08/2003]

DORSET

BEAMINSTER

John E. Spooner, 18 Glebe Court, Barnes Lane, Beaminster, DT8 3EZ. Tel: (01308) 862713. Est: 1975. Market stand/stall. Small stock. Spec: Aviation; Military; Naval. PR: £5–100. [Updated]

BLANDFORD FORUM

Ancient & Modern Bookshop, (Basement) 84 Salisbury Street, Blandford Forum, DT11 7QE. Prop: Margaret A. Davey. Tel: (01258) 455276. Website: www.ancientandmodernbooks.co.uk. E-mail: pegdavey@tinyworld.co.uk. Est: 1989. Private premises. Open: **M:** 09:30–16:30; **T:** 09:30–16:30; **Th:** 09:30–16:30; **F:** 09:30–16:30; **S:** 09:30–16:30; closed for lunch: 12:30–13:30. Large general stock. Spec: Academic/Scholarly; Alpinism/Mountaineering; Antiquarian; History - British; Science - General. PR: £1–100. CC: Cheque. Also, limited number of pictures, book rests, chairs & tables. Cata: On request. [29/06/2003]

The Dorset Bookshop, ■ 69 East Street, Blandford Forum, DT11 7DX. Ethan Golden. Tel: (01258) 452266. Est: 1950. Shop open: **M:** 10:00–17:00; **T:** 10:00–17:00; **W:** 10:00–17:00; **Th:** 10:00–17:00; **F:** 10:00–17:00; **S:** 10:00–17:00. Small general stock. Spec: PR: £1–100. Mem: BA. [Updated]

Four Tees Booksearch, P.O. Box 2701, Blandford Forum, DT11 8YR. Prop: J.A. Davis. Tel: (01725) 516425. Est: 1996. Private premises. Postal business only. Small general stock. Also, booksearch. PR: £1–120. [01/07/2003]

BOURNEMOUTH

Mary Bradley–Cox, 13 Lascelles Road, Bournemouth, BH7 6NF. Tel: (01202) 246160. Website: www.marybradleycox.com. E-mail: mbradleycox@aol.com. Est: 1992. Private premises. Internet and postal. Open: **M:** 09:00–18:00; **T:** 09:00–18:00; **W:** 09:00–18:00; **Th:** 09:00–18:00; **F:** 09:00–18:00; **S:** 09:00–17:00. Small stock. Spec: Bridge; Crime (True); Fiction - Crime, Detective, Spy, Thrillers; Medicine; Politics; Psychotherapy; Sport - Golf. PR: £5–200. CC: AE; MC; V; Switch, Solo. VAT No: GB 797 8711 57. [Updated]

Butler Books, 3 Denewood Road, Bournemouth, BH4 8EB. Prop: B.H. & M.E. Butler. Tel: (01202) 764185. Fax: (01202) 764185. E-mail: butler.books@lineone.net. Est: 1980. Private premises. Postal business only. Appointment necessary. Medium stock. Spec: History of Ideas; Oriental; Religion - General; Religion - Christian; Religion - Jewish; Theology. PR: £10–5,000. Cata: 3 – on theology and religion. Corresp: French, German. [13/03/2003]

Facet Books, 67 Bennett Road, Bournemouth, BH8 8RH. Prop: Mr James Allinson and Mrs Margit Allinson. Tel: (01202) 269269. Website: www.jallinson.freeserve.co.uk. E-mail: jim@jallinson. freeserve.co.uk. Est: 1982. Private premises. Internet and postal. Telephone first. Large general stock. Spec: Academic/Scholarly; Advertising; Aeronautics; Cartoons; Catalogues Raisonnes; Children's - General; Comedy; Comic Books & Annuals; Comics; Mysticism; Odd & Unusual; Psychic; Religion - Christian; Spiritualism; Supernatural; U.F.O.s; also Booksearch. PR: £1–2,500. CC: MC; V; Switch. Corresp: German. Mem: FSB. [Updated]

Holdenhurst Books, ■ 275, Holdenhurst Road, Bournemouth, BH8 8BZ. R.W. Reese. Tel: (01202) 397718. Est: 1985. Shop open: **M:** 10:00–17:00; **T:** 09:00–17:00; **Th:** 10:00–17:00; **F:** 10:00–17:00; **S:** 10:00–17:00. Medium stock. Spec: Motorbikes; Motoring. PR: £5–150. [Updated]

P.F. & J.R. McInnes, 59 Richmond Park Road, Bournemouth, BH8 8TU. Tel: (01202) 394609. Est: 1981. Private premises. Appointment necessary. Very small stock. Spec: Sport - Boxing. PR: £1–3,000. Research facility on premises, with B&B offered. [28/07/2002]

H. & S.J. Rowan, ■ 459 Christchurch Road, Boscombe, Bournemouth, BH1 4AD. Tel: (01202) 398820. Est: 1969. Shop open: **M:** 09:00–18:00; **T:** 09:00–18:00; **W:** 09:00–18:00; **Th:** 09:00–18:00; **F:** 09:00–18:00; **S:** 09:00–18:00. Large general stock. Spec: Antiquarian; Antiques; Art; Aviation; Topography - Local; also Booksearch. PR: £1–1,000. VAT No: GB 185 3287 39. [Updated]

Sue Sims, 21 Warwick Road, Pokesdown, Bournemouth, BH7 6JW. Tel: (01202) 432562. Fax: n/a. E-mail: reggierhino@aol.com. Est: 1978. Private premises. Postal business only. Contactable. Very small stock. Spec: Author - Brent-Dyer, Elinor M.; Author - Fairlie–Bruce, D.; Author - Forest, A; Author - Oxenham, Elsie; Children's - General; Religion - Roman Catholic; also, booksearch. PR: £1–500. Major stock of girl's books and school stories. Cata: 1 – Irregular. Corresp: French, German. [Updated]

Yesterday Tackle & Books, 42 Clingan Road, Boscombe East, Bournemouth, BH6 5PZ. Prop: David & Alba Dobbyn. Tel: (01202) 476586. Est: 1983. Private premises. Appointment necessary. Small stock. Spec: Sport - Angling/Fishing. PR: £1–100. CC: AE. Also, fishing tackle and related items. Cata: 1 occasionally. [28/04/2003]

Yesterday's Books, 6 Cecil Avenue, Bournemouth, BH8 9EH. Prop: David & Jessica L. Weir. Tel: (01202) 522442. Website: www.booksatpbfa.com. E-mail: djl.weir@btinternet.com. Est: 1974. Office &/or bookroom; Internet and postal. Telephone first. Open: **M:** 09:00–17:00; **T:** 09:00–17:00; **W:** 09:00–17:00; **Th:** 09:00–17:00; **F:** 09:00–17:00; **S:** 09:00–13:00. Medium stock. Spec: Anthropology; Countries - Africa; Egyptology; Ethnography; History - General; Literary Travel; Literature; Pacifism; Sport - Hockey; Travel - General; Travel - Africa; Tribal. PR: £5–500. CC: JCB; MC; V. Cata: 4 on Africana. Corresp: French, German. Mem: PBFA. [Updated]

BOURTON

Well–Head Books, The Old Vicarage, Bourton, Gillingham, SP8 5BJ. Prop: Stephen Mobsby. Tel: (01747) 840213. Fax: (01747) 840724. E-mail: Wellheadbk. Est: 1985. Postal business only. Open: Spec: Crafts; Dolls & Dolls' Houses; Embroidery; Lace; Needlework; Textiles; Woodwork; also, booksearch. PR: £5–500. [05/09/2003]

BRIDPORT

Bridport Old Bookshop, ■ 11 South Street, Bridport, DT6 3NR. Prop: Caroline Mactaggart & Rosie Young. Tel: (01308) 425689. E-mail: caroline@TextBiz.com. Est: 1981. Shop open: **T:** 10:00–05:00. Small stock. Spec: Children's - General. PR: £2–500. CC: MC; V. Corresp: Open 10 to 5 six days a week. Also stock books of Scottish interest. Mem: PBFA. [Updated]

Far Horizons Books, Far Horizons, Ryall, Bridport, DT6 6EG. Prop: Mrs. C.E.M. Parr. Tel: (01297) 489046. Est: 1990. Private premises. Internet and postal. Open: **M:** 10:00–19:30; **T:** 10:00–19:30; **W:** 10:00–19:30; **Th:** 10:00–19:30; **F:** 10:00–19:30. Medium stock. Spec: Esoteric; Ghosts; Gnostics; Metaphysics; Mind, Body & Spirit; Mysticism; Occult; Parapsychology; Psychic; Religion - Buddhism; Religion - Christian; Religion - Islam; Spiritualism; Supernatural; Weird & Wonderful; Witchcraft; Yoga. PR: £4–100. Cata: 4 a year on specialities. [05/09/2003]

Caroline Mactaggart, Manor Farmhouse, Swyre, Bridport, Dorchester, DT2 9DN. Tel: (01308) 898174. E-mail: caroline@textbiz.com. Est: 1984. Private premises. Shop at: Bridport Old Bookshop, 11 South Street, Bridport, Dorset. Very small stock. Spec: Scottish Interest. PR: £5–200. CC: MC; V. Mem: PBFA. [Updated]

CHARMOUTH

Charmouth Bounty Books, 1 Maycroft, Higher Sea Lane, Charmouth, DT6 6BB. Prop: Louisa Mamakou. Tel: 00 44 (0) 1297 56023. Website: http://www.clique.co.uk/members/charmouth. E-mail: louisa@charmouthbountybooks.fsnet.co.uk. Est: 2003. Private premises. Internet and postal. Appointment necessary. Very small general stock. Spec: Antiquarian; Archaeology; Astronomy; Biography; Children's - General; Countries - Cyprus; Countries - Greece; Earth Sciences; Geography; Geology; History - General; Literature; Marine Sciences; Maritime/Nautical; Medicine; Military; Modern First Editions. PR: £10–500. CC: MC; V; (via Abe). Free Worldwide Booksearch / Email Catalogues on request. Cata: 3 – a year. Corresp: French, Greek. [Updated]

The Lighthouse Books, ■ Langley House, The Street, Charmouth, DT6 6PE. Prop: Mr Jean Vaupres. Tel: (01297) 560634 (Home) Est: 2004. Shop open: **M:** 10:00–17:00; **T:** 10:00–17:00; **W:** 10:00–17:00; **Th:** 10:00–17:00; **F:** 10:00–17:00; **S:** 10:00–17:00; **Su:** 10:00–17:00. Medium stock. Spec: Architecture; Country Houses; Fashion & Costume; Folio Society, The; Irish Interest; Odd & Unusual; Sculpture; Travel - General; Welsh Interest. PR: £1–300. NB. Outside school holidays, open 10:00 – 17:00 Friday to Monday. Corresp: French, Italian. [Updated]

DORCHESTER

The Dorchester Bookshop, ■ 3 Nappers Court, Charles Street, Dorchester, DT1 1EE. Prop: Michael J. Edmonds. Tel: (01305) 269919. Est: 1993. Shop open: **T:** 10:00–17:00; **W:** 10:00–17:00; **Th:** 10:00–17:00; **F:** 10:00–17:00; **S:** 10:00–17:00. Medium stock. Spec: PR: £1–500.[Updated]

Marco Polo Travel & Adventure, Marco Polo House, West Bexington, Dorchester, DT2 9DE. Prop: Mark A. Culme-Seymour. Tel: (01308) 898420. Fax: (01308) 898416. Website: www.marcopolobooks. co.uk. E-mail: mark@marcopolobooks.co.uk. Est: 1977. Private premises. Internet and postal. Appointment necessary. Very small stock. Spec: Travel - General. PR: £15–300. CC: MC; V. Book Searches. Cata: 1 a year on Travel, Adventure, Hitory Auto/Biographies. VAT No: GB 717 8378 00. [Updated]

Judith Stinton, 21 Cattistock Road, Maiden Newton, Dorchester, DT2 OAG. Tel: (01300) 320778. Website: www.abebooks.com. E-mail: judithstinton@hardycountry.fsnet.co.uk. Est: 1989. Private premises. Internet and postal. Appointment necessary. Very small stock. Spec: Children's - General; Topography - Local. PR: £1–100. [Updated]

Steve Walker Fine Books, 1 Sydenham Way, Dorchester, DT1 1DN. Tel: 01350 260690. E-mail: vectaphile@hotmail.com. Est: 1985. Private premises. Postal business only. Appointment necessary. Very small general stock. Spec: Author - Hardy, Thomas; Author - Johnson, Samuel; Bookbinding; Books about Books; Languages - National; Literature; Religion - General. PR: £5–500. Bookbinding and Restoration. Mem: Society of Bookbinders. [Updated]

Woolcott Books, Kingston House, Higher Kingston, Dorchester, DT2 8QE. Prop: H.M. & J.R. St. Aubyn. Tel: (01305) 267773. Fax: (01305) 751899. Est: 1978. Private premises. Appointment necessary. Open: Small stock. Spec: Colonial; Countries - Africa; Countries - India; History - National; Military; Travel - Africa; Travel - Asia; Travel - Middle East; also Booksearch. PR: £5–500. Cata: 1 a year. [Updated]

Words Etcetera Bookshop, ■ 2 Cornhill, Dorchester, DT1 1BA. Prop: Julian Nangle. Tel: (01305) 251919. Fax: (01305) 251919. Website: www.wordsetcetera.co.uk. E-mail: jnangle@ wordsetcetera.co.uk. Est: 1974. Internet and postal. Shop open: **M:** 10:00–17:30; **T:** 10:00–17:30; **W:** 10:00–17:30; **Th:** 10:00–17:30; **F:** 10:00–17:30; **S:** 10:00–17:30. Medium stock. Spec: Art; Author - Hardy, Thomas; Author - Lawrence, T.E.; Author - Powys Family, The; Illustrated; Modern First Editions; Poetry; Private Press; Signed Editions; Topography - Local; also Booksearch. Illustrated and Literature. Corresp: French. Mem: PBFA; BA. [Updated]

R.A. Yates, 9 Treves Road, Dorchester, DT1 2HD. Tel: (01305) 264336. Private premises. Appointment necessary. Open: Small stock. Spec: Academic/Scholarly; Humanities. PR: £1–100. Cata: occasionally. [27/05/2003]

FERNDOWN

Janet Cherry, Highbury, Woodside Road, West Moors, Ferndown, BH22 0LY. Prop: Stanley Cherry. Tel: (01202) 874372. Fax: (01202) 874370. Est: 1970. Private premises. Appointment necessary. Very small stock. Spec: Antiquarian; Gardening; Horticulture; Voyages & Discovery; War - General. PR: £5–100. Corresp: French. [08/07/2003]

GILLINGHAM

Eden Books, PO Box 1562, Gillingham, SP8 4ZN. Prop: Grant & Tracey Eden. Tel: (01747) 831130. Website: www.edenbooks.com. E-mail: edenbooks@aol.com. Est: 1997. Private premises. Internet and postal. Spec: Publishers - Ladybird Books; Sport - Boxing; Sport - Football (Soccer); Sport - Rugby. CC: AE; E; JCB; MC; V. Mem: PBFA. VAT No: GB 762 3914 22. [23/11/2004]

Lilian Modlock, Southcote, Langham Lane, Wyke, Gillingham, SP8 5NT. Tel: (01747) 821875. Fax: (01747) 821875. E-mail: modlock3@btinternet.com. Est: 1995. Private premises. Postal business only. Appointment necessary. Medium stock. Spec: Biography; Children's - General; Cinema/Film; Cookery/Gastronomy; Illustrated; Landscape; Poetry; Topography - General; Topography - Local; Travel - General; also, booksearch. PR: £3–400. [Updated]

Available from Richard Joseph Publishers Ltd

BOOK DEALING FOR PROFIT
by Paul Minet

(Quarto H/b)   £10.00 144pp

LANGPORT

Keeble Antiques, ■ Cheapside, Langport, TA10 9PW. Prop: Clive Keeble. Tel: 01458 259627. Fax: 01458 259627. Website: www.keebleantbks.co.uk. E-mail: clive@keebleantiques.com. Est: 1998. Internet and postal. (Shop now closed in Sherborne, Dorset). Open: **M:** 09:00–18:00; **T:** 09:00–18:00; **W:** 09:00–18:00; **Th:** 09:00–18:00; **F:** 09:00–18:00; **S:** 09:00–18:00. Medium stock. Spec: Antiques; Art; Carriages & Driving; Natural History; Private Press; Rural Life; Topography - Local; Travel - General; also booksearch. PR: £1–1,000. [Updated]

LYME REGIS

Lymelight Books & Prints, ■ 1 Drakes Way, Lyme Regis, DT7 3QP. Prop: Nigel Cozens. Tel: (01297) 443464. Fax: (01297) 443464. Website: www.lymelight-books.demon.co.uk. E-mail: nigel@lymelight-books.demon.co.uk. Est: 1994. Shop open: **M:** 10:00–18:00; **T:** 10:00–18:00; **W:** 10:00–18:00; **Th:** 10:00–18:00; **F:** 10:00–18:00; **S:** 10:00–18:00; **Su:** 10:00–18:00. Medium stock. Spec: Antiquarian; Art; Atlases; Author - Darwin, Charles; Author - Fowles, John; Author - Hardy, Thomas; Author - Lawrence, T.E.; Children's - Illustrated; Colour-Plate; Geology; Illustrated; Literature; Natural History; Natural Sciences; Palaeontology. PR: £5–10,000. CC: AE; E; MC; V; Cirrus. Also, bookbinding and booksearch. Print & Mapsearch and Restoration. Cata: occasionally. Corresp: French. Mem: PBFA. VAT No: GB 684 4800 14. [Updated]

The Bookshop, ■ The Old Bonded Store, Marine Parade, The Cobb, Lyme Regis, BT7 3JF. Prop: Ms L. Forman. Tel: (01297) 444820. Est: 2003. Shop open: **F:** 11:00–16:30; **S:** 11:00–16:30. Medium stock. Spec: Fiction - General; Maritime/Nautical; Poetry. PR: £1–100. Open weekends in summer, phone first. Also, fossils. [Updated]

The Sanctuary Bookshop, 65 Broad Street, Lyme Regis, DT7 3QF. Prop: Bob Speer. Tel: (01297) 445815. Website: http://www.lyme-regis.demon.co.uk/. E-mail: books@lyme-regis.demon.co.uk. Est: 1982. Shop &/or showroom. Open: **M:** 10:30–17:30; **T:** 10:30–17:30; **W:** 10:30–17:30; **Th:** 10:30–17:30; **F:** 10:30–17:30; **S:** 10:30–17:30; **Su:** 10:30–17:30; Very large stock. Spec: Art - Reference; Military; Music - General; Music - Printed; Musical Instruments; Publishers - Penguin. PR: £1–50. CC: AE; MC; V. Booklovers Bed & Breakfast, free Booksearch, E-Mail, Antiques, Mechanical Music. [Updated]

MILBORNE PORT

Kingswood Books, 17 Wick Road, Milborne Port, Sherborne, DT9 5BT. Prop: Anne Rockall & Allan Dollery. Tel: (01963) 250280. Fax: (01963) 250280. Website: www.kingswoodbooks.btinternet.co.uk. E-mail: kingswoodbooks@btinternet.com. Est: 1985. Private premises. Internet and postal. Appointment necessary. Medium stock. Spec: Academic/Scholarly; Advertising; Anthropology; Antiquarian; Archaeology; Art - History; Egyptology; Genealogy; History - Ancient; History - Byzantine; History - Middle Ages; History - National; Medicine - History of; Palaeontology; Science - History. PR: £1–2,000. CC: JCB; MC; V; Switch. Bookbinders & restorers. See our web site. Cata: 2 a year. Mem: PBFA. Also at: Various book fairs listed on our web site. [Updated]

POOLE

Bookstand, 53 Kings Ave., Poole, BH14 9QQ. Prop: Eleanor Smith & Wendy Marten. Tel: (01202) 716229. Fax: (01202) 734663. Website: www.abebooks.com/home/bookstand. E-mail: bookstand@lineone.net. Est: 1997. Private premises. Internet. Appointment necessary. Small general stock. Spec: Author - Thelwell, N; Author - Wheatley, Dennis; Autographs; Humour; Illustrated; Manuscripts; Modern First Editions; Poetry; Private Press; Signed Editions. PR: £15–5,000. CC: V. [16/12/2004]

Branksome Books, 33a Kings Avenue, Poole, BH14 9QG. Prop: P.G. Bryer–Ash. Tel: (01202) 730235. Fax: (01202) 730235. Est: 1988. Private premises. Appointment necessary. Very small general stock. Spec: Author - Lawrence, T.E.; Sport - Angling/Fishing; Sport - Field Sports; Travel - General. PR: £5–200. Corresp: French. [27/03/2003]

ECR Books, 4 Yarmouth Road, Branksome, Poole, BH12 1JN. Prop: John Aris. Tel: (01202) 537365. Est: 1989. Private premises. Appointment necessary. Medium stock. Spec: Antiquarian; Bindings; Children's - General; Private Press; Theology; Typography; also, booksearch. PR: £10–100. Cata: occasionally. [17/06/2003]

R.H. & P. Haskell, 64 Winston Avenue, Branksome, Poole, BH12 1PG. Tel: (01202) 744310. Fax: (01202) 744310. E-mail: rhandp@btinternet.com. Est: 1973. Private premises. Postal business only. Appointment necessary. Very small stock. Spec: PR: £5–1,000. Also, bookbinding service. [Updated]

Wessex Rare Books, 10 Mallow Close, Broadstone, Poole, BH18 9NT. Prop: D. & L. Pilborough. Tel: (01252) 510297. Est: 1983. Private premises. Appointment necessary. Small stock. Spec: Biography; Ex-Libris; Linguistics; Oriental; Reference; Royalty - General; Social History; Social Sciences; Transport; War - General. PR: £1–1,000. Cata: occasionally on specialities. [Updated]

Christopher Williams, 19 Morrison Avenue, Parkstone, Poole, BH12 4AD. Prop: Christopher & Pauline Williams. Tel: (01202) 743157. Fax: (01202) 743157. Website: www.abebooks.com/home/cw. E-mail: cw4finebooks@lineone.net. Est: 1967. Private premises. Internet and postal. Appointment necessary. Very small stock. Spec: Arts, The; Bibliography; Cookery/Gastronomy; Crafts; Lace; Topography - Local. PR: £5–100. CC: MC; V. Cata: occasionally. Mem: PBFA. [Updated]

PUDDLETOWN

The Antique Map and Bookshop, ■ 32 High Street, Puddletown, DT2 8RU. Prop: C.D. & H.M. Proctor. Tel: (01305) 848633. Fax: (01305) 848992. Website: www.puddletownbookshop.co.uk. E-mail: proctor@puddletown.demon.co.uk. Est: 1976. Internet and postal. Shop open: **M:** 09:00–17:00; **T:** 09:00–17:00; **W:** 09:00–17:00; **Th:** 09:00–17:00; **F:** 09:00–17:00; **S:** 09:00–17:00. Medium stock. Spec: Author - Barnes, William; Author - Conan Doyle, Sir Arthur; Author - Hardy, Thomas; Author - Henty, G.A.; Author - Lawrence, T.E.; Author - Wells, H.G.; Fine & Rare; Illustrated; Literature; Literature - Victorian; Military; Natural History. PR: £5–3,000. CC: AE; JCB; MC; V; SW. Cata: 4 a year. Corresp: German. Mem: ABA; PBFA; ILAB. VAT No: GB 291 7495 21. [Updated]

SHAFTESBURY

Paul Goldman, Meadow View, East Orchard, Shaftesbury, SP7 0LG. Tel: (01747) 811380. Fax: (01747) 811380. Website: www.abebooks.com. E-mail: goldman@clara.net. Est: 1997. Private premises. Postal business only. Appointment necessary. Small stock. Spec: Academic/Scholarly; Art; Art - History; Art - Reference; Cartoons; Comedy; Humour; Illustrated; Literature; Printing; Victoriana. PR: £10–500. Cata: 2 on specialities. Corresp: French, Italian, Greek. Mem: ABA; PBFA; ILAB. [Updated]

Not Just Books, ■ 7A High Street, Shaftesbury, SP7 8QZ. Prop: F. W. Barrett-Selbie. Tel: (01747) 850003. E-mail: ntrevor64@supanet.com. Est: 1996. Shop open: **W:** 10:00–16:30; **Th:** 10:00–16:30; **F:** 10:00–16:30; **S:** 10:00–16:30; closed for lunch: 12:30–14:00. Medium stock. Spec: PR: £1–200. [Updated]

SHERBORNE

Chapter House Books, ■ Trendle Street, Sherborne, DT9 3NT. Claire Porter, Tudor Books Ltd. Tel: (01935) 816262. Website: www.chapterhouse-books.co.uk. E-mail: chapterhousebooks@tiscali.co.uk. Est: 1988. Shop open: **M:** 10:00–17:00; **T:** 10:00–17:00; **W:** 10:00–17:00; **Th:** 10:00–17:00; **F:** 10:00–17:00; **S:** 10:00–17:00. Large general stock. PR: £1–500. CC: MC; V. Also, booksearch, bookbinding & book repair services, secondhand CDs, videos and sheet music. VAT No: GB 799 9885 07. [Updated]

Grahame Thornton, Bookseller, Monghyr House, Spring Lane, Long Burton, Sherborne, DT9 5NZ. Grahame Thornton. Tel: (01963) 210443. Fax: (01963) 210443. Website: www.grahamethornton .f9.co.uk. E-mail: grahame@grahamethornton.f9.co.uk. Est: 1995. Private premises. Internet and postal. Telephone first. Open: **M:** 09:00–18:00; **T:** 09:00–18:00; **W:** 09:00–18:00; **Th:** 09:00–18:00; **F:** 09:00–18:00; **S:** 09:00–18:00; **Su:** 09:00–18:00. Small stock. Spec: Antiquarian; Biography; Espionage; Fiction - General; History - General; History - 19th Century; Medicine; Military; Publishers - Penguin; Travel - General; War - World War I; War - World War II; also, booksearch. CC: MC; V; SW; S. Corresp: French. [Updated]

Verandah Books, Stonegarth, The Avenue, Sherborne, DT9 3AH. Prop: Michael Hougham. Tel: (01935) 815900. Fax: (01935) 815900. Website: www.verandah.demon.co.uk. E-mail: mah@verandah.demon .co.uk. Est: 1992. Private premises. Postal business only. Appointment necessary. Medium stock. Spec: Author - Kipling, Rudyard; Countries - Afghanistan; Countries - Burma; Countries - Himalayas, The; Countries - India; Countries - Nepal; Countries - Pakistan; Countries - South East Asia; Countries - Sri Lanka. PR: £10–500. Cata: 5 a year. [Updated]

STALBRIDGE

March House Books, March House, Thornhill Road, Stalbridge, DT10 2PS. Prop: Mrs. Barbara Fisher. Tel: (01963) 364403. Fax: (01963) 364405. Website: www.marchhousebooks.com. E-mail: books@marchhousebooks.com. Est: 1997. Private premises. Internet and postal. Small stock. Spec: Children's - General; Illustrated. PR: £5–650. CC: Paypal. [Updated]

STOBOROUGH

Calluna Books, 54 Corfe Road, Stoborough, Wareham, BH20 5AF. Prop: Y. Gartshore. Tel: (01929) 552660 evenings. E-mail: neil&yuki@onaga54.freeserve.co.uk. Est: 1997. Private premises. Appointment necessary. Small stock. Spec: Entomology; Natural History; Ornithology. PR: £5–500. Also, attends specialist bird fairs. Cata: 2 to 3 a year. [Updated]

SWANAGE

New & Secondhand Books, 35 Station Road, Swanage, BH19 1AD. Prop: Jill & Mike Blanchard. Tel: (01929) 424088. PR: £1–100. [28/08/2003]

Reference Works Ltd., 9 Commercial Road, Swanage, BH19 1DF. Tel: (01929) 424423. Fax: (01929) 422597. Website: www.referenceworks.co.uk. E-mail: sales@referenceworks.co.uk. Est: 1984. Office &/or bookroom. Telephone first. Small stock. Spec: Antiques; Ceramics; Decorative Art. PR: £5–800. CC: MC; V. Cata: 8 a year. [Updated]

WAREHAM

Reads, Beehive Cottage, East Stoke, Wareham, BH20 4JW. Prop: Reg Read & Anthony Hessey. Tel: (01929) 554971, or 5. E-mail: reginaldreads@aol.com. Est: 1998. Private premises. Postal business only. Small stock. Spec: Anthroposophy; Applied Art; Archaeology; Architecture; Art; Autobiography; Biography; Cinema/Film; Geology; Music - Classical; Performing Arts; Philosophy; Politics; Theatre; Topography - General; Topography - Local; Town Planning; Windmills & Watermills. PR: £5–3,000. CC: JCB; MC; V. Exhibits at major PBFA fairs. Corresp: French. Mem: PBFA. [Updated]

WEYMOUTH

Books & Bygones, ■ 26, Great George Street, Weymouth, DT4 7AS. Mrs. D. Nash. Tel: (01305) 777231. Est: 1983. Shop open: **M:** 12:00–17:00; **T:** 12:00–17:00; **W:** 12:00–17:00; **Th:** 12:00–17:00; **F:** 12:00–17:00; **S:** 12:00–17:00; **Su:** 12:00–17:00. Medium stock. PR: £1–1,000. [23/06/2002]

Books Afloat, ■ 66 Park Street, Weymouth, DT4 7DE. John Ritchie. Tel: (01305) 779774. Est: 1983. Shop open: **M:** 09:30–17:30; **T:** 09:30–17:30; **W:** 09:30–17:30; **Th:** 09:30–17:30; **F:** 09:30–17:30; **S:** 09:30–17:30. Large general stock. Spec: Author - Hardy, Thomas; Author - Powys Family, The; Aviation; Canals/Inland Waterways; Fiction - General; Maritime/Nautical; Military History; Navigation; Railways; Sport - Yachting; Topography - General; Topography - Local; Transport; Travel - General. PR: £1–140. [Updated]

The Nautical Antique Centre, ■ 3 Cove Passage, Hope Square, Weymouth, DT4 8TR. Prop: Mr D.C. Warwick. Tel: (01305) 777838. Website: www.nauticalantiques.org. E-mail: info@nauticalantiques .org. Est: 1989. Internet and postal. Telephone first. Shop open: **T:** 10:00–17:00; **W:** 10:00–17:00; **Th:** 10:00–17:00; **F:** 10:00–17:00. Closed for lunch: 13:00–14:00. Very small stock. Spec: Journals - Maritime; Manuals - Seamanship; Maritime/Nautical; Maritime/Nautical - Log Books; Naval; Navigation; Shipbuilding; Steam Engines. PR: £5–300. CC: MC; V. [Updated]

WIMBORNE

John Graham, 52 Blandford Road, Corfe Mullen, Wimborne, BH21 3HQ. Prop: John Graham. Tel: (01202) 692397. Fax: (01202) 692397. Est: 1987. Private premises. Postal business only. Small stock. Spec: Biography; History - General; History - Industrial; History - Local; History - National; Social History. PR: £1–100. [Updated]

DURHAM

BARNARD CASTLE

Books on the Bank, ■ 3 The Bank, Barnard Castle, DL12 8PH. Prop: Colin and Cathy Robinson. Tel: (01833) 695123. E-mail: bankbooks@btinternet.com. Est: 1999. Shop open: **T:** 10:00–16:00; **W:** 10:00–16:00; **Th:** 10:00–16:00; **F:** 10:00–16:00; **S:** 10:00–17:00. Medium stock. Spec: Art - Reference; History - General; Rural Life; Topography - Local. PR: £1–300. CC: AE; E; JCB; MC; V. Internet sales via abebooks.com. [Updated]

Greta Books, Lodge Farm, Scargill, Barnard Castle, DL12 9SY. Prop: Gordon Thomson. Tel: (01833) 621000. Fax: (01833) 621000. E-mail: Gretabooks@xemaps.com. Postal business only. Spec: Author - Priestley, J.B.; Author - Walsh, M.; Building & Construction; Countries - Scotland; Farming & Livestock; Fiction - General; First Editions; History - General; Literature - Scottish; Maritime/ Nautical; Salvation Army; Scottish Interest. PR: £5–50. [Updated]

BISHOP AUCKLAND

Vinovium Books, Wear Valley Business Centre, 27 Longfield Road, Bishop Auckland, DL14 6XB. Prop: Paul Hughes. Tel: (01388) 777770. Website: www.vinoviumbooks.co.uk. E-mail: enqrj@ vinoviumbooks.co.uk. Est: 1996. Office &/or bookroom. Internet and postal. Appointment necessary. Small stock. Spec: Academic/Scholarly; Antiquarian; History - Local; Military History; Sport - Angling/Fishing; Sport - Field Sports; Topography - Local. PR: £10–3,000. CC: JCB; MC; V; Switch. Mem: PBFA. VAT No: GB 746 9734 81. [Updated]

DARLINGTON

Combat Arts Archive, 12 Berkeley Road, Darlington, DL1 5ED. Prop: Mr. J. Sparkes. Tel: (01325) 465286. Website: http://www.combatbooks.co.uk. E-mail: johnsparkes@ntlworld.com. Est: 1995. Private premises. Postal business only. Appointment necessary. Small stock. Spec: Physical Culture; Sport - Boxing; Sport - Duelling; Sport - Fencing; Sport - Martial Arts,; Sport - Weightlifting/ Bodybuilding; Sport - Wrestling. PR: £1–150. CC: JCB; MC; V. Cata: 4 every 3 months. [Updated]

Tony and Gill Tiffin, 144 Coniscliffe Road, Darlington, DL3 7RW. Prop: G.A. & M.G. Tiffin. Tel: (01325) 487274. E-mail: tony.tiffin@btinternet.com. Est: 1992. Private premises. Book fairs only. Telephone first. Spec: Academic/Scholarly; Children's - General; Literature; Military; Military History; Poetry; School Registers/Rolls of Honour; Sport - Cricket; War - World War I. PR: £3–200. Mem: PBFA. [Updated]

Jeremiah Vokes, ■ 61 Coniscliffe Road, Darlington, DL3 7EH. Prop: Jeremiah Vokes. Tel: (01325) 469449. Est: 1979. Shop open: **M:** 09:30–17:30; **T:** 09:30–17:30; **W:** 09:30–17:30; **Th:** 09:30–17:30; **F:** 09:30–17:30; **S:** 09:30–17:30; Medium stock. Spec: Fiction - Crime, Detective, Spy, Thrillers; Sherlockiana; also, booksearch. PR: £5–1,000. Mem: PBFA. [Updated]

MIDDLETON–IN–TEESDALE

The Village Bookshop, 36 Market Place, Middleton–in–Teesdale, DL12 0RJ. Prop: Susan and David Fielden. Tel: (01833) 640373. Fax: (01833) 640373. Website: www.villagebookshop.co.uk. E-mail: david.fielden@talk21.com. Est: 2000. Spec: Crafts; Rural Life; Topography - Local. PR: £1–50. [05/ 09/2003]

STOCKTON–ON–TEES

Norton Books, 18 Wolviston Road, Billingham, Stockton–on–Tees, TS22 5AA. (*) Prop: C. Casson. Tel: (01642) 553965. Fax: (01642) 553965. E-mail: sales@ricardmarketing.com. Est: 1981. Private premises. Internet and postal. Appointment necessary. Spec: Antiquarian; Author - Beckett, S.; Author - Crane, Hall; Author - Crosby, Harry & Caresse; Author - Cunard, Nancy; Author - Durrell, Lawrence; Author - Eliot, T.S.; Author - Hemingway, Ernest; Author - Joyce, James; Author - Kerouac, Jack. PR: £10–2,000. Mem: PBFA. [Updated]

P.R. Brown (Books), 39 Sussex Walk, Norton–on–Tees, Stockton-on-Tees, Cleveland, TS20 2RG. (*) Prop: P. Robinson–Brown. Tel: (01642) 871704. Est: 1975. Private premises. Appointment necessary. Very small stock. Spec: Botany; History - Local; Ornithology. PR: £5–500. [Updated]

WILLINGTON

John Turton, 83 High Street, Willington. Tel: (01388) 747600. Fax: (01388) 746741. Also at: 1-2 Cochrane Terrace, Willington (q.v.). [05/09/2003]

John Turton, 1–2 Cochrane Terrace, Willington, Crook, DL15 0HN. Tel: (01388) 745770. Fax: (01388) 746741. E-mail: johnturton@turtome.co.uk. Est: 1978. Spec: Antiquarian; Bindings; Ecclesiastical History & Architecture; Free Thought; Genealogy; Heraldry; Journals - General; Military History; Mining; Parish Registers; School Registers/Rolls of Honour; Topography - General; Topography - Local. PR: £5–2,000. Also at: 83 High Street, Willington (q.v.). [25/06/2003]

EAST SUSSEX

David Summerfield Books, 4 Wingrove, The Tye, Alpriston, BN26 5TL. Tel: (01323) 870003. Est: 1987. Private premises. Appointment necessary. Small stock. Spec: Sport - Cricket. PR: £5–500. [Updated]

BEXHILL

Raymond Elgar, 6 Blackfields Avenue, Bexhill, TN39 4JL. Tel: (01424) 843539. Private premises. Postal business only. Very small stock. Spec: Bindings; Bookbinding; Magic & Conjuring; Music - General; Musical Instruments. Cata: 1 on bookbinding sundries and tools. [Updated]

BRIGHTON

Breese Books Ltd, 10 Hanover Crescent, Brighton, BN2 9SB. Prop: Martin Breese. Tel: (01273) 687 555. Website: www.sherlockholmes.co.uk. E-mail: MBreese999@aol.com. Est: 1988. Private premises. Postal business only. Small stock. Spec: Author - Blyton, Enid; Author - Crompton, Richmal; Author - Greene, Graham; Fiction - General; Magic & Conjuring; Sherlockiana. PR: £35–5,000. CC: MC; V. Also, specialist publishers. [14/04/2003]

Brighton Books, ■ 18 Kensington Gardens, Brighton, BN1 4AL. Prop: Paul Carmody & Catherine Clement. Tel: (01273) 693845. Fax: (01273) 693845. Est: 1996. Shop open: **M:** 10:00–18:00; **T:** 10:00–18:00; **W:** 10:00–18:00; **Th:** 10:00–18:00; **F:** 10:00–18:00; **S:** 10:00–18:00. Large stock. Spec: Academic/Scholarly; Architecture; Art; Biography; Children's - General; Cinema/Film; Drama; Fiction - General; First Editions; Gardening; Illustrated; Mythology; Photography; Poetry. PR: £1–500. CC: AE; JCB; MC; V; SW. Corresp: French, German. [Updated]

Cooks Books, 34 Marine Drive, Rottingdean, Brighton, BN2 7HQ. Prop: Tessa McKirdy. Tel: (01273) 302707. Fax: (01273) 301651. Est: 1975. Private premises. Appointment necessary. Medium stock. Spec: Cookery/Gastronomy; Food & Drink. PR: £1–500. CC: MC; V. Cata: 2 a year on gastromony. Corresp: French. VAT No: GB 509 0878 31. [Updated]

Dinnages Transport Publishing, P.O. Box 2210, Brighton, BN1 9WA. Prop: Mr. G. & Mrs. C. Dinnage. Tel: (01273) 601001. Fax: (0871) 433-8096. Website: www.transport-postcards.co.uk. E-mail: mail@dinnages.org.uk. Est: 1989. Storeroom; Showroom open at selected Saturdays by prior arrangement. Regular stall at Maidstone Collectors Fair (5 a year). Internet and postal. Appointment necessary. Very small stock. Spec: Buses/Trams; History - Local; Publishers - General; Railways; Transport. PR: £1–25. CC: PayPal/Nox. Also publishers of nostalgic transport & local photographs and postcards, and book distributor. [updated]

Turner Donovan Military Books, 12 Southdown Avenue, Brighton, BN1 6EG. Tel: (01273) 566230. E-mail: tom@turnerdonovan.com. Est: 1985. Postal business only. Spec: Countries - India; Military; Military History; War - Napoleonic; War - World War II. PR: £15–2,500. [15/05/2003]

Fisher Nautical, Huntswood House, St. Helena Lane, Streat, Hassocks, Brighton, BN6 8SD. (*) Prop: S. & J. Fisher. Tel: (01273) 890273. Fax: (01273) 891439. Website: www.fishernauticalbooks.co.uk. E-mail: fishernautical@seabooks.fsnet.co.uk. Est: 1969. Private premises. Postal business only. Very large stock. Spec: Maritime/Nautical; also, booksearch. PR: £10–3,000. CC: MC; V. Cata: 12 – every 4-6 weeks on nautical. Mem: PBFA. [Updated]

Invisible Books, Unit 8, 15-26 Lincoln Cottage Works, Lincoln Cottages, Brighton, BN2 9UJ. Prop: Paul Holman & Bridget Penney. Tel: (01273) 694574. Fax: (0870) 052 2755. Website: www. invisiblebooks.net. E-mail: invisible@invisiblebooks.demon.co.uk. Est: 1994. Storeroom; Internet and postal. Appointment necessary. Medium stock. Spec: Academic/Scholarly; Counterculture; New Age. PR: £1–1,000. VAT No: GB 825 8052 27. [Updated]

Kenya Books, 31 Southdown Ave., Brighton, BN1 6EH. Prop: J. McGivney. Tel: (01273) 556029. Website: www.abebooks.com/home/kenyabooks. E-mail: info@kenyabooks.com. Private premises. Internet and postal. Open: **M:** 09:00–19:00; **W:** 09:00–19:00; **Th:** 09:00–19:00; **F:** 09:00–19:00; **S:** 09:00–19:00. Medium stock. Spec: Africana; Countries - Africa; Countries - France; Countries - Indian Ocean, The; Countries - Ireland; Countries - Kenya; Countries - South Africa; Countries - Tanzania; Countries - Uganda; Irish Interest; Languages - African; Linguistics; Police Force Histories. PR: £1–500. Corresp: French; Swahili. [Updated]

Moviedrome, 8 Friar Crescent, Brighton, BN1 6NL. Prop: Don Shiach. Tel: (01273) 881611. E-mail: moviedrome@fastnet.co.uk. Est: 1993. Internet and postal. Spec: Cinema/Film. PR: £1–500. [29/06/ 2003]

Colin Page Antiquarian Books, ■ 36 Duke Street, Brighton, BN1 1AG. Prop: John Loska. Tel: (01273) 325954. E-mail: cpagebooks@aol.com. Est: 1969. Shop open: **M:** 09:30–17:30; **T:** 09:30–17:30; **W:** 09:30–17:30; **Th:** 09:30–17:30; **F:** 09:30–17:30; **S:** 09:30–17:30. Large stock. Spec: Bindings; Children's - General; Colour-Plate; Illustrated; Literature; Natural History; Topography - General; Travel - General. PR: £1–10,000. CC: AE; JCB; MC; V. Cata: 1 on request. Mem: ABA. [17/07/2003]

Rainbow Books, ■ 28 Trafalgar Street, Brighton, BN1 4ED. Prop: Kevin Daly. Tel: (01273) 605101. Est: 1998. Shop open: **M:** 10:30–18:00; **T:** 10:30–18:00; **W:** 10:30–18:00; **Th:** 10:30–18:00; **F:** 10:30–18:00; **S:** 10:30–18:00. Very large general stock. Spec: PR: £1–20. [Updated]

Savery Books and Antiques, ■ 257 Ditchling Road, Brighton, BN1 6JG. Prop: James, Sarah, Marianne, & Anne, Savery. Tel: (01273) 564899 and 5. E-mail: saverybooks@aol.com. Est: 1990. Shop open: **M:** 10:00–16:00; **T:** 10:00–14:00; **W:** 10:00–16:00; **Th:** 10:00–16:00; **F:** 10:00–16:00; **S:** 10:00–16:00. Medium stock. Spec: Academic/Scholarly; Art; Aviation; Biography; Children's - General; Cookery/ Gastronomy; Fiction - General; Gardening; History - General; Literary Criticism; Literature; Maritime/Nautical; Military; Philosophy; Psychology/Psychiatry. PR: £1–10. CC: MC; V. Also, antiques & small furniture. [Updated]

Liz Seeber, Old Vicarage, 3 College Road, Brighton, BN2 1JA. Tel: (01273) 684949. Website: www. lizseeberbooks.co.uk. E-mail: seeber.books@virgin.net. Est: 1994. Private premises. Postal business only. Appointment necessary. Small stock. Spec: Cookery/Gastronomy; Gardening; also Booksearch. PR: £5–3,000. CC: MC; V. Cata: quarterly. VAT No: GB 629 3954 04. [Updated]

Studio Bookshop, ■ 68 St. James's Street, Brighton, BN2 1PJ. Prop: Paul Brown. Tel: (01273) 691253. Website: www.abebooks.com/home/studiobookshop. E-mail: studiobookshop@btconnect.com. Est: 1995. Shop open: **M:** 11:00–17:00; **T:** 11:00–17:00; **W:** 11:00–19:00; **F:** 11:00–17:00; **S:** 11:00–17:00. Medium stock. Spec: Academic/Scholarly; Antiques; Applied Art; Architecture; Art; Art - Reference; Ceramics; First Editions; Glass; History - General; Humanities; Literary Criticism; Literature; Literature in Translation; Modern First Editions; Stained Glass. PR: £5–450. CC: JCB; MC; V. [Updated]

The Trafalgar Bookshop, ■ 44 Trafalgar Street, Brighton, Prop: David Boland. Tel: (01273) 684300. Est: 1979. Shop. Medium stock. Spec: Colour-Plate; Journals - General; Literature; Sport - General; Sport - Horse Racing (all aspects); also Booksearch. [Updated]

CROWBOROUGH

Ray Hennessey Bookseller, Panfield House, Crowborough Hill, Crowborough, TN6 2HJ. Prop: Ray & Deanna Hennessey. Tel: (01892) 653704. Fax: (0870) 0548776. E-mail: rayhen@books4.demon.co.uk. Est: 1954. Private premises. Internet and postal. Appointment necessary. Shop at: Olinda House Antiques Rotherfield East Sussex. Open: **M:** 10:10–17:17; **T:** 10:10–17:17; **W:** 10:10–17:17; **Th:** 10:00– 17:00; **F:** 10:00–17:00; **S:** 10:00–17:00; **Su:** 11:00–16:00. Medium stock. Spec: Africana; Antiquarian; Antiques; Applied Art; Art; Bibles; Canals/Inland Waterways; Children's - Illustrated; Gardening; Illustrated; Lace; Literature; Miniature Books; Needlework; Poetry; Publishers - Batsford; Sport - Golf; Tapestry; Textiles. PR: £6–1,000. CC: AE; E; JCB; MC; V. Mem: PBFA. [Updated]

Simply Read Books, Fielden Rd, Crowborough, TN6 2TR. Prop: W.L. & W.P. Banks. Tel: (01892) 664584. Website: www.abebooks.com/home/simplyread. E-mail: simplyreadbook@aol.com. Est: 1998. Private premises. Internet and postal. Telephone first. Shop at: Badgers Wood, Fielden Rd., Crowborough, East Sussex TN6 1TP. Spec: Crime (True); Modern First Editions; Travel - General; also Booksearch. PR: £2–20. CC: MC; V. [08/07/2003]

EASTBOURNE

Camilla's Bookshop, ■ 57 Grove Road, Eastbourne, BN21 4TX. Prop: Camilla Francombe & Stuart Broad. Tel: (01323) 736001. E-mail: camillasbooks@tiscali.co.uk. Est: 1976. Shop open: **M:** 10:00–17:30; **T:** 10:00–17:30; **W:** 10:00–17:30; **Th:** 10:00–17:30; **F:** 10:00–17:30; **S:** 10:00–17:30. Very large stock. Spec: Archaeology; Art; Art - History; Cinema/Film; Embroidery; History - General; Juvenile; Literature; Military; Military History; Mind, Body & Spirit; Modern First Editions; Music - General; Mysticism; Naval; Palmistry & Fortune Telling; Poetry. PR: £1–1,000. CC: MC; V. VAT No: GB 583 7350 18. [Updated]

Roderick Dew, 10 Furness Road, Eastbourne, BN21 4EZ. Tel: (01323) 720239. Est: 1975. Private premises. Appointment necessary. Small stock. Spec: Applied Art; Architecture; Bibliography; Fine Art. PR: £5–500. Cata: 4 a year on art and bibliography. Corresp: French, German. [Updated]

A. & T. Gibbard, ■ 1 and 2 Calverley Walk, Eastbourne, BN21 4UP. Alan & Maria Tania Gibbard. Tel: (01323) 734128. Fax: (01323) 734128. Est: 1909. Shop open: **T:** 10:00–17:00; **W:** 10:00–17:00; **Th:** 10:00–17:00; **F:** 10:00–17:00; **S:** 10:00–17:00. Medium stock. Spec: Literature; Natural History; Railways; Topography - Local; Transport. PR: £1–1,000. CC: AE; MC; V. Corresp: Italian, Spanish. Mem: PBFA. VAT No: GB 621 5744 53. [Updated]

Berry Harper, Books, 4 Friston Downs, Friston, Eastbourne, BN20 0ET. Prop: Mrs. B. Harper. Tel: (01323) 423335. E-mail: berry@pavilion.co.uk. Est: 1986. Private premises. Internet and postal. Telephone first. Open: **M:** 09:00–18:00; **T:** 09:00–18:00; **W:** 09:00–18:00; **Th:** 09:00–18:00; **F:** 09:00–18:00; **S:** 09:00–18:00. Very small stock. Spec: Publishers - General; Publishers - Ladybird Books. PR: £1–50. Corresp: French, German. [Updated]

London & Sussex Antiquarian Books, Southwood, 15 Dittons Road, Eastbourne, BN21 1DR. Prop: Dr. G.B. Carruthers. Tel: (01323) 730857. Fax: (01323) 737550. E-mail: doctor.johnsons@virgin.net. Est: 1970. Postal business only. Spec: Alternative Medicine; Dogs; Medicine - History of. PR: £10–100. [Updated]

R. & A. Books, 4 Milton Grange, 6 Arundel Road, Eastbourne, BN21 2EL. Prop: Robert Manning and Alan Millard. Tel: (01323) 647690. Website: http://www.raenterprises.co.uk/. E-mail: robert.manning @btinternet.com. Est: 2000. Private premises. Internet and postal. Contact by email please. We will search sell and buy. Large general stock. Spec: Academic/Scholarly; Advertising; Aeronautics; Africana; Agriculture; Almanacs; Alpinism/Mountaineering; Animals and Birds; Annuals; Anthropology; Antiquarian; Antiques; Archaeology; Arms & Armour; Art; Art - History; Art - Reference; Arthurian. PR: £1–500. Worldwide orders accepted. Payment in sterling through PayPal. UK cheques accepted. [Updated]

HASTINGS

Calendula Horticultural Books, 3 Amherst Garden, Hastings, TN34 1TU. Prop: Heiko Miles. Tel: (01424) 437591. Website: www.calendulabooks.com. E-mail: heiko@calendulabooks.com. Est: 1987. Private premises. Postal business only. Small stock. Spec: Flower Arranging; Gardening; Herbalism; Horticulture; Landscape; Ornithology; Plant Hunting. PR: £5–10,000. CC: JCB; V. [Updated]

Chthonios Books, 7 Tamarisk Steps, Off Rock-a-Nores Road, Hastings, TN34 3DN. Prop: Stephen Ronan. Tel: (01424) 433302. Website: www.esotericism.co.uk/index.htm. E-mail: service@ esotericism.co.uk. Est: 1985. Private premises. Internet and postal. Telephone first. Small stock. Spec: Alchemy; Classical Studies; Earth Mysteries; Egyptology; Hermeticism; Humanism; Literature in Translation; Occult; Paganism; Philosophy; Religion - Christian; Spiritualism; Witchcraft; also, booksearch. PR: £3–300. CC: MC; V; SW. SO. Cata: 8 Email catalogues of new stock. Corresp: French. [Updated]

Hoovey's Books, P.O. Box 27, St. Leonards–on–Sea, Hastings, TN37 6TZ. (*). Tel: (01424) 753407. Fax: (01424) 753407. Website: www.hooveys.co.uk. E-mail: books@hooveys.com. Est: 1968. Office &/or bookroom; appointment necessary. Small general stock. Spec: booksearch. Catalogue printing, cleaning materials, jacket coverings. VAT No: GB 397 8504 94. [19/08/2003]

Howes Bookshop, ■ Trinity Hall, Braybrooke Terrace, Hastings, TN34 1HQ. Prop: Miles Bartley. Tel: (01424) 423437. Fax: (01424) 460620. Website: www.howes.co.uk. E-mail: rarebooks@howes.co.uk. Est: 1921. Shop open: **M:** 09:30–17:00; **T:** 09:30–17:00; **W:** 09:30–17:00; **Th:** 09:29–17:00; **F:** 09:30–17:00. Closed for lunch: 13:00–14:00. Very large stock. Spec: Academic/Scholarly; Antiquarian; Arts, The; Bibliography; Classical Studies; History - General; Literature; Philosophy; Theology; Travel - General. PR: £10–5,000. CC: MC; V. Cata: 5 on speciailities. Mem: ABA; PBFA; ILAB. VAT No: GB 201 2142 45. [07/07/2003]

Robert Mucci, ■ 68 High Street, Old Town, Hastings, TN34 3EW. Prop: Robert M. Mucci. Tel: (01424) 445340. Est: 1989. Shop open: **M:** 11:00–18:00; **T:** 11:00–18:00; **W:** 11:00–18:00; **Th:** 11:00–18:00; **F:** 11:00–18:00; **S:** 11:00–18:00; **Su:** 11:00–18:00. Very small general stock. PR: £1–8. [Updated]

Olio Books, 43 Robertson Street, Hastings, TN34 1HL. Prop: Philip & Denise Rees. Tel: (01424) 428987. Est: 1981. Spec: Antiques; Art; Art - Reference; Author - General; Children's - General; Fiction - General; History - General; Military; Music - General; Topography - General; Travel - General. PR: £1–100. [28/08/2003]

The Paperback Reader, ■ 82 Queens Road, Hastings, TN34 1RL. Prop: Rog and Amanda Read. Tel: (01424) 446749. Est: 1972. Shop open: **M:** 09:00–17:00; **T:** 09:00–17:00; **Th:** 09:00–17:00; **F:** 09:00–17:00; **S:** 09:00–17:00; Large stock. Spec: Comics. PR: £1–4. [27/05/2003]

Anthony Sillem, 9 Tackleway, Old Town, Hastings, TN34 3DE. Prop: Anthony Sillem. Tel: (01424) 446602. Fax: (01424) 446602. Website: tackletext@btopenworld.com. E-mail: tackletext@btopenworld.com. Est: 1994. Private premises. Appointment necessary. Small stock. Spec: First Editions; Illustrated; Literature; Literature in Translation; Memoirs; Modern First Editions. PR: £10–2,000. CC: MC; V. Cata: 3 a year. Mem: PBFA. [Updated]

HEATHFIELD

Botting & Berry, ■ 31 High Street, Heathfield, TN21 8HU. Prop: John Botting and Dave Berry. Tel: (01435) 868555. Est: 2001. Shop open: **M:** 10:00–17:00; **T:** 10:00–17:00; **W:** 10:00–17:00; **Th:** 10:00–17:00; **F:** 10:00–17:00; **S:** 10:00–17:00. Small stock. PR: £1–500. Fairs: Royal National, Bloomsbury, London. [30/06/2003]

HOVE

J.F. Holleyman, 3 Portland Avenue, Hove, BN3 5NP. Tel: (01273) 410915. Private premises. Postal business only. Appointment necessary. Small stock. Spec: Photography. Cata: 3 a year. [Updated]

Simon Hunter Antique Maps, 21 St Johns Road, Hove, BN3 2FB. Prop: Simon Hunter. Tel: (01273) 746983. Website: www.antiquemaps.org.uk. E-mail: simonhunter@fastnet.co.uk. Internet and postal. Medium stock. Spec: PR: £5–1,000. CC: AE; E; JCB; MC; V. Antique Maps only. Corresp: French. Mem: IMCoS. VAT No: GB 587 4541 02. [Updated]

Whitehall Books, 3 Leighton Road, Hove, BN3 7AD. Prop: Peter Batten. Tel: (01273) 735252. Website: www.whitehallbooks.co.uk. E-mail: peterbatten@whitehallbooks.co.uk. Est: 1991. Private premises. Internet and postal. Appointment necessary. Very small stock. Spec: Antiques; Art; Countries - Russia; Crime (True); Criminology; Illustrated; Literary Criticism; Literature. PR: £1–100. Translation. Literary detective work and general literary information. Corresp: French, Russian. [Updated]

LEWES

Richard Beaton, 24 Highdown Road, Lewes, BN7 1QD. Prop: Dr. Richard Beaton. Tel: (01273) 474147. Fax: (01273) 474147. Website: www.victorian-novels.co.uk. E-mail: richard@victorian-novels.co.uk. Est: 1996. Private premises. Internet and postal. Appointment necessary. Open: **M:** 09:00–18:00; **T:** 09:00–18:00; **W:** 09:00–18:00; **Th:** 09:00–18:00; **F:** 09:00–18:00; **S:** 09:00–18:00. Small stock. Spec: Fiction - General; Literature - Victorian. PR: £5–1,000. CC: JCB; MC; V; SW. Cata: 5 every 2 - 3 months. Corresp: French. Mem: PBFA. [Updated]

John Beck, 29 Mill Road, Lewes, BN7 2RU. Tel: (01273) 477555. Est: 1982. Office &/or bookroom. Postal business only. Appointment necessary. Shop at: The Boxroom, Needlemakers, Lewes. Open 7 days. Open: **M:** 10:00–16:00; **T:** 10:00–16:00; **W:** 10:00–16:00; **Th:** 10:00–16:00; **F:** 10:00–16:00; **S:** 10:00–16:00; **Su:** 10:00–16:00. Small stock. Spec: Children's - General; Comic Books & Annuals; Comics; Juvenile. PR: £1–1,000. [Updated]

Bow Windows Book Shop, ■ 175 High Street, Lewes, BN7 1YE. Prop: Alan & Jennifer Shelley. Tel: (01273) 480780. Fax: (01273) 486686. Website: www.bowwindows.com. E-mail: rarebooks@bowwindows.com. Est: 1964. Shop open: **M:** 09:30–05:00; **T:** 09:30–05:00; **W:** 09:30–05:00; **Th:** 09:30–05:00; **F:** 09:30–05:00; **S:** 09:30–05:00. Medium stock. Spec: Antiquarian; Artists; Author - Bloomsbury Group, The; Author - Rackham, Arthur; Author - Sackville-West, Vita; Author - Woolf, Virginia; Children's - Illustrated; Countries - China; Countries - Japan; Geology; Literature; Modern First Editions. PR: £1–5,000. CC: AE; MC; V. Cata: 4 a year. Corresp: German. Mem: ABA; PBFA; ILAB. VAT No: GB 370 1163 88. [Updated]

A. & Y. Cumming Limited, ■ 84 High Street, Lewes, BN7 1XN. Prop: A.J. Cumming. Tel: (01273) 472319. Fax: (01273) 486364. E-mail: a.y.cumming@ukgateway.net. Est: 1976. Shop open: **M:** 10:00–17:00; **T:** 10:00–17:00; **W:** 10:00–17:00; **Th:** 10:00–17:00; **F:** 10:00–17:00; **S:** 10:00–17:30. Very large stock. Spec: Art; Bindings; Illustrated; Literature; Natural History; Topography - General; Travel - General. Mem: ABA. VAT No: GB 412 4098 80. [Updated]

Ruth Kidson, ■ 31 Western Road, Lewes, BN7 1RL. Prop: Mrs. G.R. Kidson. Tel: (01273) 487087. Fax: (01273) 487087. Website: www.ruth.kidson@virgin.net. E-mail: books@ruthkidson.co.uk. Est: 1992. Shop; Internet and postal. Telephone first. Open: **T:** 11:00–16:30; **Th:** 11:00–16:30; **F:** 11:00–16:30; **S:** 11:00–17:00. Small general stock. Spec: PR: £2–1,000. CC: MC; V; Delta, Mae. Opening times may vary, please phone ahead if coming any distance. Mem: ABA; PBFA; ILAB; Rare Books Society. VAT No: GB 777 7852 58. [Updated]

T.F.S. Scott, 37 St. Anne's Crescent, Lewes, BN7 1SB. Tel: (01273) 473619. Est: 1979. Private premises. Appointment necessary. Small general stock. Spec: Fiction - General; First Editions; Literature; Memoirs; Topography - General; Topography - Local; Travel - Africa; Travel - Asia; Travel - Europe; Travel - Middle East. PR: £2–700. Mem: PBFA. [25/06/2002]

Derek Wise, Berewood House, Barcombe, Lewes, BN8 5TW. Tel: (01273) 400559. Fax: (01273) 400559. E-mail: derekwise@pavilion.co.uk. Est: 1986. Private premises. Internet and postal. Appointment necessary. Small stock. Spec: Author - Byron, Lord; Education & School; Literature; Maritime/Nautical; Military; Military History; Natural History; Naval; Public Schools; School Registers/Rolls of Honour. PR: £1–1,500. Cata: 1 occasionally. Corresp: French. Mem: PBFA. [Updated]

PORTSLADE

Peter Scott, 14 Vale Road, Portslade, BN41 1GF. Prop: Peter Scott. Tel: (01273) 410576. Website: www.scottbooks.freeuk.com. E-mail: peter.scott45@btopenworld.com. Est: 1986. Private premises. Internet and postal. Appointment necessary. Small general stock. Spec: Academic/Scholarly; Art; History - General; Literature; Religion - General. PR: £1–200. [Updated]

ROBERTSBRIDGE

Spearman Books, ■ The Old Saddlery Bookshop, 56 High Street, Robertsbridge, TN32 5AP. John & Janet Brooman. Tel: (01580) 880631. Fax: (01580) 880631. E-mail: saddlerybooks@aol.com. Est: 1970. Shop open: **M:** 10:00–17:00; **T:** 10:00–17:00; **W:** 10:00–17:00; **Th:** 10:00–17:00; **F:** 10:00–17:00; **S:** 09:00–17:00. Closed for lunch: 13:00–14:00. Medium stock. Spec: Travel - General. PR: £1–500. [03/03/2003]

ROTHERFIELD

Kennedy & Farley, 2 Brook Cottages, New Road, Rotherfield, TN6 3JT. Prop: Helen Kennedy & Fran Farley. Tel: (01444) 412785. E-mail: kennedyandfarley@care4free.net. Est: 1987. Private premises. Internet and postal. Telephone first. Small general stock. Spec: Modern First Editions; Sport - Horse Racing (all aspects); Sport - Hunting. Corresp: French. Mem: PBFA. [Updated]

RYE

Chapter and Verse Booksellers, ■105 High Street, Rye, TN31 7JE. Prop: Spencer James Rogers. Tel: (01797) 222692. E-mail: chapterandverse@btconnect.com. Est: 1993. Shop open: **M:** 10:00–17:00; **T:** 10:00–17:00; **W:** 10:00–17:00; **F:** 10:00–17:00; **S:** 10:00–17:00. Medium stock. Spec: Antiquarian; Art; Art - History; Art - Reference; Author - Woolf, Virginia; Autobiography; Bindings; Biography; Colour-Plate; Topography - General; Topography - Local; Travel - General; War - General; also Booksearch. PR: £10–27,500. CC: MC; V; SW. [23/04/2003]

The Meads Book Service, ■ 4 & 5 Lion Street, Rye, TN31 7LB. Prop: Clive Ogden. Tel: (01797) 227057. Fax: (01797) 223769. E-mail: meadsbookservice@freenet.co.uk. Est: 1988. Shop open: **M:** 10:15–17:30; **T:** 10:15–17:30; **W:** 10:15–17:30; **Th:** 10:15–17:30; **F:** 10:15–17:30; **S:** 10:15–17:30; **Su:** 10:15–17:30. Small stock. Spec: Author - Benson, A.C.; Author - Benson, E.F.; Author - Benson, R.H.; Author - Madox Ford, Ford; Author - Thorndike, Russell; Biography; Children's - General; Fiction - General; Military; Military History; Natural History; Topography - Local; also Booksearch. PR: £1–200. [Updated]

ST. LEONARD'S–ON–SEA

The Book Jungle, ■ 24 North Street, St. Leonard's–on–Sea, TN38 0EX. Prop: Michael Gowen. Tel: (01424) 421187. E-mail: mrgowen@yahoo.co.uk. Est: 1991. Shop open: **T:** 10:00–16:00; **Th:** 10:00–16:00; **F:** 10:00–16:00; **S:** 10:00–16:00. Large general stock. Spec: PR: £1–20. [Updated]

Raymond Kilgarriff, 15 Maze Hill, St. Leonards–on–Sea, TN38 0HN. Tel: (01424) 426146. Website: www.ilab.org. E-mail: rmkilgarriff@btinternet.com. Est: 1947. Private premises. Internet and postal. Appointment necessary. Very small stock. Spec: Academic/Scholarly; Antiquarian; Fine & Rare; History - General; Literature. PR: £100–2,000. CC: MC; V. Mem: ABA; ILAB. VAT No: GB 794 2047 15. [Updated]

TICEHURST

Piccadilly Rare Books, ■ Church Street, Ticehurst, TN5 7AA. Prop: Paul P.B. Minet. Tel: (01580) 201221. Fax: (01580) 200957. Website: www.picrare.com. E-mail: Picrare@btinternet.com. Est: 1972. Shop open: **M:** 10:00–17:00; **T:** 10:00–17:00; **W:** 10:00–17:00; **Th:** 10:00–17:00; **F:** 10:00–17:00; **S:** 10:00–18:00. Large general stock. Spec: Diaries; Royalty - General; Royalty - European. PR: £5–1,000. CC: AE; MC; V. Also, publishers of 'Royalty Digest' (monthly); 'British Diarist' (quarterly). Rates on request. Reprinters. Mem: PBFA; AVBA. VAT No: GB 583 9618 89. [Updated]

EAST YORKSHIRE

ALLERTHORPE

K. Books, Waplington Hall, Allerthorpe, York, YO42 4RS. Prop: B.J. & S.M. Kaye, M.J. Rose. Tel: (01759) 302142. Fax: (01759) 305891. Website: www.kbooks.uk.com. E-mail: kaye@kbooks.uk.com. Est: 1966. Private premises. Internet and postal. Very large stock. Spec: Antiquarian; History - General; Literature; Natural History; Printing; Topography - General; also Booksearch. PR: £10–2,000. CC: V. Corresp: French. Mem: ABA. VAT No: GB 161 1956 22. [13/07/2003]

BEVERLEY

Beverley Old Bookshop, ■ 2 Dyer Lane, Beverley, HU17 8AE. Prop: Colin Tatman. Tel: (01482) 880611. Est: 1993. Shop open: **M:** 10:00–17:00; **T:** 10:00–17:00; **W:** 10:00–17:00; **Th:** 10:00–17:00; **F:** 10:00–17:00; **S:** 10:00–17:00. Medium stock. Spec: Bookbinding; Children's - General; History - Local; Illustrated. PR: £1–200. Also, book restoration. [Updated]

Countryman Books, 37 North Bar Without, Beverley, HU17 7AG. Prop: Christine Swift. Tel: (01482) 869710. Fax: (01482) 869710. Website: www.countryman.co.uk. E-mail: books@countryman.co.uk. Spec: Author - Aldin, Cecil; Dogs; Sport - Angling/Fishing; Sport - Big Game Hunting; Sport - Falconry; Sport - Hunting; Sport - Polo; Sport - Shooting. PR: £5–150. CC: MC; V; Switch. Mem: ABA. [Updated]

Eastgate Bookshop, ■ 11 Eastgate, Beverley, HU17 0DR. Prop: Barry Roper. Tel: (01482) 868579. E-mail: barry@eastgatebooks.karoo.co.uk. Est: 1983. Shop open: **W:** 10:00–17:00; **Th:** 10:00–17:00; **F:** 10:00–17:00; **S:** 10:00–16:30. Large general stock. Spec: Archaeology; Crime (True); History - Local; Military; Topography - Local; Travel - Asia; also Booksearch. PR: £1–500. CC: JCB; MC; V; Switch. Open Monday and Tuesday by appointment only. Cata: occasionally on local history, Borneo, true crime. Also at: Sarawak Books, Beverley (q.v.) [Updated]

Peter Riddell, Hall Cottage, Main St., Cherry Burton, Beverley, HU17 7RF. Tel: (01964) 551453. E-mail: bkscherryb@aol.com. Est: 1989. Private premises. Internet and postal. Appointment necessary. Very small general stock. Spec: Alpinism/Mountaineering; Countries - Central Asia; Countries - Polar. PR: £1–250. [Updated]

BRIDLINGTON

Family Favourites (Books), 51 First Avenue, Bridlington, YO15 2JR. Prop: Shirley Jackson. Tel: (01262) 606061. E-mail: shirleyjackson@telco4u.net. Est: 1989. Private premises. Postal business only. Medium stock. Spec: Annuals; Autobiography; Biography; Drawing; Fiction - General; Modern First Editions; Ornithology; Topography - General, also Booksearch. PR: £3–500. [15/04/03]

J.L. Book Exchange, ■ 72 Hilderthorpe Road, Bridlington, YO15 3BQ. Prop: John Ledraw. Tel: (01262) 601285. Est: 1971. Shop open in summer: **M:** 08:30–18:00; **T:** 08:30–18:00; **W:** 08:30–18:00; **Th:** 08:30–18:00; **F:** 08:30–18:00; **S:** 08:30–18:00; **Su:** 08:30–18:00. Medium stock. Spec: PR: £1–80. Winter opening: Mon-Sat 09.30–17.30. Mem: PBFA. [Updated]

DRIFFIELD

Solaris Books, Flat 4, 13 Lockwood St., Driffield, YO25 6RU. Prop: Jim Goddard. Tel: (01377) 272022. Website: www.solaris-books.co.uk. E-mail: jim@solaris-books.co.uk. Private premises. Internet and postal. Telephone first. Medium stock. Spec: Fiction - Fantasy, Horror; Fiction - Science Fiction; Military History; Modern First Editions; Photography; also Booksearch. PR: £2–1,200. Cata: 4 – [Updated]

FLAMBOROUGH

Resurgam Books, ■ The Manor House, Flamborough, Bridlington, York, YO15 1PD. Prop: Geoffrey Miller. Tel: (01262) 850943. Fax: (01262) 850943. Website: www.resurgambooks.co.uk. E-mail: gm@resurgambooks.co.uk. Est: 1998. Internet and postal. Shop open: **M:** 09:00–17:00; **T:** 09:00–17:00; **W:** 09:00–17:00; **Th:** 09:00–17:00; **F:** 09:00–17:00; **S:** 09:00–17:00; **Su:** 10:00–16:00. Very small stock. PR: £1–400. CC: E; JCB; MC; V. [Updated]

GREAT DRIFFIELD

The Driffield Bookshop, ■ 21 Middle Street North, Great Driffield, YO25 6SW. Prop: G.R. Stevens. Tel: (01377) 254210. Est: 1981. Shop open: **M:** 10:00–07:30; **T:** 10:00–17:30; **W:** 10:00–17:30; **Th:** 10:00– 17:30; **F:** 10:00–17:30; **S:** 10:00–17:30; Medium stock. Spec: Fiction - Science Fiction; History - General; Literature; Military History; Modern First Editions; Travel - General. PR: £1–150. Cata: 3 a year. [Updated]

HOWDEN

Kemp Booksellers, ■ 5–7 Vicar Lane, Howden, DN14 7BP. Prop: Mike Kemp. Tel: (01430) 432071. Fax: (01430) 431666. Website: www.kempbooksellers.co.uk. E-mail: enquiries@kempbooksellers.co.uk. Est: 1979. Shop open: **T:** 10:00–17:00; **W:** 10:00–17:00; **Th:** 10:00–17:00; **F:** 10:00–17:00; **S:** 10:00– 16:00; Closed for lunch: 13:00–13:30. Large stock. Spec: Antiquarian; Author - Peake, Mervyn; Fiction - Science Fiction; Modern First Editions; Topography - General; Topography - Local. PR: £1–1,000. CC: MC; V. Cata: 2 a year. Corresp: French. Mem: ABA; PBFA; BA; ILAB. [Updated]

HULL

Bowie Books & Collectables, 19 Northolt Close, Hull, HU8 0PP. Prop: James Bowie. Tel: (01482) 374609. E-mail: bowiebooks@hotmail.co.uk. Est: 2003. Private premises. Internet and postal. Appointment necessary. Shop at: http://stores.ebay.com/Bowies-Books-And-Collectables_W0QQsspagenameZME. Open: **M:** 09:00–18:00; **T:** 09:00–18:00; **W:** 09:00–18:00; **Th:** 09:00–18:00; **F:** 09:00–18:00; **S:** 09:00– 15:00. Small general stock. Spec: Antiquarian; Fiction - General; First Editions; Literature; Modern First Editions; Religion - General. PR: £2–150. [Updated]

Harry Holmes Books, 85 Park Avenue, Hull, HU5 3EP. Prop: H.H. & P.A. Purkis. Tel: (01482) 443220. Est: 1989. Private premises. Appointment necessary. Open: Small stock. Spec: Alpinism/ Mountaineering; Biography; Countries - Scotland; Literature; Religion - Christian; Spiritualism; Topography - Local; Travel - Polar; Voyages & Discovery; also Booksearch. PR: £1–100. Books on literary biography are also stocked. Cata: 5 on Polar exploration and mountaineering. Corresp: French and German. Mem: PBFA. [17/05/2003]

hullbooks.com, ■ 165 Newland Avenue, Hull, HU5 2EP. Prop: Ian & Karren Barfield. Tel: 01482 444677. Website: www.hullbooks.com. E-mail: hullbooks@yahoo.co.uk. Shop open: **M:** 10:00–17:00; **T:** 10:00–17:00; **W:** 10:00–17:00; **Th:** 10:00–17:00; **F:** 10:00–17:00; **S:** 10:00–17:00. Large general stock. Spec: Academic/Scholarly; History - Local; Humanities; Social Sciences. PR: £2–200. CC: E; JCB; MC; V. Mem: PBFA. [Updated]

Colin Martin - Bookseller, 3 Village Road, Garden Village, Hull, HU8 8QP. Prop: Colin and Jane Martin, L.L.B., B.A. Tel: (01482) 585836. Website: www.colinmartinbooks.com. E-mail: enquiries@ colinmartinbooks.com. Est: 1991. Storeroom. Shop at: Holderness Road, Hull. Open: **M:** 10:00– 16:00; **T:** 10:00–16:00; **W:** 10:00–16:00; **Th:** 10:00–16:00; **F:** 10:00–16:00. Very large stock. Spec: Applied Art; Architecture; Art; Art - History; Art - Reference; Artists; Arts, The; Design; Interior Design; Sculpture. PR: £3–600. CC: AE; D; JCB; MC; V; SW, SO. Cata: 1 occasionally. Corresp: French, German, Italian. VAT No: GB 780 4607 24. [Updated]

KIRKELLA

East Riding Books, 13 Westland Road, Kirkella, HU10 7PH. Prop: Gill Carlile. Tel: (01482) 650674. Website: www.eastridingbooks.co.uk. E-mail: info@eastridingbooks.co.uk. Est: 1996. Private premises. Internet and postal. Small stock. Spec: Music - General; Music - Classical; Music - Composers; Music - Jazz; Music - Musicians; Music - Opera; Musical Instruments. PR: £1–500. CC: MC; V. Mem: PBFA. VAT No: GB 747 0534 31. [Updated]

MILLINGTON

Quest Books, Harmer Hill, Millington, York, YO42 1TX. Prop: Dr. Peter Burridge. Tel: (01759) 304735. Fax: (01759) 306820. E-mail: questbyz@aol.com. Est: 1984. Private premises. Postal business only. Appointment necessary. Very small stock. Spec: Academic/Scholarly; Archaeology; Architecture; Classical Studies; Countries - Arabia; Asia Minor; Balkans, The; Cyprus; Egypt; Greece; Iran; Turkey; Travel - General. PR: £5–1,000. CC: JCB; MC; V. Cata: 2 a year. Mem: PBFA. [Updated]

SWANLAND

Cygnet Books, 86 Main Street, Swanland, HU14 3QR. (*) Prop: Mrs. Jackie Kitchen. Tel: (01482) 635610. Website: www.cygnetbooks.co.uk. E-mail: jackie@cynetbooks.co.uk. Est: 2000. Private premises. Postal business only. Open: **M:** 09:00–17:00 **T:** 09:00–17:00; **W:** 09:00–17:00; **Th:** 09:00–17:00; **F:** 09:00–17:00; **S:** 09:00–17:00. Small stock. Spec: Children's - General; Comic Books & Annuals; Disneyana; Fables; First Editions; Pop-Up, 3D, Cut Out & Movable, also Booksearch. PR: £2–100. CC: JCB; MC; V; Maestro. VAT No: GB 817 0861 29. [Updated]

WINESTEAD

Alex Alec–Smith Books, The Old Rectory, Winestead, Hull, HU12 0NN. Tel: (01964) 630548. Fax: (01964) 631160. E-mail: alex@aasbooks.demon.co.uk. Est: 1985. Private premises. Appointment necessary. Small stock. Spec: Author - Byron, Lord; Bibliography; Books about Books; Dictionaries; Literary Criticism; Literature; Topography - Local. PR: £5–3,000. CC: MC; V. Cata: 4 on Byron & the Romantics, bibliography & dictionary. Mem: ABA; PBFA; ILAB. VAT No: GB 433 6879 22. [Updated]

ESSEX

BILLERICAY

Engaging Gear Ltd., Lark Rise, 14 Linkdale, Billericay, CM12 9QW. Prop: D.E. Twitchett. Tel: (01277) 624913. Est: 1965. Private premises. Postal business only. Very small stock. Spec: Author - Moore, John; Horology; Sport - Cycling; Travel - General. PR: £5–500. Stock includes titles on cycling history and travel. [Updated]

BIRCH

John Cowley, Auto–in–Print, Mill Lodge, Mill Lane, Birch, Colchester, CO2 0NG. Tel: (01206) 331052. Fax: (01206) 330438. Website: www.autoinprint.freeserve.co.uk. E-mail: cowley@autoinprint .freeserve.co.uk. Est: 1975. Private premises. Internet and postal. Appointment necessary. Open: Very large stock. Spec: Motoring, also Booksearch. [26/02/03]

BRAINTREE

Lawful Occasions, 68 High Garrett, Braintree, CM7 5NT. Prop: M.R. Stallion. Tel: (01376) 551819. Fax: (01376) 326073. Website: www.lawfuloccasions.co.uk. E-mail: stallion@supanet.com. Est: 1997. Private premises. Internet and postal. Appointment necessary. Very small stock. Spec: Crime (True); Criminology; Police Force Histories; also Booksearch. PR: £1–100. Stock and booksearch on police history only. Credit/debit cards accepted via Paypal. Publisher of bibliographies on police history. Cata: quarterly on police history. Corresp: French. [Updated]

BRENTWOOD

Book End, ■ 36–38 Kings Road, Brentwood, CM14 4DW. Prop: G.E. & M.K. Smith. Tel: withheld. Est: 1980. Shop open: **M:** 10:00–17:30; **T:** 10:00–17:30; **W:** 10:00–17:30; **Th:** 10:00–13:00; **F:** 10:00–17:30; **S:** 10:00–17:00. Medium stock. Spec: PR: £1–100. [Updated]

Fortune Books, 94 Shenfield Road, Brentwood, CM15 8ET. Prop: J.H. Jeffries. Tel: not given. E-mail: Est: 1980. Private premises. Appointment necessary. Very small stock. Spec: Fiction - Crime, Detective, Spy, Thrillers. PR: £1–150. Cata: 2 a year [updated]

CHELMSFORD

Christopher Heppa, 48 Pentland Avenue, Chelmsford, CM1 4AZ. Prop: Christopher Heppa. Tel: (01245) 267679. E-mail: christopher@heppa4288.fsnet.co.uk. Est: 1982. Private premises. Internet and postal. Appointment necessary. Medium stock. Spec: Author - Bates, H.E.; Author - Buchan, John; Author - Wodehouse, P.G.; Children's - General; Fiction - Crime, Detective, Spy, Thrillers; Fiction - Historical; First Editions; Illustrated; Literature; Military History; Modern First Editions; Signed Editions. PR: £1–3,000. Cata: 4 – intermittently. Corresp: Spanish. Mem: PBFA. [Updated]

CLACTON–ON–SEA

Bookworm, ■ 100 Kings Ave., Holland–on–Sea, Clacton-on-Sea, CO15 5EP. Prop: Mr Andrew M. M'Garry-Durrant. Tel: (01255) 815984. Website: www.bookwormshop.com. E-mail: question@bookwormshop.com. Est: 1994. Shop open: **M:** 09:00–14:30; **T:** 09:00–14:30; **W:** 09:00–14:30; **Th:** 09:00–14:30; **F:** 09:00–14:30; **S:** 09:00–16:00. Medium stock. Spec: Cinema/Film; Military; Modern First Editions; Sport - Motor Racing. PR: £5–500. CC: AE; D; E; JCB; MC; V. [Updated]

COGGESHALL

John Lewis, 35 Stoneham Street, Coggeshall, CO3 1UH. Tel: (01376) 561518. Website: www.abebooks .com. E-mail: LewisLynet@aol.com. Est: 1985. Private premises. Appointment necessary. Very small stock. Spec: Maritime/Nautical; Travel - General; Travel - Africa; Travel - Americas; Travel - Asia; Travel - Australasia/Australia; Travel - Europe; Travel - Middle East; Travel - Polar; Voyages & Discovery; also Booksearch. PR: £25–2,000. CC: MC; V. Cata: 3 – or 4 a year on specialities. Corresp: French. Mem: PBFA. [Updated]

COLCHESTER

Book–Worm International, 5 Pointwell Lane, Coggeshall Hamlet, Colchester, SS11 7PP. Prop: Donna Collins. Tel: (07754) 583759. Website: www.abebooks.com/home/donnasbookworm. E-mail: donna@bookworm.fsnet.co.uk. Est: 1999. Private premises. Internet and postal. Appointment necessary. Medium stock. Spec: Children's - General; Cookery/Gastronomy; Countries - Mexico; Crime (True); History - General; Humour; Literature; Modern First Editions; Poetry; Royalty - General. PR: £1–200. CC: E; MC; V; Switch. Cata: on request. [13/04/2003]

Castle Bookshop, ■ 40 Osborne St., Colchester, CO2 7DB. Prop: J.R. Green. Tel: (01206) 577520. Fax: (01206) 577520. Est: 1947. Shop open: **M:** 09:00–17:00; **T:** 09:00–17:00; **W:** 09:00–17:00; **Th:** 09:00–17:00; **F:** 09:00–17:00; **S:** 09:00–17:00. Very large stock. Spec: Archaeology; Aviation; First Editions; History - Local; Military; Modern First Editions; Topography - General; Topography - Local; Transport, also Booksearch. PR: £1–1,000. CC: MC; V. Mem: PBFA. VAT No: GB 360 3502 89. [Updated]

Farringdon Books, Shrubland House, 43 Mile End Road, Colchester, CO4 5BU. Prop: Alan Austin. Tel: (01206) 855 771. E-mail: alan@farringdon-books.demon.co.uk. Est: 1972. Private premises. Postal business only. Medium stock. Spec: Fiction - Crime, Detective, Spy, Thrillers; Fiction - Fantasy, Horror; Fiction - Science Fiction. PR: £1–200. [Updated]

Greyfriars Books: the Colchester, ■ 92 East Hill, Colchester, CO1 2QN. Prop: Pauline & Simon Taylor. Tel: (01206) 563138. Website: www.greyfriarsbooks.co.uk. E-mail: simon@greyfriarsbooks.co.uk. Est: 1983. Shop open: **M:** 10:00–17:30; **T:** 10:00–17:30; **W:** 10:00–17:30; **Th:** 10:00–17:30; **F:** 10:00–17:30; **S:** 10:00–17:30. Very large stock. Spec: Academic/Scholarly; Archaeology; Architecture; Art; Art - Reference; Gardening; History - Ancient; History - British; Literary Criticism; Literature; Mathematics; Natural History; Philosophy; Poetry; Psychology/Psychiatry; Science - General; Topography. PR: £2–200. Corresp: French. VAT No: GB 759 8699 37. [Updated]

Quentin Books Ltd, 38 High Street, Wivenhoe, Colchester, CO7 9BE. Prop: Mr Paterson. Tel: (01206) 825433. Fax: (01206) 822990. E-mail: quentin_books@lineone.net. Est: 1990. Storeroom. Appointment necessary. Medium stock. Spec: Bibliography; Bindings; Biography; Books about Books; History - General; History - American; Maritime/Nautical; Natural History; Psychoanalysis; Psychology/Psychiatry; Psychotherapy; Topography - General. PR: £1–1,000. Local topography majors on Essex. Cata: occasionally on psychology. Corresp: French, German. [Updated]

DAGENHAM

John Thorne, 19 Downing Road, Dagenham, RM9 6NR. Tel: (020) 8592-0259. Fax: (020) 8220-0082. E-mail: liquidliterature@aol.com. Est: 1985. Private premises. Postal business only. Very small stock. Spec: Brewing; Public Houses; Viticulture; Whisky; Wine. PR: £1–300. CC: PayPal. Cata: 1 a year. [Updated]

EPPING

Browsers Bookshop, ■ 9 Station Road, Epping, CM16 4HA. Prop: Brian & Moira Carter. Tel: (01992) 572260. Est: 1990. Shop open: **Th:** 10:00–16:00; **F:** 10:00–16:00; **S:** 10:00–16:00; Medium stock. Spec: PR: £1–800. [Updated]

GREAT BARDFIELD

Ken & Jenny Jacobson, 'Southcotts', Petches Bridge, Great Bardfield, CM7 4QN. Prop: Ken Jacobson. Tel: (01371) 810566. Fax: (01371) 810845. Website: www.jacobsonphoto.com. E-mail: ken@ jacobsonphoto.com. Est: 1970. Private premises. Internet and postal. Appointment necessary. Very small stock. Spec: Photography. PR: £100–3,000. Also, 19th century photographs. Corresp: French. Mem: AIPAD. [19/03/2003]

GREAT DUNMOW

Clive Smith, Brick House, North Street, Great Dunmow, CM6 1BA. Tel: (01371) 873171. Fax: (01371) 873171. E-mail: clivesmith@route56.co.uk. Est: 1975. Private premises. Appointment necessary. Small stock. Spec: Antiquarian; Cookery/Gastronomy; Medicine; Military; Natural History; Topography - General; Topography - Local; Travel - General; Travel - Asia; Voyages & Discovery. PR: £10–1,000. Cata: 40 a year. Corresp: French, Indonesian. VAT No: GB 571 600 167. [Updated]

GREAT LEIGHS

Missing Books, 'Coppers', Main Road, Great Leighs, CM3 1NR. Prop: Chris Missing. Tel: (01245) 361609. E-mail: missingbooks@madasafish.com. Est: 1994. Private premises. Internet and postal. Small stock. Spec: Architecture; Biography; City of London; Countries - England; History - Local; Publishers - Black, A. & C.; Rural Life; Topography - General; Topography - Local. PR: £2–500. CC: MC; V. Mem: PBFA. [Updated]

HARWICH

Harwich Old books, ■ 21, Market Street, Harwich, CO12 3DX. Prop: Peter J. Hadley. Tel: (01255) 551667. Fax: (01255) 554539. Website: books@hadley.co.uk. E-mail: books@hadley.co.uk. Est: 1982. Shop open: **F:** 10:00–17:00; **S:** 10:00–17:00; **Su:** 13:00–17:00. Medium stock. Spec: Academic/ Scholarly; Architecture; Art - Reference; Artists; Arts, The; Illustrated; Limited Editions; Literature. CC: MC; V; Switch. Cata: 6 a year on Architecture / Literature. Corresp: French, Italian. Mem: ABA; PBFA; ILAB. VAT No: GB 489 0588 89. [09/09/2003]

ILFORD (SEE ALSO UNDER LONDON OUTER)

June Rhoda, 43 Redbridge Lane East, Ilford, IG4 5EU. Prop: J.R. Arnold. Tel: (020) 8550-5256. Fax: (020) 8550-5256. E-mail: Est: 1983. Private premises. Postal business only. Very small stock. Spec: Alpinism/Mountaineering; History - Local. PR: £1–100. [06/09/2003]

LEIGH–ON–SEA

Leigh Gallery Books, ■ 135–137 Leigh Road, Leigh–on–Sea, SS9 1JQ. Prop: Barrie Gretton. Tel: (01702) 715477. Fax: (01702) 715477. Website: www.abebooks.com/home/BOO/. E-mail: leighgallerybooks @bigfoot.com. Est: 1983. Shop open: **Th:** 10:00–17:00; **F:** 10:00–17:00; **S:** 10:00–17:00. Large general stock. Spec: Art; Illustrated; Literature; Topography - Local. PR: £1–200. CC: AE; MC; V. [Updated]

Othello's Bookshop, ■ 1376 London Road, Leigh–On–Sea, SS9 2UH. Prop: F.G. Bush & M.A. Layzell. Tel: (01702) 473334. E-mail: othellos@hotmail.com. Est: 1999. Shop. Medium stock. Spec: PR: £6–200. Cata: general. [Updated]

LITTLE HALLINGBURY

Assinder Books, Windy Walls, Dell Lane, Little Hallingbury, Essex. CM22 7SH. Prop: N.M. & I. Assinder. Tel: 01279654479. Website: www.abebooks.com. E-mail: assinbooks@aol.com. Est: 1992. Private premises. Internet and postal. Telephone first. Open: Medium stock. Spec: Art - Reference; Children's - General; Illustrated. PR: £2–300. Corresp: Norwegian. [Updated]

MALDON

All Books, ■ 2 Mill Road, Maldon, CM9 5HZ. Prop: Mr. Kevin Peggs. Tel: (01621) 856214. Website: www.allbooks.demon.co.uk. E-mail: kevin@allbooks.demon.co.uk. Est: 1970. Internet and postal. Shop open: **M:** 10:00–17:00; **T:** 10:00–17:00; **W:** 10:00–16:00; **Th:** 10:00–17:00; **F:** 10:00–16:00; **S:** 10:00–17:30; **Su:** 13:30–17:00. Very large general stock. Spec: Academic/Scholarly; Advertising; Aeronautics; Africana; Arts, The; Aviation; History - General; History - Renaissance, The; Maritime/ Nautical; Steam Engines. PR: £1–500. CC: MC; V. [Updated]

MANNINGTREE

John Drury Rare Books, Strandlands, Wrabness, Manningtree, CO11 2TX. Prop: David Edmunds. Tel: (01255) 886260. Fax: (01255) 880303. Website: www.johndrury.co.uk. E-mail: mail@ johndrury.co.uk. Est: 1971. Private premises. Appointment necessary. Small stock. Spec: Antiquarian; Economics; Education & School; Fine & Rare; History of Ideas; Humanities; Irish Interest; Law; Manuscripts; Philosophy; Politics; Social History; Women. PR: £30–3,000. CC: MC; V. Cata: irregularly. Corresp: French. Mem: ABA. VAT No: GB 325 6594 41. [Updated]

RAYLEIGH

Fantastic Literature Limited, 35 The Ramparts, Rayleigh, SS6 8PY. Prop: Simon G. Gosden. Tel: (01268) 747564. Fax: (01268) 747564. Website: www.fantasticliterature.com. E-mail: sgosden@ netcomuk.co.uk. Est: 1984. Private premises. Postal business only. Large stock. Spec: Author - Blackwood, A.; Author - King, Stephen; Author - Pratchett, Terry; Author - Wells, H.G.; Fiction - Crime, Detective, Spy, Thrillers; Fiction - Fantasy, Horror; Fiction - Historical; Fiction - Science Fiction; Publishers - Ghost Story Press. PR: £1–900. CC: E; MC; V; Switch. Also, booksearch and scans available of any title. Cata: 6 on specialities. Corresp: French. Mem: IBN. [Updated]

ROMFORD

J.V.A. Jones, 68 Sedgefield Crescent, Romford, RM3 9RS. Prop: John V.A. & Trudi Jones. Tel: (01708) 340864. Est: 1994. Private premises. Postal business only. Medium stock. Spec: Children's - General; Entertainment - General; Fiction - General. PR: £1–20. [14/03/2003]

Ken Whitfield, 5 Eugene Close, Romford, RM2 6DJ. Tel: (01708) 474763. E-mail: kenkwhitfield@ aol.com. Est: 1984. Private premises. Internet and postal. Small stock. Spec: Art; Biography; Entertainment - General; Fiction - General; History - General; Military; Sport - Football (Soccer); Topography - General; Transport; Travel - General. PR: £2–80. Cata: 3 a year. [29/06/2003]

SAFFRON WALDEN

Lankester Antiques and Books, ■ The Old Sun Inn, Church Street and Market Hill, Saffron Walden, CB10 1HQ. Prop: Paul Lankester. Tel: (01799) 522685. Est: 1964. Shop open: **M:** 10:00–17:00; **T:** 10:00–17:00; **W:** 10:00–17:00; **Th:** 10:00–17:00 **F:** 10:00–17:00. Very large general stock. PR: £1–50. [updated]

SHENFIELD

Booknotes, 6 York Road, Shenfield, CM15 8JT. Prop: Tony Connolly. Tel: (01277) 226130. Website: www.ascon.demon.co.uk. E-mail: booknotes@ascon.demon.co.uk. Est: 1985. Private premises. Internet and postal. Medium stock. [Updated]

SOUTHEND–ON–SEA

Tony Peterson, 11 Westbury Road, Southend–on–Sea, SS2 4DW. Prop: Tony Peterson. Tel: (01702) 462757. Website: www.chessbooks.co.uk. E-mail: tony@chessbooks.co.uk. Est: 1993. Private premises. Internet and postal. Appointment necessary. Very small stock. Spec: PR: £4–200. CC: PayPal. Cata: 4 on chess. [Updated]

Gage Postal Books, P.O. Box 105, Westcliff–on–Sea, Southend–on–Sea, SS0 8EQ. (*) Prop: Simon A. Routh. Tel: (01702) 715133. Fax: (01702) 715133. Website: www.gagebooks.com. E-mail: gagebooks@clara.net. Est: 1971. Storeroom; Internet and postal. Appointment necessary. Very large stock. Spec: Ecclesiastical History & Architecture; Religion - General; Theology. PR: £3–1,000. CC: MC; V. Cata: 12 a year. Corresp: German. Mem: PBFA. [Updated]

STANFORD–LE–HOPE

Atticus Books, ■ 54 Bramleys, Stanford–Le–Hope, SS17 8AG. Prop: Robert Drake. Tel: Shop (01375) 371200. Est: 1981. Shop at: 8 London Road, Grays, Essex RM17 5XY. Open: **Th:** 09:00–16:00; **F:** 09:00–16:00; **S:** 09:00–00:00. Medium stock. Spec: Antiquarian; Arms & Armour; Aviation; Bindings; Dogs; Fiction - General; Firearms/Guns; History - Local; Maritime/Nautical; Military; Occult; Private Press; Spiritualism; Sport - Field Sports; Topography - Local; also Booksearch. PR: £1–400. [27/05/2003]

STANSTEAD

Paul Embleton, 12 Greenfields, Stansted, CM24 8AH. Tel: (01279) 812627. Fax: (01279) 817576. Website: www.abebooks.com/home/embleton. E-mail: paulembleton@btconnect.com. Est: 1994. Private premises. Internet and postal. Appointment necessary. Small stock. Spec: Children's - Early Titles; Children's - Illustrated; Illustrated; Maritime/Nautical; Military; also Booksearch. PR: £3–1,000. CC: Paypal. Also, a booksearch service. Cata: list available. [Updated]

WESTCLIFF–ON–SEA

Clifton Books, 34 Hamlet Court Road, Westcliff–on–Sea, SS0 7LX. Prop: John R. Hodgkins. Tel: (01702) 331004. Fax: (01702) 346304. Website: www.cliftonbooks.co.uk. E-mail: jhodgk9942@ aol.com. Est: 1970. Private premises. Internet and postal. Appointment necessary. Large stock. Spec: Academic/Scholarly; Agriculture; Economics; History - British; Social History; Trade Unions; Transport. CC: AE; D; E; JCB; MC; V. Cata: 12 - one a month. Mem: PBFA. [04/06/2003]

Barrie E. Ellen, The Bookshop, ■ 262 London Road, Westcliff–on–Sea, SS0 7JG. Tel: (01702) 338763. Website: www.abebooks.com/home/barrieellen. E-mail: barrie_ellen@hotmail.com. Est: 1976. Shop open: **M:** 10:00–17:00; **T:** 10:00–17:00; **Th:** 10:00–17:00; **F:** 10:00–17:00; **S:** 10:00–17:00. Large stock. Spec: Chess; Games. PR: £1–400. CC: AE; E; JCB; MC; V; SW. [Updated]

Marjon Books, 16 Mannering Gardens, Westcliff–on–Sea, SS0 0BQ. Prop: R.J. Cooper. Tel: (01702) 347119. Est: 1975. Private premises. Appointment necessary. Very small stock. Spec: PR: £2–120. Cata: 2 on detective fiction. [Updated]

WICKFORD

Mr. H. Macfarlane, 40 Chaucer Walk, Wickford, SS12 9DZ. Tel: (01268) 570892. Website: www.tudorblackpress.co.uk. E-mail: jmba21803@blueyonder.co.uk. Est: 1997. Private premises. Internet and postal. Very small stock. Spec: Astronomy; Medicine; Printing; Private Press; Science - General. PR: £2–150. Also, a booksearch service (relating to scientific books only). Cata: 1 – a year on medicine. [Updated]

WICKHAM BISHOPS

Baldwin's Scientific Books, 18, School Road, Wickham Bishops, Witham, CM8 3NU. Prop: Stuart A. Baldwin. Tel: (01621) 891526. Fax: (01621) 891522. Website: www.secondhandsciencebooks.com. E-mail: sbaldwin@fossilbooks.co.uk. Est: 1972. Private premises. Internet and postal. Appointment necessary. Medium stock. Spec: Academic/Scholarly; Animals and Birds; Antiquarian; Archaeology; Astronomy; Biography; Biology; Botany; Evolution; Geology; Herpetology; Journals - General; Mineralogy; Mining; Natural History; Palaeontology; Science - History of. PR: £5–5,000. CC: MC; V. Also, journals and offprints of scientific articles, (over 50,000 in stock) and general stock. Cata: occasionally. Mem: PBFA. VAT No: GB 219 1793 51. [Updated]

WITHAM

Phoenix Fine Books, Hatchcroft House, White Notley, Witham, CM8 1RG. Prop: Diane Barber. Tel: (01376) 326283. E-mail: Est: 1972. Postal business only. Spec: Artists; Guide Books; Literature. PR: £5–500. [28/08/2003]

WOODFORD GREEN

Handsworth Books, 8 Warners Close, Woodford Green, IG8 0TF. Prop: Stephen Glover. Tel: (07976) 329042. Fax: (0870) 0520258. Website: www.handsworthbooks.co.uk. E-mail: steve@handsworthbooks .demon.co.uk. Est: 1987. Private premises. Postal business only. Medium stock. Spec: Academic/Scholarly; Applied Art; Company History; Fine Art; History - General; Literary Criticism; Military History; Music - General; Philosophy; Religion - General; Topography - General; War - General. PR: £2–650. CC: AE; E; JCB; MC; V. Mem: PBFA. [Updated]

Salway Books, 47 Forest Approach, Woodford Green, IG8 9BP. Prop: Barry Higgs. Tel: (020) 8491 7766. E-mail: salway.books@ntlworld.com. Est: 1993. Small stock. Spec: Aviation; Canals/Inland Waterways; Company History; Industry; Mining; Railways; Topography - Local; Traction Engines. PR: £1–500. CC: E; MC; V. Mem: PBFA. [Updated]

GLOUCESTERSHIRE

ALMONDSBURY

Michael Garbett Antiquarian Books, 1 Over Court Mews, Over Lane, Almondsbury, BS32 4DG. Prop: Michael & Jeanne Garbett. Tel: (01454) 617376. Fax: (01454) 617376. Website: www.michaelgarbett .theanswer.co.uk. E-mail: migarb@overcourtmews.freeserve.co.uk. Est: 1965. Private premises. Appointment necessary. Open: Small stock. Spec: Bindings; Miniature Books. Cata: 1 a year on miniature books. Mem: ABA. VAT No: GB 358 1080 58. [updated]

BADMINTON

Mrs. P.A. Sheppard, 2 Rose Cottage, Hawkesbury Upton, Badminton, GL9 1AU. Mrs. P.A. Sheppard. Tel: (01454) 238686. Website: http://ukbookworld.com/cgi-bin/search.pl?s_i_DLR_I. E-mail: annesbookroom@aol.com. Est: 1998. Private premises. Internet and postal. Appointment necessary. Small general stock. Spec: PR: £1–350. CC: PayPal. [14/04/2003]

BERKELEY

Volumes of Motoring, Hertsgrove, Wanswell, Berkeley, GL13 9RR. Prop: Terry Wills. Tel: (01453) 811819. Fax: (01453) 811819. E-mail: twills@breathemail.net. Est: 1979. Private premises. Internet and postal. Open: **M:** 08:00–22:00; **T:** 08:00–22:00; **W:** 08:00–22:00; **Th:** 08:00–22:00; **F:** 08:00–22:00; **S:** 08:00–21:00; **Su:** 09:00–22:00. Spec: Motoring; Sport - Motor Racing. PR: £2–60. CC: MC; V. Wide range of motoring remainders available to the trade. [19/08/2003]

CHELTENHAM

R. Andrews, 3 Huntsmans Meet, Andoversford, Cheltenham, GL54 4JR. Tel: (01242) 820904. Est: 1977. Private premises. Appointment necessary. Medium stock. Spec: Crime (True); Fiction - Crime, Detective, Spy, Thrillers. Cata: occasionally. [updated]

David Bannister, 26 Kings Road, Cheltenham, GL52 6BG. Tel: (01242) 514287. Fax: (01242) 513890. Website: www.antiquemaps.co.uk. E-mail: db@antiquemaps.co.uk. Est: 1963. Private premises. Internet and postal. Appointment necessary. Very small stock. Spec: Atlases; Cartography; Reference. PR: £10–5,000. CC: JCB; MC; V. VAT No: GB 391 9317 27. [Updated]

Cotswold Internet Books, Maida Vale Business Centre, Maida Vale Road, Cheltenham, GL53 7ER. Prop: John & Caro Newland. Tel: (01242) 261428. E-mail: jnewland@v21mail.co.uk. Est: 1989. Warehouse; Internet and postal. Telephone first. Open: **M:** 08:30–19:00; **T:** 08:30–19:00; **W:** 08:30–19:00; **Th:** 08:30–19:00; **F:** 08:30–00:00; **S:** 09:00–17:00. Very large general stock. Spec: PR: £5–500. CC: AE; E; JCB; MC; V; Maestro. VAT No: GB 535 5039 51. [Updated]

Bruce Marshall Rare Books, Foyers, 20 Gretton Road, Gotherington, Cheltenham, GL52 9QU. Tel: (01242) 672997. Fax: (01242) 675238. E-mail: marshallrarebook@aol.com. Private premises. Appointment necessary. Very small stock. Spec: Atlases; Colour-Plate; Natural History; Travel - General. Mem: ABA; ILAB. [Updated]

Moss Books, ■ 8–9 Henrietta Street, Cheltenham, GL50 4AA. Prop: Christopher Moss. Tel: (01242) 222947. E-mail: chris.moss@virgin.net. Est: 1992. Shop open: **M:** 10:00–18:00; **T:** 10:00–18:00; **W:** 10:00–18:00; **Th:** 10:00–18:00; **F:** 10:00–18:00; **S:** 09:00–18:00. Large general stock. PR: £1–100. Corresp: Japanese. VAT No: GB 618 3105 62. [Updated]

Peter Lyons Books, ■ 11 Imperial Square, Cheltenham, GL50 1QB. Prop: Peter Lyons. Tel: (01242) 260345. Est: 2001. Shop open: **W:** 10:00–17:00; **Th:** 10:00–17:00; **F:** 10:00–17:00; **S:** 10:00–17:00. Spec: Applied Art; Art; Art - History; Art - Reference; Artists; Arts, The; Biography; Children's - General; Modern First Editions; Poetry. PR: £2–50. Open at other times by appointment. [Updated]

Nick Thorne, 6 Cleeveview Road, Cheltenham, GL52 5NH. Tel: E-mail: the.thornes@btinternet.com. Est: 1994. Spec: Author - Carroll, Lewis; Children's - General; Sport - Boxing. PR: £1–250. [18/08/ 2003]

Available from Richard Joseph Publishers Ltd

BOOK DEALING FOR PROFIT
by Paul Minet

Quarto H/b
£10.00 144pp

John Wilson Manuscripts Ltd, Painswick Lawn, 7 Painswick Road, Cheltenham, GL50 2EZ. Prop: John & Gina Wilson. Tel: (01242) 580344. Fax: (01242) 580355. Website: www.manuscripts.co.uk. E-mail: mail@manuscripts.co.uk. Est: 1967. Private premises. Internet and postal. Appointment necessary. Very large stock. Spec: Autographs; Documents - General; Manuscripts. PR: £20–50,000. CC: AE; MC; V. Cata: 1 a year. Mem: ABA; ILAB; PADA. VAT No: GB 194 9050 39. [Updated]

CHIPPING CAMPDEN

Draycott Books, ■ 2 Sheep Street, Chipping Campden, GL55 6DX. Prop: Robert & Jane McClement. Tel: Business (01386) 841. E-mail: draycottbooks@hotmail.com. Est: 1981. Shop open: **M:** 10:00–17:00; **T:** 10:00–17:00; **W:** 10:00–17:00; **Th:** 10:00–17:00; **F:** 10:00–17:00; **S:** 10:00–17:00. Medium stock. PR: £1–1,000. [Updated]

CIRENCESTER

Aviabooks, ■ 8 Swan Yard, West Market Place, Cirencester, GL7 2NH. Prop: Paul Gentil. Tel: (01285) 641700. Website: www.abebooks.com. E-mail: paul@gentil.demon.co.uk. Est: 1997. Shop open: **M:** 09:30–17:00; **T:** 09:30–17:00; **Th:** 09:30–17:00; **F:** 09:30–17:00; **S:** 09:30–18:00. Small general stock. Spec: Aeronautics; Antiques; Applied Art; Architecture; Art; Art - History; Art - Reference; Art - Technique; Artists; Astronomy; Aviation; Botany; Ceramics; Entomology; History - Ancient; History - British; History - Roman; Lepidopterology / Lepidoptery. PR: £1–1,000. CC: MC; V; Maestro. Also, book fairs & specialist events, bookbinding & repair service. Cata: on Aviation, Natural History. Mem: PBFA. [Updated]

The Bookroom, ■ Cirencester Arcade, Market Place, Cirencester, GL7 2NX. Prop: Tetbury Old Books Ltd. Tel: (01285) 644214. Fax: (01285) 504458. E-mail: bookroom@tetbury.co.uk. Est: 1998. Shop open: **M:** 10:00–17:00; **T:** 10:00–17:00; **W:** 10:00–17:00; **Th:** 10:00–17:00; **F:** 10:00–17:00; **S:** 10:00–17:00; **Su:** 12:00–17:00. Very small general stock. PR: £3–100. CC: MC; V. [Updated]

Books for Collectors, 9 The Pheasantry, Down Ampney, Cirencester, GL7 5RE. Prop: Jon Edgson. Tel: (01793) 750152. Website: www.booksforcollectors.co.uk. E-mail: jonedgson@aol.com. Private premises. Appointment necessary. Small stock. Spec: Art; Design; Fashion & Costume; Illustrated; Interior Design; Performing Arts; Photography; Vintage Paperbacks. PR: £5–500. Regularly attends book fairs. Cata: occasionally on design, fashion, costume, photography. Mem: PBFA. [04/06/2003]

COLEFORD

Simon Lewis Transport Books, PO Box 9, Coleford, GL16 8YF. Prop: Simon Lewis. Tel: (01594) 839369. Website: www.simonlewis.com. E-mail: simon@simonlewis.com. Est: 1985. Office &/or bookroom. Internet and postal. Contactable. Open: Medium stock. Spec: Buses/Trams; Motorbikes; Motoring; Railways; Sport - Motor Racing; Steam Engines; Transport; Vintage Cars. PR: £1–500. CC: E; MC; V. Cata: on request. VAT No: GB 575 9030 21. [Updated]

FAIRFORD

Jacques Gander, 14 Keble Lawns, Fairford, GL7 4BQ. Tel: (01285) 712988. E-mail: jacques@ jgander.fsnet.co.uk. Private premises. Internet and postal. Spec: Children's - General; Modern First Editions. [Updated]

GLOUCESTER

Internet Bookshop UK Ltd., ■ Unit 2, Wisloe Road, Gloucester, GL2 7AF. Prop: Mr. G. Cook. Tel: (01453) 890278. Fax: (0870) 442 5292. Website: www.ibuk.com. E-mail: orders@ibuk.com. Est: 1996. Internet and postal. Telephone first. Shop open: **M:** 09:00–17:00; **T:** 09:00–17:00; **W:** 09:00–17:00; **Th:** 09:00–17:00; **F:** 09:00–17:00. Very large stock. Spec: Academic/Scholarly; Alpinism/Mountaineering; Art; Aviation; Children's - General; Cookery/Gastronomy; Gardening; Military; Music - General; Naval; Ornithology; Politics; Railways; Sport - Angling/Fishing; Sport - Cricket; Sport - Diving/Sub-Aqua. PR: £8–1,000. CC: AE; MC; V; Switch. [Updated]

KEMPSFORD

Ximenes Rare Books Inc., Kempsford House, Kempsford, GL7 4ET. Prop: Stephen Weissman. Tel: (01285) 810640. Fax: (01285) 810650. E-mail: steve@ximenes.com. Est: 1965. Small stock. Spec: Antiquarian. PR: £50–10,000. CC: MC; V. Cata: 3 a year. Corresp: French. Mem: ABA; PBFA; ILAB; ABAA. VAT No: GB 672 4533 30. [12/08/2003]

LECHLADE

Evergreen Livres, The Old School, Kelmscot, Lechlade, GL7 3HG. Prop: N.S. O'Keeffe. Tel: (01367) 252558. Fax: (01367) 250081. E-mail: ocker@oxfree.com. Est: 1984. Private premises. Postal business only. Very small stock. Spec: Dogs; Farming & Livestock; Gardening; Horticulture; Natural History. PR: £2–500. [Updated]

MORETON–IN–MARSH

Jeffrey Formby Antiques, Orchard Cottage, East Street, Moreton–in–Marsh, GL56 0LQ. Tel: (01608) 650558. Fax: (01608) 650558. Website: www.formby-clocks.co.uk. E-mail: jeff@formby-clocks.co.uk. Est: 1993. Shop &/or gallery; Telephone first. Open: **F:** 10:00–17:00; **S:** 10:00–17:00. Very small stock. Spec: Horology; Scientific Instruments. PR: £5–500. CC: E; JCB; MC; V. Cata: 2 a year. [Updated]

Four Shire Bookshops, ■ 17 High Street, Moreton–in–Marsh, GL56 0AF. Prop: Hazel & David Potten. Tel: (01608) 651451. Fax: (01608) 650827. E-mail: fourshirebooks@aol.com. Est: 1981. Shop open: **M:** 09:30–16:00; **T:** 09:30–16:00; **W:** 09:30–16:00; **Th:** 09:30–17:00; **F:** 09:30–17:00; **S:** 08:30–17:00; closed for lunch: 13:00–14:00. Medium stock. Spec: Embroidery; History - Local; Needlework; Topography - Local; also Booksearch. PR: £1–100. CC: E; JCB; MC. Cata: 2 a year on embroidery & quilting. [Updated]

NAILSWORTH

Keogh's Books, ■ Market St, Nailsworth, GL6 0BX. Prop: J. Keogh. Tel: (01453) 833922. Website: www.keoghsbooks.co.uk. E-mail: joekeogh@keoghbooks.fsnet.co.uk. Est: 1985. Internet and postal. Shop open: **M:** 10:00–17:00; **T:** 10:00–17:00; **W:** 10:00–17:00; **Th:** 10:00–17:00; **F:** 10:00–17:00; **S:** 10:00–17:30. Small stock. Spec: Art; Art - History; Art - Reference. PR: £2–200. CC: AE; MC; V; SW. [Updated]

NEWENT

Oakwood Books, 37 Church Street, Newent, GL18 1AA. Prop: Jim Haslem, A.L.A. Tel: (01531) 821040. Website: www.abebooks.com/home/oakwoodbooks. E-mail: jim@haslem.fsnet.co.uk. Est: 1987. Private premises. Internet and postal. Appointment necessary. Small stock. Spec: Topography - Local. PR: £2–450. Cata: subject lists sent on request. [Updated]

NEWNHAM ON SEVERN

Marcus Niner, Newnham Old Books, 48 High Street, Newnham on Severn, GL14 1AA. Tel: (01594) 516088. E-mail: mail@ninerbooks.co.uk. Private premises. Telephone first. Very small stock. Spec: Art; Literature; Topography - Local; Travel - General. PR: £10–2,000. CC: MC; V. Mem: PBFA. [Updated]

Christopher Saunders (Orchard Books), Kingston House, High Street, Newnham on Severn, GL14 1BB. Prop: Chris Saunders. Tel: (01594) 516030. Fax: (01594) 517273. Website: www.cricket-books.com. E-mail: chrisbooks@aol.com. Est: 1981. Office &/or bookroom. Appointment necessary. Large stock. Spec: CC: MC; V. Cata: 4 – on cricket. Mem: ABA; PBFA; ILAB. [Updated]

STOW–ON–THE–WOLD

Wychwood Books, ■ Sheep Street, Stow–on–the–Wold, GL54 1AA. Prop: Miss. Lucy Baggott & Mr. Henry Baggott. Tel: (01451) 831880. E-mail: wychwoodbooks@btopenworld.com. Est: 1985. Shop open: **M:** 09:30–17:30; **T:** 09:30–17:30; **W:** 09:30–17:30; **Th:** 09:30–17:30; **F:** 09:30–17:30; **S:** 09:30–17:30. Large stock. Spec: Antiques; Architecture; Art; Author - Murdoch, I.; Biography; First Editions; Literature; Natural History; Sport - Field Sports; Sport - Horse Racing (all aspects); Sport - Hunting; Sport - Shooting; Topography - General; Topography - Local. PR: £3–4,000. CC: MC; V. Mem: PBFA. [Updated]

STROUD

Anthroposophical Books, Fromehall Mill - Blk 2, Rm 9, 2nd Flr, Lodgemore Lane, Stroud, GL5 3EH. Prop: H. & A. Tandree. Tel: (01453) 764 932. Fax: same. E-mail: herb@philosophy-books.co.uk. Est: 1988. Office &/bookroom. Appointment necessary. Open: **M:** 09:00–05:00. Small general stock. Spec: Anthroposophy; Author - Steiner, Rudolf; Occult. PR: £8–50. CC: MC; V. Cata: 1 a year on Rudolf Steiner & anthroposophy. Corresp: French, German. [Updated]

Herb Tandree Philosophy Books, Fromehall Mill - Blk 2/Rm 9, Lodgemore Lane, Stroud, GL5 3EH. Prop: Herb Tandree. Tel: (01453) 764 932. Fax: (01453) 764 932. Website: www.philosophy-books.co.uk. E-mail: herb@philosophy-books.co.uk. Est: 2000. Private premises. Internet and postal. Appointment necessary. Medium stock. Spec: Academic/Scholarly; Economics; History of Ideas; Philosophy; Religion - General. CC: AE; JCB; MC. Cata: 6 – bi-monthly. Corresp: French, German. VAT No: GB 783 4154 17. [Updated]

Ian Hodgkins and Company Limit, Upper Vatch Mill, The Vatch, Slad, Stroud, GL6 7JY. Prop: G.A. Yablon & I. Hoy. Tel: (01453) 764270. Fax: (01453) 755233. Website: www.ianhodgkins.com. E-mail: i.hodgkins@dial.pipex.com. Est: 1974. Private premises. Internet and postal. Appointment necessary. Medium stock. Spec: Applied Art; Art; Art - Reference; Artists; Author - Austen, Jane; Author - Brontes, The; Author - Crane, Walter; Author - Gaskell, E.; Author - Lang, Andrew; Author - Morris, William; Author - Potter, Beatrix; Author - Rossetti, C.; Author - Ruski PR: £5–5,000. CC: MC; V. Cata: 4 a year. Mem: ABA. [25/06/2003]

Inprint, ■ 31 High Street, Stroud, GL5 1AJ. Prop: Joy & Mike Goodenough. Tel: (01453) 759731. Fax: (01453) 759731. Website: www.inprint.co.uk. E-mail: enquiries@inprint.co.uk. Est: 1978. Internet and postal. Shop open: **M:** 10:00–17:00; **T:** 10:00–17:00; **W:** 10:00–17:00; **Th:** 10:00–17:00; **F:** 10:00–17:00; **S:** 10:00–17:00. Medium stock. Spec: Applied Art; Cinema/Film; Fine Art; Gardening; Performing Arts. PR: £5–500. CC: AE; D; E; JCB; MC; V. [Updated]

Alan & Joan Tucker, The Bookshop, Old Stationmaster's House, Station Road, Stroud, GL5 3AP. Tel: (01453) 764738. Fax: (01453) 766899. Website: www.abebooks.com/home/SANDITON. E-mail: at80jt@globalnet.co.uk. Est: 1963. Storeroom; Appointment necessary. Open: **M:** 09:30–17:00; **T:** 09:30–17:00; **W:** 09:30–17:00; **Th:** 09:30–17:00; **F:** 09:30–17:00; closed for lunch: 12:00–14:15. Very small general stock. Spec: Arts, The; Authors - Women; Children's - General; Fine Printing; Limited Editions; Literary Criticism; Literary Travel; Literature; Literature in Translation; Poetry; Topography - Local. PR: £1–100. CC: MC; V. Please phone before visiting storeroom. Also, new maps. Stock also on www.bookline. Cata: rarely - on literature. Mem: BA. VAT No: GB 275 0258 60. [Updated]

TETBURY

Tetbury Old Books Limited, ■ 4, The Chipping, Tetbury, GL8 8ET. Prop: Tetbury Old Books Ltd. Tel: (01666) 504330. Fax: (01666) 504458. E-mail: oldbooks@tetbury.co.uk. Est: 1994. Shop open: **M:** 10:00–18:00; **T:** 10:00–18:00; **W:** 10:00–18:00; **Th:** 10:00–18:00; **F:** 10:00–18:00; **S:** 10:00–18:00; **Su:** 11:00–18:00. Small general stock. PR: £1–5,000. CC: AE; E; JCB; MC; V. Mem: TADA. Also at: The Bookroom, Cirencester. [Updated]

TEWKESBURY

Avonbridge Books, 8 Churchill Grove, Newtown, Tewkesbury, GL20 8EL. Tel: (01684) 295785. Fax: (01684) 291823. Website: www.avonbridgebooks.com. E-mail: libris@avonbridgebooks.com. Private premises. Internet and postal. Medium stock. Spec: Academic/Scholarly; Antiquarian; Books about Books; Maritime/Nautical. PR: £5–1,000. CC: JCB; MC; V; Switch. Also, a booksearch service. Mem: PBFA. [25/06/2003]

Cornell Books, ■ The Wheatsheaf, 132 High Street, Tewkesbury, GL20 5AR. Prop: D.W. Hall & G.T. & C.L. Cornell. Tel: (01684) 293337. Fax: (01684) 273959. E-mail: gtcornell@aol.com. Est: 1996. Shop; open: **M:** 10:30–17:00; **T:** 10:30–17:00; **W:** 10:30–17:00; **Th:** 10:30–17:00; **F:** 10:30–17:00; **S:** 10:30–17:00. Large general stock. Spec: Author - Moore, John; Children's - General; Colour-Plate; Natural History; Topography - General; Topography - Local; Travel - General, also Booksearch. PR: £1–500. CC: MC; V. [Updated]

UPPER RISSINGTON

Aquarius Books Ltd., Unit 132, Rissington Business Park, Upper Rissington, GL54 2QB. Prop: Mrs Valerie Dumbleton. Tel: (01451) 820352. Website: www.ukbookworld.com/members/aquarius. E-mail: aquarius.bks@virgin.net. Est: 1993. Office and/or bookroom; Internet and postal. Appointment necessary. Large general stock. Spec: booksearch. PR: £2–750. CC: MC; V. [29/06/2003]

UPTON SAINT LEONARDS

John Bush, Bookdealer, Hazel Grove House, Upton Hill, Upton St. Leonards, GL4 8DE. Tel: (01452) 814386. Fax: (01452) 814386. E-mail: john.bush@virgin.net. Est: 1990. Private premises. Internet and postal. Appointment necessary. Very large general stock. Spec: Academic/Scholarly; Antiquarian; Biography; Fiction - General; History - General; Limited Editions; Sport - Cricket. PR: £5–200. [06/06/2003]

WESTBURY-ON-SEVERN

Dive In Books, ■ Dive In, Lecture Hall, The Village, Westbury-on-Severn, GL14 1PA. Prop: Patricia Larkham. Tel: (01452) 760124. Fax: (01452) 760590. Website: www.diveinbooks.co.uk. E-mail: mydive@globalnet.co.uk. Est: 1975. Internet and postal. Shop open: **M:** 09:00–14:00; **T:** 09:00–14:00; **W:** 09:00–14:00; **Th:** 09:00–14:00; **F:** 09:00–14:00. Small stock. Spec: Archaeology; Calligraphy; D.I.Y (Do It Yourself); Deep Sea Diving; Maritime/Nautical; Natural History; Pacifism; Sport - Cycling; Travel - General. PR: £1–150. [Updated]

GREATER MANCHESTER

ALTRINCHAM

Christopher Baron, 15 Crossfield Road, Hale, Altrincham, WA15 8DU. Tel: (0161) 980-1014. Fax: (0161) 980-1415. Website: www.abebooks.com. E-mail: BaronBook@aol.com. Est: 1979. Private premises. Internet and postal. Large stock. Spec: Games; Horology; Locks & Locksmiths; Microscopy; Natural History; Science - General; Science - History of; Scientific Instruments; Sport - Angling/Fishing; Technology. CC: JCB; MC; V; Maestro. Mem: PBFA. [Updated]

Edward Yarwood Rare Books, 61 Fairywell Road, Timperley, Altrincham, WA15 6XB. Tel: (withheld). Est: 1994. Private premises. Postal business only. Medium stock. Spec: Author - Gurdjieff, W.I.; Author - Wilson, Colin; Biography; Philosophy. PR: £5–250. Also; book plates, manuscripts, booksearch and attends fairs. Cata: 4 a year on Gurdjieff. [Updated]

BOLTON

Martin Bott (Bookdealers) Ltd., ■ 28-30 Lee Lane, Horwich, BL6 7BY. (*) Prop: M.L.R. & M.H. Bott. Tel: (01204) 691489. Fax: (01204) 698729. Website: www.bottbooks.com. E-mail: martin.bott@ btinternet.com. Est: 1997. Shop; Internet and postal. Telephone first. Shop At and postal address - 6 St. Leonards Avenue, Lostock, Bolton, BL6 4JE. Open: **M:** 10:15–15:30; **T:** 10:15–15:00; **Th:** 10:15–15:00; **F:** 10:15–15:00; **S:** 10:30–16:00. Large stock. Spec: Aviation; Buses/Trams; Canals/Inland Waterways; Company History; Engineering; Geology; Industry; Maritime/Nautical; Mining; Naval; Railways; Steam Engines; Technology; Traction Engines; Transport, also Booksearch. PR: £1–1,000. CC: AE; JCB; MC; V; SW. Booksearch for Railway & Industrial History titles only. [Updated]

Delph Books, 437 Bury & Bolton Road, Radcliffe, Bolton, M26 4LJ. Prop: Frank Lamb. Tel: (0161) 764-4488. E-mail: Est: 1979. Private premises. Appointment necessary. Medium stock. Spec: Company History; Genealogy; Military; Parish Registers; Police Force Histories; School Registers/Rolls of Honour; Topography - Local; also Booksearch. PR: £1–200. [18/06/2003]

Siri Ellis Books, ■ The Last Drop Village, Bromley Cross, Bolton, BL7 9PZ. Prop: Siri E. Ellis. Tel: (01204) 597511. Website: www.siriellisbooks.co.uk. E-mail: mail@siriellisbooks.co.uk. Est: 1998. Shop open: **M:** 12:00–17:00; **T:** 12:00–17:00; **Th:** 12:00–17:00; **F:** 12:00–17:00; **S:** 11:00–17:00; **Su:** 11:00–17:00. Small stock. Spec: Children's - General; Children's - Illustrated; Illustrated. PR: £1–1,000. CC: AE; V; Switch. Booksearch for childhood favourites. Mem: PBFA. [Updated]

CHEADLE (SEE ALSO UNDER CHESHIRE)

Clifford Elmer Books, 8 Balmoral Avenue, Cheadle Hulme, Cheadle, SK8 5EQ. Prop: Clifford & Marie Elmer. Tel: (0161) 485-7064. Website: www.truecrime.co.uk. E-mail: sales@cliffordelmerbooks.com. Est: 1978. Private premises. Appointment necessary. Medium stock. Spec: Crime (True); Criminology. PR: £3–500. CC: JCB; MC. Cata: 8 a year. Mem: PBFA. [Updated]

Mainly Fiction, 21 Tennyson Road, Cheadle, SK8 2AR. Prop: Christopher J. Peers. Tel: (0161) 428-6836. E-mail: mainly.fiction@ntlworld.com. Est: 1986. Private premises. Postal business only. Spec: Children's - General; Fiction - Crime, Detective, Spy, Thrillers; First Editions; Modern First Editions. PR: £5–200. CC: V. Mem: PBFA. [Updated]

DIDSBURY

Barlow Moor Books, 29 Churchwood Road, Didsbury, M20 6TZ. Prop: Dr. Roger & Dr. L.A. Finlay. Tel: (0161) 434 5073. Fax: (0161) 448 2491. E-mail: books@barlowmoorbooks.com. Est: 1990. Private premises. Postal business only. Contactable. Very small general stock. Corresp: French. VAT No: GB 560 9236 38. [Updated]

E.J. Morten (Booksellers), ■ 6–9 Warburton Street, Didsbury, Manchester, M20 6WA. Prop: John A. Morten. Tel: (0161) 445-7629. Fax: (0161) 448-1323. E-mail: morten.booksellers@lineone.net. Est: 1959. Shop open: **M:** 10:00–17:30; **T:** 09:00–17:29; **W:** 10:00–17:30; **Th:** 10:00–17:30; **F:** 10:00–17:30; **S:** 10:00–00:30. Large stock. Spec: Military History; Sport - General; Travel - General. Cata: 2 a year. Corresp: French, German. Mem: PBFA; BA; ILAB; BT, NBL. [updated]

DUNKINFIELD

Starlord Books, 72 Chester Avenue, Dukinfield, SK16 5BW. Prop: Starlord. Tel: 0161-338-8465. E-mail: Starlord@Starlord-Enterprises.freeserve.co.uk. Est: 1995. Private premises. Internet and postal. Appointment necessary. Open: **M:** 10:00–18:00; **T:** 09:00–12:00; **W:** 10:10–18:00; **Th:** 10:00–16:00; **F:** 12:00–16:00; **S:** 10:00–16:00; **Su:** 12:00–16:00. Medium stock. Spec: Academic/Scholarly; Alternative Medicine; Astrology; Biography; Comic Books & Annuals; Crime (True); Earth Mysteries; Esoteric; Fiction - Crime, Detective, Spy, Thrillers; Fiction - Fantasy, Horror; Fiction - Science Fiction; Metaphysics; Mind, Body & Spirit. PR: £1–100. [Updated]

LITTLEBOROUGH

George Kelsall Booksellers, ■ The Bookshop, 22 Church Street, Littleborough, OL15 9AA. Tel: (01706) 370244. E-mail: kelsall@bookshop22.fsnet.co.uk. Est: 1979. Shop open: **M:** 11:00–17:00; **T:** 13:00–17:00; **W:** 10:00–17:00; **Th:** 10:00–17:00; **F:** 10:00–17:00; **S:** 10:00–17:00. Large stock. Spec: Architecture; Art - History; Art - Reference; History - General; History - Industrial; Politics; Social History; Topography - Local; Transport. PR: £1–500. Mem: PBFA. VAT No: GB 306 0657 8. [Updated]

MANCHESTER

The Bookshop, ■ 441 Wilmslow Road, Withington, Manchester, M20 4AN. Prop: Paul Johnson and Jon Heddon. Tel: (0161) 445 4345. Fax: (0161) 445 4345. Website: www.bookacademy.co.uk. E-mail: sales@bookacademy.co.uk. Est: 1996. Internet and postal. Shop open: **M:** 10:00–18:00; **T:** 10:00–18:00; **W:** 10:00–18:00; **Th:** 10:00–18:00; **F:** 10:00–18:00; **S:** 10:00–18:00; **Su:** 12:00–17:00. Large general stock. Spec: Academic/Scholarly; Black Studies; Culture - Popular; History - General; Holocaust; Homosexuality & Lesbianism; Irish Interest; Philosophy; Politics, also Booksearch. PR: £1–50. CC: MC; V; Maestro. Also at: The Bookshop, 11 Grove Street, Wilmslow, SK9 1DU and The Bookshop, 488 Wilbraham Rd, Chorlton, M21 9AS. [Updated]

Browzers, 2, Buckingham Road, Prestwich, Manchester, M25 9NE. Prop: Alan E. Seddon. Tel: (0161) 7732327. Fax: 01617732327. Website: http://www.browzersbooks.co.uk. E-mail: aseddon@ browzersbooks.co.uk. Est: 1980. Private premises. Postal business only. Small stock. Spec: Antiques; Collecting; Sport - Horse Racing (all aspects). PR: £1–300. CC: MC; V; Switch. Cata: 2 a year on horse racing. Mem: PBFA. [Updated]

Classic Crime Collections, 95a Boarshaw Road, Middleton, Manchester, M24 6AP. Prop: Rob Wilson. Tel: (0161) 653-4145. E-mail: Rob@mtwilson.freeserve.co.uk. Est: 1989. Private premises. Postal business only. Small stock. Spec: Author - Christie, Agatha; Author - Creasey, John; Author - Fleming, Ian; Buses/Trams; Canals/Inland Waterways; Crime (True); Fiction - Crime, Detective, Spy, Thrillers; Crime (True); Railways; Sport - Cricket; Sport - Golf; Topography - Local; Transport. PR: £2–400. Also, a booksearch service. [Updated]

Franks Booksellers, Suite 33, 4th Floor, St Margaret's Chambers, 5 Newton Street, Piccadilly, Manchester, M1 1HL. Tel: (0161) 237-3747. Fax: (0161) 237-3747. Est: 1960. Office. &/or bookroom; Open: **M:** 10:00–14:00; **T:** 10:00–14:00; **W:** 10:00–14:00; **Th:** 10:00–14:00; **F:** 10:00–14:00. Small stock. Spec: Advertising; Autographs; Children's - General; Cinema/Film; Comic Books & Annuals; Magic & Conjuring; Performing Arts; Periodicals & Magazines; Private Press; Sport - Boxing; Sport - Football (Soccer); Sport - Rugby. PR: £1–1,000. Also, postcards. [Updated]

Gibbs Bookshop Ltd., ■ 13 Howard Road, Northenden, Manchester, M22 4EG. Tel: (0161) 998-2794. Fax: (0161) 998-2794. Website: www.gibbsbookshop.co.uk. E-mail: gibbsbookshop@beeb.net. Est: 1922. Internet and postal. Shop open: **M:** 10:00–17:00; **T:** 10:00–17:00; **W:** 10:00–17:00; **Th:** 10:00–17:00; **F:** 10:00–17:00; **S:** 10:00–17:00. Very large general stock. PR: £5–50. CC: JCB; MC; V. Mem: ABA. VAT No: GB 145 4624 68. [Updated]

Tim Kendall–Carpenter, 633 Wilmslow Road, Manchester, M20 6DF. Tel: (0161) 445-6172. Fax: (0161) 438-8445. E-mail: timkcbooks@aol.com. Est: 1996. Private premises. Internet and postal. Appointment necessary. Medium stock. Spec: First Editions; Modern First Editions; Poetry; Proof Copies. PR: £5–1,000. CC: AE; MC; V; Maestro. VAT No: GB 781 2657 13. [Updated]

The Little Bookshop & Thanatos, ■ The Basement, Friends Meeting House, 6 Mount Street, Manchester, M2 5NS. Prop: Valerie Clark. Tel: (0161) 834-9898. Website: http:// thantatosbooks.seekbooks.co.uk. E-mail: thantaosbooks@excite.com. Est: 1989. Shop open: **M:** 15:00–18:00; **T:** 15:00–18:00; **Th:** 11:00–18:00; **F:** 11:00–18:00. Medium stock. Spec: Arts, The; Autobiography; Biography; Fiction - General; History - General; Poetry; Religion - General; Travel - General; also Booksearch. PR: £1–100. Also, contactable on (07815) 560872. [Updated]

Philip Nevitsky, P.O. Box 364, Manchester, M60 1AL. Tel: (0161) 228-2947. Fax: (0161) 236-0390. Est: 1974. Storeroom; Postal business only. Small stock. Spec: Cinema/Film; Entertainment - General; Music - Popular. [Updated]

V.M. Riley Books, 3 Leyburn Avenue, Stretford, Manchester, M32 8DZ. Prop: Mrs. Valerie M. Riley. Tel: (0161) 865-6543. Website: ukbookworld.com/members/vmriley. E-mail: val@rileyv.fsnet.co.uk. Est: 1989. Private premises. Postal business only. Small general stock. Spec: PR: £1–50. [Updated]

The Treasure Island, 4 Evesham Road, Blackley, Manchester, M9 7EH. Prop: Ray Cauwood. Tel: (0161) 795 7750. Website: www.abebooks.com/home/RAYJC2000. E-mail: ray@the-treasure-island.com. Est: 2003. Private premises. Postal business only. Appointment necessary. Small stock. Spec: Animals and Birds; Art; Aviation; Languages - National; Maritime/Nautical; Medicine; Philately; Photography; Railways; Sport - Angling/Fishing; Sport - Cricket; Sport - Horse Racing (all aspects); Sport - Rugby; Travel - General. PR: £1–50. CC: V. Cata: 1 – a year. [Updated]

MOTTRAM IN LONGDENDALE

Rose Books, 26 Roe Cross Green, Mottram in Longdendale, Hyde, SK14 6LP. (*) Prop: E. Alan Rose. Tel: (01457) 763485. Fax: (01457) 763485. Est: 1990. Private premises. Appointment necessary. Very small stock. Spec: History - Local; Religion - Christian; Theology. PR: £2–150. Cata: 2 – a year on church history. [Updated]

OLDHAM

Moorland Books, ■ 1 Smithy Lane, Uppermill, Oldham, OL3 6AH. Prop: Mrs. C.M. Bennett. Tel: (01457) 871306. E-mail: moorlandbooks@ntlworld.com. Est: 1982. Open: **T:** 10:30–16:00; **W:** 10:30–16:30; **Th:** 09:30–16:30; **F:** 10:30–16:30; **S:** 10:30–16:30; **Su:** 11:00–16:30. Medium stock. Spec: Also, booksearch. PR: £1–100. CC: MC; V. [Updated]

Towpath Bookshop, ■ 27 High Street, Uppermill, Oldham, OL3 6HS. (*) Prop: Janet Byrom. Tel: (01457) 877078. Est: 1992. Shop open: **T:** 11:00–16:30; **W:** 10:30–17:00; **Th:** 10:30–17:00; **F:** 10:30–17:00; **S:** 10:30–17:00; **Su:** 11:00–17:00. Very small general stock. [Updated]

ROCHDALE

Empire Books, 61 Broad Lane, Rochdale, OL16 4PL. Prop: Robert Oliver. Tel: (01706) 666678. Fax: (01706) 666678. Website: www.empiremilitarybooks.co.uk. E-mail: empirebooks@boltblue.com. Est: 1993. Private premises. Internet and postal. Appointment necessary. Large stock. Spec: Arms & Armour; Aviation; Biography; Colonial; Countries - Australia; Espionage; Firearms/Guns; Maritime/ Nautical; Memoirs; Military; Military History; Naval; Newspapers - General; War - General; War - American Civil War; War - Boer, The; War - English Civil Wars. PR: £1–200. CC: JCB; MC; V; Switch. Also, Australian military specialist. Mem: PBFA. [14/04/2003]

Rochdale Book Company, ■ 399 Oldham Road, Rochdale, OL16 5LN. Prop: J.S. & S.M. Worthy. Tel: (01706) 658300. Fax: (01706) 713294. E-mail: worthybooks@aol.com. Est: 1971. Shop. Telephone first. Open: **S:** 10:30–17:30. Large stock. Spec: Antiquarian; Architecture; Canals/Inland Waterways; Children's - General; Company History; Fine & Rare; History - Industrial; Illustrated; Industry; Military History; Motoring; Railways; Topography - Local; Transport; Travel - General. CC: MC; V. Mem: PBFA. [Updated]

STOCKPORT

Richard Coulthurst, 97 Green Pastures, Stockport, SK4 3RB. Tel: (0161) 431-3864. E-mail: richard .coulthurst@btinternet.com. Est: 1995. Private premises. Postal business only. Very small stock. Spec: Canals/Inland Waterways; History - Industrial; Publishers - Oakwood Press; Railways; Steam Engines; Transport; also Booksearch. PR: £5–100. Cata: 1 a year. [Updated]

Robin S. Hunt, 6 Alford Road, Heaton Chapel, Stockport, SK4 5AW. Prop: Robin Hunt. Tel: (0161) 285-9670. E-mail: robin@rashalf.freeserve.co.uk. Est: 1975. Postal business only. Very small stock. Spec: Crime (True); History - General; Nostalgia; Royalty - General; Social History. PR: £1–50. Very few books, mainly ephemera. See entry on www.sheppardsworld.co.uk. [Updated]

WIGAN

R.D.M. & I.M. Price (Books), 25 Coniston Avenue, Whitley, Wigan, WN1 2EY. Prop: Robert and Irene Price. Tel: (01942) 242607. Est: 1997. Private premises. Postal business only. Very small stock. Spec: Autobiography; Biography; Colonial; Fiction - General; also Booksearch. PR: £1–65. [Updated]

Wiend Books & Collectables, ■ 8–12 The Wiend, Wigan, Lancashire, WN1 1PF. Prop: Paul Morris. Tel: (01942) 820500. Fax: (01942) 820500. Website: www.wiendbooks.co.uk. E-mail: wiendbooks@ lycos.co.uk. Shop. Spec: Archaeology; Architecture; Art; Children's - General; Cinema/Film; Collecting; Company History; Cookery/Gastronomy; Fiction - Crime, Detective, Spy, Thrillers; Fiction - Science Fiction; History - Ancient; Magic & Conjuring; Maritime/Nautical; Military History; Music - PR: £3–250. [Updated]

HAMPSHIRE

ALRESFORD

Bolton Books, 60, The Dean, Alresford, SO24 9BD. Prop: David Bolton. Tel: (01962) 734435. Fax: (10962) 734435. Website: www.boltonbooks.com. E-mail: david@boltonbooks.com. Est: 1997. Private premises. Internet and postal. Appointment necessary. Very small stock. Spec: Colour-Plate; Illustrated; Publishers - Black, A. & C.; Publishers - Foulis, T.N.; Topography - General. PR: £5–1,250. Also exhibits at bookfairs. Cata: 4 – A. & C. Black Colour Books. Mem: PBFA. [Updated]

Laurence Oxley Ltd, ■ The Studio Bookshop, 17 Broad Street, Alresford, Nr. Winchester, SO24 9AW. Prop: Anthony Oxley. Tel: (01962) 732188. E-mail: aoxley@freenet.co.uk. Est: 1950. Shop open: **M:** 09:00–17:00; **T:** 09:00–17:00; **W:** 09:00–17:00; **Th:** 09:00–17:00; **F:** 09:00–17:00; **S:** 09:00–17:00. Large stock. Spec: Countries - Far East, The; Countries - India; Topography - General; Topography - Local. PR: £1–25,000. CC: AE; D; MC; V. Also, picture dealers, picture frame makers and restoration work. Cata: 2 – Watercolour pictures. Mem: ABA; BA; ABA, FATG. VAT No: GB 188 5081 31. [Updated]

ALTON

Soldridge Books Ltd, Soldridge House, Soldridge Road, Medstead, Alton, GU34 5JF. Prop: Jan & John Lewis. Tel: (01420) 562811. Fax: (01420) 562811. Website: www.soldridgebooks.co.uk. E-mail: lewis@soldridgebooks.co.uk. Est: 1991. Private premises. Internet and postal. Appointment necessary. Open: **M:** 09:00–18:00; **T:** 09:00–18:00; **W:** 09:00–18:00; **Th:** 09:00–18:00; **F:** 09:00–18:00; **S:** 09:00–13:00. Medium stock. Spec: Aeronautics; Aviation; First Editions; Photography; Poetry. PR: £3–400. CC: MC; V; Maestro. Cata: 6 a year. Corresp: French. Mem: PBFA. VAT No: GB 799 6939 25. [Updated]

Alton Secondhand Books, ■ 43 Normandy Street, Alton, GU34 1DQ. Prop: Mrs. J. Andrews. Tel: (01420) 89352. E-mail: joan.andrews@virgin.net. Est: 1989. Shop open: **M:** 09:30–17:30; **T:** 09:30–17:30; **W:** 09:30–17:00; **Th:** 09:30–17:30; **F:** 09:30–17:30; **S:** 09:30–17:00. Medium stock. Also, booksearch. PR: £1–100. VAT No: GB 631 9874 13. [Updated]

Dance Books Ltd, The Old Bakery, 4 Lenten St., Alton, GU34 1HG. Prop: David Leonard. Tel: (01420) 86138. Fax: (01420) 86142. Website: www.dancebooks.co.uk. E-mail: dwl@dancebooks.co.uk. Est: 1960. Storeroom. Appointment necessary. Open: **M:** 10:00–17:00; **T:** 10:00–17:00; **W:** 10:00–17:00; **Th:** 10:00–17:00; **F:** 10:00–17:00. Small stock. Spec: Dance. PR: £1–1,000. CC: AE; E; MC; V. Mem: BA. VAT No: GB 238 6405 53. [Updated]

Nebulous Books, Cromwell House, 11 Oliver Rise, Alton, GU34 2BN. Prop: Peter Bancroft. Tel: (01420) 89264. Est: 1986. Private premises. Appointment necessary. Small stock. Spec: Canals/Inland Waterways; Railways; Transport. PR: £1–40. [01/07/2003]

Peter White Books, Westbrooke House, 76 High Street, Alton, GU34 1EN. Peter White. Tel: 01420-86745. Fax: 01420-86745. E-mail: pwbooks@btconnect.com. Est: 1995. Office. &/or bookroom. Internet and postal. Telephone first. Very small stock. Spec: History - Local; Modern First Editions; Railways; Sport - Football (Soccer); Topography - General; Transport. PR: £4–60. Also, stocks titles on local history in most counties. Corresp: French. [Updated]

ALVERSTOKE

R.W. Forder, 12 St Mark's Road, Alverstoke, Gosport, PO12 2DA. Prop: R.W. Forder. Tel: (023) 9252-7965. E-mail: forder@marksrd.freeserve.co.uk. Est: 1985. Private premises. Internet and postal. Telephone first. Spec: Free Thought; Humanism; Radical Issues. PR: £1–200. Also, a booksearch service. Corresp: German. [Updated]

ANDOVER

Armchair Auctions, 98 Junction Road, Andover, SP10 3JA. Prop: George Murdoch. Tel: (01264) 362048. Fax: (01264) 362048. Est: 1989. Private premises. Small stock. Spec: Aviation; Military; Naval; War - World War I, also Booksearch. PR: £5–500. CC: AE; MC; V. Main activity: postal auctions. Cata: ten a year. [Updated]

ASHURST

Les Alpes Livres, 'Arcadia', Hazel Grove, Ashurst, SO40 7AJ. Prop: Tony Astill. Tel: (023)-8029 3767. Website: www.les-alpes-livres.co.uk. E-mail: alpes@supanet.com. Est: 1993. Private premises. Internet and postal. Telephone first. Small stock. Spec: Alpinism/Mountaineering; Bindings; Countries - Central Asia; Countries - Switzerland; Countries - Tibet. PR: £5–1,000. CC: D; MC; V. Cata: quarterly. Corresp: French. VAT No: GB 631 6744 41. [09/09/2003]

BASINGSTOKE

Byblos Antiquarian & Rare Books, Broadmead, 5 Worting Road, Basingstoke, RG21 8TL. Tel: (01256) 417092. Website: www.byblos.uk.com. E-mail: Henry.Stanton@byblos.uk.com. Est: 2005. Private premises. Internet and postal. Very small stock. Spec: Antiquarian; Fine & Rare; also Booksearch. PR: £5–200. CC: MC; V. Corresp: French, Italian. Mem: IOAB. [Updated]

EMSWORTH

Bookends, ■ 7 High St., Emsworth, PO10 7AQ. Prop: Carol Waldron. Tel: (01243) 372154. E-mail: cawaldron@tinyworld.co.uk. Est: 1982. Shop open: **M:** 09:00–17:00; **T:** 09:00–17:00; **W:** 09:00–17:00; **Th:** 09:00–17:00; **F:** 09:00–17:00; **S:** 09:00–17:00; **Su:** 10:00–15:00. Large stock. Spec: PR: £1–300. Corresp: French. [Updated]

Peter Hill, 3 Westbourne Avenue, Emsworth, PO10 7QT. Tel: (01243) 379956. Fax: (01243) 379956. E-mail: peterhill.books@btinternet.com. Est: 1986. Private premises. Appointment necessary. Open: **M:** 09:00–17:00; **T:** 09:00–17:00; **W:** 09:00–17:00; **Th:** 09:00–17:00; **F:** 09:00–17:00. Small stock. Spec: Alpinism/Mountaineering; Classical Studies; Travel - General. PR: £10–2,000. Corresp: French. Mem: ABA; PBFA. [Updated]

FARNBOROUGH

Farnborough Gallery, 26 Guildford Road West, Farnborough, GU14 6PU. Prop: P.H. Taylor. Tel: (01252) 518033. Fax: (01252) 511503. Website: www.farnboroughgallery.co.uk. E-mail: peter-t@btconnect.com. Est: 1978. Storeroom. Internet and postal. Appointment necessary. Open: **M:** 08:00–18:00; **T:** 08:00–18:00; **W:** 08:00–18:00; **Th:** 08:00–18:00; **F:** 08:00–18:00; **S:** 08:00–17:00. Spec: Academic/Scholarly; Art; Art - Technique; First Editions; History - General; Military; Military History. PR: £5–1,000. CC: AE; MC; V. Also, picture framing , mount cutting, framed artwork for sale. Cata: 4 a year on military history, art, general railways. Mem: Fine Art Trade Guild. VAT No: GB 296 4807 13. [Updated]

FLEET

War & Peace Books, 32 Wellington Ave., Fleet, GU51 3BF. Prop: Dr G.M. Bayliss. Tel: (01252) 677902. Fax: (01252) 677902. Website: www.abebooks.com. E-mail: gwyn.bayliss@ntlworld.com. Est: 1998. Private premises. Postal business only. Contactable. Very small stock. Spec: Aviation; Biography; Literary Travel; Literature; Maritime/Nautical; Military; Military History; Naval; Poetry; Politics. PR: £5–100. [Updated]

FORDINGBRIDGE

Bristow & Garland, ■ 45–47 Salisbury Street, Fordingbridge, SP6 1AB. Prop: David Bristow & Victoria Garland. Tel: (01425) 657337. Fax: (01425) 657337. Website: www.bristowandgarland.co.uk. E-mail: mail@bristowandgarland.co.uk. Est: 1970. Shop open: **M:** 10:00–17:00; **T:** 10:00–17:00; **W:** 10:00–17:00; **Th:** 10:00–13:00; **F:** 10:00–17:00; **S:** 10:00–17:00. Small general stock. Spec: Autographs; Fine & Rare; Manuscripts. PR: £5–5,000. CC: JCB; MC. [29/06/2003]

GOSPORT

Richard Martin Bookshop & Gallery, ■ 19-23 Stoke Road, Gosport, PO12 1LS. Tel: (023) 9252-0642. Fax: (023) 9252-0642. Website: www.richardmartingallery.co.uk. E-mail: enquiries@ richardmartingallery.co.uk. Est: 1976. Shop open: **T:** 10:30–16:30; **Th:** 10:30–16:30; **F:** 10:30–16:30; **S:** 10:30–13:00; Closed for lunch: 13:00–14:15. Medium stock. Spec: Illustrated; Maritime/Nautical; Topography - General; Travel - General. PR: £10–3,000. CC: MC; V. Also, restoration work, frames and mounts. Cata: occasionally on thematic. Mem: PBFA. VAT No: GB 430 6603 81. [Updated]

Sub Aqua Prints and Books, 3 Crescent Road, Alverstoke, Gosport, PO12 2DH. Prop: Kevin F. Casey. Tel: (023) 9252 0426. Fax: (023) 9250 2428. Website: www.subaquaprints.com. E-mail: kevin@ subaquaprints.com. Est: 1991. Private premises. Internet and postal. Appointment necessary. Small stock. Spec: Deep Sea Diving; Marine Sciences; Maritime/Nautical; Naval. PR: £5–1,000. CC: JCB; MC; V. [Updated]

HORDLE

Alastor Books, 12 Wisbech Way, Hordle, SO41 0YQ. Prop: J.A. Eaton. Tel: (01425) 629756. E-mail: alastor.books@virgin.net. Internet and postal. Spec: Antiquarian; Bibliography; Books about Books; Travel - General. PR: £15–1,000. Mem: PBFA. [12/08/2003]

HORNDEAN

Milestone Publications Goss & Crested China Club, 62 Murray Road, Horndean, PO8 9JL. Prop: Mrs. Lynda Pine. Tel: (023) 9259-7440. Fax: (023) 9259-1975. Website: www.gosschinaclub.demon.co.uk. E-mail: info@gosschinaclub.co.uk. Est: 1975. Spec: Author - Goss, W.H.; Author - Hall, S.C.; Author - Jewitt, Llewellynn; Ceramics. PR: £1–40. Also, dealers in souvenir ware china, Goss & Crested china c.1850-1940, heraldic porcelain & new books of the same topics. [Updated]

Tobo Books, 10 London Road, Horndean, Waterlooville, PO8 0BZ. Prop: Matthew Wingett. Tel: 07985 053777. Website: www.tobo-books.com. E-mail: sheppards@tobo-books.com. Est: 2000. Office. &/or bookroom. Internet. Contactable. Open: **M:** 09:00–17:00; **T:** 09:09–17:00; **W:** 09:09–17:00; **Th:** 09:09–17:00; **F:** 09:00–17:00. Small stock. Spec: Antiquarian; Architecture; Author - Byron, Lord; Author - Cruickshank, G.; Author - Dickens, Charles; Author - Fleming, Ian; Author - Greene, Graham; Author - Milne, A.A.; Author - Tolkien, J.R.R.; Author - Trollope, Anthony; Bindings; Fine & Rare; PR: £1–10,000. CC: JCB; MC; V. Corresp: Schoolboy French; Schoolboy Spanish. Mem: PBFA. VAT No: GB 812 1985 36. [Updated]

LIPHOOK

Pauline Harries Books, 4 Willow Close, Liphook, GU30 7HX. Tel: (01428) 723764. Fax: (01428) 722367. Website: www.abebooks.com/home/paulineharriesbooks. E-mail: paulineharriesbooks@lineone.net. Est: 1982. Private premises. Appointment necessary. Medium stock. Spec: Booksearch. PR: £2–1,000. CC: JCB; MC; V; Delta. [22/10/2004]

LISS

William Duck, Highfield Farm, Hatch Lane, Liss, GU33 7NH. Prop: William Duck. Tel: (01730) 895594. Fax: (01730) 894548. Est: 1963. Private premises. Appointment necessary. Very small stock. Spec: Aeronautics; Architecture; Arms & Armour; Astronautics; Aviation; Canals/Inland Waterways; Cities; Country Houses; Design; Engineering; Firearms/Guns; Gardening; Geology; Industry; Landscape; Maritime/Nautical; Meteorology; Mining; Motorbikes; Motoring. PR: £10–5,000. Cata: 2 on specialities. Mem: ABA; PBFA. [Updated]

LYMINGTON

M. & B. Clapham, ■ 7 Emsworth Road, Lymington, SO41 9BL. Prop: Barbara & Peter Clapham. Tel: (01590) 673178. Est: 1978. Shop at: Lymington Antiques Centre, 75 High Street, Lymington. Open: **M:** 10:00–17:00; **T:** 10:00–17:00; **W:** 10:00–17:00; **Th:** 10:00–17:00; **F:** 10:00–17:00; **S:** 09:00–17:00. Medium stock. Spec: Music - General; Sport - Yachting. Cata: occasionally. Corresp: French, Italian. [Updated]

MINSTEAD

Nova Foresta Books, 17 Castle Malwood Lodge, Minstead, SO43 7HB. Prop: Georgina Babey & Peter Roberts. Tel: (023) 8081-2475. Website: www.novaforestabooks.co.uk. E-mail: postmaster@ novaforestabooks.co.uk. Est: 1994. Private premises. Appointment necessary. Very small stock. Spec: Topography - Local. PR: £1–1,000. Research into family histories and property relating to New Forest area. Also publishers. [Updated]

NEW MILTON

J.H. Day, 33 Ashley Common Road, Ashley, New Milton, BH25 5AL. Prop: J.H. Day. Tel: (01425) 619406. Website: www.abebooks.com. E-mail: jamesjday@aol.com. Est: 1983. Private premises. Internet and postal. Appointment necessary. Medium stock. Spec: Sport - Horse Racing (all aspects). PR: £5–200. CC: Paypal. Also at: Lyminton Antique Centre. [Updated]

OVERTON

David Esplin, 30 High Street, Overton, RG25 3HA. Tel: (01256) 771108. E-mail: books@desplin .freeserve.co.uk. Est: 1978. Postal business only. Spec: Medicine - History of; Science - History of; Technology. PR: £5–1,000. [Updated]

PETERSFIELD

The Petersfield Bookshop, ■ 16a Chapel Street, Petersfield, GU32 3DS. Prop: Frank, Ann, John & David Westwood. Tel: (01730) 263438. Fax: (01730) 269426. Website: www.petersfieldbookshop.com. E-mail: sales@petersfieldbookshop.com. Est: 1918. Shop open: **M:** 09:00–17:30; **T:** 09:00–17:30; **W:** 09:00–17:30; **Th:** 09:00–17:30; **F:** 09:00–17:30; **S:** 09:00–17:30. Spec: Sport - Angling/Fishing; Travel - General, also Booksearch. PR: £1–2,000. CC: AE; D; MC; V. Also, maps, prints, new books, art materials, picture framing. Cata: 4 a year. Mem: ABA; PBFA; BA; ILAB. VAT No: GB 192 6013 72. [Updated]

David Schutte, 'Waterside', 119 Sussex Road, Petersfield, GU31 4LB. Tel: (01730) 269115. Fax: (01730) 231177. Website: http://davidschutte.co.uk. E-mail: david.schutte@virgin.net. Est: 1980. Private premises. Internet and postal. Appointment necessary. Spec: Author - Blyton, Enid; Author - Buckeridge, A.; Author - Crompton, Richmal; Author - Johns, W.E.; Author - Ransome, Arthur; Author - Saville, M.; Author - Wodehouse, P.G.; Children's - General. PR: £3–1,500. CC: MC; V. Cata: 6 a year. Mem: PBFA. [Updated]

PORTSMOUTH

Abbey Bookshop, ■ 69 Fawcett Road, Southsea, Portsmouth, PO4 ODB. Prop: Nick Purkis. Tel: (023) 9273-7077. Est: 1986. Shop open: **T:** 12:00–18:00; **W:** 12:00–18:00; **Th:** 12:00–18:00; **F:** 12:00–18:00; **S:** 11:00–18:00. Very large stock. Spec: Art; Chess; Children's - General; Esoteric; Fiction - General; Fine Art; First Editions; History - General; Military; Military History; Mind, Body & Spirit; Natural History; Naval; Poetry; Politics; Railways; Topography - General; Travel - General. PR: £1–100. Cata: 1 a year. Corresp: French. [Updated]

Art Reference Books, 3 Portswood Road, Portsmouth, PO2 9QX. Prop: Andy Ralph. Tel: (02392) 790861. Fax: (02392) 650756. Website: www.artreferencebooks.com. E-mail: artreferencebooks@ hotmail.com. Est: 1999. Private premises. Internet and postal. Appointment necessary. Medium stock. Spec: Antiquarian; Antiques; Applied Art; Architecture; Art; Art - History; Art - Reference; Artists; Ceramics; Children's - Illustrated; Collecting; Country Houses; Decorative Art; Design; Dolls & Dolls' Houses; Fashion & Costume; Fine Art; Furniture. PR: £2–1,000. [07/09/2003]

Jade Mountain, ■ 17–19 Highland Road, Southsea, Portsmouth, PO4 9DA. Prop: Ian Stemp. Tel: (023) 92 732951. Website: ianstemp@btinternet.com. E-mail: ianstemp@btinternet.com. Est: 1992. Internet and postal. Shop open: **M:** 09:30–17:30; **W:** 09:30–17:30; **F:** 09:30–17:30; **S:** 09:30–17:30. Large stock. Spec: Animals and Birds; Cinema/Film; Dictionaries; Fiction - General; Food & Drink; Gardening; History - General; Languages - Foreign; Literature; Music - General; Natural History; Plays; Poetry; Psychology/Psychiatry; Publishers - Pelican; Railways. PR: £1–80. [Updated]

Roadster Motoring Books, 33 Martin Road, Copnor, Portsmouth, PO3 6JZ. Prop: Peter Cockburn. Tel: (023) 9266-5632. Est: 1991. Private premises. Appointment necessary. Small stock. Spec: Motorbikes; Motoring; Sport - Motor Racing; Vintage Cars. PR: £5–200. [01/07/2003]

www.artreferencebooks.com, Portswood Road, Portsmouth, PO2 9QX. Prop: Andy Ralph. Tel: (023) 9279 0861. Website: www.artreferencebooks.com. E-mail: artreferencebooks@hotmail.com. Est: 1999. Internet and postal. Shop at: 3 Portswood road, Hilsea, Portsmouth, Hampshire, PO2 9QX. Medium stock. Spec: Academic/Scholarly; Aesthetic Movement; Antiquarian; Antiques; Applied Art; Architecture; Art; Art - History; Art - Reference; Art - Technique; Art - Theory; Art Deco; Art Nouveau; Artists; Carpets; Ceramics; Collecting; Country Houses; Decorative Art, PR: £2–600. CC: E; MC; V. [Updated]

RINGWOOD

E. Chalmers Hallam, Trees, 9 Post Office Lane, St. Ives, Ringwood, BH24 2PG. Prop: Laura Hiscock. Tel: (01425) 470060. Fax: (01425) 470060. Website: www.hallam-books.co.uk. E-mail: laura@ chalmershallam.freeserve.co.uk. Est: 1946. Private premises. Appointment necessary. Large stock. Spec: Anthropology; Author - Watkins–Pitchford, Denys ('B.B.'); Cockfighting; Countries - Africa; Countries - India; Dogs; Firearms/Guns; Fishes; Sport - Angling/Fishing; Sport - Archery; Sport - Big Game Hunting; Sport - Coursing; Sport - Falconry; Sport - Fencing. PR: £5–5,000. CC: MC; V; Debit card. Cata: 2 a year. Mem: PBFA. [13/03/2003]

ROMSEY

Bufo Books, 32 Tadfield Road, Romsey, SO51 5AJ. Prop: Ruth Allen & Peter Hubbard. Tel: (01794) 517149. Fax: (08700) 516786. Website: www.bufobooks.demon.co.uk. E-mail: bufo@bufobooks .demon.co.uk. Est: 1979. Private premises. Internet and postal. Appointment necessary. Medium stock. Spec: Children's - General; Military; War - General. PR: £1–200. CC: MC; V; Bartercard. Attends bookfairs. Cata: occasionally. Corresp: French. Mem: PBFA. VAT No: GB 522 4988 32. [Updated]

SOUTHAMPTON

Vincent G. Barlow, 24 Howerts Close, Warsash, Southampton, SO31 9JR. Tel: (01489) 582431. Est: 1981. Storeroom; Appointment necessary. Small stock. Spec: Art - Reference; Catalogues Raisonnes; Children's - General; Decorative Art; Fine Printing; Illustrated; Interior Design; Limited Editions; Monographs; Private Press. PR: £3–2,000. Attends monthly fairs at Royal National. Also prints. Mem: PLA; IBIS. [Updated]

Broadwater Books, 62 Britannia Gardens, Hedge End, Southampton, SO30 2RP. Prop: J.B. & A.B. Dancy. Tel: (01489) 786035. E-mail: john@jdancy.fsnet.co.uk. Est: 1988. Private premises. Postal business only. Large stock. Spec: Countries - England; Countries - Melanesia; Countries - Scotland; History - General; Religion - General; Theology; Travel - General. PR: £1–400. Also, wants lists welcomed. [Updated]

Ellwood Books, ■ 22 Northam Road, Southampton, SO14 0PA. Prop: Mark Harrison and Helen Ford. Tel: (02380) 232300. Website: www.ellwoodbooks.com. E-mail: info@ellwoodbooks.com. Est: 2001. Shop open: **M:** 10:30–16:30; **T:** 10:30–16:30; **Th:** 10:30–16:30; **F:** 10:30–16:30; **S:** 10:30–16:30. Small stock. Spec: Fiction - General; Fine & Rare; Modern First Editions; Poetry; Signed Editions. PR: £5– 30. CC: E; JCB; MC; V; Switch; Solo. Also attends London & Farnham HD bookfairs & Internet trading. Cata: occasionally on specialities. VAT No: GB 832 0693 40. [Updated]

W.E. Jackson, 6 Shepherds Close, Bartley, Southampton, SO40 2LJ. Prop: Bill Jackson. Tel: (02380) 812640. E-mail: bill@bilberry.ndo.co.uk. Est: 1988. Private premises. Postal business only. Small general stock. PR: £1–100. [Updated]

Morley Case, 24 Wildburn Close, Calmore, Southampton, SO40 2SG. Prop: David Case. Tel: (023) 8086-4264. Website: www.abebooks.com/home/case. E-mail: morleycase@aol.com. Est: 1973. Private premises. Internet and postal. Appointment necessary. Small general stock. Spec: Art; Aviation; Military; Sport - Golf. PR: £5–200. [13/03/2003]

Peter Rhodes, Bookseller, ■ 21 Portswood Road, Southampton, SO17 2ES. Tel: (02380) 399003. E-mail: peterrhodes.books@virgin.net. Est: 1996. Shop open: **T:** 10:00–17:00; **W:** 10:00–17:00; **Th:** 10:00– 17:00; **F:** 10:00–17:00; **S:** 10:00–17:00. Large general stock. Spec: Anthropology; Author - 20th Century; Children's - Illustrated; Countries - India; Photography; Theatre. Also, insurance and probate valuation, coffee shop. [Updated]

Signature Books, 22 Taranto Road, Southampton, SO16 5PN. Prop: Mrs Rowena Adams. Tel: (023) 8078 7756. Website: www.signaturebookco.com. E-mail: signaturebookco@aol.com. Est: 2002. Private premises. Internet and postal. Very small stock. Spec: Children's - General; Countries - Polar; Fiction - General; Maritime/Nautical; Military; Natural History; Performing Arts; Poetry; Politics; Religion - General; Science - General; Signed Editions; Sport - General; Topography - General; Transport. PR: £5–160. Cata: 4 a year. [Updated]

SOUTHSEA

Palladour Books, 23, Eldon Street, Southsea, PO5 4BS. Prop: Jeremy & Anne Powell. Tel: (02392) 826935. Fax: (02392) 826935. E-mail: palladour@powellj33.freeserve.co.uk. Est: 1985. Private premises. Internet and postal. Appointment necessary. Open: Very small stock. Spec: First Editions; Literature; Military; Periodicals & Magazines; Poetry; School Registers/Rolls of Honour; War - General; War - World War I; War - World War II; also Booksearch. PR: £1–500. Cata: 2 – Military Literature and Poetry of WW1. [Updated]

WARSASH

Warsash Nautical Bookshop, ■ 6 Dibles Road, Warsash, Southampton, SO31 9HZ. Prop: Mr. Andrew Marshall. Tel: (01489) 572384. Fax: (01489) 885756. Website: www.nauticalbooks.co.uk. E-mail: orders@nauticalbooks.co.uk. Est: 1973. Internet and postal. Shop open: **M:** 09:00–17:45; **T:** 09:00–17:45; **W:** 09:00–17:45; **Th:** 09:00–17:45; **F:** 09:00–17:45; **S:** 09:30–17:00. Small stock. Spec: Academic/Scholarly; Maritime/Nautical; Maritime/Nautical - Log Books; Navigation, also Booksearch. PR: £5–500. CC: AE; D; E; JCB; MC; V. Cata: 2 Half Yearly. Mem: BA. VAT No: GB 108 3293 82. [Updated]

WINCHESTER

John Barton, 84 Old Kennels Lane, Winchester, SO22 4JT. Tel: (01962) 866543. E-mail: jgbarton@virgin.net. Est: 1966. Private premises. Postal business only. Telephone first. Very small stock. Spec: Archaeology; Architecture; History - General; History - Local; History - National; Topography - General. PR: £2–100. [updated]

Boris Books, Winnall Manor Farm, Wales Street, Winchester, SO23 0HA. Prop: Pam Stevenson. Tel: (01962) 890355. Website: www.borisbooks.co.uk. E-mail: pam@borisbooks.fsnet.co.uk. Est: 1995. Office &/or bookroom; Internet and postal. Appointment necessary. Shop at: 2 Holland Close, Chandler's Ford, Eastleigh, Hants SO53 3NA. Open: **M:** 09:30–16:30; **T:** 09:30–16:30; **W:** 09:30–16:30; **Th:** 09:30–16:30; **F:** 09:30–16:30; Closed for lunch: 13:15–14:15. Small general stock. Spec: Author - Heyer, Georgette; Children's - General; Fiction - General; Fiction - Historical; First Editions; Illustrated; Literature; Music - General; Music - Composers. PR: £1–200. CC: MC; V. Mem: PBFA. VAT No: GB 717 6806 15. [Updated]

Peter M. Daly, 6 Ronald Bowker Court, Greenhill Road, Winchester, SO22 5EA. Prop: Peter M. Daly. Tel: (01962) 867732. E-mail: petermdaly@rarebooks.fsnet.co.uk. Est: 1984. Private premises. Internet and postal. Appointment necessary. Small general stock. Spec: Africana; Agriculture; Alpinism/Mountaineering; Animals and Birds; Antiquarian; Countries - Afghanistan; Countries - Africa; Countries - Arabia; Countries - Central Asia; Countries - Far East, The; Countries - India; Countries - Kenya. T PR: £1–1,000. CC: JCB; MC; V; SW. Mem: PBFA. VAT No: GB 411 8630 76. [Updated]

H.M. Gilbert & Son, 5 Rooks Down, Winchester, SO22 4QN. Prop: Richard Gilbert. Tel: (023) 8022-6420. Est: 1859. Private premises. Appointment necessary. Small stock. Spec: Antiquarian; Literature; Maritime/Nautical; Topography - General; Topography - Local. PR: £1–500. CC: MC; V. Mem: PBFA. [updated]

Kingsgate Books & Prints, ■ Kingsgate Arch, Winchester, SO23 9PD. Prop: Michael Fowkes. Tel: (01962) 864710. Fax: (01962) 864710. Est: 1992. Shop open: **T:** 12:30–17:00; **W:** 12:30–17:00; **Th:** 12:30–17:00; **F:** 12:30–17:00; **S:** 10:00–17:00. Very small stock. Spec: Art - History; Art - Reference; History - Local; Literary Criticism; Literature; Natural History; Poetry. PR: £1–150. CC: MC; V. Corresp: French. Mem: BA. [23/08/2002]

S.P.C.K., ■ 24 The Square, Winchester, SO23 9EX. Tel: (01962) 866617. Fax: (01962) 890312. E-mail: winchester@spck.org.uk. Est: 1698. Shop open: **M:** 09:00–16:30; **T:** 08:00–17:30; **W:** 09:00–17:30; **Th:** 09:00–17:30; **F:** 09:00–17:30; **S:** 08:00–17:30. Large stock. Spec: Religion - Christian; Theology; also Booksearch. PR: £1–300. CC: MC; V. Also, wide Christian booksearch service. Mem: BA. VAT No: GB 232 8071 82. [Updated]

Available from Richard Joseph Publishers Ltd
BOOKDEALING FOR PROFIT
by Paul Minet

Quarto H/b   £10.00 144pp

Sen Books, 3 Long Barrow Close, South Wonston, Winchester, SO21 3ED. Prop: Andrew Duckworth. Tel: (01962) 884405. Fax: (01962) 884405. E-mail: andrew.duckworth_senbooks@btopenworld.com. Est: 1975. Private premises. Appointment necessary. Small general stock. Spec: Author - Trollope, Anthony; Author - White, Gilbert, also Booksearch. PR: £1–200. [Updated]

The Winchester Bookshop, ■ (next to Ladbroke's), 10a St. George's Street, Winchester, SO23 8BG. Prop: J. Barton, R. Brown, D. Barnes & M. Green. Tel: (01962) 855630. E-mail: books.winchester@ btinternet.com. Est: 1991. Shop open: **M:** 10:00–17:00; **T:** 10:00–17:00; **W:** 10:00–17:00; **Th:** 10:00–17:00; **F:** 10:00–17:00; **S:** 10:00–17:30. Medium stock. Spec: Academic/Scholarly; Advertising; Anthologies; Archaeology; Bindings; Literature; Sport - Angling/Fishing; Topography - General; Topography - Local; also Booksearch. PR: £1–300. CC: MC; V. Corresp: German. [Updated]

HEREFORDSHIRE

ASHPERTON,

Books for Content, Spring Grove Farm, Wood End, Ashperton, Ledbury, HR8 2RS. Prop: H.M. & M.G. Jones. Tel: (01432) 890279. Est: 1989. Private premises. Postal business only. Small stock. Spec: Agriculture; Cookery/Gastronomy; Farming & Livestock; Gardening; Horticulture; Rural Life. PR: £3–100. [Updated]

BISHOP'S FROME

T. Bicknell, 1 Mudwalls, Bishop's Frome, WR6 5DB. (*). Tel: (01885) 490723. E-mail: mail@bicknellbooks .freeserve.co.uk. Est: 2000. Private premises. Internet and postal. Very small stock. Spec: Bindings; Churchilliana. PR: £10–1,000. [08/09/2003]

DILWYN

Mary Bland, 3 Castle Barn, Dilwyn, HR4 8HZ. Tel: (01544) 318750. Est: 1978. Private premises. Appointment necessary. Small stock. Spec: Botany; Gardening. PR: £1–200. Cata: 2 occasionally. [27/04/2003]

GLASBURY

babelog books, Victoria House, Glasbury, Hereford, HR3 5NR. Prop: Simon Cartwright. Tel: (01497) 847190. Website: www.ukbookworld.com/members/mason. E-mail: babelog.books@ukgateway.net. Est: 2000. Private premises. Postal business only. Appointment necessary. Very small stock. Spec: Literature; Literature in Translation; Modern First Editions; Poetry. PR: £5–1,000. [08/09/2003]

HAY–ON–WYE (SEE ALSO UNDER POWYS, WALES)

HEREFORD

Acer Books, Penworlodd Farm, Rowlestone, Hereford, HR2 0DS. Prop: Kevin Desforges BSc (Hons). Tel: (01981) 241176. Fax: (01981) 241176. E-mail: acerbooks@bigfoot.com. Est: 1998. Private premises. Postal business only. Contactable. Open: **M:** 09:00–18:00; **T:** 09:00–18:00; **W:** 09:00–18:00; **Th:** 09:00–18:00; **F:** 09:00–18:00; **S:** 09:00–18:00. Medium stock. Spec: Animals and Birds; Botany; Conservation; Forestry; Geography; Landscape; Natural History; New Naturalist; Ornithology; Rural Life; Signed Editions; Topography - General; also Booksearch. PR: £1–3,000. Exhibits at natural history fairs, inc. British Birdwatching Fair. Cata: occasionally on natural history, new naturalist. [Updated]

The New Strand Bookshop, ■ Eardisley, Hereford, HR3 6PW. Prop: R. & A. Cardwell. Tel: (01544) 327285. Shop open: **W:** 09:30–18:00; **Th:** 09:30–18:00; **F:** 09:30–18:00; **S:** 09:30–18:00; **Su:** 09:30–18:00; Very large stock. Spec: Children's - General; Fiction - General; Fiction - Crime, Detective, Spy, Thrillers; Fiction - Science Fiction; Natural History. PR: £1–250. [Updated]

O'Donoghue Books, PO Box 162, Hereford, HR3 5WZ. Prop: Sean O'Donoghue. Tel: (020) 7610-3004. Fax: (078160) 821745. Website: www.intertextuality.com. E-mail: odonoghue.books@virgin.net. Est: 1994. Private premises. Internet. Large stock. Spec: Academic/Scholarly; Biography; Philosophy; Politics; Psychology/Psychiatry; Social Sciences. PR: £10–50. CC: MC; V; Switch. Also on: Ibooknet. VAT No: GB 751 8509 19. [Updated]

B.A. & C.W.M. Pratt, Huntington House, Huntington Lane, Hereford, HR4 7RA. Tel: (01432) 350927. Fax: (01432) 350927. Est: 1967. Private premises. Postal business only. Spec: Medicine. [Updated]

KINGTON

Castle Hill Books, ■ 12 Church Street, Kington, HR5 3AZ. Prop: Peter Newman. Tel: (01544) 231195. Fax: (01544) 231161. Website: www.castlehillbooks.co.uk. E-mail: sales@castlehillbooks.co.uk. Est: 1987. Shop open: **M:** 10:30–13:00; **T:** 10:30–13:00; **W:** 10:30–13:00; **Th:** 10:30–13:00; **F:** 10:30–13:00; **S:** 10:30–16:00. Very large stock. Spec: Academic/Scholarly; Agriculture; American Indians; Antiquarian; Archaeology; History - General; Natural History; Topography - General; Topography - Local. PR: £3–15,000. CC: MC; V. Also, new books. and maps in stock. Cata: 1 – lists sent on request. Mem: PBFA. VAT No: GB 489 2054 19. [Updated]

Courtyard Books, Gladestry, Kington, HR5 3NR. Prop: M Johnson. Tel: (01544) 370296. Website: www.courtyardbooks.org.uk. E-mail: info@courtyardbooks.org.uk. Est: 2002. Shop &/or showroom. Internet and postal. Telephone first. Open: **M:** 10:00–17:00; **T:** 10:00–17:00; **W:** 10:00–17:00; **Th:** 10:00–17:00; **F:** 10:00–17:00. Very small stock. Spec: Author - 20th Century; Author - Cornwell, Bernard; Author - Hemingway, Ernest; Author - Kerouac, Jack; Author - Le Carre, John; Author - Pinter, Harold; Author - Rankin, Ian; Author - Rushdie, Salman; Espionage; Fiction - Crime, Detective, Spy, Thrillers. PR: £8–300. CC: JCB; MC. Cata: 1 a year. [Updated]

Fineart Photographer, The Courtyard Barns, Gladestry, Kington, HR5 3NR. Prop: Michael Johnson. Tel: (01544) 370296. Website: www.fineart-photographer.com. Est: 2002. Shop &/or showroom. Internet and postal. Telephone first. Open: **M:** 10:00–17:00; **T:** 10:00–17:00; **W:** 10:10–17:00; **Th:** 10:00–17:00; **F:** 10:00–16:00. Very small stock. Spec: Art; Art - History; Fine Art; Illustrated; Photography. PR: £5–200. CC: MC; V. Cata: 1 a year. Also at: Courtyard Books, Kington (q.v.). [12/04/2003]

LEDBURY

David Thomas Motoring Books, ■ Redsul, Upperfields, Ledbury, HR8 1LE. Tel: (01531) 635114. Fax: (01531) 635114. Website: www.allautobooks.com. E-mail: davidthomas@tesco.net. Est: 1997. Appointment necessary. Shop at: New shop opening in Ledbury October 2003 - please contact for address. Medium stock. Spec: Motoring. PR: £3–500. CC: MC; V; Switch. Corresp: French, German, Italian. Mem: FSB. [19/08/2003]

Keith Smith Books, ■ 78b The Homend, Ledbury, HR8 1BX. Prop: Keith Smith. Tel: Day (01531) 635336. E-mail: keith@ksbooks.demon.co.uk. Est: 1986. Shop open: **M:** 10:00–17:00; **T:** 10:00–17:00; **W:** 10:00–17:00; **Th:** 10:00–17:00; **F:** 10:00–17:00; **S:** 10:00–17:00; Medium stock. Spec: Author - Dymock Poets, The; Author - Masefield, John; Embroidery; History - Local; Needlework; Poetry; Rugs; Topography - Local; War - World War I. PR: £1–250. CC: E; JCB; MC; V; De, SW. Cata: 4 a year. [Updated]

LEOMINSTER

Hummingbird Books, ■ 16 South Street, Leominster, HR6 8JB. Prop: Jill Gibbs. Tel: (01568) 616471. Website: hummingbirdbooks@btinternet.com. E-mail: hummingbirdbooks@btinternet.com. Est: 2001. Shop open: **M:** 10:00–17:30; **T:** 10:00–17:30; **Th:** 10:00–17:30; **F:** 10:00–17:30; **S:** 09:00–16:00; Medium stock. Spec: Maritime/Nautical; Military History; Sport - General. CC: MC; V. Also at: Concession at 6 Broad Street, Hay-on-Wye. [Updated]

ROSS–ON–WYE

Ross Old Books & Prints, ■ 51 & 52 High Street, Ross–on–Wye, HR9 5HH. Prop: Phil Thredder. Tel: +44 (0)1989 567458. Website: www.rossoldbooks.co.uk. E-mail: enquiries@rossoldbooks.co.uk. Est: 1986. Internet and postal. Shop at and open: **W:** 10:00–17:00; **Th:** 10:00–17:00; **F:** 10:00–17:00; **S:** 10:00–17:00; or by appointment. Medium stock. Spec: Folio Society, The; History - Local; Topography - General. PR: £1–500. CC: AE; MC; V; SW, SO. Also, British county maps. Mem: PBFA; BA. VAT No: GB 435389233. [Updated]

WEOBLEY

Hereford Booksearch (John Trev, Church Road, Weobley, HR4 8SD. Tel: 01544 318388. E-mail: john@trevitt.freeserve.co.uk. Est: 2004. Private premises. Postal business only. Appointment necessary. Very small stock. [Updated]

The Weobley Bookshop, ■ 5 Portland Street, Weobley, HR4 8SB. Tel: Shop (01544) 319292. Fax: (01544) 319292. E-mail: karen@grovedesign.co.uk. Est: 1999. Shop at: Broad Street Books, 18 Broad Street, Ludlow, Shropshire, SY8 1NG. Open: **T:** 10:00–17:00; **W:** 10:00–17:00; **Th:** 10:00–17:00; **F:** 10:00–17:00; **S:** 10:00–17:00. Medium stock. Spec: Booksearch. PR: £2–100. CC: MC; V. Mem: BA. VAT No: GB 489 1728 94. [11/05/2003]

HERTFORDSHIRE

BERKHAMSTEAD

David Mundy at Heritage Antiques, ■ 24 Castle Street, Berkhamstead, HP4 2DD. Prop: David Mundy. Tel: (020) 7482 7087. Est: 1994. Shop open: **M:** 10:00–17:30; **T:** 10:00–17:30; **W:** 10:00–17:30; **Th:** 10:00–17:30; **F:** 10:00–17:30; **S:** 10:00–17:30; **Su:** 10:00–17:30. Small stock. Spec: Antiques; Art; Fiction - General; History - General; Literature; Military; Sport - General; Topography - General; Topography - Local; Travel - General. PR: £1–50. CC: MC; V. Mem: Also at: Nooks & Crannies, Chesham, Bucks HP5 1HG (q.v.). [Updated]

Richard Frost, 'Sunhaven', Northchurch Common, Berkhamsted, HP4 1LR. Tel: (01442) 862011. E-mail: frost.family@freeuk.com. Est: 1989. Private premises. Book fairs only. Telephone first. Spec: Biography; First Editions; History - General; Literary Criticism; Philately; Topography - General; Travel - General. PR: £1–200. [Updated]

Red Star Books, 4 Hamilton Road, Berkhamsted, HP4 3EF. Prop: Conor Pattenden. Tel: (01442) 870775. Website: www.abebooks.com/home/conorpattenden. E-mail: redstarbooks@ btopenworld.com. Est: 2001. Private premises. Internet and postal. Appointment necessary. Medium stock. Spec: Academic/Scholarly; History - Anarchism; History - Labour/Radical Movements; Marxism; Politics; Radical Issues; Social History; Socialism; Trade Unions; War - Spanish Civil War. PR: £2–1,000. [Updated]

BISHOPS STORTFORD

www.AntiqueWatchStore.com, Grooms Cottage, Elsenham Hall, Bishops Stortford, CM22 6DP. Tel: 01279-814 946. Fax: 01279-814 962. Website: www.antiquewatchstore.com. E-mail: info@davidpenney.co.uk. Est: 1994. Private premises. Internet and postal. Appointment necessary. Very small stock. Spec: Antiques. CC: AE; MC; V. Mem: FBHI. VAT No: GB 354 3041 82. [Updated]

Sheila Rainford, White Pine Cottage, High St., Henham, Bishop's Stortford, CM22 6AS. Tel: (01279) 851129. Fax: (01279) 851129. E-mail: sheilarainford@talk21.com. Est: 1983. Private premises. Internet and postal. Small stock. Spec: Banking & Insurance; Cookery/Gastronomy; Economics; History - Industrial; Industry; Literature. PR: £5–1,000. CC: V. Cata: 2 annually. Corresp: French and German. Mem: PBFA. VAT No: GB 632 2122 89. [Updated]

Ray Smith, 'Lynwood', 111 Parsonage Lane, Bishop's Stortford, CM23 5BA. Tel: (01279) 324780. E-mail: raymond.smith63@ntlworld.com. Est: 1994. Postal business only. Spec: Travel - Africa. PR: £3–200. [Updated]

Edwin Trevorrow, 5 Pryors Close, Bishop's Stortford, CM23 5JX. Tel: (01279) 652902. E-mail: Est: 1994. Spec: Biography; Fiction - General; Fiction - Historical; Fiction - Science Fiction; First Editions; Literature; Modern First Editions; Vintage Paperbacks; also Booksearch. PR: £1–200. [30/08/2003]

BUSHEY

Aviation Book Supply, ■ 10 Pasture Close, Bushey, WD23 4HP. Prop: R.K. Tomlinson. Tel: (07831) 073531. Website: www.aero-shop.co.uk. Est: 1996. Shop. Appointment necessary. Medium stock. Spec: Aviation. PR: £5–250. CC: MC; V. Cata: 2 a year. [Updated]

CHESHUNT

Denis W. Amos, 10 Mill Lane, Cheshunt, Waltham Cross, EN8 0JH. Tel: (01992) 630486. Est: 1948. Private premises. Postal business only. Large stock. Spec: Gambling; Sport - General; Sport - Football (Soccer); Sport - Horse Racing (all aspects); Sport - Olympic Games, The; Sport - Racket Sports; Sport - Tennis; also Booksearch. [Updated]

Sheppard's Book Dealers in
JAPAN

Order the next printed edition – or search on www.sheppardsworld.co.uk

ELSTREE

Elstree Books, 12 West View Gardens, Elstree, WD6 3DD. Prop: Mrs. S. Herbert. Tel: (020) 8953-2999. Website: www.welcome.to/elstreebooks. E-mail: elstreebooks@hotmail.com. Est: 1991. Postal business only. Spec: Fine & Rare; First Editions; Illustrated; Limited Editions; Private Press; Signed Editions; Topography - General; Travel - General, also Booksearch. PR: £2–250. [Updated]

HARPENDEN

Mavis Eggle, 34 Cowper Road, Harpenden, AL5 5NG. Tel: (01582) 762603. Fax: (01582) 762603. Est: 1979. Private premises. Appointment necessary. Small stock. Spec: Antiquarian; Social History; Sport - Angling/Fishing; Technology. PR: £1–500. Mem: PBFA. [Updated]

HATFIELD

Edna Whiteson Ltd., 22 Cornflower Way, Hatfield, AL10 9FU. Tel: (01707) 647716. Fax: (01707) 647716. E-mail: ednawhiteson_books@lineone.net. Est: 1962. Private premises. Appointment necessary. Medium stock. Spec: First Editions; Limited Editions; Modern First Editions; Signed Editions; Topography - General; Travel - General, also Booksearch. Cata: 4 a year. Mem: ABA; PBFA. [01/07/2003]

HERTFORD

Gillmark Gallery, 25 Parliament Square, Hertford, SG14 1EX. Prop: Mark Pretlove & Gill Woodhouse. Tel: (01992) 534444. Fax: (01992) 554734. Website: www.gillmark.com. E-mail: gillmark@btinternet.com. Est: 1997. Market stand/stall. Open: **T:** 10:00–17:00; **W:** 10:00–17:00; **Th:** 10:00–14:00; **F:** 10:00–17:00; **S:** 10:00–05:00. Medium stock. Spec: Antiquarian; Atlases; Natural History; Topography - General; Topography - Local, also Booksearch. PR: £1–3,000. CC: AE; JCB; MC; V. VAT No: GB 740 8541 36. [Updated]

HITCHIN

Adrem Books, 7 Bury End, Pirton, Hitchin, SG5 3QB. Prop: David Braybrooke. Tel: (07778) 394923. Fax: (01462) 712668. E-mail: braybrooke35@aol.com. Est: 1990. Private premises. Internet and postal. Appointment necessary. Medium stock. Spec: Academic/Scholarly; Almanacs; Cartoons; Children's - General; Computing; Criminology; Fables; First Editions; Law; Literature; Music - General; Poetry; Technical; Travel - General; Typography; War - General. PR: £3–500. CC: AE; E; MC; V; PayPal. Cata: occasionally. Corresp: French. [Updated]

The Bookbug, 1, The Arcade, Hitchin, SG5 1ED. Prop: T.W. & S. Jevon. Tel: (01462) 431309. E-mail: Est: 1986. Spec: PR: £1–10. [28/08/2003]

Eric T. Moore Books, ■ 24 Bridge Street, Hitchin, SG5 2DF. Tel: (01462) 450497. Website: www.erictmoore.co.uk. E-mail: booksales@erictmoore.co.uk. Est: 1965. Shop open: **M:** 08:30–18:00; **T:** 08:30–18:00; **W:** 08:30–18:00; **Th:** 08:30–18:00; **F:** 08:30–18:00; **S:** 08:30–18:00; **Su:** 11:00–17:00. Very large stock. CC: MC; V. VAT No: GB 759 7801 77. [Updated]

Phillips of Hitchin (Antiques), ■ The Manor House, Hitchin, SG5 1JW. Prop: Jerome Phillips. Tel: (01462) 432067. Fax: (01462) 441368. Est: 1884. Shop open: **M:** 09:00–17:30; **T:** 09:00–17:30; **W:** 09:00–17:30; **Th:** 09:00–17:30; **F:** 09:00–17:30. Medium stock. Spec: Antiques; Applied Art; Architecture; Interior Design; Woodwork; also Booksearch. PR: £5–3,000. CC: AE; E; MC; V. Open Saturdays by appointment. Also, antique furniture. Cata: 1 a year. Corresp: French, German, Italian, Spanish, Russian, Portuguese. Mem: PBFA. VAT No: GB 197 1842 28. [Updated]

LETCHWORTH GARDEN CITY

Barry Meaden (Aviation Books), Silverbirch Cottages, 26 Station Road, Letchworth Garden City, SG6 3BE. Prop: Barry Meaden. Tel: (01462) 678912. Website: www.ukbookworld.com/members/spitfire. E-mail: barrymeaden@waitrose.com. Est: 1998. Private premises. Postal business only. Telephone first. Small stock. Spec: Aeronautics; Aviation; Military; Military History; Naval; War - World War I; War - World War II; also Booksearch. PR: £5–200. Cata: 4 a year on Aviation. [Updated]

RADLETT

G.L. Green Ltd., 18 Aldenham Avenue, Radlett, WD7 8HX. Prop: G. L. Grenn. Tel: (01923) 857077. Fax: (01923) 857077. Website: www.glgreen.com. E-mail: orders@glgreenbooks.com. Est: 1972. Storeroom. Internet and postal. Appointment necessary. Small general stock. Spec: Deep Sea Diving; Maritime/Nautical; Naval; Shipbuilding; War - World War I; War - World War II. PR: £1–1,000. CC: AE; JCB; V. Cata: 6 a year on naval & maritime. [Updated]

RICKMANSWORTH

Clive A. Burden Ltd., Elmcote House, The Green, Croxley Green, Rickmansworth, WD3 3HN. Tel: (01923) 778097. Fax: (01923) 896520. E-mail: pburdea@caburdea.com. Est: 1966. Private premises. Appointment aecessary. Spec: Academic/Scholarly; Atlases; Illustrated; Travel - Geaeral. PR: £5–10,000. Also, decorative books. Mem: ABA; ILAB; IMCoS. [updated]

SAINT ALBANS

Thomas Thorp, 64 Lancaster Road, St. Albans, AL1 4ET. Prop: J.H.Thorp. Tel: 01727 864778. Fax: (01727) 854778. Website: www.abebooks.com/home/thorpbooks. E-mail: thorpbooks@compuserve.com. Est: 1883. Private premises. Internet and postal. Appointment necessary. Very small stock. Spec: Antiquarian; Private Press. PR: £25–5,000. CC: MC; V. And on ILAB's web site. Cata: 1 a year. Mem: ABA; PBFA; ILAB. [Updated]

L.M.S. Books, 28 Orchard Street, St. Albans, AL3 4HL. Prop: Chris Fruin. Tel: (01727) 864339. Website: www.lmsbooks.co.uk. E-mail: lmsbooks@hotmail.com. Est: 1993. Office &/or bookroom; Appointment necessary. Medium stock. Spec: Author - Pratchett, Terry; Countries - Mexico; Fiction - General; First Editions; Literature; Modern First Editions; Mysteries; Signed Editions. PR: £10–350. CC: MC; V; SW. Also, a selection of stock at: Biblion, London W1. Cata: bi-monthly. [07/08/2003]

RM Books, 18 Cornwall Road, St. Albans, AL1 1SH. Prop: Robert Moore. Tel: (01727) 830058. Website: www.rmbooks.co.uk. E-mail: rmbooks@verulamium94.freeserve.co.uk. Est: 1988. Private premises. Postal business only. Very small stock. Spec: Medicine; Medicine - History of; Science - General; Science - History of. PR: £10–100. Cata: 1 a year on request. Mem: ABA; PBFA. [Updated]

TRING

David Ford Books, Midwood, Shire Lane, Cholesbury, Tring, HP23 6NA. Tel: (01494) 758663. E-mail: dford.books@ukgateway.net. Est: 1985. Private premises. Internet and postal. Telephone first. Large stock. Spec: Animals and Birds; Art - History; Cinema/Film; Egyptology; Fiction - General; First Editions; Gardening; History - General; History - Ancient; Military; Topography - General; Topography - Local; Travel - General. PR: £1–500. CC: JCB; MC; V. Mem: PBFA. Also at: Hertford Antique Centre, St Andrews St., Hertford and The Gillmark Gallery, Parliament Square, Hertford. [Updated]

WATFORD

G. & R. Leapman Ltd., 37 Hogarth Court, High Street, Bushey, Watford, WD23 1BT. (*) Prop: Gillian Leapman. Tel: (020) 8950-2995. Fax: (020) 8950-4131. E-mail: gleapman1@compuserve.com. Est: 1970. Private premises. Appointment necessary. Very small stock. Spec: Countries - Caribbean, The; Travel - Americas, also Booksearch. PR: £10–1,000. [Updated]

Peter Taylor & Son, 1 Ganders Ash, Leavesden, Watford, WD25 7HE. Tel: (01923) 663325. E-mail: taylorbooks@clara.co.uk. Est: 1973. Storeroom. Postal business only. Medium stock. Spec: Academic/Scholarly; Antiquarian; Archaeology; Art - History; Bibliography; Biography; Ecclesiastical History & Architecture; Fine & Rare; Heraldry; History - British; History - Irish; History - Local; History of Civilisation; History of Ideas. PR: £15–1,000. CC: MC; V. Cata: 4 a year on the Middle Ages, Renaissance & early modern British history. Corresp: French. [Updated]

Westons Booksellers Ltd., 44 Stratford Road, Watford, WD17 4NZ. Prop: Jeremy Weston. Tel: (01923) 229081. Fax: (01923) 243343. Website: www.westons.co.uk. E-mail: books@westons.co.uk. Est: 1977. Private premises. Appointment necessary. Medium stock. Spec: Engineering; Medicine; Science - General; Technology. PR: £3–300. CC: E; MC; V. Cata: 11 a year and on the internet. VAT No: GB 225 0259 93. [Updated]

Norman Wright, 60 Eastbury Road, Watford, WD19 4JL. Tel: (01923) 232383. Est: 1989. Private premises. Postal business only. Small stock. Spec: Children's - General; Comic Books & Annuals; Comics. PR: £5–500. Cata: 4 a year on specialities. [Updated]

ISLE OF WIGHT

BEMBRIDGE

Black & White Books, 7 The Ruskins, King's Road, Bembridge, PO35 5NY. Prop: M.T. Kirk. Tel: 01983 875494. Website: www.ukbookworld.com. E-mail: m.kirk@which.net. Est: 1990. Private premises. Internet and postal. Appointment necessary. Very small general stock. Spec: Booksearch. PR: £4–100. Also at: Books for sale at the Hungerford Arcade, Berkshire. [30/07/2003]

COWES

Curtle Mead Books, Curtle Mead, Baring Road, Cowes, PO31 8DS. Prop: John Lucas. Tel: (01983) 294312. E-mail: lucas@curtlemead.demon.co.uk. Est: 1999. Private premises. Telephone first. Medium stock. Spec: Maritime/Nautical; Natural History; Naval; Navigation; Ornithology; Ship Modelling; Shipbuilding; Sport - Yachting; Topography - Local; also Booksearch. PR: £1–500. Cata: occasional. Corresp: German. Mem: PBFA. [Updated]

FRESHWATER

David G. Bancroft, Little Orchard, Court Road, Freshwater, PO40 9NU. Tel: (01983) 759069. Est: 1995. Private premises. Postal business only. Open: **M:** 08:00–21:00; **T:** 08:00–21:00; **W:** 08:00–21:00; **Th:** 08:00–21:00; **F:** 08:00–21:00; **S:** 08:00–21:00 **Su:** 08:00–00:00. Small stock. Spec: Aviation. PR: £3–150. Catalogues also include gliding and technical aspects of aviation. Cata: 6 a year on aviation: pioneer, military, civil, WW1, WWII. [Updated]

Cameron House Books, ■ Dimbola Lodge, Terrace Lane, Freshwater, PO40 9QE. Prop: L.J. Sklaroff. Tel: (01983) 754960. Fax: (01983) 755578. Website: www.cameronhousebooks.com. E-mail: ljs@cambooks-dimbola.freeserve.co.uk. Est: 1994. Internet and postal. Shop open: **T:** 10:00–16:00; **W:** 10:00–16:00; **Th:** 10:00–16:00; **F:** 10:00–16:00; **S:** 10:00–16:00; **Su:** 10:00–16:00. Medium stock. Spec: Author - Cameron, Julia Margaret; Author - Keeping, Charles; Author - Peake, Mervyn; Author - Tennyson, Lord Alfred; Fine & Rare; First Editions; Illustrated; Limited Editions; Literature; Modern First Editions; Photography; Poetry; Private Press. PR: £1–3,000. Also, a booksearch service. Corresp: French, German, Spanish. Mem: PLA. [Updated]

NEWPORT

Firsts in Print, 95 St. John's Road, Newport, PO30 1LS. Prop: Peter Elliston. Tel: (01983) 521748. Website: www.firsts-in-print.co.uk. E-mail: peter@firsts-in-print.co.uk. Est: 1984. Private premises. Internet and postal. Appointment necessary. Shop at: Corner House, 68-70 Lugley St, Newport, Isle of Wight. Open: **M:** 09:00–17:00; **T:** 09:00–17:00; **W:** 09:00–17:00; **Th:** 09:00–17:00; **F:** 09:00–17:00. Medium stock. Spec: Literature; Modern First Editions; Proof Copies; Signed Editions. PR: £3–1,000. CC: MC; V; Switch. Cata: 5 - Every two months. VAT No: GB 768 9507 66. [Updated]

RYDE

Heritage Books, ■ 7 Cross Street, Ryde, PO33 2AD. Prop: Rev. D.H. Nearn. Tel: (01983) 562933. Fax: (01983) 812634. E-mail: heritagebooksryde@btconnect.com. Est: 1978. Shop open: **M:** 10:00–17:00; **T:** 10:00–17:00; **W:** 10:00–17:00; **F:** 10:00–17:00; **S:** 10:00–17:00. Large general stock. Spec: Countries - Africa; Countries - Isle of Wight; Theology. PR: £1–500. CC: MC; V. Corresp: French, Portuguese. VAT No: GB 339 0615 58. [Updated]

The Ryde Bookshop, ■ 135 High Street, Ryde, PO33 2RJ. Prop: M.D. Sames. Tel: (01983) 565227. Est: 1988. Shop open: **M:** 08:30–17:45; **T:** 08:30–17:45; **W:** 08:30–17:00; **Th:** 08:30–17:00; **F:** 08:30–17:45; **S:** 08:30–17:45. Very large general stock. CC: AE; E; JCB; MC; V. Also, new books. [Updated]

SAINT HELENS

Mother Goose Bookshop, West Green House, Upper Green Road, St. Helens. Prop: Valerie Edmondson. Tel: shop (01983) 874063. E-mail: mothergoosebooks@lycos.com. Est: 1980. Spec: Alpinism/Mountaineering; Author - General; Maritime/Nautical; Military. PR: £300–3,000. [28/08/2003]

VENTNOR

Shirley Lane Books, St. Lawrence Dene, Undercliff Drive, Ventnor, PO38 1XJ. Prop: Shirley Lane. Tel: (01983) 852309. Website: www.ukbookworld.com/members/Shirleylane. E-mail: shirleylane@talk21.com. Est: 1976. Private premises. Internet and postal. Appointment necessary. Small stock. Spec: Authors - Women; Feminism; Women. PR: £1–500. Corresp: French. [Updated]

Ventnor Rare Books, ■ 32 Pier Street, Ventnor, PO38 1SX. Prop: Nigel & Teresa Traylen. Tel: (01983) 853706. Fax: (01983) 854706. E-mail: vrb@andytron.demon.co.uk. Est: 1989. Shop open: **M:** 10:00–17:00; **T:** 10:00–17:00; **Th:** 10:00–17:00; **F:** 10:00–17:00; **S:** 10:00–17:00; Medium stock. Spec: Academic/Scholarly; Antiquarian; Art - Reference; Bibliography; Bindings; Fiction - General; Literature; Military History; Royalty - General; Topography - General; Topography - Local; Transport. PR: £1–500. CC: MC; V; UK Switch. Corresp: French. Mem: ABA; PBFA; ILAB. VAT No: GB 566 5246 19. [Updated]

YARMOUTH

Alan Argent, Two Ways, Sconce Road, Norton, Yarmouth, PO41 0RT. Tel: (01983) 760851. Storeroom. Appointment necessary. Very small stock. Spec: Maritime/Nautical. PR: £3–100. Also, attends the occasional bookfair. [Updated]

KENT

ASHFORD

D.R. & A.K. Flawn, 42 Magazine Road, Ashford, TN24 8NT. Prop: David Richard Flawn, Anna Flawn. Tel: (01233) 638217. E-mail: familyflawn@dungeon.netlink.co.uk. Est: 1990. Private premises. Postal business only. Small stock. Spec: Law; Medicine - History of; Sport - Cricket; Sport - Rowing; also Booksearch. PR: £1–120. Corresp: French. [01/09/2003]

Woodside Books, 1 Woodside Cottages, Westwell Lane, Ashford, TN26 1JB. Prop: Ann Gipps. Tel: (01233) 624495. E-mail: ann.gipps@btinternet.com. Est: 1991. Private premises. Internet and postal. Appointment necessary. Very small stock. Spec: Botany; Entomology; Natural History; Ornithology. PR: £1–500. CC: MC; V. Cata: 4 – 3 monthly. [Updated]

BECKENHAM

Julia Sesemann, 10 Kemerton Road, Beckenham, BR3 6NJ. Tel: (020) 8658-6123. Est: 1977. Private premises. Appointment necessary. Very small stock. Spec: Author - Blyton, Enid; Children's - General; Comic Books & Annuals; Illustrated; Juvenile. PR: £2–250. Cata: occasionally. [Updated]

BIDDENHAM

P.R. & V. Sabin (Printed Works, Saxton House, The Nightingales, Biddenden, TN27 8HN. Tel: (01580) 715603. Fax: (01580) 714603. E-mail: paulsabin@btopenworld.com. Private premises. Appointment necessary. Medium stock. Spec: Illustrated; Limited Editions; Private Press. Mem: PBFA. [Updated]

BROMLEY (SEE ALSO BROMLEY IN GREATER LONDON OUTER)

Barry Chambers, 55 Recreation Road, Shortlands, Bromley, BR2 0DY. (*). Tel: (020) 8464-7354. E-mail: barrychambers@onetel.net.uk. Est: 1997. Private premises. Postal business only. Very small stock. Spec: Natural History; Ornithology. [14/04/2003]

CANTERBURY

The Canterbury Bookshop, ■ 37 Northgate, Canterbury, CT1 1BL. Prop: David Miles. Tel: (01227) 464773. Fax: (01227) 780073. E-mail: canterburybookshop@btconnect.com. Est: 1980. Shop open: **M:** 10:00–17:00; **T:** 10:00–17:00; **W:** 10:00–17:00; **Th:** 10:00–17:00; **F:** 10:00–17:00; **S:** 10:00–17:00. Small stock. Spec: Children's - General; Illustrated; Juvenile; Typography. PR: £1–2,000. CC: MC; V. Fairs attended: all London, ABA, Olympia, Chelsea and in USA. Cata: occasionally. Mem: ABA; PBFA; ILAB. [29/06/2003]

The Chaucer Bookshop, ■ 6 & 7 Beer Cart Lane, Canterbury, CT1 2NY. Prop: Sir Robert Sherston–Baker, Bt. Tel: (01227) 453912. Fax: (01227) 451893. Website: www.chaucer-bookshop.co.uk. E-mail: chaucerbooks@btconnect.com. Est: 1956. Shop open: **M:** 10:00–17:00; **T:** 10:00–17:00; **W:** 10:00–17:00; **Th:** 10:00–17:00; **F:** 10:00–17:00; **S:** 10:00–17:00. Large stock. Spec: Antiquarian; Archaeology; Art; Bindings; Biography; History - General; Topography - General; Topography - Local. PR: £5–150. CC: AE; D; E; JCB; MC; V; SW. Mem: ABA; PBFA. VAT No: GB 332 9825 44. [Updated]

Little Stour Books, North Court House, West Stourmouth, Nr Preston, Canterbury, CT3 1HT. Prop: Colin Button. Tel: (01227) 722371. Fax: (01227) 722021. Website: www.littlestourbooks.com. E-mail: sales@littlestourbooks.com. Est: 1996. Private premises. Internet and postal. Appointment necessary. Large stock. Spec: Author - Blyton, Enid; Author - Buckeridge, A.; Author - Crompton, Richmal; Author - Henty, G.A.; Author - Johns, W.E.; Author - Maclean, Alistair; Author - Oxenham, Elsie; Author - Rackham, Arthur; Author - Wodehouse, P.G.; Children's - General. PR: £6–500. CC: JCB; MC; V; SW, SO. Cata: 4 a year. Mem: PBFA. [Updated]

Oast Books, 1 Denstead Oast, Chartham Hatch, Canterbury, CT4 7SH. Prop: Bill & Jennie Reading. Tel: (01227) 730808. Website: members.aol.com/oastbooks/home.htm. E-mail: oastbooks@aol.com. Est: 1997. Market stand/stall. Postal business only. Small stock. Spec: Counselling; Psychoanalysis; Psychology/Psychiatry; Psychotherapy. PR: £2–40. CC: Paypal. Cata: 3 a year. [Updated]

Periwinkle Press, ■ 197 Ashford Road, Canterbury, CT1 3XS. Prop: Antony & Clare Swain. Tel: (01227) 768516. E-mail: cswain1805@aol.com. Est: 1968. Internet and postal. Shop at: Faversham Antique Centre,7 Court Street, Faversham, (01795) 591471. Open: **M:** 10:00–17:00; **T:** 10:00–17:00; **W:** 10:00–14:00; **Th:** 10:00–17:00; **F:** 10:00–17:00; **S:** 10:00–17:00. Medium stock. Spec: Author - Ardizzone, Edward; Children's - General; Self-Sufficiency; Topography - Local. PR: £1–100. CC: AE; JCB; V. Also, print and picture restoration, picture framing. [10/05/2003]

Tiger Books, Yew Tree Cottage, Westbere, Canterbury, CT2 0HH. Prop: Dr. Bryan & Mrs. Sylvia Harlow. Tel: (01227) 710030. Fax: (01227) 712066. E-mail: tiger@sharlow.fsbusiness.co.uk. Est: 1988. Private premises. Internet and postal. Appointment necessary. Large stock. Spec: Antiquarian; Author - Dickens, Charles; Fiction - Women; Literary Travel; Literature; Literature in Translation; Periodicals & Magazines; also Booksearch. PR: £10–5,500. CC: E; JCB; MC; V. Cata: 6 on specialities. Mem: ABA; BA; ILAB. [Updated]

CHATHAM

Roadmaster Books, P.O. Box 176, Chatham, ME5 9AQ. Prop: Malcolm & Sue Wright. Tel: (01634) 862843. Fax: (01634) 201555. E-mail: info@roadmasterbooks.co.uk. Est: 1976. Private premises. Postal business only. Spec: Canals/Inland Waterways; Company History; Conservation; Dolls & Dolls' Houses; Flower Arranging; Geography; Geology; Motoring; Publishers - David & Charles; Publishing; Railways; Rural Life; Shipbuilding; Social History; Steam Engines; Topography - Local. PR: £1–350. Cata: quarterly transport, annually-general. Corresp: French. VAT No: GB 619300952. [Updated]

Sandstone Books, 14 Seymour Road, Chatham, ME5 7AE. Tel: (01634) 306437. Website: www.sandstonebooks.co.uk. E-mail: verne@sandstonebooks.co.uk. Est: 1989. Private premises. Internet and postal. Appointment necessary. Open: **M:** 09:00–20:00; **T:** 09:00–20:00; **W:** 09:00–20:00; **Th:** 09:00–20:00; **F:** 09:00–20:00; **S:** 09:00–20:00; **Su:** 09:00–20:00. Small stock. Spec: Modern First Editions. PR: £10–500. Cata: 4 a year. [17/06/2003]

DARTFORD

Douglas Biswell, 3 Keith Ave., Sutton at Hone, Dartford, DA4 9HH. Tel: (01322) 225522. E-mail: dougrbiswell@aol.com. Postal business only. Very small stock. Spec: Astronomy. PR: £1–1,000. [11/05/2003]

Third Reich Books, 34 Walnut Tree Avenue, Dartford, DA1 1LJ. Prop: Mr. Jeremy Dixon. Tel: (01322) 279026. Fax: (01322) 279026. Website: www.thirdreichbooks.com. E-mail: trbooks@aol.com. Est: 1991. Private premises. Postal business only. Telephone first. Very small stock. Spec: Holocaust; Memoirs; Military History; War - World War II. PR: £5–300. Also, a booksearch (Nazi Germany only). [10/05/2003]

DEAL

Books, ■ 168 High Street, Deal, CT14 6BQ. Prop: Peter Ritchie. Tel: (01304) 368662. Shop open: **Th:** 10:00–17:00; **F:** 10:00–17:00; **S:** 10:00–17:00. Medium stock. Spec: Antiques; Architecture; Art; Collecting. PR: £2–300. [Updated]

J. Clarke–Hall Limited, 75 Middle Street, Deal, CT14 6HN. Prop: S.M. Edgecombe. Tel: (01304) 375467. Est: 1934. Private premises. Appointment necessary. Very small general stock. Spec: PR: £5–750. Attends Bonnington Fair in June. Cata: occasionally on Samuel Johnson and his world. [08/07/2003]

The Golden Hind Bookshop, ■ 85 Beach Street, Deal, CT14 6JB. Prop: Josephine & Colin Whittington. Tel: (01304) 375086/37553. Fax: (01304) 375533. E-mail: goldenhind@freeuk.co.uk. Est: 1989. Shop open: **Th:** 10:30–17:00; **F:** 10:30–17:00; **S:** 10:30–17:00; **Su:** 10:30–17:00. Medium stock. Spec: Biography; Children's - General; Fiction - General; History - General; Humour; Military; Poetry; Topography - General; Topography - Local; War - General. PR: £1–100. Corresp: French, Spanish, German, Italian. [16/03/2003]

McConnell Fine Books, ■ The Golden Hind, 85 Beach Street, Deal, CT14 6JB. Prop: Nick McConnell. Tel: (01304) 375086. Website: www.abebooks.com/home/sandwichfinebooks. E-mail: mcconnellbooks@aol.com. Est: 1972. Shop. Telephone first. Open: **W:** 10:30–17:00; **Th:** 10:30–17:00; **F:** 10:30–17:00; **S:** 10:30–17:00. Medium stock. Spec: Antiquarian; Bindings; Maritime/Nautical. PR: £2–1,000. CC: MC; V. Corresp: French, Russian. Mem: ABA; PBFA; ILAB. [Updated]

Twiggers Booksearch, 44 The Strand, Walmer, Deal, CT14 7DX. Prop: M. Thiry. Tel: (013)0436 5511. Fax: (013)0437 5209. Website: www.twiggers.com. E-mail: booksearch @twiggers.com. Est: 1980. Private premises. Postal business only. Contactable: M: 09:00–17:30; T: 09:00–17:30; W: 09:00–17:30; Th: 09:00–17:30; F: 09:00–17:30; S: 10:00–16:00. Very small general stock. Spec: Booksearch. CC: SW. VAT No: GB 726 1475 36. [Updated]

DOVER

Pat Castleton, 26 Kearsney Avenue, Dover, CT16 3BU. Prop: Pat Castleton. Tel: (01304) 330371. Website: www.abebooks.com/home/PATCASTLETON. E-mail: patriciacastleton@hotmail.com. Est: 1992. Private premises. Internet and postal. Telephone first. Small general stock. Spec: Academic/Scholarly; Agriculture; Animals and Birds; Author - General; Author - 20th Century; Biography; Botany; Cats; Children's - General; Children's - Illustrated; Christmas; Cookery/Gastronomy; Dogs; Farming & Livestock; Fiction - General. PR: £5–50. Also stock shown on www.ukbookworld.com/members/patcastleton and www.ukbookworld.com. Corresp: French. [Updated]

EGERTON

Mindreaders Books, Forstal Corner Cottage, Egerton, TN27 9EH. (*) Prop: Ali Jones. Tel: (01233) 756490. E-mail: info@mindreaders.co.uk. Est: 2000. Private premises. Internet and postal. Small stock. Spec: Psychotherapy. PR: £1–50. CC: MC; V. [09/09/2003]

FARNBOROUGH

Lewis First Editions, 9 Ferndale Way, Farnborough, BR6 7EL. Prop: David Fordyce. Tel: (01689) 854261. Website: www.abebooks.com/home/davidfordyce/. Est: 2000. Internet and postal. Small stock. Spec: Author - Lewis, C.S.; Author - Saville, M.; Author - Shute, Neville; Modern First Editions. PR: £5–2,000. [09/05/2003]

FARNINGHAM

Wadard Books, ■ 6 High Street, Farningham, DA4 0DG. Tel: (01322) 863151. E-mail: wadardbooks@ btinternet.com. Est: 2001. Shop open: T: 10:00–18:00; Th: 10:00–18:00; F: 10:00–18:00; S: 10:00–18:00; Medium stock. Spec: Alchemy; Antiquarian; Art; Aviation; Children's - Early Titles; Children's - General; Children's - Illustrated; Churchilliana; Cookery/Gastronomy; Culture - Foreign; Fiction - General; Gardening; Herbalism; Military; Natural History; Naval. PR: £1–5,000. CC: AE; JCB; MC; V. VAT No: GB 586 5906 86. [Updated]

FAVERSHAM

Faversham Antique Centre, ■ 7 Court Street, Faversham, ME13 QBS. Prop: Antony Swain. Tel: (01795) 591471. Website: cswain1805@aol.com. E-mail: cswain1805@aol.com. Est: 1968. Internet and postal. Shop at: Periwinkle Press , 197 Ashford Road, Canterbury, Kent. CT1 3XS. Open: M: 10:00–17:00; T: 10:00–17:00; W: 10:00–14:30; Th: 10:00–17:00; F: 10:00–17:00; S: 10:00–17:00. Very small general stock. Spec: Topography - Local, also Booksearch. PR: £1–100. CC: MC; V. [16/05/2003]

Faversham Books, 49 South Road, Faversham, ME13 7LS. Prop: Mr. & Mrs. C.M. Ardley. Tel: (01795) 532873. Est: 1979. Postal business only. Spec: Author - Kipling, Rudyard. PR: £1–500. [updated]

John O'Kill, 'Coulthorn Lodge', 9 Ospringe Road, Faversham, ME13 7LJ. Tel: (01795) 534510. E-mail: john.o'kill@virgin.net. Est: 1990. Private premises. Postal business only. Small general stock. Spec: Antiquarian; Illustrated. PR: £1–500. [Updated]

FOLKESTONE

Jenny Hurst, The Old Coach House, Rectory Lane, Lyminge CT18 8EG. Tel: (01303) 862693. Website: www.abebooks.com. E-mail: intabooks@btopenworld.com. Private premises. Internet and postal business only. Medium stock. Spec: Architecture; Art; Autobiography; Biography; Children's; Fiction - General; History - General; Military; Music - General; Philosophy; Politics; Pschic; Physchology/Psychiatry; Science - General; Travel - General. PR: £5–100. CC: Paypal via abebooks.com, and cheques drawn on sterling banks only. Also, large print books.

Marrin's Bookshop, ■ 149 Sandgate Road, Folkestone, CT20 2DA. Prop: Patrick Marrin. Tel: (01303) 253016. Fax: (01303) 850956. Website: www.marrinbook.co.uk. E-mail: enquiries@ marrinbook.co.uk/marrinbook@clara.co.uk. Est: 1940. Shop open: T: 09:30–17:30; W: 09:30–17:30; Th: 09:30–17:30; F: 09:30–17:30; S: 09:30–17:30. Medium stock. Spec: Antiquarian; Fine & Rare; History - Local; Incunabula; Topography - Local. PR: £1–5,000. CC: MC; V; Debit. Cata: 4 a year – Kent topography. Mem: ABA; PBFA; ILAB. VAT No: GB 316 6132 80. [Updated]

MilitaryHistoryBooks.com, PO Box 590, Folkestone, CT20 2WX. Prop: Ian H. & Gillian M. Knight. Tel: (01303) 246500. Fax: (01303) 245133. Website: www.militaryhistorybooks.com. E-mail: info@militaryhistorybooks.com. Est: 1970. Private premises. Internet and postal. Open: **M:** 10:00–17:00; **T:** 10:00–17:00; **W:** 10:00–17:00; **Th:** 10:00–17:00; **F:** 10:00–17:00; **S:** 09:00–14:00. Large stock. Spec: Arms & Armour; Aviation; Espionage; Firearms/Guns; Military; Military History; War - General; Wargames; also Booksearch. PR: £10–500. CC: AE; D; E; JCB; MC; V; SW. Cata: 4 – quarterly. VAT No: GB 770 7124 36. [Updated]

Nick Spurrier, 27 Plain Road, Folkestone, CT20 2QF. Tel: (01303) 246100. Fax: (01303) 245800. Website: www.nick-spurrier.co.uk. E-mail: spurrier@btconnect.com. Est: 1977. Private premises. Internet and postal. Appointment necessary. Medium stock. Spec: Black Studies; Company History; Economics; Feminism; History - General; Marxism; Pacifism; Philosophy; Politics; Psychology/Psychiatry; Radical Issues; Socialism; Trade Unions; War - General; Women; also Booksearch. PR: £1–50. CC: JCB; MC. Cata: 8 – on economic history & other specialities. VAT No: GB 362 1931 64. [Updated]

GRAVESEND

L.J. Berry Books and Pictures, 4, Manor Road, Gravesend, DA12 1AA. Tel: (020) 8854-6753. E-mail: lesberry@berrybooks.freeserve.co.uk. Est: 1987. Shop &/or gallery. Open: **F:** 10:30–17:30; **S:** 09:00–17:00. Spec: Archaeology; Architecture; Art; Art - History; Art - Reference; Design; Fine Art; History - General; History - Ancient; Literary Criticism; Military History; Photography; War - World War I; War - World War II. PR: £5–200. [Updated]

HERNE BAY

Barber Music, 85 Sea Street, Herne Bay, CT6 8QQ. Prop: Denis M. Allen. Tel: (01227) 375341. E-mail: Est: 2000. Spec: Dance; Music - General; Musical Instruments. PR: £1–20. [28/08/2003]

Herne Bay Books, 22 Western Esplanade, Herne Bay, CT6 8RW. Prop: Mr. R.J.C. Eburne (Dick). Tel: (01227) 743201. E-mail: dickeburne@yahoo.co.uk. Est: 1995. Private premises. Postal business only. Appointment necessary. Small general stock. PR: £1–20. [22/12/2004]

HYTHE

The Old Gallery Bookshop, ■ 125 High Street, Hythe, CT21 5JJ. Prop: David & Philippa Hadaway. Tel: (01303) 269339. Est: 1990. Shop open: **M:** 10:00–17:00; **T:** 10:00–17:00; **W:** 10:00–13:00; **Th:** 10:00–17:00; **F:** 10:00–17:00; **S:** 09:00–17:00. Medium stock. Spec: Aviation; Maritime/Nautical; Military; Motoring; Ornithology; Railways; Transport. PR: £1–400. CC: E; MC; V. Winter: open 10:00 to 16:00 and closed Wednesday and Sunday. [Updated]

LEIGH

Peter Davis, Old Farm Cottage, Lealands Avenue, Leigh, Tonbridge, TN11 8QU. Tel: (01732) 832275. Est: 1984. Private premises. Appointment necessary. Small stock. Spec: Circus; Entertainment - General; Fairgrounds; Magic & Conjuring; Music - Music Hall; Performing Arts; Puppets & Marionettes. PR: £2–100. *Also at:* Kent Book Fairs. Corresp: French, German. [27/04/2003]

LYMINGE

Scott Brinded, 17 Greenbanks, Lyminge, CT18 8HG. Tel: (01303) 862258. Fax: (01303) 862660. Est: 1991. Private premises. Postal business only. Small stock. Spec: Antiquarian; Bibliography; Books about Books; Literature; Palaeography; Papermaking; Printing; Topography - General; Typography. PR: £1–5,000. CC: MC; V. Cata: 2 a year. [Updated]

MAIDSTONE

Peter Blest, Little Canon Cottage, Wateringbury, Maidstone, ME18 5PJ. Prop: Peter & Jan Blest. Tel: (01622) 812940. Est: 1974. Private premises. Postal business only. Very large stock. Spec: Agriculture; Animals and Birds; Botany; Cockfighting; Entomology; Flower Arranging; Gardening; Herbalism; Herpetology; Horticulture; Natural History; New Naturalist; Ornithology; Plant Hunting; Poultry; Rural Life; Sport - Angling/Fishing. PR: £5–5,000. CC: E; MC; V. Cata: 1 on natural history, gardening, field sports. Mem: PBFA. [22/08/2002]

Cobnar Books, 567 Red Hill, Wateringbury, Maidstone, ME18 5BE. Prop: Larry Ilott. Tel: (01622) 813230. Fax: (0870) 0567232. Website: books@cobnar.co.uk. E-mail: books@cobnar.demon.co.uk. Private premises. Postal business only. Appointment necessary. Spec: Antiquarian; Bibliography; Printing; Topography - Local. PR: £10–2,000. CC: MC; V. Cata: occasionally. Mem: PBFA. VAT No: GB 702 4681 56. [04/06/2003]

Jill Howell, Photographic Book, Hopview Cottage, 1, Hilltop, Hunton, Maidstone, ME15 0QP. Prop:Jill Howell. Tel: (01622) 820899. Fax: (01622) 820899. E-mail: jillphotobooks@aol.com. Est: 1993. Private premises. Postal business only. Appointment necessary. Small stock. PR: £3–1,500. Also, a booksearch service in specialist subject only. Cata: 3 Photography. Corresp: French. Mem: PBFA. [Updated]

MARGATE

Sun House Books, 72 Northumberland Avenue, Margate, CT9 3LY. Tel: (0709) 2841342. Fax: (0709) 2024636. Website: www.sunhousebooks.co.uk. E-mail: sales@sunhousebooks.co.uk. Est: 1999. Private premises. Internet. Appointment necessary. Small stock. Spec: Academic/Scholarly; Architecture; Civil Engineering; Ecclesiastical History & Architecture; Engineering; History - Design; Interior Design; Teaching; Town Planning; Urban History. PR: £3–200. CC: Paypal. [Updated]

ORPINGTON

Roland Books, 60 Birchwood Road, Petts Wood, Orpington, BR5 1NZ. Prop: A.R. Hughes. Tel: (01689) 838872. Fax: (01689) 838872. E-mail: py32@dial.pipex.com. Private premises. Internet and postal. Open: **M:** 09:00–17:00; **T:** 09:00–17:00; **W:** 09:00–17:00; **Th:** 09:00–17:00; **F:** 09:00–17:00. Medium stock. Spec: Architecture; Art; Buses/Trams; Business Studies; Crime (True); Entertainment - General; Fiction - General; History - General; Military History; Motoring; Music - Rock; Natural History; Philosophy; Railways; Sport - General; Transport; Travel - PR: £1–75. CC: MC; V; Switch. [Updated]

RAINHAM

The Book Mark, Unit 15c, Rainham Shopping Centre, Rainham, ME8 9HW. Prop: G. Harrison. Tel: (01634) 365987. Est: 1992. PR: £1–30. [28/08/2003]

RAMSGATE

michaelsbookshop.com, ■ 72 King St., Ramsgate, CT11 8NY. Prop: Michael Child. Tel: (01843) 589500. Website: www.michaelsbookshop.com. E-mail: michaelsbookshop@aol.com. Est: 1984. Internet and postal. Shop open: **M:** 09:30–17:30; **T:** 09:30–17:30; **W:** 09:30–17:30; **Th:** 09:30–17:30; **F:** 09:30–17:30; **S:** 09:30–17:30; **Su:** 11:00–16:00. Very large general stock. Spec: PR: £1–100. CC: MC; V. [11/04/2003]

Yesteryear Railwayana, Stablings Cottage, Goodwin Road, Ramsgate, CT11 0JJ. Prop: Patrick & Mary Mullen. Tel: 01843 587283. Fax: 01843 587283. Website: www.yesrail.com. E-mail: mullen@yesrail.com. Est: 1978. Private premises. Internet and postal. Large stock. Spec: Railways. PR: £1–500. CC: AE; JCB; MC. Cata: 9 every six weeks. [Updated]

ROCHESTER

Baggins Book Bazaar Ltd., ■ 19 High Street, Rochester, ME1 1PY. Manager: Godfrey George. Tel: (01634) 811651. Fax: (01634) 840591. Website: www.bagginsbooks.co.uk. E-mail: godfreygeorge@btconnect.com. Est: 1986. Shop open: **M:** 10:00–18:00; **T:** 10:00–18:00; **W:** 10:00–18:00; **Th:** 10:00–18:00; **F:** 10:00–18:00; **S:** 10:00–18:00; **Su:** 10:00–18:00. Very large general stock. Spec: Booksearch. PR: £1–200. CC: AE; D; E; JCB; MC; V; Maestro. Cata: misc. see list on abebooks. VAT No: GB 472 9061 36. [Updated]

Stained Glass Books, 13, Parkfields, Rochester, ME2 2TW. Prop: K.R. & S.J. Hill. Tel: (01634)719050. Website: www.glassconservation.com. E-mail: bookmail@glassconservation.com. Est: 1987. Private premises. Postal business only. Contactable. Very small stock. Spec: Glass; Stained Glass. PR: £5–500. [Updated]

SEVENOAKS

Roderick M. Barron, The Antiq, P.O. Box 67, Sevenoaks, TN13 3WW. Tel: (01732) 742558. Fax: (01732) 742558. Website: www.barron.co.uk. E-mail: rod@barron.co.uk. Est: 1989. Postal business only. Spec: Atlases. PR: £100–10,000. [15/05/2003]

Felstead Books, Phildon Lodge, Seal Hollow Road, Sevenoaks, TN13 3SL. Prop: P.M. Smith. Tel: (01732) 456928. Fax: (01732) 740253. E-mail: smith@phildon.freeserve.co.uk. Est: 1979. Postal business only. Small stock. Spec: Genealogy; Heraldry; also Booksearch. PR: £20–1,000. [Updated]

Garwood & Voigt, 55 Bayham Road, Sevenoaks, TN13 3XE. Prop: Nigel Garwood & Rainer G. Voigt. Tel: (01732) 460025. Fax: (01732) 460026. Website: www.garwood-voigt.com. E-mail: gv@garwood-voigt.com. Est: 1977. Office &/or bookroom. Appointment necessary. Small stock. Spec: Atlases; Cookery/Gastronomy. CC: E; MC; V. Corresp: German, French. Mem: ABA; PBFA; ILAB; IMCoS. [Updated]

Chas J. Sawyer, P.O. Box 170, Sevenoaks, TN13 3QF. Tel: (01732) 457262. Fax: (01732) 742026. E-mail: cjsbks@compuserve.com. Est: 1894. Private premises. Appointment necessary. Very small stock. Spec: Africana; Bibliography; Bindings; Churchilliana; City of London. PR: £20–5,000. CC: AE; MC; V. Cata: occasionally. Also at: Stock also at: Jonathan Potter Ltd, London W. (q.v.). [09/05/2003]

Martin Wood Cricket Books, 1c Wickenden Road, Sevenoaks, TN13 3PJ. Tel: (01732) 457205. Fax: (01732) 457205. Website: www.martinwoodcricketbooks.co.uk. Est: 1970. Private premises. Appointment necessary. Small stock. Spec: Sport - Cricket. PR: £1–500. Cata: online@ www.martinwoodcricketbooks.co.uk. [Updated]

SIDCUP

Mark W. Corder, 9 Townshend Close, Sidcup, DA14 5HY. Prop: Mark Corder. Tel: (020) 8309-5665. Website: mark.corder.btinternet.co.uk. E-mail: mark.corder@btinternet.com. Est: 1988. Private premises. Internet and postal. Appointment necessary. Open: **M:** 08:00–00:00. Small stock. Spec: Academic/Scholarly; History - British; Reference; Theology; Topography - Local. PR: £10–500. Cata: occasional. [Updated]

SITTINGBOURNE

J. & J. Fox Books, 48 Woodstock Road, Sittingbourne, ME10 4HN. Prop: M.V. Fox. Tel: (01795) 470310. Fax: (01795) 470310. Est: 1981. Storeroom. Appointment necessary. Small stock. Spec: Antiquarian; Cookery/Gastronomy; Maritime/Nautical; Military; Typography. PR: £10–1,500. CC: AE; D; E; JCB; MC; V. Cata: occasionally. Corresp: French, Portugese, Spanish. Mem: PBFA. [24/02/2003]

Underwater Antiques, 123 Peregrine Drive, Sittingbourne, ME10 4UG. Tel: (01795) 472664. E-mail: philsidey@aol.com. Postal business only. Spec: Antiquarian; Author - Cecil, H; Crime (True); Maritime/Nautical; Modern First Editions; Sport - Diving/Sub-Aqua. PR: £3–300. [15/05/2003]

SMARDEN

Mrs Janet Cameron, The Meeting House, Smarden, TN27 8NR. Tel: (withheld). Est: 1992. Private premises. Postal business only. Small general stock. [Updated]

TONBRIDGE

C. & A.J. Barmby, 140 Lavender Hill, Tonbridge, TN9 2AY. Prop: Chris & Angela Barmby. Tel: (01732) 771590. Fax: (01732) 771590. Website: bookpilot@aol.com. E-mail: bookpilot@aol.com. Est: 1981. Storeroom Internet and postal. Appointment necessary. Large stock. Spec: Antiquarian; Antiques; Applied Art; Archaeology; Architecture; Art; Art - Reference; Author - 20th Century; Author - Durrell, Lawrence; Author - Fowles, John; Author - Graves, Robert; Author - Steadman, Ralph; Carpets; Ceramics; Collecting; Decorative Art. PR: £5–4,000. CC: MC; V; Switch. VAT No: GB 367 4200 58. [Updated]

Grant Demar Books, 15 White Cottage Road, Tonbridge, TN10 4PX. Tel: (01732) 360208. Est: 1977. Private premises. Appointment necessary. Small stock. Spec: Animals and Birds; Conservation; Entomology; Natural History; Ornithology; Zoology. PR: £1–1,000. Cata: 2 a year. [30/04/2003]

Tony Skelton, The Old School House, Shipbourne, Tonbridge, TN11 9PB. Prop: D.A.L. Skelton. Tel: (01732) 810481. E-mail: tskelt@waitrose.com. Est: 1992. Private premises. Internet and postal. Contactable. Open: **M:** 08:08–20:20; **T:** 08:08–20:20; **W:** 08:00–20:00; **Th:** 08:00–20:00; **F:** 08:00–20:00; **S:** 09:00–20:00; **Su:** 09:00–20:00; Small stock. Spec: Countries - Ireland; First Editions; Literature; Modern First Editions; Publishers - Penguin; also Booksearch. PR: £5–500. Corresp: French, German. Mem: PBFA. VAT No: GB 796 5067 79. [Updated]

P. & F. Whelan, 68 The Drive, Tonbridge, TN9 2LR. Prop: Tony & Mary Whelan. Tel: (01732) 354882. Fax: (01732) 354882. E-mail: whelanirishbooks@lineone.net. Est: 1986. Private premises. Postal business only. Small stock. Spec: Countries - Ireland; History - National; Irish Interest. PR: £5–250. Cata: 3 – history of Ireland, Irish literature & guidebooks. [Updated]

Anthony Whittaker, Four Seasons, Chillmill Green, Brenchley, Tonbridge, TN12 7AL. Tel: (01892) 723494. E-mail: bookant@hotmail.com. Est: 1980. Private premises. Book fairs only. Appointment necessary. CC: MC; V. Mem: PBFA. [Updated]

TUNBRIDGE WELLS

Hall's Bookshop, ■ 20–22 Chapel Place, Tunbridge Wells, TN1 1YQ. Prop: Sabrina Izzard. Tel: (01892) 527842. Fax: (01892) 527842. E-mail: sabizzard@waitrose.com. Est: 1898. Shop open: **M:** 09:30–17:00; **T:** 09:30–17:00; **W:** 09:30–17:00; **Th:** 09:30–17:00; **F:** 09:30–17:00; **S:** 09:30–17:00; Large stock. Spec: Art; Bindings; Biography; History - General; Literature; Natural History; Topography - General; Travel - General; also Booksearch. Mem: PBFA. [Updated]

Politicos.co.uk, PO Box 279, Tunbridge Wells, TN2 4WJ. Prop: Iain Dale. Tel: 0870 850 1110. Fax: 0870 850 0176. Website: www.politicos.co.uk. E-mail: iain.dale@politicos.co.uk. Est: 1996. Warehouse. Internet and postal. Very large stock. Spec: Autobiography; Autographs; Biography; History - National; Memoirs; Politics. PR: £1–1,000. CC: AE; MC; V; SW. Also, new books. Mem: PBFA. [Updated]

Stanley Fish & Co., 26 Grosvenor Park, Tunbridge Wells, Kent, TN1 2BD. Prop: Robin Peterson. Tel: (01892) 527537. Website: www.stanleyfish.com. E-mail: stanleyfish@aol.com. Est: 1992. PR: £1–300. [Updated]

World War Books, Oaklands, Camden Park, Tunbridge Wells, TN2 5AE. Prop: Tim Harper. Tel: (01892) 538465. Fax: (01892) 538465. Website: www.worldwarbooks.com. E-mail: wwarbooks @btinternet.com. Est: 1993. Private premises. Internet and postal. Contactable. Medium stock. Spec: Aviation; Holocaust; Maritime/Nautical; Military; School Registers/Rolls of Honour; War - General. PR: £10–5,000. CC: MC; V. Cata: 2. Mem: PBFA; OMRS. [Updated]

WESTERHAM

Derek Stirling Bookseller, 1 Quebec Avenue, Westerham, TN16 1BJ. Tel: (01959) 561 822. Fax: (01959) 561 822. E-mail: derekfs@dialstart.net. Est: 1999. Private premises. Internet and postal. Appointment necessary. Very small stock. Spec: Academic/Scholarly; Antiquarian; Author - Dickens, Charles; Bibles; Ex-Libris; Fables; History - General; History - 19th Century; Illustrated; Journals - General; Languages - National; Linguistics; Literature; Literature - Victorian; Newspapers - General. PR: £5–1,000. [Updated]

The Design Gallery 1850-1950, 5 The Green, Westerham, RH7 6NR. Prop: Chrissie Painell. Tel: (01959 561234. Website: www.designgallery.co.uk. E-mail: sales@designgallery.co.uk. Spec: Bindings; Crafts. Also, Victorian fine bindings, and original illustrations. [Updated]

WHITSTABLE

Alan & Margaret Edwards, 10 Meteor Avenue, Whitstable, CT5 4DH. Tel: (01227) 262276. Fax: (01227) 261158. E-mail: a.m.books@lineone.net. Est: 1988. Private premises. Postal business only. Appointment necessary. Small stock. Spec: Ecclesiastical History & Architecture; Theology; Topography - General. PR: £1–500. Exhibits at book fairs. Cata: 3 a year. Corresp: French, German. [Updated]

LANCASHIRE

BLACKBURN

The Bookshelf, c/o 10 Pendle Road, Great Harwood, Blackburn, BB6 7TN. Prop: Jeff & Jean Taylor. Tel: (01254) 884242. Fax: (01254) 876233. Website: www.abebooks.com. E-mail: thebshelf@aol.com. Est: 1998. Private premises. Internet. Small stock. Spec: PR: £1–50. CC: AE; MC; V. [11/05/2003]

Neil Summersgill, Pigeon Hall, Abbott Brow, Mellor, Blackburn, BB2 7HT. Tel: (01254) 813559. E-mail: summersgillbooks@btinternet.com. Est: 1984. Private premises. Internet and postal. Appointment necessary. Very small stock. Spec: Antiquarian; Atlases; Autographs; Bindings; Letters; Manuscripts; Natural History; Sport - Field Sports; Travel - General. PR: £10–5,000. CC: MC; V. Mem: PBFA. [Updated]

BLACKPOOL

Bob Dobson, 3 Staining Rise, Staining, Blackpool, FY3 0BU. Tel: (01253) 895678. Fax: (01253) 895678. E-mail: bobdobson@amserve.com. Est: 1969. Private premises. Appointment necessary. Large stock. Spec: History - Local; Topography - Local. PR: £1–100. Incl: books on Lancashire, Yorkshire and Cheshire. Also publishes as Landy Publishing. Cata: 6 – 2 each year on Lancashire, Yorkshire, Cheshire. VAT No: GB 534 3982 30. [Updated]

John McGlynn, 173 Newton Drive, Blackpool, FY3 8ND. Tel: (01253) 300100. Fax: (01253) 300020. Website: www.vintagetechnology.org. E-mail: johnmcglynn@blueyonder.co.uk. Est: 1996. Private premises. Postal business only. Shop open 7 days a week. Medium stock. Spec: Motoring; Transport. PR: £10–200. Also, collectables and ephemera. [Updated]

BRINSCALL

Modern Firsts Etc., Hilltops, Windsor Drive, Brinscall, PR6 8PX. Prop: R.J. Leek. Tel: (01254) 830861. Est: 1985. Private premises. Postal business only. Very small stock. Spec: Autographs; First Editions; Painting. PR: £1–500. [Updated]

BURY

Richard Byrom Textile Bookroom, 3 Hawkshaw Lane, Bury, BL8 4JZ. Tel: (01204) 880155. Fax: (01204) 880155. Est: 1984. Private premises. Appointment necessary. Medium stock. Spec: Carpets; Company History; Crochet; Embroidery; Fashion & Costume; Industry; Knitting; Lace; Sheep/Shepherding; Social History; Tapestry; Textiles; Trade Unions. PR: £1–500. [Updated]

CARNFORTH

The Carnforth Bookshop, ■ 38–42 Market Street, Carnforth, LA5 9JX. Prop: P. & G. Seward. Tel: (01524) 734588. Fax: (01524) 735893. Website: www.carnforthbooks.co.uk. E-mail: carnforthbkshop@aol.com. Internet and postal. Shop open: **M:** 09:00–17:30; **T:** 09:00–17:30; **W:** 09:00–17:30; **Th:** 09:00–17:30; **F:** 09:00–17:30; **S:** 09:00–17:30. Very large stock. Spec: Alpinism/Mountaineering; Art; Art - History; Biography; Classical Studies; Fiction - General; Fine & Rare; History - General; History - Local; History - National; Languages - Foreign; Literature; Military History; Music - General; Natural History; also Booksearch. PR: £1–500. CC: AE; E; MC; V. Mem: BA. VAT No: GB 306 8293 93. [Updated]

F.N. Crack (Books), 2 Sawmill Cottages, Burton–in–Lonsdale, Carnforth, LA6 3JS. Prop: Noel Crack. Tel: (015242) 61244. Est: 1978. Private premises. Appointment necessary. Small stock. Spec: Animals and Birds; Botany; Entomology; Gardening; Natural History; Natural Sciences; Ornithology; Sport - Falconry; Sport - Field Sports; Taxidermy. PR: £2–600. Cata: 2 a year. Mem: PBFA. [08/07/2003]

CHORLEY

Bowland Bookfinders, 88 Bury Lane, Withnell, Chorley, PR6 8SD. Prop: D.S. Suttie. Tel: (01254) 830619. E-mail: david@bookfind.freeserve.co.uk. Est: 1987. Private premises. Postal business only. Appointment necessary. Spec: Academic/Scholarly; Advertising; War - General; also Booksearch. [Updated]

Browse Books, 10 Silverdale Close, Worden Park, Leyland, Chorley, PR25 3BY. (*) Prop: T.B. Bowe.
Tel: (01772) 431608. E-mail: b_bowe@hotmail.com. Est: 1989. Display/stand. Internet and postal.
Telephone first. Shop at: at: Bygone Times Antique Centre, The Green, Eccleston Chorley,Lancs.
Open: **M:** 10:00–17:00; **T:** 10:00–17:00; **W:** 10:00–20:00; **Th:** 10:00–15:00; **F:** 10:00–17:00; **S:** 10:00–
16:00; **Su:** 10:00–17:00. Spec: Antiques; Buses/Trams; Crafts; Embroidery; Gardening; Humour;
Motoring; Poetry; Sets of Books; Transport. PR: £2–50. Extensive Sheet Music Stock. [Updated]

CLITHEROE

Bowdon Books, ■ 33 Lowergate, Clitheroe, BB7 1AD. Prop: Gordon & Gillian Hill. Tel: (01200) 425333.
Fax: (01200) 443490. Est: 1987. Shop open: **Th:** 10:00–16:00; **F:** 10:00–16:30; **S:** 10:00–16:30. Medium
stock. Spec: Fashion & Costume; Needlework; Textiles; Topography - Local. PR: £5–500. CC: JCB;
MC; V; Switch. Also, book fairs. Mem: PBFA. [Updated]

Moorside Books Ltd, ■ Moorside Cottage, Whalley Old Road, Billington, Clitheroe, BB7 9JF. Prop:
David Sedgwick. Tel: (01254) 824104. E-mail: dsbooks@easynet.co.uk. Est: 1985. Internet and postal.
Shop at: Moorside Cottage, Whalley Old Road, Billington, Clitheroe, BB7 9JF. Open: **T:** 10:00–17:00;
Th: 10:00–17:00; **F:** 10:00–17:00; **S:** 10:00–17:00; Small stock. Spec: Astronomy; Author - Lawrence,
T.E.; Bindings; Physics; Science - General; Science - History of; Travel - Asia; Travel - Middle East.
PR: £5–10,000. CC: MC; V; Switch. Cata: 1 – T E Lawrence. Mem: PBFA. Also at: 29 Moor Lane,
Clitheroe, Lancs. VAT No: GB 787 8011 92. [Updated]

Roundstone Books, 29 Moor Lane, Clitheroe, BB7 1BE. Prop: Jo Harding. Tel: (01200) 444242. Website:
www.roundstonebooks.co.uk. E-mail: joharbooks@aol.com. Est: 1995. Spec: Academic/Scholarly;
Alternative Medicine; Biography; Children's - General; Countries - Poland; Drama; Feminism; First
Editions; History - General; Languages - Foreign; Literary Criticism; Literature; Poetry; Travel -
General. PR: £1–100. Free booksearch service. [14/04/2003]

DARWEN

Bygone Books, 27 Glenshiels Avenue, Hoddlesden, Darwen, BB3 3LS. Prop: Gordon French. Tel:
(01254) 703077. Website: www.bygonebooks.fsnet.co.uk. E-mail: gordonandjen@
bygonebooks.fsnet.co.uk. Est: 1992. Private premises. Internet and postal. Telephone first. Very
small stock. Spec: Children's - General; Fiction - General; First Editions; Topography - General; also
Booksearch. PR: £2–80. CC: MC; V. Mem: PBFA. [29/06/2003]

Red Rose Books, 478, Bolton Road, Darwen, BB3 2JR. Prop: K.M. Tebay. Tel: (01254) 776767. Website:
www.redrosebooks.co.uk. E-mail: info@redrosebooks.co.uk. Est: 1993. Private premises. Internet
and postal. Appointment necessary. Small stock. Spec: Sport - Cricket. PR: £1–1,000. CC: AE; MC;
V. Cata: 5 a year. Mem: PBFA. VAT No: GB 693 2135 32. [Updated]

FENCE

Pendleside Books, 359 Wheatley Lane Road, Fence, Nr. Burnley, BB12 9QA. Prop: E. & B. Sutcliffe. Tel:
(01282) 615617. Est: 1974. Private premises. Appointment necessary. Very small stock. Spec:
Entomology; Mycology; Topography - Local. PR: £5–500. CC: JCB; MC; V. Cata: 2 a year on
mycology, entomology. Corresp: French, Italian. [Updated]

HALTON

Mark Towers, 45 Beech Road, Halton, LA2 6QQ. Tel: (01524) 811556. Website: www.royoftherovers
.com. E-mail: mark@royoftherovers.com. Postal business only. Spec: Comic Books & Annuals;
Comics. PR: £2–50. [Updated]

LANCASTER

Hardback Hotel, 68 Windermere Road, Lancaster, LA1 3EZ. Prop: J. Bean. Tel: (07763) 814587.
Website: www.hardbackhotel.co.uk. E-mail: mail@hardbackhotel.co.uk. Est: 2001. Private premises.
Internet and postal. Small stock. Spec: Modern First Editions; Proof Copies. PR: £2–400. CC:
Paypal. [Updated]

PRESTON

Great Grandfather's, ■ 82 Towngate, Leyland, Preston, PR25 2LR. Prop: Greg D. Smith. Tel: (01772) 422268. E-mail: books@greatgrandfathers.fsnet.co.uk. Est: 1985. Shop open: **T:** 10:00–17:30; **Th:** 10:00–16:30; **F:** 10:00–17:30; **S:** 10:00–17:30. Large stock. Spec: Natural History; Topography - Local. PR: £1–200. Open other times by appointment. Corresp: French, German. Mem: PBFA. [11/03/2003]

Bygone Tunes, 19 Churchside, New Longton, Preston, PR4 4LU. Prop: Jean Billington. Tel: (01772) 613729. E-mail: jean@bygonetunes.com. Est: 1975. Private premises. Postal business only. Large general stock. Spec: Music - General; Music - Jazz; Music - Printed. PR: £3–10. [13/08/2003]

V.J. Moss Antiquarian Books, 83 Chaigley Road, Longridge, Preston, PR3 3TQ. Tel: (01772) 782943. Fax: (01772) 782943. E-mail: vjmoss@onetel.net.uk. Est: 1982. Private premises. Internet and postal. Appointment necessary. Large stock. Spec: Bibliography; Bindings; Books about Books; Collecting; Papermaking; Printing; Publishing; Typography; also Booksearch. PR: £10–2,000. Cata: 2 – books about books. VAT No: GB 604 5317 68. [29/06/2003]

O'Connor Fine Books, 9 Garrison Road, Fulwood, Preston, PR2 8AL. Prop: John and Evelyn O'Connor. Tel: (01772) 719359. E-mail: oconnorfinebooks@hotmail.com. Est: 2002. Private premises. Appointment necessary. Very small stock. Spec: Bibliography; Bindings; Collecting; Design; Illustrated; Papermaking; Printing; Private Press; Publishing; Typography. Cata: 2 a year. Corresp: French. [12/07/2003]

Preston Book Company, ■ 68 Friargate, Preston, PR1 2ED. Prop: M. Halewood. Tel: (01772) 252613. E-mail: prestonrarebooks@halewood221b.freeserve.co.uk. Est: 1960. Internet and postal. Shop open: **M:** 10:00–17:00; **T:** 10:00–17:00; **W:** 10:00–17:00; **Th:** 10:00–17:00; **F:** 10:00–17:00; **S:** 10:00–17:00. Large general stock. Spec: Americana; Atlases; Author - Conan Doyle, Sir Arthur; Colour-Plate; Sherlockiana; Travel - General. PR: £10–1,000. CC: JCB; MC. [29/06/2003]

SAINT ANNES ON SEA

BookstopUK, 47 St. David's Road North, Saint Annes on Sea, FY8 2BS. Prop: Ian & Jackie Allen. Tel: (01253) 721676. Fax: (0870) 129 4686. Website: www.bookstopuk.co.uk. Est: 2000. Private premises. Internet and postal. Appointment necessary. Very small general stock. Spec: Academic/Scholarly; Advertising; Aeronautics; Fiction - General; Fiction - Crime, Detective, Spy, Thrillers; Fiction - Fantasy, Horror; Fiction - Historical; Fiction - Science Fiction; Modern First Editions; Proof Copies. [1803/2003]

THORNTON CLEVELEYS

Seabreeze Books, 39 Woodfield Road, Thornton Cleveleys, FY5 4EQ. Prop: Martin L. Johnson. Tel: (01253) 850075. Est: 1994. Private premises. Appointment necessary. Stock at: Skipton Antique Centre, Skipton, North Yorks. (q.v.). Medium stock. Spec: Antiquarian; Art; Books about Books; Children's - General; Churchilliana; Fiction - General; Limited Editions; Literature - Victorian; Military; Modern First Editions; Mysteries; Poetry; Pop-Up, 3D, Cut Out & Movable; Sport - Golf. PR: £1–5,000. Cata: 1 – literature. Mem: Also at: Skipton Antiques Centre, Skipton (q.v.). [Updated]

LEICESTERSHIRE

HINCKLEY

Caduceus Books, 28 Darley Road, Burbage, Hinckley, LE10 2RL. Prop: Ben Fernee. Tel: (01455) 250542. Fax: (0870) 055-2982. Website: www.caduceusbooks.com. E-mail: ben@caduceusbooks.com. Est: 1989. Private premises. Appointment necessary. Very small stock. Spec: Alchemy; Astrology; Esoteric; Occult; Supernatural; Witchcraft. PR: £1–1,000. CC: MC; V; Switch. Also, manuscripts, associated items. Cata: on occult, witchcraft, esoteric. [Updated]

KIBWORTH HARCOURT

Pam Turnbull - The Countryman', The Croft, 14 Leicester Road, Kibworth Harcourt, LE8 0NN. Prop: Pamela M. Turnbull. Tel: (0116) 279-3211. Fax: (0116) 279-2437. E-mail: pamturnbull@countrymansgallery.fsnet.co.uk. Est: 1980. Private premises. Appointment necessary. Small stock. Spec: Children's - General; Dogs; Ornithology; Poultry; Sport - Angling/Fishing; Sport - Field Sports; Sport - Hunting; Sport - Shooting. PR: £1–500. CC: MC. Cata: on request. [Updated]

LEICESTER

Black Cat Bookshop, ■ 90 Charles St., Leicester, LE1 1GE. Prop: Philip & Karen Woolley. Tel: (0116) 251-2756. Fax: (0116) 281-3545. Website: www.blackcatbookshop.com. E-mail: blackcatuk@aol.com. Est: 1987. Internet and postal. Shop at: www.blackcatbookshop.com. Open: **M:** 09:30–17:00; **T:** 09:30–17:00; **W:** 09:30–17:00; **Th:** 09:30–17:00; **F:** 09:30–17:00; **S:** 09:30–17:00. Large general stock. Spec: Author - Conan Doyle, Sir Arthur; Author - Fleming, Ian; Children's - General; Comic Books & Annuals; Comics; Counterculture; Countries - Melanesia; Countries - Mexico; Fiction - General; Fiction - Historical; Fiction - Science Fiction; Music - Popular. PR: £1–500. CC: E; JCB; MC; V; SW, Delta. Cata: 5 on various subjects 2-3 times a years. Mem: PBFA. [Updated]

Cottage Books, Gelsmoor, Coleorton, Leicester, LE67 8HR. Prop: Jennifer M. Boyd–Cropley. Tel: None. Est: 1970. Private premises. Postal business only. Medium stock. Spec: Agriculture; Architecture; Canals/Inland Waterways; Crafts; Fairgrounds; Folklore; Gypsies; History - Local; Landscape; Rural Life; Scottish Interest; Social History; Traction Engines; Windmills & Watermills. PR: £1–2,000. Cata: 10 – 6 on rural subjects & 4 on Gypsies and fairs. Mem: PBFA. [Updated]

Cyclamen Books, P.O. Box 69, Leicester, LE1 9EW. Prop: D. & Y. Abramski. Tel: n/a. Fax: (0116) 270-4623. E-mail: rara@cyclamenbooks.com. Est: 1976. Storeroom. Postal business only. Shop at: 18 Ashclose Avenue, Leicester LE2 3WA. Very large general stock. Spec: Academic/Scholarly; Advertising; Africana; Countries - Balkans, The; Countries - Central Asia; Countries - East Europe; Countries - France; Countries - Middle East, The; Countries - Russia; Criminology; Feminism; Languages - Foreign; Media; Pacifism PR: £10–100. Corresp: French. [25/06/2003]

Rebecca Dearman Rare Books, ■ 2 Francis Street, Stonygate, Leicester, LE2 BD. Tel: (0116) 270-9666. Website: rebeccadearmanrarebooks.co.uk. E-mail: rebeccadearman@hotmail.com. Est: 1967. Internet and postal. Shop open: **T:** 09:00–17:30; **W:** 09:00–17:30; **Th:** 09:00–17:30; **F:** 09:00–17:30; **S:** 09:00–18:00. Large general stock. PR: £1–1,000. Cata: 3 a year. [17/06/2003]

Howarth Antiques, 60 Manor Road, Desford, Leicester, LE9 9JS. Prop: Mike Barlow. Tel: to come. E-mail: info@forgottenwords.com. Private premises. Internet and postal. Spec: Stock can be searched via abebooks and biblio.com under 'Forgotten Words'. Also, valuer. [Updated]

Ice House Books, 19 Hall Road, Leicester, LE7 9SY. Prop: Eleanor S Davidson. Tel: (0116) 292 1964. Fax: 0116 292 1963. Website: www.icehousebooks.co.uk. E-mail: eleanor@icehousebooks.co.uk. Est: 2000. Warehouse; Internet and postal. Appointment necessary. Open: **M:** 09:00–19:00; **T:** 09:00–19:00; **W:** 09:00–19:00; **Th:** 09:00–19:00; **F:** 09:00–19:00; **S:** 09:00–17:00; **Su:** 10:00–17:00; Closed for lunch: 12:00–13:00. Large stock. Spec: Academic/Scholarly; Africana; Animals and Birds; Anthropology; Art; Arts, The; Biography; Biology; Botany; Building & Construction; Business Studies; Cartoons; Chemistry; Chess; Cinema/Film; Classical Studies; Comedy; Conservation; Countries - Africa. PR: £5–2,000. CC: JCB; MC; V. Cata: weekly website updates. [Updated]

Bruce Main–Smith & Co. Ltd., 132, Saffron Road, Wigston, Leicester, LE18 4UP. (*) Prop: D.R. & M.E. Mitchell (Directors). Tel: (0116) 277-7669. Fax: (0116) 277-7669. Website: www.brucemainsmith.com. E-mail: sales@brucemainsmith.com. Est: 1972. Spec: Motorbikes. PR: £4–100. CC: MC; V; SW. Also, virtually a complete stock of all new motor cycle books, plus 4,000 photocopied manuals, spares lists & brochures. [Updated]

Maynard & Bradley, ■ 1 Royal Arcade, Silver Street, Leicester, LE1 5YW. Prop: David Maynard & Stephen Bradley. Tel: (0116) 253-2712. Website: www.maynardandbradley.com. E-mail: books@maynardandbradley.com. Est: 1971. Shop open: **M:** 09:15–17:15; **T:** 09:15–17:15; **W:** 09:15–17:15; **Th:** 09:15–17:15; **F:** 09:15–17:15; **S:** 09:00–17:00. Medium stock. Spec: Bindings; Colour-Plate; Cookery/Gastronomy; Illustrated; Private Press; Sport - Cricket; Sport - Field Sports; Topography - General, also Booksearch. PR: £1–3,000. CC: MC; V; Solo. Also, pictures, picture-framing, conservation services, print colouring & decorative mount cutting service (trade). Mem: PBFA. VAT No: GB 416 3807 58. [Updated]

Pooks Motor Books, ■ Unit 4, Fowke Street, Rothley, Leicester, LE7 7PJ. (*) Prop: Barrie Pook & John Pook. Tel: (0116) 237-6222. Fax: (0116) 237-6491. E-mail: pooks.motorbooks@virgin.net. Shop open: **M:** 09:00–17:00; **T:** 09:00–17:00; **W:** 09:00–17:00; **Th:** 09:00–17:00; **F:** 09:00–17:00. Very large stock. Spec: Biography; Marque Histories (see also motoring); Motorbikes; Motoring; Transport; Vintage Cars. PR: £3–1,000. CC: MC; V. Also, sales catalogues for cars & motorcycles. [08/07/2003]

Rosanda Books, 11 Whiteoaks Road, Oadby, Leicester, LE2 5YL. Prop: David Baldwin BA, M. Phil, & Joyce Baldwin. Tel: (0116) 2713880. E-mail: dbaldwin@themutual.net. Est: 1994. Private premises. Appointment necessary. Spec: History - Ancient; History - British; History - European; History - Middle Ages. PR: £2–50. Cata: 3 – History. [Updated]

Treasure Trove Books, ■ 21 Mayfield Road, Leicester, LE2 1LR. Prop :Linda Sharman. Tel: (0116) 2755933. E-mail: sales@treasuretrovebooks.co.uk. Est: 1993. Internet. Shop open: **M:** 09:30–17:30; **T:** 09:30–17:30; **W:** 09:30–17:30; **Th:** 09:30–17:30; **F:** 09:30–17:30; **S:** 09:30–17:30. Very large stock. Spec: Annuals; Author - Bellairs, George; Author - Blyton, Enid; Author - Brent-Dyer, Elinor M.; Author - Buckeridge, A.; Author - Christie, Agatha; Author - Johns, W.E.; Author - Potter, Beatrix; Author - Simenon, Georges; Authors - Women; Botany; Childrens. PR: £1–500. [Updated]

Tony Yates Antiquarian Books, 3 Melton Avenue, Leicester, LE4 7SE. Tel: (0116) 266-1891. Website: TonyYatesBooks@Btopenworld.com. E-mail: tonyyatesbooks@btopenworld.com. Est: 1989. Private premises. Appointment necessary. Small stock. Spec: Antiquarian; Children's - General; Education & School; Illustrated; Literature; Psychology/Psychiatry; Topography - Local. PR: £5–1,000. Cata: 1 – a year. Mem: PBFA. [Updated]

LOUGHBOROUGH

Booklore, 6 The Green, East Leake, Loughborough, LE12 6ld. (*) Prop: Ralph & Simon Corbett. Tel: (01509) 820614. E-mail: Ralphcorbett@aol.com. Private premises. Internet and postal. Appointment necessary. Open: **M:** 09:30–17:30; **T:** 09:30–17:30; **W:** 09:30–17:30; **Th:** 09:30–17:30; **F:** 09:30–17:30; **S:** 09:00–16:00. Large stock. Spec: Antiquarian; Bindings. PR: £10–1,000. CC: MC; V. Mem: ABA; PBFA. VAT No: GB 815 6907 13. [Updated]

Eric Goodyer, Natural History, Hathern, Loughborough, LE12 5LE. Prop: Sue Duerdoth & Eric Goodyer. Tel: (01509) 844473. Fax: (01509) 844473. Website: http://www.abebooks.com/home/ ERICGOODYER/. E-mail: eg@dmu.ac.uk. Est: 1992. Very small stock. Spec: Antiquarian; Natural History. PR: £5–300. CC: PayPal. [Updated]

Malcolm Hornsby, Antiquarian and Secondhand Books, ■ 41 Churchgate, Loughborough, LE11 1UE. Prop: Malcolm Hornsby. Tel: (01509) 269860. Website: hornsbybooks.co.uk. E-mail: info@hornsbybooks.co.uk. Est: 1993. Shop open: **M:** 10:00–17:30; **T:** 10:00–17:30; **W:** 10:00–17:30; **Th:** 10:00–17:30; **F:** 10:00–17:30; **S:** 10:00–17:30. Medium stock. Spec: Academic/Scholarly; Antiquarian; Art; Aviation; History - General. CC: AE; E; JCB; MC; V. Corresp: French, German, Greek. Mem: PBFA. [Updated]

Magis Books, 64 Leopold Street, Loughborough, LE11 5DN. Prop: Tom Clarke. Tel: (01509) 210626. Fax: (01509) 238034. Website: www.magis.co.uk. E-mail: enquiries@magis.co.uk. Est: 1975. Private premises. Internet and postal. Telephone first. Very large stock. Spec: Alchemy; Astrology; Earth Mysteries; Esoteric; Folklore; Fore-Edge Paintings; Freemasonry & Anti-Masonry; Ghosts; Mysticism; Mythology; New Age; Occult; Paganism; Philosophy; Psychic; Spiritualism; Witchcraft. PR: £1–1,200. CC: AE; D; MC; V. Also, distributor of new books & publishers (Thoth Publications). Mem: PBFA. [Updated]

MARKET HARBOROUGH

Bowden Books, 14 Station Road, Great Bowden, Market Harborough, LE16 7HN. Prop: Terry Bull. Tel: (01858) 466832. Est: 1986. Private premises. Postal business only. Very small stock. Spec: Architecture; Art; Colour-Plate; Publishers - Black, A. & C.; Topography - General; Travel - General. PR: £5–750. Corresp: French, Italian. Mem: PBFA. [23/08/2002]

Christine's Book Cabin, ■ Rear of 7–9 Coventry Road, Market Harborough, LE16 9BX. Prop: Malcolm & Christine Noble. Tel: (01858) 433233. Website: www.bookcabin.co.uk. E-mail: bookcabin@ harborough.uk.com. Est: 1997. Shop open: **M:** 10:00–16:30; **T:** 10:00–16:30; **Th:** 10:00–16:30; **F:** 10:00–16:30; **S:** 10:00–16:30. Small general stock. Spec: Booksearch. PR: £1–300. CC: AE; JCB; MC; V; SW. See also Malcolm and Christine Noble. Cata: catalogue available on website. [14/04/2003]

Malcolm & Christine Noble, 1 Stuart Crescent, Lubenham, Market Harborough, LE16 7RL. Tel: (01858) 434671. Website: www.bookcabin.co.uk. E-mail: malcolm@bookcabin.co.uk. Est: 1992. Private premises. Postal business only. Spec: Entertainment - General; Nostalgia; Periodicals & Magazines; Topography - Local; also Booksearch. CC: AE; JCB; MC; V. [Updated]

MELTON MOWBRAY

Witmeha Productions, The Orchard, Wymondham, Melton Mowbray, LE14 2AZ. [Updated]

ROTHLEY

Whig Books Ltd., 11 Grangefields Drive, Rothley, Prop: Dr. J. Pollock & Mrs. A. Hinchliffe. Tel: (0116) 237-4420. Est: 1985. Private premises. Appointment necessary. Very small stock. Spec: Art; History - General; Literature. PR: £1–500. Cata: occasionally. Mem: PBFA. [Updated]

THURCASTON

Ian Kilgour (Sporting Books), 3 Hall Farm Road, Thurcaston, LE7 7JF. Prop: Ian Kilgour. Tel: (0116) 235-0025. E-mail: sportingbooks@ntlworld.com. Est: 1972. Private premises. Internet and postal. Appointment necessary. Small stock. Spec: Cockfighting; Dogs; Farming & Livestock; Firearms/ Guns; Rural Life; Sport - Angling/Fishing; Sport - Field Sports; Sport - Hunting; Sport - Shooting. PR: £2–500. Cata: 8 a year. [Updated]

BARTON–ON–HUMBER

Humber Books, Rozel House, 4 St. Mary's Lane, Barton–on–Humber, DN18 5EX. Prop: Peter M. Cresswell. Tel: (01652) 634958. Fax: (01652) 634965. Website: www.netguides.co.uk/uk/humber.html. E-mail: pmc@humberbooks.co.uk. Est: 1972. Spec: Antiquarian; Bibles; Hymnology; Manuscripts; Religion - Christian; Religion - Methodism; Religion - Non-conformity; Religion - Protestantism; Religion - Puritanism; Theology. PR: £20–2,000. [Updated]

Roger & Sylvia Shakeshaft, Pinewoods, High Street, South Ferriby, Barton–upon–Humber. Tel: (01652) 661185. Est: 1995. Private premises. Appointment necessary. Very small general stock. Spec: Americana; Children's - Illustrated; Illustrated; Modern First Editions; Natural History. PR: £1–25. Corresp: French. [09/07/2003]

BILLINGBOROUGH

Brockwells Booksellers, Unit 1C, White Leather Square, Billingborough, NG34 0QP. Prop: Matthew & Richard Peace. Tel: (01529)241222. Fax: (01529)455890. Website: www.brockwells .co.uk. E-mail: books@brockwells.co.uk. Est: 1997. Warehouse. Internet and postal. Telephone first. Open: **M:** 09:00–16:00; **T:** 09:00–16:00; **W:** 09:00–16:00; **Th:** 09:00–16:00; **F:** 09:00–16:00. Large stock. Spec: Academic/Scholarly; Antiquarian; Business Studies; Engineering; History - General; Military History; Politics; Travel - General; Voyages & Discovery. PR: £7–2,250. CC: AE; MC; V; Maestro. Prints and maps selling. New Boook Sales, Secure Credit Card Facility on Website. Mem: Bibliographical Society. [Updated]

BILLINGHAY

Not JUST Books, 27-29 High Street, Billinghay, Lincoln, LN4 4AU. Prop: Maggy Browne. Tel: (01526) 860294. Fax: (0870) 7059623. Website: www.notjustbooks.f9.co.uk. E-mail: books@ notjustbooks.f9.co.uk. Est: 1981. Private premises. Internet and postal. Appointment necessary. Medium stock. Spec: Biography; Crime (True); Fiction - General; Fire & Firefighters; History - General; Police Force Histories; Politics; Publishers - Chambers; Publishers - Guinness Publishing Ltd.; Radio/Wireless; Religion - General; Social History; Television. PR: £5–50. CC: AE; JCB; MC; Switch. Props for Theatre, Film and TV. Mem: FSB. [Updated]

BOSTON

Libra Books, Church House, Wigtoft, Boston, PE20 2NJ. Prop: Paul & Linda Daunter. Tel: (01205) 460829. Fax: (01205) 460829. Website: : http://www.ukbookworld.com/members/LibraBooks. E-mail: libra.books@btinternet.com. Est: 1994. Private premises. Internet and postal. Telephone first. Large general stock. Spec: Biography; Ex-Libris; Fiction - General; Fiction - Crime, Detective, Spy, Thrillers; Fiction - Historical; Fiction - Science Fiction; Fiction - Women; Gardening; History - General; Juvenile; Memoirs; Modern First Editions; Music - General. PR: £1–100. [Updated]

CLEETHORPES

Soccer Books Limited, 72 St Peters Avenue, Cleethorpes, DN35 8HU. Prop: John Robinson. Tel: (01472) 696226. Fax: (01472) 698546. Website: www.soccer-books.co.uk. E-mail: info@soccer-books.co.uk. Est: 1983. Office &/or bookroom. Postal business only. Appointment necessary. Open: **M:** 09:00–17:00; **T:** 09:00–17:00; **W:** 09:00–17:00; **Th:** 09:00–17:00; **F:** 09:00–17:00. Small stock. Spec: Sport - Football (Soccer). PR: £1–500. CC: AE; E; JCB; MC; V. Mem: PBFA. VAT No: GB 546 5008 49. [19/08/2003]

FOLKINGHAM

David Strauss, The White House, 25 Market Place, Folkingham, NG34 0SE. Prop: David & Victoria Strauss. Tel: (01529) 497298. Fax: (01529) 497298. Website: www.abebooks.com/home/davidstrauss. E-mail: david.strauss@btinternet.com. Est: 1977. Private premises. Internet and postal. Telephone first. Medium stock. Spec: Academic/Scholarly; Architecture; Art - History; History - General; Literary Criticism; Philosophy; Theology. PR: £8–3,500. CC: MC; V; Switch. [28/05/2003]

GRANTHAM

Bookwyze, 42 Castlegate, Grantham, NG31 6SS. Prop: Tony Midgley. Tel: (01476) 579887. Website: www.bookwyze.co.uk. E-mail: tony.midgley@talk21.com. Est: 1990. Private premises. Internet and postal. Telephone first. Medium stock. Spec: Academic/Scholarly; Advertising; Antiquarian; Bibles; Bindings; Fine & Rare; First Editions; History - General; Illuminated Manuscripts; Illustrated; Manuscripts; Topography - General; Travel - General, also Booksearch. £10–1,000. CC: Paypal. Corresp: French, Latin, German. [11/04/2003]

Gravity Books, 110 Harrowby Road, Grantham, NG31 9DS. Prop: Mr. P.N. Emery. Tel: (01476) 564233. Website: www.gravitybooks.co.uk. E-mail: gravitybks@aol.com. Est: 1999. Private premises. Internet and postal. Appointment necessary. Large stock. Spec: Architecture; Music - Popular; Music - Rock; Sport - General; also Booksearch. PR: £2–200. CC: MC; V; SW. Corresp: French. [19/03/2003]

Midas Books & Prints, Hillside House, Beacon Lane, Grantham, NG31 9DQ. Prop: Tricia Daniels and Carolin Midgley. Tel: (01476) 566730. Fax: (01476) 566730. Est: 1990. Storeroom. Appointment necessary. Very small stock. Spec: Art; Children's - General; Design. PR: £5–100. Corresp: French. Also at: Broad Street Book Centre, Hay-on-Wye, Hereford. [28/05/2003]

HOLBEACH

P. Cassidy (Bookseller), ■ 1 Boston Road, Holbeach, PE12 7LR. Tel: (01406) 426322. Website: ukbookworld.com/members/7676. E-mail: bookscass@aol.com. Est: 1975. Shop open: **M:** 10:00–17:30; **T:** 10:00–17:30; **W:** 10:00–17:30; **Th:** 10:00–17:30; **F:** 10:00–17:30; **S:** 10:00–17:30. Medium stock. Spec: Topography - Local. PR: £1–250. CC: AE; MC; V; PayPal. [Updated]

HORNCASTLE

Good for Books, ■ 23 North Street, Horncastle, LN9 5DX. Prop: Richard & Sarah Ingram-Hill. Tel: (01507) 524415. Fax: (01507) 524415. Website: www.gaslightbooks.com. E-mail: books@gaslightbooks.com. Est: 1997. Shop open: **T:** 10:00–16:30; **Th:** 10:00–16:30; **F:** 10:00–16:30; **S:** 10:00–16:30. Medium stock. Spec: Academic/Scholarly; Agriculture; Alternative Medicine; Animals and Birds; Annuals; Antiquarian; Archaeology; Architecture; Art; Artists; Author - General; Aviation; Bibles; Bindings; Biography; Bridge; Calligraphy; Children's - Early Titles; Childrens. Also at: Pickering Antiques Centre, North Yorks Stand 23. [Updated]

Roger Lucas, 44 Queen Street, Horncastle, LN9 6BG. Tel: (01507) 522261. Website: www.rogerlucasbooksellers.com. E-mail: rogerbks@aol.com. Est: 1984. Private premises. Internet and postal. Appointment necessary. Medium stock. Spec: Art; Fiction - General; Literary Criticism; New Age. PR: £5–150. CC: MC; V; PayPal. [Updated]

KIRTON

D.C. Books, Parker House, 61a Horseshoe Lane, Kirton, Boston, PE20 1LW. Prop: D.J. & C. Lidgett. Tel: (01205) 724507. Fax: (01205) 724507. Est: 1984. Private premises. Postal business only. Very small stock. Spec: Travel - General; also Booksearch. PR: £3–5. [08/07/2003]

LINCOLN

Autumn Leaves, ■ 19 The Green, Nettleham, Lincoln, LN2 2NR. Prop: Ian & Sue Young. Tel: (01522) 750779. E-mail: leaves@onetel.com. Est: 1997. Shop open: **T:** 09:15–16:30; **W:** 09:30–16:30; **Th:** 09:30–16:30; **F:** 09:15–17:00; **S:** 09:15–12:30. Medium stock. Spec: Antiques; Art; Cookery/ Gastronomy; Drama; Entertainment - General; Fiction - General; Health; History - General; Humour; Knitting; Languages - Foreign; Literary Criticism; Literature; Music - General; Natural History; Sport - General; Transport PR: £2–100. CC: AE; JCB; MC; V; Maestro. Corresp: French, German, Swedish. VAT No: GB 737 8648 80. [Updated]

Chapter & Verse, 17 Queensway, Lincoln, LN2 4AJ. Prop: Roy Fines. Tel: (01522) 523202. E-mail: roy@fines18.freeserve.co.uk. Est: 1977. Private premises. Internet and postal. Appointment necessary. Open: **M:** 09:00–18:00; **T:** 09:00–18:00; **W:** 09:00–18:00; **Th:** 09:00–18:00; **F:** 09:00–18:00; **S:** 09:00–18:00; **Su:** 09:00–18:00. Very small stock. Spec: Topography - Local. PR: £1–5,000. CC: AE; MC; V; SW. Corresp: German. [Updated]

Golden Goose Books, ■ 20–21 Steep Hill, Lincoln, LN2 1LT. Prop: Mrs Anna Cockram & Richard West–Skinn. Tel: (01522) 522589. E-mail: harlequin@acockram.fsbusiness.co.uk. Est: 1984. Shop open: **M:** 11:00–17:00; **T:** 11:00–17:00; **Th:** 11:00–17:00; **F:** 11:00–17:00; **S:** 11:00–17:15. Spec: Antiques; Art; Illustrated. Mem: PBFA. Also at: Harlequin Gallery, 20-22, Steep Hill, Lincoln (q.v.). [Updated]

Harlequin Gallery, ■ 22 Steep Hill, Lincoln, LN2 1LT. Prop: Richard West–Skinn. Tel: (01522) 522589. E-mail: harlequin@acockram.fsbusiness.co.uk. Est: 1964. Shop open: **M:** 11:00–17:00; **T:** 11:00–17:00; **Th:** 11:00–17:00; **F:** 11:00–17:00; **S:** 11:00–17:15. PR: £1–15,000. Also, Golden Goose Globe restorers, R.W. & S.J. West-Skinn. Also at: Golden Goose Books, 20-21, Steep Hill, Lincoln LN2 1LT. [Updated]

Orlando Booksellers, 1 Rasen Lane, Lincoln, LN1 3EZ. Prop: Alison Smith & Christopher McKee. Tel: (01522) 510828. Fax: (01522) 544322. Website: www.abebooks.com/home/ORLAN_DO/. E-mail: orlando@booksellers.fsworld.co.uk. Est: 1994. Private premises. Internet and postal. Contactable. Small stock. Spec: Beat Writers; Fine & Rare; Literature; Modern First Editions; Photography; Poetry; Publishers - Hogarth Press; Publishers - Pan; Publishers - Penguin; Women. PR: £20–1,000. CC: AE; JCB; MC; V; Switch. VAT No: GB 629 3707 21. [08/07/2003]

Readers Rest, ■ 13–14 Steep Hill, Lincoln, LN2 1LT. Prop: Nick Warwick. Tel: (01522) 543217. Est: 1982. Open: **M:** 09:30–16:00; **T:** 09:30–16:00; **W:** 09:30–16:00; **Th:** 09:30–16:00; **F:** 09:30–16:00; **S:** 09:30–16:00; **Su:** 11:00–16:00. Very large general stock. PR: £1–50. Also at: Readers Rest Hall of Books, Steep Hill, Lincoln. [Updated]

Smallwood Books, 37 Cranwell Street, Lincoln, LN5 8BH. Prop: Thomas & Steven Smallwood. Tel: (01522) 822834. Website: www.smallwoodbooks.co.uk. Est: 1995. Private premises. Internet and postal. Appointment necessary. Medium stock. Spec: Academic/Scholarly; Antiquarian; Fore-Edge Paintings; Literary Criticism; Topography - Local; also Booksearch. PR: £1–5,000. CC: AE; MC; V. Corresp: Italian French. Also at: Astra Antiques Centre, Old RAF Hemswell, Lincolnshire. [19/03/ 2003]

MARKET RASEN

Croft Selections, ■ Corner Croft, Main St., Bishop Norton, Market Rasen, LN8 2BE. Prop: Bob Mould and Christine Pawson. Tel: (01633) 818711. Fax: (01633) 818711. Website: www.croft-selections.co.uk. E-mail: croftselections@btinternet.com. Est: 1999. Telephone first. Shop open: **M:** 08:00–19:00; **T:** 08:00–19:00; **W:** 08:00–19:00; **Th:** 08:00–19:00; **F:** 08:00–19:00; **S:** 08:00–19:00; **Su:** 08:00–19:00. Large general stock. Spec: Art; Biography; Children's - General; Crime (True); Dogs; Fiction - General; Gardening; History - General; Military; Music - General; Politics; Royalty - General; Travel - General; U.F.O.s, also Booksearch. PR: £10–100. CC: AE; JCB; MC; V. [26/02/2003]

SCUNTHORPE

Butterwick Books, The Old Chapel, 33 West Street, West Butterwick, Scunthorpe, DN17 3JZ. Prop: John Hardy. Tel: Website: www.ukbookworld.com/members/butterbooks. E-mail: butterwickbooks@hotmail.com. [15/05/2003]

Richard Williams (Bookdealer), 15 High Street, Dragonby, Scunthorpe, DN15 0BE. Prop: Richard Williams. Tel: (01724) 840645. Website: www.freespace.virgin.net/rah.williams/. E-mail: rah.williams @virgin.net. Est: 1975. Private premises. Appointment necessary. Very large stock. Spec: Author - Wallace, Edgar; Bibliography; Cinema/Film; Crime (True); Fiction - General; Fiction - Crime, Detective, Spy, Thrillers; Fiction - Fantasy, Horror; Fiction - Romantic; Fiction - Science Fiction; Fiction - Women; First Editions; Periodicals. PR: £3–100. CC: MC; V. Cata: 4 a year. Corresp: French, German. [11/04/2003]

SLEAFORD

Phillip Austen, 50 Main Street, Ewerby, Sleaford, NG34 9PJ. Tel: (01529) 461074. E-mail: phillip-austen@militarybooks.f9.co.uk. Est: 1989. Private premises. Postal business only. Medium stock. Spec: Military. Cata: 2 a year. Mem: PBFA. [08/07/2003]

Mark Evans, 34 Northgate, Sleaford, NG34 7DA. Prop: Mark Evans. Tel: Withheld. Est: 1985. Private premises. Postal business only. Very small general stock. Spec: Cinema/Film; Music - General; Sport - General; Television; Theatre; also Booksearch. PR: £3–100. [Updated]

Julian Roberts Fine Books, Hill House, Braceby, Sleaford, NG34 0TA. Tel: (01529) 497271. Fax: (01529) 497271. Website: www.abebooks.com/home/JULIANROBERTS/. E-mail: jrfinebooks@aol.com. Private premises. Appointment necessary. Small stock. Spec: Author - Blyton, Enid; Author - Crompton, Richmal; Author - Dahl, Roald; Author - Johns, W.E.; Children's - General; Fables; Fiction - General; Fiction - Crime, Detective, Spy, Thrillers; Fiction - Fantasy, Horror; Fiction - Historical. PR: £10–5,000. CC: MC; V. Mem: PBFA. [01/04/2003]

Westgate Bookshop, ■ 45 Westgate, Sleaford, NG34 7PU. Prop: Geoffrey Almond. Tel: (01529) 304276. Website: www.abebooks.com/home/WESTGATEBOOKSHOP/. E-mail: geoff.almond@btinternet.com. Est: 1986. Shop open: **M:** 10:00–17:00; **T:** 10:00–17:00; **W:** 10:00–17:00; **F:** 10:00–17:00; **S:** 10:00–17:00. Small stock. PR: £1–15. CC: MC; V. [Updated]

SOUTH KELSEY

Winghale Books Ltd., Grassmere Cottage, Brigg Road, South Kelsey, LN7 6PH. Directors: Irwin & Hilary Johnston. Tel: (01652) 678752. Fax: (01652) 678881. E-mail: winghale@enterprise.net. Est: 1984. Private premises. Internet and postal. Open in summer. Medium stock. Spec: Academic/Scholarly; Classical Studies; Colonial; Ecclesiastical History & Architecture; History - National; Philosophy; Politics. PR: £10–200. CC: AE; MC; V. Cata: 3 a year on history & related subjects. Mem: PBFA. VAT No: GB 365 1833 46. [Updated]

SPALDING

Anchor Books, 51 Langwith Gardens, Holbeach, Spalding, PE12 7JJ. Prop: Mr. C.R. Dunn. Tel: 01476 550103. E-mail: c.r.dunn@btinternet.com. Est: 1990. Private premises. Postal business only. Medium stock. Spec: Aeronautics; Aviation; Canals/Inland Waterways; History - General; Maritime/Nautical; Military; Naval. CC: MC; V. Corresp: German. Mem: PBFA. [Updated]

Robin Peake, 26 Balmoral Avenue, Spalding, PE11 2RN. Tel: (01775) 724050. E-mail: robin.peake@btinternet.com. Est: 1989. Postal business only. Spec: Motorbikes; Motoring; Vintage Cars. PR: £2–250. [Updated]

Michael Prior, 34 Fen End Lane, Spalding, PE12 6AD. Prop: Michael Prior. Tel: (01775) 761851. Fax: (01775) 761733. Est: 1970. Private premises. Internet and postal. Appointment necessary. Open: Medium stock. Spec: Advertising; Aeronautics; Author - Churchill, Sir Winston; Author - Forester, C.S.; Author - Masefield, John; Aviation; Maritime/Nautical; Military; Military History; Naval; Nostalgia; Ship Modelling; Shipbuilding; Sport - Yachting; Transport. PR: £10–250. Cata: irregularly. Corresp: French. [08/07/2003]

Ken Shultz, Whynacres, Shepeau Stow, Whaplode Drove, Spalding, PE12 0TU. Tel: (01406) 330352. E-mail: whynacres@bushinternet.com. Est: 1978. Private premises. Postal business only. Very small general stock. Spec: Booksearch. PR: £5–25. [Updated]

STAMFORD

St. Mary's Books & Prints, ■ 9 St. Mary's Hill, Stamford, PE9 2DP. Prop: N.A.M., M.G.D. P.A. Tyers. Tel: (01780) 763033. Fax: 01780 763033. Website: www.stmarysbooks.com. E-mail: orders@ stmarysbooks.com. Est: 1971. Internet. Shop open: **M:** 08:00–18:30; **T:** 08:00–18:30; **W:** 08:00–18:30; **Th:** 08:00–18:30; **F:** 08:00–18:30; **S:** 08:00–18:00; **Su:** 09:00–18:00. Spec: Academic/Scholarly; Almanacs; Archaeology; Architecture; Author - Fleming, Ian; Author - Rackham, Arthur; Author - Rowling, J.K.; Author - Watkins–Pitchford, Denys ('B.B.'); Bell-Ringing (Campanology); Bindings; Children's - General; Fine & Rare. I PR: £10–30,000. CC: AE; D; E; JCB; MC; V. Cata: 5 a year. Wisdens, Sporting. Corresp: German, Latin, French, Spanish, Italian. [Updated]

St. Paul's Street Bookshop, ■ 7, St. Paul's Street, Stamford, PE9 2BE. Prop: James Blessett. Tel: (01780) 482748. Fax: (01778) 380538. E-mail: jimblessett@aol.com. Est: 1986. Shop open: **M:** 10:00–17:00; **T:** 10:00–17:00; **Th:** 10:00–17:00; **F:** 10:00–17:00; **S:** 10:00–17:00; Medium stock. PR: £1–500. CC: E; MC; V. Cata: 4 on motoring & motor sport. Corresp: French, German. Mem: PBFA. VAT No: GB 551 0471 74. [Updated]

Staniland (Booksellers), ■ 4/5 St. George's Street, Stamford, PE9 2BJ. Prop: V.A. & B.J. Valentine Ketchum. Tel: (01780) 755800. Fax: (01780) 755800. E-mail: stanilandbooksellers@btinternet.com. Est: 1972. Internet. Shop open: **M:** 10:00–17:00; **T:** 10:00–17:00; **W:** 10:00–17:00; **F:** 10:00–17:00; **S:** 10:00–17:00; Closed for lunch: 13:00–14:00. Large general stock. Spec: Academic/Scholarly; Applied Art; Archaeology; Architecture; Art; Art - History; Art - Reference; Bindings; Building & Construction; Country Houses; Ecclesiastical History & Architecture; Gardening; History - General; Interior Design; Literary Criticsim. PR: £1–3,000. CC: MC; V.Mem: PBFA. VAT No: GB 200 8434 08. [Updated]

Undercover Books, ■ 30 Scotgate, Stamford, PE9 2YQ. Tel: 01780 438098. Fax: 01780 763963. Website: http://www.clique.co.uk/members/undercover/heading. E-mail: undercoverbooks@btinternet.com. Est: 1980. Internet and postal. Shop open: **M:** 10:00–00:17; **T:** 10:00–00:00; **W:** 10:00–00:17; **Th:** 10:00–00:17; **F:** 10:00–00:17; **S:** 10:00–00:17. Large stock. Spec: CC: AE; D; E; JCB; MC; V. Corresp: all. Mem: Police History Ass. [Updated]

LONDON
(EAST LONDON POSTAL DISTRICTS)

Bibliophile Books, Unit 5 Industrial Estate, Thomas Road, E14 7BN. Prop: A. Quigley. Tel: (0207) 515-9222. Fax: (0207) 538-4115. Website: www.bibliophilebooks.com. E-mail: customercare@ bibliophilebooks.co.uk. Est: 1978. Storeroom. Open: **M:** 08:30–17:00; **T:** 08:30–17:00; **W:** 08:30–17:00; **Th:** 08:30–17:00; **F:** 08:30–17:00. Medium stock. Spec: First Editions; Signed Editions; Social History. PR: £1–30. CC: AE; MC; V. Also, re-prints & remainders. Cata: 10 – monthly. Corresp: French, German, Spanish. VAT No: GB 242 6934 55. [Updated]

Birchden Books, 3 Edith Road, East Ham, London, E1 1DE. Prop: Michael Vetterlein. Tel: (020) 8472-3654. E-mail: mike@mvetterlein.freeserve.co.uk. Est: 2001. Private premises. Appointment necessary. Very small stock. Spec: Ecclesiastical History & Architecture; Illuminated Manuscripts; Sculpture; Stained Glass; Topography - Local. PR: £2–500. Cata: 4 – on specialities. [Updated]

Crimes Ink, 35 Moreton Close, Upper Clapton, London, E5 9EP. Prop: Nigel S. Piercy. Tel: (020) 8806-1895. E-mail: crimesink@q-serve.com. Est: 1987. Private premises. Appointment necessary. Medium stock. Spec: Assassinations; Crime (True); Criminology; Espionage; Fiction - General; Fiction - Crime, Detective, Spy, Thrillers; Fiction - Science Fiction; Law; Police Force Histories. PR: £1–150. Corresp: French. [29/06/2003]

Flora Books, 10 Wotton Court, 6 Jamestown Way, London, E14 2DB. Prop: Barrie Macey. Tel: (07785) 525685. Website: www.abebooks.com. E-mail: florabooks@btinternet.com. Est: 1998. Private premises. Postal business only. Medium stock. Spec: Antiquarian; Gardening. PR: £2–1,000. CC: MC; V. [19/08/2003]

Goldhold Ltd., 55 Ravenscroft Road, Canning Town, London, E16 4AF. Prop: A. McKenzie. Tel: (020) 7473-5091. Website: www.goldhold.co.uk. E-mail: sales@goldhold.co.uk. [28/08/2003]

David Houston - Bookseller, 26 North Birkbeck Road, London, E11 4JG. Tel: (020) 8556-9048. Fax: (020) 8556-9048. Website: www.abebooks.com/home/dghbooks. E-mail: scotsbooks@aol.com. Est: 1997. Private premises. Postal business only. Small stock. Spec: Scottish Interest. PR: £5–100. CC: MC; V. Cata: 4 a year. Corresp: French. [Updated]

Dr Jeremy Parrott, 31A Beacontree Avenue Elm Road, Mannamead, Walthamstow, E17 4BU. Tel: (0208) 5274315. Fax: (0036) 62-409107. Website: www.abebooks.com. E-mail: jeremyparrott@ collectedworks.fsnet.co.uk. Est: 1985. Private premises. Internet and postal. Appointment necessary. Shop at: Kezdi utca 3, Szeged 6726, Hungary. Open: Large stock. Spec: Author - Beckett, S.; Author - Benson, E.F.; Author - Stevenson, Robert Louis; Author - Twain, Mark; Author - Verne, Jules; Bibliography; Books about Books; Countries - Hungary; Literary Criticism; Literature; Literature - Victorian; Literature in T PR: £5–1,000. Book search for any book in Hungarian. Corresp: French, German, Spanish, Hungarian. [Updated]

M.A. Stroh, Riverside House, Leaside Road, Upper Clapton, E5 9LU. Tel: (0208) 806 3690. Fax: (0208) 806 3690. Website: www.webspawner.com/users/Buttonbook/. E-mail: patent@stroh.demon.co.uk. Est: 1956. Storeroom. Appointment necessary. Open: **M:** 10:00–22:00; **T:** 10:00–22:00; **W:** 10:00–22:00; **Th:** 10:00–22:00; **F:** 10:00–22:00. Very large stock. Spec: Mathematics; Medicine; Science - General; Technology. PR: £10–1,000. Cata: occasionally. Corresp: French. [Updated]

Brian Troath Books, 106 Graham Road, London, E8 1BX. Tel: (020) 7254-2912. Fax: (020) 7254-2912. Website: www.ukbookworld.com/members/ariel. E-mail: briantroathbooks@onetel.net.uk. Est: 1970. Private premises. Internet and postal. Appointment necessary. Medium stock. Spec: Books about Books; Cinema/Film; Classical Studies; Drama; Fine & Rare; First Editions; History - General; Limited Editions; Literary Criticism; Literature; Performing Arts; Periodicals & Magazines; Poetry; Private Press. PR: £10–1,000. Cata: very occasionally. [15/07/2003]

LONDON
(EAST CENTRAL POSTAL DISTRICTS)

The Amwell Book Company, ■ 53 Amwell St., London, London, EC1R 1UR. Prop: Charlotte Robinson. Tel: (020) 7837 4891. E-mail: sixrobins@aol.com. Est: 1980. Internet and postal. Open: **T:** 11:00–18:00; **W:** 11:00–18:00; **Th:** 11:00–18:00; **F:** 11:00–18:00; **S:** 13:00–17:00. Small stock. Spec: Applied Art; Architecture; Children's - Illustrated; Fashion & Costume; Fiction - Crime, Detective, Spy, Thrillers; Fiction - Women; Fine & Rare; Juvenile; Modern First Editions; Photography. PR: £5–1,000. CC: MC; V; Switch. Corresp: French. Mem: PBFA. Also at: Biblion, Davies Street, London W1. [Updated]

Elizabeth Crawford, 5 Owen's Row, London, EC1V 4NP. Tel: (020) 7278-9479. Fax: (020) 7278-9479. E-mail: E.Crawford@sphere20.freeserve.co.uk. Est: 1984. Private premises. Postal business only. Appointment necessary. Very small stock. Spec: Authors - Women; Women. PR: £5–5,000. Cata: 10 a year on Women's history/literature/women's studies. Mem: PBFA. [Updated]

Andrew Sclanders (Beatbooks), Apt. 32 St Paul's View, 15 Amwell Street, London, EC1R 1UP. Prop: Andrew Sclanders. Tel: (020) 7278-5034. Fax: (020) 7278-5034. Website: www.beatbooks.com. E-mail: sclanders@beatbooks.com. Est: 1990. Private premises. Internet and postal. Appointment necessary. Small stock. Spec: Art; Author - Burroughs, William; Author - Kerouac, Jack; Avant-Garde; Beat Writers; Counterculture; Music - Rock. PR: £5–2,500. CC: AE; E; JCB; MC; V. Cata: 3 – Beat Literature, '60s Counterculture, & the Avant-Gardes. [Updated]

LONDON
(NORTH POSTAL DISTRICTS)

Alpha Books, 60 Langdon Park Road, London, N6 5QG. Prop: Tony Maddock. Tel: (020) 8348-2831. Fax: (020) 8348-2831. E-mail: alpha@dircon.co.uk. Est: 1983. Private premises. Appointment necessary. Medium stock. Spec: Academic/Scholarly; Alchemy; Astrology; Egyptology; Esoteric; Folklore; Freemasonry & Anti-Masonry; Hermeticism; Metaphysics; Mythology; Occult; Palmistry & Fortune Telling; Psychic; Theosophy; Travel - Asia; U.F.O.s; Witchcraft. PR: £1–500. CC: MC; V. Cata: 4 a year. Mem: PBFA. [Updated]

G.W. Andron, 162a Brunswick Park Road, London, N11 1HA. Tel: (020) 8361-2409. Est: 1972. Private premises. Postal business only. Medium stock. Spec: Aeronautics; Aviation; Bibliography; Bookbinding; Books about Books; Maritime/Nautical; Military; Military History; Natural History; Naval; Printing; Topography - General; Topography - Local; Travel - General; Typography; War - General. PR: £1–100. Cata: 2 – one general & one military/naval or travel & topog. [Updated]

Antique Prints of the World, 6 Livingstone Road, Palmers Green, London, N13 4SD. Prop: Mr Mel Menelaou. Tel: (020) 8292-0622. Fax: (020) 8292-0622. Website: www.antique19thcenturyprints.com. E-mail: mel@worldprints.freeserve.co.uk. Est: 1994. Private premises. Appointment necessary. Spec: Countries - Cyprus; Countries - Greece. CC: PayPal. Corresp: Greek. [Updated]

The Aviation Bookshop, ■ 656 Holloway Road, London, N19 3PD. Prop: David Hatherell. Tel: (020) 7272-3630. Fax: (020) 7272-9761. E-mail: info@aviation-bookshop.com. Est: 1948. Shop open: **M:** 09:30–17:30; **T:** 09:30–17:30; **W:** 09:30–17:30; **Th:** 09:30–17:30; **F:** 09:30–17:30; **S:** 09:30–17:30; Large stock. Spec: Aviation. PR: £1–200. CC: AE; D; E; JCB; MC; V. Mem: BA. VAT No: GB 232 6072 90. [13/03/2003]

Church Street Bookshop, 142 Stoke Newington, Church Street, London, N16 0JU. Prop: Tim Watson. Tel: (0171) 241-5411. E-mail: Est: 1984. Spec: Academic/Scholarly. PR: £1–50. [28/08/2003]

Michael Cuddy Books, 29 Highwood Avenue, London, N12 8QL. Tel: (020) 8445-7768. Est: 1977. Private premises. Postal business only. Small stock. Spec: Aviation; Maritime/Nautical; Military; also Booksearch. PR: £3–100. Cata: occasionally. Corresp: French. [27/05/2003]

Fantasy Centre, ■ 157 Holloway Road, London, N7 8LX. Prop: Ted Ball & Erik Arthur. Tel: (020) 7607-9433. Fax: (020) 7607-9433. Website: www.fantasycentre.demon.co.uk. E-mail: books@fantasycentre.biz. Est: 1972. Open: **M:** 10:00–18:00; **T:** 10:00–18:00; **W:** 10:00–18:00; **Th:** 10:00–18:00; **F:** 10:00–18:00; **S:** 10:00–18:00; Medium stock. Spec: Fiction - Fantasy, Horror; Fiction - Science Fiction. CC: E; MC; V. website: fantasycentre.biz. Stock available on abe. Cata: 5 a year. VAT No: GB 227 3306 83. [25/02/2003]

Fisher & Sperr, ■ 46 Highgate High Street, London, N6 5JB. Tel: (020) 8340-7244. Fax: (020) 8348-4293. Est: 1939. Open: **M:** 10:00–17:00; **T:** 10:00–17:00; **W:** 10:00–17:00; **Th:** 10:00–17:00; **F:** 10:00–17:00; **S:** 10:00–17:00. Very large stock. Spec: Art; Art - History; Folio Society, The; Literary Criticism; Philosophy; Sets of Books; Topography - General. PR: £1–10. Corresp: French. Mem: ABA; ILAB. VAT No: GB 229 2603 70. [Updated]

Gate Memorabilia, 35 Nether Close, Finchley, London, N3 1AA. Prop: Jon Baldwin. Tel: (020) 8346 1090. Website: ukbookworld.com/members/Jonnyb. Est: 1981. Private premises. Internet and postal. Appointment necessary. Very small general stock. Spec: Animals and Birds; Annuals; Archaeology; Art; Autobiography; Biography; Cinema/Film; Dance; Drama; Fiction - Crime, Detective, Spy, Thrillers. PR: £3–500. CC: MC; V. [08/05/2003]

Nancy Sheiry Glaister, Fine &, Fine & Rare Books, 18 Huntingdon Street, London, N1 1BS. Prop: Nancy Sheiry Glaister. Tel: (020) 7609-1605. Fax: (020) 7607-2641. E-mail: glaisterbooks@ btinternet.com. Est: 1985. Private premises. Appointment necessary. Very small stock. Spec: Architecture; Landscape; Town Planning. PR: £20–7,500. CC: None. Cata: occasionally. Corresp: French, German, Italian. Mem: ABA; PBFA; ILAB. [Updated]

Nicholas Goodyer, 8 Framfield Road, Highbury Fields, London, N5 1UU. Tel: (020) 7226-5682. Fax: (020) 7354-4716. Website: www.nicholasgoodyer.com. E-mail: email@nicholasgoodyer.com. Private premises. Internet and postal. Telephone first. Open: **M:** 10:00–17:00; **T:** 10:00–17:00; **W:** 10:00–17:00; **Th:** 10:00–17:00; **F:** 10:00–17:00. Very small stock. Spec: Animals and Birds; Architecture; Art; Botany; Colour-Plate; Decorative Art; Fashion & Costume; Gardening; Illustrated; Natural History; Ornithology; Topography - General; Travel - General. CC: MC; V. Business operates by appointment or by chance, weekdays. Cata: 4 – regularly. Corresp: French, German, Italian, Spanish, Portuguese. Mem: ABA; PBFA. VAT No: GB 629 6750 05. [Updated]

F. & J. Hogan, 31 Tranmere Road, Edmonton, London, N9 9EJ. Prop: Frederick & Joan Hogan. Tel: (020) 8360-6146. Est: 1969. Private premises. Postal business only. Small stock. Spec: Atlases; Caricature; Cartography. PR: £5–1,000. [Updated]

Idle Genius Books, 115 Cluse Court, St. Peter Street, London, N1 8PE. Prop: Philip Obeney. Tel: (020) 7704-3193. E-mail: p.obeney@btopenworld.com. Est: 2000. Storeroom. Small stock. Spec: Archaeology; Literature; Modern First Editions; Topography - Local. PR: £5–400. Attends HD Book Fairs. Also, ephemera on London in wartime. [25/06/2003]

InterCol London, ■ 43 Templars Crescent, London, N3 3QR. Prop: Yasha Beresiner. Tel: (020) 8349-2207. Fax: (020) 8346-9539. Website: www.intercol.co.uk. E-mail: yasha@compuserve.com. Est: 1981. Shop open: **T:** 10:30–17:00; **W:** 10:30–17:00; **Th:** 10:30–17:00; **F:** 10:30–17:00; **S:** 10:30–17:00; Small stock. Spec: Banking & Insurance; Cartography; Erotica; Freemasonry & Anti-Masonry; Gambling; Games; Numismatics; Topography - General. PR: £5–500. CC: AE; E; JCB; MC; V. Corresp: French, Italian, Spanish, Turkish, Hebrew. Mem: ANA; IBNS; IMCoS; IPCS. VAT No: GB 350 6069 69. [24/09/2003]

M.E. Korn Books, 5 Dolphin Court, 42 Carleton Road, London, N7 0ER. Prop: Eric Korn. Tel: (020) 7609-7100. Fax: (020) 7609-7100. E-mail: eric@mekornbooks.freeserve.co.uk. Est: 1969. Private premises. Book fairs only. Contactable. Small stock. Spec: Children's - General; Linguistics; Natural History; Science - General; also Booksearch. PR: £5–500. Also, a booksearch service. Cata: very seldom. Corresp: French Russian. Mem: ABA; PBFA. VAT No: GB 234 2420 04. [Updated]

Barrie Marks Limited, 24 Church Vale, Fortis Green, London, N2 9PA. Tel: (020) 8883-1919. Spec: Fine & Rare; Illustrated; Limited Editions; Literature; Private Press. [Updated]

Ian McKelvie, 45 Hertford Road, London, N2 9BX. Tel: (020) 8444-0567. Fax: (020) 8444-0567. Website: http://ukbookworld.com/members/Dudley1. E-mail: ianmckelvie@supanet.com. Est: 1969. Private premises. Internet and postal. Appointment necessary. Large stock. Spec: Author - Bloomsbury Group, The; Fiction - General; Fiction - Crime, Detective, Spy, Thrillers; First Editions; Limited Editions; Literature; Modern First Editions; Plays; Poetry; Proof Copies; Signed Editions. CC: AE; JCB; MC; V; Maestro. Cata: 2 a year.

Mountaineering Books, 6 Bedford Road, London, N8 8HL. Prop: Mr. R. & Mrs. A. Court. Tel: (020) 8340-1953. Est: 1990. Private premises. Appointment necessary. Open: Very small stock. Spec: Alpinism/Mountaineering; Author - Buchan, John. PR: £10–500. Cata: 2 – a year on alpinism/ mountaineering. [Updated]

Pendleburys Bookshop, Church House, Portland Avenue, Stamford Hill, London, N16 6HJ. Prop: Jonathan Pendlebury. Tel: (020) 8809-4922. Website: www.pendleburys.com. E-mail: books@ pendleburys.com. Est: 1984. Spec: Bibles; Ecclesiastical History & Architecture; History of Ideas; Philosophy; Prayer Books; Religion - General; Religion - Christian; Religion - Islam; Religion - Jewish. PR: £1–300. [Updated]

John Price, 8 Cloudesley Square, London, N1 0HT. Tel: (020) 7837-8008. Fax: (020) 7278-4733. Website: www.johnpriceantiquarianbooks.com. E-mail: books@jvprice.com. Est: 1988. Private premises. Internet and postal. Appointment necessary. Very small stock. Spec: Antiquarian; Cookery/ Gastronomy; History of Ideas; Literature; Music - General; Performing Arts; Philosophy; Scottish Interest. PR: £45–4,500. CC: AE; E; MC; V. Corresp: French, German. Mem: ABA; PBFA; BA; ILAB. [Updated]

Ripping Yarns, ■ 355 Archway Road, London, N6 4EJ. Prop: Celia Mitchell. Tel: (020) 8341-6111. Fax: (020) 7482-5056. Website: www.rippingyarns.co.uk. E-mail: yarns@rippingyarns.co.uk. Est: 1984. Internet and postal. Shop open: **T:** 11:00–17:00; **W:** 11:00–17:00; **Th:** 11:00–17:00; **F:** 11:00–17:00; **S:** 10:00–17:00; **Su:** 11:00–16:00; Very large stock. Spec: Children's - General; Illustrated; Literature. PR: £1–500. Corresp: French Spanish. Mem: PBFA. [Updated]

Susanne Schulz–Falster, 22 Compton Terrace, London, N1 2UN. Prop: Susanne Schulz-Falster. Tel: (020) 7704-9845. Fax: (020) 7354-4202. E-mail: sfalster@btinternet.com. Est: 1997. Private premises. Appointment necessary. Very small stock. Spec: Antiquarian; Early Imprints; Economics; History of Ideas; Linguistics; Philosophy; Printing; Women; also Booksearch. PR: £100–10,000. CC: MC; V. Also, building collections, valuations. Cata: 3 a year. Corresp: German, Italian, French. Mem: ABA; ILAB; VDA. VAT No: GB 714 4200 79. [Updated]

John Singleton, 8 Gladsmuir Road, London, N19 3JX. Tel: (020) 7263-9179. Website: jsingl1920@ aol.com. E-mail: jsingl1920@aol.com. Est: 1995. Private premises. Internet and postal. Appointment necessary. Large stock. Spec: Children's - General; Cinema/Film; Modern First Editions; Performing Arts; Poetry. PR: £5–300. [14/04/2003]

Stanhope Bibliophiles, P.O. Box 6754, London, N3 3NT. Prop: Mr. Smith. Tel: (withheld). Est: 1975. Private premises. Postal business only. Very small stock. Spec: Atlases; Dictionaries; Parish Registers; Railways; Sport - Hunting; Topography - Local. PR: £5–500. Also, books on English counties; Devon & Dorset parish registers, and Devon topography. [26/09/2004]

STM Books, 2 Castle Mews, North Finchley, London, N12 9EH. Tel: 020 8492 7324. Website: www.stmbooks.co.uk. E-mail: sales@stmbooks.co.uk. Est: 1984. Shop &/or showroom; Internet and postal. Telephone first. Open: **M:** 08:00–16:00; **T:** 08:00–16:00; **W:** 08:00–16:00; **Th:** 08:00–16:00; **F:** 08:00–16:00. Very small stock. Spec: Medicine; Medicine - History of; Veterinary. PR: £10–500. CC: AE; D; JCB; MC. Also, new books. Mem: PBFA. [19/08/2003]

Robert Temple, 65 Mildmay Road, London, N1 4PU. Prop: P.J. Allen. Tel: (020) 7254-3674. Fax: (020) 7254-3674. Website: www.telinco.co.uk/RobertTemple/. E-mail: roberttemple@telinco.co.uk. Est: 1977. Warehouse; Internet and postal. Appointment necessary. Medium stock. Spec: Academic/ Scholarly; Anthologies; Antiquarian; Fiction - General; Fiction - Crime, Detective, Spy, Thrillers; Fiction - Fantasy, Horror; Fiction - Historical; Fiction - Science Fiction; Fiction - Women; First Editions; Journals - General; Juvenile. PR: £5–15,000. CC: PayPal. Credit and Debit cards taken via the PayPal secure server only (VISA, non-corporate AmEx, MasterCard, Discover, Switch, Solo). Corresp: French. VAT No: GB 292 2648 41. [Updated]

Richard Thornton Books, 25 Beechdale, Winchmore Hill, N21 3QE. Prop: Richard Thornton. Tel: (020) 8886 8202. Website: www.abebooks.com/home/NEVILLE/. E-mail: richard.thorntonbooks@ btinternet.com. Est: 1994. Private premises. Internet and postal. Telephone first. Open: **M:** 09:00– 20:00; **T:** 09:00–20:00; **W:** 09:00–20:00; **Th:** 09:00–20:00; **F:** 09:00–20:00; **S:** 09:00–20:00; **Su:** 10:00– 18:00. Medium stock. Spec: Art; Children's - General; Fiction - Crime, Detective, Spy, Thrillers; First Editions; History - British; History - South Africa; Literature; Military; Modern First Editions; Motoring; Natural History; Sport - General; Sport - Angling/Fishing. PR: £10–2,000. CC: AE; D; E; JCB; MC; V. Cata: 15 a year. Mem: PBFA; BIB. Also, books rooms available to view near Southgate Tube. [Updated]

John Trotter Books, 80 East End Road, London, N3 2SY. Prop: John Trotter. Tel: (020) 8349-9484. Website: www.bibliophile.net/John-Trotter-Books.htm. E-mail: jtrotter@freenetname.co.uk. Est: 1973. Office &/or bookroom. Internet and postal. Open: **M:** 09:00–17:00; **T:** 09:09–17:00; **W:** 09:00–17:00; **Th:** 09:00–17:00; **Su:** 10:00–13:00. Large stock. Spec: Countries - Middle East, The; History - Ancient; Religion - Jewish; Travel - Middle East, also Booksearch. PR: £5–1,500. CC: AE; MC; V. Mem: PBFA; BA. [Updated]

Tyger Press, 41 Cheverton Road, London, N19 3BA. Prop: Alaric Bamping. Tel: (020) 7272-3234. Fax: (020) 7272-8898. Website: www.abebooks.com. E-mail: tygerpress@clara.net. Est: 1984. Postal business only. Spec: Genealogy; History - General; History - Local; Manuscripts; Topography - General. PR: £1–750. [Updated]

Graham Weiner, 78 Rosebery Road, London, N10 2LA. Tel: (020) 8883-8424. Fax: (020) 8444-6505. E-mail: graham.weiner@btinternet.com. Est: 1973. Private premises. Internet and postal. Appointment necessary. Medium stock. Spec: Chemistry; Geology; History - General; Medicine; Physics; Science - General; Science - History of; Technology; Transport. PR: £15–2,500. CC: MC; V. Cata: 1 a year. Corresp: French. Mem: ABA; IEE. VAT No: GB 230 6110 23. [Updated]

Woburn Books, 5 Caledonian Road, London, N1 9DX. Prop: Andrew Burgin. Tel: (020) 7263 5196. Fax: (020) 7263-5196. E-mail: woburn@burgin.freeserve.co.uk. Est: 1991. Office &/or bookroom. Internet and postal. Medium stock. Spec: Academic/Scholarly; Africana; Anthropology; Antiquarian; Architecture; Art; Arts, The; Avant-Garde; Beat Writers; Black Studies; Economics; Health; History - Labour/Radical Movements; Marxism; Pacifism; Philosophy; Photography; Poetry; Politics. PR: £1–500. CC: JCB; V; SW. Mem: PBFA. [25/06/2003]

LONDON
(NORTH WEST POSTAL DISTRICTS)

Archive Books & Music, ■ 83 Bell Street, London, Marylebone, London, NW1 6TB. Prop: Tim Meaker. Tel: (020) 7402-8212. Website: www.archivebookstore.com. Est: 1973. Open: **M:** 10:30–18:00; **T:** 10:30–18:00; **W:** 10:30–18:00; **Th:** 10:30–18:00; **F:** 10:30–18:00; **S:** 10:30–18:00. Medium stock. Spec: Antiquarian; Music - General; Music - Classical; Music - Popular. PR: £1–150. CC: MC; V. [13/09/2003]

Aurelian Books, 31 Llanvanor Road, London, NW2 2AR. Prop: David Dunbar. Tel: (020) 8455 9612. E-mail: dgldunbar@aol.com. Est: 1970. Private premises. Appointment necessary. Small stock. Spec: Colour-Plate; Conservation; Entomology; Lepidopterology / Lepidoptery; Natural History. PR: £5–5,000. CC: MC; V; SW. Cata: 2 a year. Mem: PBFA. [Updated]

H. Baron, 121 Chatsworth Road, London, NW2 4BH. Prop: Christel Wallbaum. Tel: (020) 8459-2035. Fax: (020) 8459-2035. Est: 1949. Private premises. Postal business only. Spec: Autographs; Iconography; Letters; Music - General. CC: E; MC; V. Cata: 2 – antiquarian music, books on music, autographs. Corresp: French, German. Mem: ABA. VAT No: GB 227 1452 82. [Updated]

The Book Depot, 111 Woodcote Avenue, Mill Hill, London, NW7 2PD. Prop: Conrad Wiberg. Tel: (020) 8906-3708. E-mail: conrad@adword.fsnet.co.uk. Est: 1980. Postal business only. Spec: Booksearch. PR: £5–10. [25/06/2003]

Cranhurst Books, 20 Cranhurst Road, Willesden Green, London, NW2 4LN. Prop: Heidi Stransky. Tel: (020) 8452-7845. Fax: (020) 8452-0689. E-mail: HStransky@aol.com. Est: 1997. Private premises. Appointment necessary. Small stock. Spec: Children's - General; Comic Books & Annuals; Modern First Editions. PR: £5–2,500. [Updated]

P.G. de Lotz Books, 20 Downside Crescent, Belsize Park, London, NW3 2AP. Tel: (020) 7794-5709. Est: 1968. Private premises. Appointment necessary. Medium stock. Spec: Aviation; Bibliography; Maritime/Nautical; Military; War - General. Cata: 1 a year. [22/08/2002]

Keith Fawkes, ■ 1–3 Flask Walk, Hampstead, London, NW3 1HJ. Prop: Keith Fawkes. Tel: (020) 7435-0614. Est: 1970. Open: **M:** 10:00–18:00; **T:** 09:00–18:00; **W:** 10:00–18:00; **Th:** 09:00–18:00; **F:** 10:00–18:00; **S:** 10:00–18:00; **Su:** 13:00–18:00. Large general stock. PR: £1–100. Also, bric a brac. VAT No: GB 232 0644 04. [Updated]

Fishburn Books, 43 Ridge Hill, London, NW11 8PR. Prop: Jonathan Fishburn. Tel: (0208) 455-9139. Fax: (0208) 922-5008. Website: www.fishburnbooks.com. E-mail: fishburnbooks@yahoo.co.uk. Est: 2000. Private premises. Appointment necessary. Spec: Countries - Middle East, The; Holocaust; Judaica; Religion - Hebraica; Religion - Jewish. PR: £15–5,000. CC: AE; MC; V. Cata: 3 – Mem: PBFA. VAT No: GB 805 4965 16. [Updated]

Fortune Green Books, 74 Fortune Green Road, London, NW6 1DS. Prop: Eric Stevens & Jane Bell. Tel: (020) 7435-7545. E-mail: belleric@dircon.co.uk. Est: 1992. Office &/or bookroom. Internet and postal. Appointment necessary. Medium stock. Spec: Academic/Scholarly; Art; Feminism; Fiction - General; Fiction - Women; Literary Criticism; Literature; Women. PR: £1–50. CC: MC; V. Mem: PBFA. [Updated]

Stephen Foster, ■ 95 Bell Street, London, NW1 6TL. Prop: Stephen Foster. Tel: (020) 7724-0876. Fax: (020) 7724-0927. Website: www.95bellstreet.com. E-mail: stephen.foster@sfbooks.co.uk. Est: 1987. Open: **M:** 10:30–18:00; **T:** 10:30–18:00; **W:** 10:30–18:00; **Th:** 10:30–18:00; **F:** 10:30–18:00; **S:** 10:30–18:00; Medium stock. Spec: Antiquarian; Antiques; Architecture; Art - History; Art - Reference; Artists; Arts, The; Decorative Art; History - General; Iconography; Interior Design; Literature. PR: £1–1,000. CC: AE; JCB; MC; V; Switch; Maestro. Also, a booksearch service; new books at a discount and stock on ibooknet. Mem: ABA; PBFA; ILAB. Also at: stock at Biblion, Davies Mews. VAT No: GB 521 5504 81. [Updated]

Hellenic Bookservices, ■ 91 Fortess Road, Kentish Town, London, NW5 1AG. Prop: M. Williams & Andrew Stoddart. Tel: (020) 7267-9499. Fax: (020) 7267-9498. Website: www.hellenicbookservice.com. E-mail: info@hellenicbookservice.com. Est: 1966. Large stock. Spec: Academic/Scholarly; Byzantium; Classical Studies; Countries - Cyprus; Countries - Greece; Foreign Texts; Guide Books; Literary Criticism; Poetry; Theology. CC: AE; JCB; MC; V. Also, a booksearch service, school supplies – all subjects. Corresp: Modern Greek. Mem: PBFA. [Updated]

C.R. Johnson Rare Book Collect, 4, Keats Grove, Hampstead, NW3 2RT. Prop: C.R. Johnson & C.A. Forster. Tel: (020) 7794-7940. Fax: (020) 7433-3303. Website: www.crjohnson.com. E-mail: mail@crjohnson.com. Est: 1970. Private premises. Internet and postal. Appointment necessary. Very large general stock. Spec: Authors - Women; Fiction - General; Literature. PR: £25–5,000. CC: MC; V. Cata: 1 a year. Mem: PBFA; CERL. [Updated]

Terence Kaye - Bookseller, 52 Neeld Crescent, London, NW4 3RR. Prop: H Terence Kaye. Tel: (020) 8202-8188. Fax: (020) 8202-8188. E-mail: kforbook@onetel.com. Est: 1996. Office &/or bookroom. Appointment necessary. Open: **M:** 09:00–20:00; **T:** 09:00–20:00; **W:** 09:00–20:00; **Th:** 09:00–20:00; **F:** 09:00–18:00; **S:** 10:00–20:00; **Su:** 10:00–20:00. Small stock. Spec: Cinema/Film; Circus; Drama; Entertainment - General; Fairgrounds; Music - Music Hall; Performing Arts; Television; Theatre, also Booksearch (specialist subjects only). PR: £10–200. Also, library/collection development. Corresp: Hebrew. Mem: Ephemera Society. [Updated]

Loretta Lay Books, 24 Grampian Gardens, London, NW2 1JG. Tel: (020) 8455-3069. Website: www.laybooks.com. E-mail: lorettalay@hotmail.com. Est: 2001. Private premises. Postal business only. Appointment necessary. Very small stock. Spec: Crime (True); Criminology; Fiction - Crime, Detective, Spy, Thrillers. PR: £5–1,000. CC: JCB; MC; V; SW. Also at: Black-Bird Books, 24 Grampian Gardens, London. [10/12/2004]

Richard Lucas, 114 Fellows Road, London, NW3 3JH. Tel: (020) 7449-9431. Est: 1975. Private premises. Appointment necessary. Medium stock. Spec: Brewing; Cookery/Gastronomy; Etiquette; Food & Drink; Herbalism; Public Houses; Travel - General; Viticulture; Whisky; Wine. PR: £10–1,000. Cata: 1 a year occasionally. [Updated]

Nicholas Morrell (Rare Books), 77 Falkland Road, London, NW5 2XB. Tel: (020) 7485-5205. Fax: (020) 7485-2376. Website: www.morbook.com. E-mail: morbook@aol.com. Est: 1982. Private premises. Appointment necessary. Very small stock. Spec: Travel - General. PR: £5–5,000. Cata: 1 a year. Corresp: French, German. Mem: ABA; PBFA. VAT No: GB 370 7735 39. [03/08/2003]

Moss Books, 14 Manor Park Gardens, Edgware, London, HA8 7NA. Tel: (020) 8386-2707. Fax: (020) 8386-2707. E-mail: moss.books@ntlworld.com. Est: 2002. Market stand/stall; Internet and postal. Appointment necessary. Medium stock. Spec: Archaeology; Architecture; Ceramics; Ecclesiastical History & Architecture; Lepidopterology / Lepidoptery; Odd & Unusual; Ornithology; Pacifism; Religion - General. PR: £5–800. CC: PayPal. VAT No: GB 805 4666 26. [29/06/2003]

Neil's Books, 151 Fordwych Road, London, NW2 3NG. Prop: Neil Aptaker. Tel: (020) 8452–0933. Fax: (02082) 2082434. E-mail: neilsbooks@lineone.net. Est: 1990. Internet and postal. Shop at: Portobello Road nr. Flyover. Open: **M:** 10:00–18:45; **Th:** 10:00–18:45; Medium stock. Spec: Fiction - General; Modern First Editions. PR: £2–200. [Updated]

Primrose Hill Books, 134 Regents Park Road, London, NW1 8XL. Tel: (0207) 586 2027. Fax: (0207) 722 9653. E-mail: phbooks@btconnect.com. Est: 1987. Storeroom. Internet and postal. Appointment necessary. Medium stock. Spec: Biography; First Editions; Poetry; Theatre. PR: £4–1,000. CC: AE; E; JCB; MC; V. Mem: PBFA. VAT No: GB 523 4672 53. [Updated]

Paul Rassam, Flat 5, 18 East Heath Road, London, NW3 1AJ. Tel: (020) 7794-9316. Fax: (020) 7794-7669. E-mail: paul@rassam.demon.co.uk. Est: 1972. Private premises. Appointment necessary. Very small stock. Spec: Autographs; First Editions; Literature; Manuscripts. CC: MC; V. Cata: occasionally. Mem: ABA. [Updated]

Robert G Sawers Ltd, No.5, Inglewood Road, London, NW6 1OT. Tel: (0207) 794 9618. Fax: (0207) 794 9571. Website: bobsawers@clara.net. E-mail: bobsawers@clara.net. Est: 1970. Private premises. Internet and postal. Appointment necessary. Very small stock. Spec: Countries - Far East, The; Countries - Japan. Corresp: French, Spanish, Japanese. Mem: ABA. VAT No: GB 233 701 02. [Updated]

Visit www.sheppardsworld.co.uk

to order directories and related titles – and to search for overseas

book dealers – ephemera dealers – print & map sellers

San Expedito Books, 18 Wentworth Mansions, Keats Grove, London, NW3 2RL. Prop: Dr. J.Q.C. Mackrell. Tel: (020) 7794-8414. Fax: (020) 7794-8414. E-mail: jqcmackrell@hotmail.com. Est: 1998. Private premises. Spec: Booksearch. [19/03/2003]

Sevin Seydi Rare Books, 13 Shirlock Road, London, NW3 2HR. Prop: Sevin Seydi & Maurice Whitby. Tel: (020) 7485 9801. Fax: (020) 7428 9313. E-mail: sevin@seydi.fsnet.co.uk. Est: 1970. Private premises. Appointment necessary. Large stock. Spec: Architecture; Art - History; Bindings; Classical Studies; Countries - Greece; Countries - Italy; Countries - Turkey; Early Imprints; Emblemata; History of Ideas; Illustrated; Incunabula; Manuscripts; Philology. CC: MC; V. Cata: 3 – irregularly on specialities. Corresp: French, Turkish. Mem: PBFA. [Updated]

Unsworths Booksellers, ■ 101 Euston Road, London, NW1 2RA. Charlie Unsworth. Tel: 020 7383 5507. Fax: 020 7383 5507. Website: www.unsworths.com. E-mail: books@unsworths.com. Est: 1986. Open: **M:** 10:00–18:30; **T:** 10:00–18:30; **W:** 10:00–18:30; **Th:** 10:00–18:30; **F:** 10:00–18:30; **S:** 10:00–18:30. Very large stock. Spec: Academic/Scholarly; Advertising; Anthropology; Antiquarian; Archaeology; Architecture; Art; Bibliography; Bindings; Books about Books; Byzantium; Cinema/Film; Classical Studies; Early Imprints; Ecclesiastical History & Architecture; Egyptology. PR: £1–1,000. CC: AE; D; E; JCB; MC; V. Mem: ABA; PBFA; BA; ILAB. Also at: 12 Bloomsbury Street, London WC1B 3QA. VAT No: GB GB480114575. [Updated]

Walden Books, ■ 38 Harmood Street, London, NW1 8DP. Prop: David Tobin. Tel: (020) 7267-8146. Fax: (020) 7267-8147. Website: www.ukbookworld/members/waldenbooks. E-mail: waldenbooks@ lineone.net. Est: 1979. Open: **Th:** 10:30–18:30; **F:** 10:30–18:30; **S:** 10:30–18:30; **Su:** 10:30–18:30; Medium stock. Spec: Architecture; Art; Art - History; Literature; Philosophy; also Booksearch. PR: £1–450. CC: AE; MC; V. Mem: PBFA. VAT No: GB 564 4805 26. [Updated]

Eva M. Weininger, Antiquarian Bookseller, 79 Greenhill, London, NW3 5TZ. Tel: (020) 7435-2334. Est: 1979. Private premises. Appointment necessary. Very small stock. Spec: Courtesy; Culture - Foreign; Culture - National; Etiquette; History of Ideas; Social History. PR: £10–150. [Updated]

J. & S. Wilbraham, 1 Wise Lane, Mill Hill, London, NW7 2RL. Prop: John and Shahin Wilbraham. Tel: (0208) 9593709. Website: www.wilbraham.demon.co.uk. E-mail: john@wilbraham.demon.co.uk. Est: 1981. Private premises. Postal business only. Contactable. Very small stock. Spec: Antiquarian; Children's - General; Literature. PR: £10–1,000. CC: AE; MC; V. Cata: 6 a year. Corresp: French. [Updated]

LONDON
(SOUTH EAST POSTAL DISTRICTS)

The Bookshop on the Heath, ■ 74 Tranquil Vale, Blackheath, London, SE3 0BW. Prop: Richard Platt. Tel: (020) 8852-4786. Website: www.bookshopontheheath.co.uk. E-mail: tboth@btopenworld.com. Est: 2003. Open: **M:** 10:00–18:00; **T:** 10:00–18:00; **W:** 10:00–18:00; **Th:** 10:00–18:00; **F:** 10:00–18:00; **S:** 10:00–18:00; **Su:** 12:00–18:00. Medium stock. Spec: Author - Fleming, Ian; Children's - General; Fiction - Crime, Detective, Spy, Thrillers; Modern First Editions; Topography - Local. PR: £1–5,000. CC: AE; MC; V. Switch. Corresp: German, Mandarin. VAT No: GB 831112578. [Updated]

Fiona Campbell, 158 Lambeth Road, London, SE1 7DF. Tel: (020) 7928-1633. Fax: (020) 7928-1633. E-mail: fcampbell@britishlibrary.net. Est: 1970. Private premises. Appointment necessary. Small stock. Spec: Countries - Italy; Travel - General; Travel - Europe. CC: JCB; MC; V. Also, a booksearch service, and bookbinding. Cata: 2 – a year. Corresp: French, German and Italian. Mem: ABA; PBFA. ILAB. [Updated]

Marcus Campbell Art Books, ■ 43 Holland Street, Bankside, London, SE1 9JR. Prop: Marcus Campbell. Tel: (020) 7261-0111. Fax: (020) 7261-0129. Website: www.marcuscampbell.demon.co.uk. E-mail: campbell@marcuscampbell.demon.co.uk. Est: 1998. Internet and postal. Shop open: **M:** 10:30–18:30; **T:** 10:30–18:30; **W:** 10:30–18:00; **Th:** 10:30–18:06; **F:** 10:30–18:30; **S:** 10:30–18:30; **Su:** 12:00–18:00. Very large stock. Spec: Art; Art - Reference; Artists; Monographs. PR: £2–2,000. CC: E; MC; V; Switch. Cata: 1 a year infrequently. Corresp: French. Mem: PBFA. VAT No: GB 605 8695 15. [12/03/2003]

Chapter Two, Fountain House, Conduit Mews, London, SE18 7AP. Manager: Miss P. Brachotte. Tel: (020) 8316-5389. Website: www.chaptertwobooks.org.uk. E-mail: chapter2uk@aol.com. Est: 1976. Office &/or bookroom. Internet and postal. Telephone first. Open: **M:** 09:00–17:00; **T:** 09:00–17:00; **W:** 09:00–17:00; **Th:** 09:00–17:00; **F:** 06:00–17:00; Closed for lunch: 13:00–14:30. Medium stock. Spec: Author - Baring-Gould, S.; Author - Blyton, Enid; Author - Johns, W.E.; Bibles; Children's - General; Countries - Africa; Countries - Asia; Irish Interest; Publishers - Black, A. & C.; Publishers - Ladybird Books; Religion - Christian, also Booksearch PR: £2–500. CC: AE; MC; V. Also, publisher/ retailer of new books & foreign language Christian literature, Bible distributor, archive & booksearch service. Cata: 3 a year. Corresp: Afrikaans, French, German, Dutch, Spanish, Norwegian. [Updated]

Nigel A. Clark, 28 Ulundi Road, Blackheath, London, SE3 7UG. Tel: (020) 8858-4020. Est: 1975. Private premises. Postal business only. Appointment necessary. Very small stock. Spec: Antiques; Art - History; Art - Reference; Artists; Ceramics; Collecting; Horology; Numismatics; Philately; Theatre, also Booksearch. PR: £1–100. [Updated]

Collectable Books, 15 West Park, London, SE9 4RZ. Partners: Tom & Sue Biro. Tel: (020) 8851-8487. Website: www.collectablebooks.co.uk. E-mail: biro@collectablebooks.co.uk. Est: 1992. Private premises. Appointment necessary. Very small stock. Spec: Antiquarian; Architecture; Arts, The; Food & Drink; Health; Medicine; Natural History; Religion - General; Travel - General; Wine. PR: £10–20,000. CC: E; JCB; MC; V; SO, SW. Corresp: French, German, Italian, Hungarian, Portuguese. Mem: PBFA. VAT No: GB 299 3282 10. [Updated]

Peter Ellis, Bookseller, ■ 18 Cecil Court, London, WC2N 4HE. Tel: (020) 7836 8880. Fax: (020) 8318-4748. Website: www.peter-ellis.co.uk. E-mail: ellisbooks@lineone.net. Est: 1999. Shop at: 18 Cecil Court, London WC2 4HE. Open: **M:** 10:30–19:00; **T:** 10:30–19:00; **W:** 10:30–19:00; **Th:** 10:30–19:00; **F:** 10:30–19:00; **S:** 10:30–17:30. Medium stock. Spec: Art; Artists; Arts, The; Beat Writers; Biography; Children's - General; Fiction - General; First Editions; Gardening; Limited Editions; Literary Criticism; Literature; Modern First Editions; Private Press; Signed Editions; Surrealism. PR: £10–1,000. CC: AE; MC; V. Cata: 6 a year. Modern literature/illustrated. Corresp: French, German. Mem: ABA; ILAB. VAT No: GB 751 8751 12. [Updated]

Fine Art, 75, London, SW11 1DP. Prop: Robert Walker. Tel: (07970) 616325. Fax: (07970) 616325. Website: www.fineart.tm. E-mail: sheppards@fineart.tm. Est: 1991. Private premises. Internet and postal. Appointment necessary. Open: **M:** 10:00–17:17; **T:** 10:00–17:17; **W:** 10:00–17:17; **Th:** 10:00–17:00; **F:** 10:00–17:00. Small general stock. Spec: Antiquarian; Arts, The; Bindings; Colour-Plate; Early Imprints; First Editions; Fore-Edge Paintings; Illuminated Manuscripts; Illustrated; Incunabula; Limited Editions; Natural History; Topography - General; Topography - Local. PR: £100–20,000. CC: AE; MC; V. Mem: PBFA. [Updated]

Jane Gibberd, ■ 20 Lower Marsh, London, SE1 7RJ. Tel: (020) 7633-9562. Est: 1968. Open: **W:** 11:00–19:00; **Th:** 11:00–19:00; **F:** 11:00–19:00. Small general stock. Spec: PR: £1–25. [Updated]

Hava Books, 110 Aspinall Road, Brockley, SE4 2EG. Prop: John Havercroft. Tel: (020) 7639-8339. Website: www.havabooks.com. E-mail: jhavercroft@rmplc.co.uk. Est: 2000. Office &/or bookroom. Internet. Appointment necessary. Small stock. Spec: Academic/Scholarly; Antiquarian; Atlases; Books about Books; Illustrated; Languages - Foreign; Literature - Victorian; Literature in Translation; Travel - General. PR: £10–3,000. CC: Paypal. Corresp: French, Spanish. Mem: PBFA. VAT No: GB 782 4918 92. [Updated]

Kirkdale Bookshop, ■ 272 Kirkdale, Sydenham, SE26 4RS. Prop: Ms. Geraldine A. Cox. Tel: (020) 8778-4701. Fax: (020) 8776-6293. E-mail: kirkdalebookshop@hotmail.com. Est: 1966. Shop open: **M:** 09:00–17:30; **T:** 09:00–17:30; **W:** 09:00–17:30; **Th:** 09:00–17:30; **F:** 09:00–17:30; **S:** 09:00–17:30. Medium stock. Spec: CC: MC; V. Also, new books, & greetings cards. Mem: BA. [Updated]

Peter Marcan, Bookseller, P.O. Box 3158, London, SE1 4RA. Tel: (020) 7357 0368. Est: 2000. Private premises. Appointment necessary. Open: **M:** 10:00–19:00; **T:** 10:00–19:00; **W:** 10:00–19:00; **Th:** 10:00–19:00; **F:** 10:00–19:00; **S:** 10:00–19:00. Very small stock. Spec: Architecture; Arts, The; Cities; Horticulture; Music - Classical; Social History; Urban History. PR: £3–50. Publishing - reprints, directories, catalogues. Cata: 3 a year. [Updated]

Marcet Books, ■ 4a Nelson Road, Greenwich, London, SE10 9JB. Prop: Martin Kemp. Tel: (020) 8853-5408. Website: www.marcetbooks.co.uk. E-mail: marcetbooks@btconnect.com. Est: 1980. Shop; Internet and postal. Open: **M:** 10:00–18:00; **T:** 10:00–18:00; **W:** 10:00–18:00; **Th:** 10:00–18:00; **F:** 10:00–18:00; **S:** 10:00–18:00; **Su:** 10:00–18:00. Medium stock. Spec: Art; Bibliography; Fiction - Crime, Detective, Spy, Thrillers; First Editions; Maritime/Nautical; Naval; Sport - Cricket; Sport - Yachting; Topography - General; Travel - General. PR: £1–100. CC: AE; MC; V; Paypal. Attends book fairs monthly at Russell Hotel, London. Cata: 1 a year. on foreign travel. Mem: PBFA. [Updated]

Military Bookworm, P.O. Box 235, London, SE23 1NS. Prop: David W. Collett. Tel: (020) 8291-1435. Fax: (020) 8291-1435. Website: www.militarybookworm.co.uk. E-mail: info@militarybookworm .co.uk. Est: 1975. Storeroom. Internet. Contactable. Medium stock. Spec: Military; Military History; School Registers/Rolls of Honour. PR: £5–300. CC: MC; V. [13/07/2003]

Richard Platt Rare Books, 84 Red Lion Lane, Shooters Hill, London, SE18 4LE. Tel: (020) 8856-4202. Fax: (020) 8856-4211. Website: www.abebooks.com/home/richardplatt. E-mail: richardplatt .books@btinternet.com. Est: 1997. Private premises. Appointment necessary. Small stock. Spec: Author - Christie, Agatha; Author - Conan Doyle, Sir Arthur; Author - Fleming, Ian; Author - Freeman, R A; Author - Gilbert, Michael; Author - Rankin, Ian; Fiction - Crime, Detective, Spy, Thrillers; First Editions; Signed Editions. PR: £10–3,000. Also, at Biblion and at Bookshop Blackheath, London SE3. [12/05/2003]

Hilary Rittner Booksearch, 30 Crooms Hill, Greenwich, London, SE10 8ER. Prop: Hilary Rittner. Tel: (020) 8858-7759. Private premises. Postal business only. Spec: Artists; Author - Ardizzone, Edward; Illustrated; also Booksearch. [Updated]

John Rolfe, 39 Combe, Blackheath, London, SE3 7PZ. Prop: John Rolfe. Tel: (020) 8858-3349. Website: abebooks.com/home/johnrolfe. E-mail: johnrolfebooks@tinyworld.co.uk. Private premises. Internet and postal. Appointment necessary. Very small stock. Spec: Dogs. PR: £5–500. [Updated]

Ruskin Books, 49 Dighton Court, John Ruskin Street, London, SE5 0PR. Prop: Frederick W. Lidyard. Tel: (020) 7703 0567. Spec: Booksearch. [13/05/2003]

Michael Silverman, P.O. Box 350, London, SE3 0LZ. Tel: (020) 8319-4452. Fax: (020) 8856-6006. Website: www.michael-silverman.com. E-mail: ms@michael-silverman.com. Est: 1989. Private premises. Postal business only. Appointment necessary. Medium stock. Spec: Art; Autographs; Documents - General; History - General; Letters; Literature; Manuscripts. CC: AE; MC; V. Cata: 2 a year. Mem: ABA; ILAB. VAT No: GB 532 9017 59. [Updated]

Spread Eagle Bookshop, ■ 8 Nevada Street, Greenwich, London, SE10. Prop: Richard F. Moy. Tel: (020) 8305-1666. Fax: (020) 8305 0447. Website: www.spreadeagle.org. E-mail: books@ spreadeagle.org. Est: 1960. Shop open: **M:** 10:00–17:00; **T:** 10:00–17:00; **W:** 10:00–17:00; **Th:** 10:00–17:00; **F:** 10:00–17:00; **S:** 10:00–17:00; **Su:** 10:00–17:00; Closed for lunch: 13:00–14:00. Large stock. Spec: Advertising; Animals and Birds; Antiquarian; Arts, The; Author - Churchill, Sir Winston; Bindings; Children's - General; Children's - Illustrated; Cinema/Film; City of London; Collecting; D.I.Y (Do It Yourself); Decorative Art; Documents - General. PR: £3–100. CC: AE; D; E; JCB; MC; V. Also, ephemera, picture framing and restoration, collectables and antiques. Corresp: French, Italian. [13/09/2003]

Stephen E. Tilston, 7 Dartmouth House, Dartmouth Row, Greenwich, SE10 8BF. Prop: Steve & Frances Tilston. Tel: (020) 8691 3108. Website: http://www.ukbookworld.com/members/tilston. E-mail: tilston@attglobal.net. Est: 1985. Private premises. Internet and postal. Appointment necessary. Medium stock. Spec: Architecture; Art; Biography; Cookery/Gastronomy; Fiction - General; History - General; Maritime/Nautical; Military; Military History; Naval; Poetry; Politics; Topography - General; Travel - General; War - World War I; War - World War II. PR: £5–1,000. CC: MC; V; Maestro. [Updated]

Tower Bridge Books, 72 Gainsford Street, Tower Bridge Square, London, SE1 2NB. Prop: Tom Hoffman. Tel: (020) 7403-5485. Fax: (020) 7403-5485. Est: 1990. Private premises. Appointment necessary. Small stock. Spec: Antiquarian; Fine & Rare; History - Guilds and Livery Companies; Sport - Rowing. PR: £5–500. Cata: 2 a year on rowing. [18/06/2003]

LONDON
(SOUTH WEST POSTAL DISTRICTS)

Ancient Art Books, 34 East Sheen Ave., East Sheen, London, SW14 8AS. Prop: D.G. Giles. Tel: (020) 8878-8951. Fax: (020) 8878-9201. E-mail: Ancientartbooks@aol.com. Est: 1999. Private premises. Postal business only. Small stock. Spec: Applied Art; Glass. PR: £10–15,000. Also at Biblion, London. Cata: 1 a year on ancient glass. Mem: Also at: Biblion. [Updated]

Ash Rare Books, 43 Huron Road, London, SW17 8RE. Prop: Laurence Worms. Tel: (020) 8672-2263. Website: www.ashrare.com. E-mail: books@ashrare.com. Est: 1946. Private premises. Internet and postal. Appointment necessary. Open: **M:** 10:00–17:00; **T:** 10:00–17:00; **W:** 10:00–17:00; **Th:** 10:00–17:00; **F:** 10:00–17:00. Medium stock. Spec: Bibliography; City of London; First Editions; Poetry. PR: £20–5,000. CC: AE; D; E; JCB; MC; V. Cata: 4 a year. Mem: ABA; ILAB. VAT No: GB 244 2896 45. [Updated]

Chris Beetles Ltd., 8 & 10 Ryder Street, St. James's, London, SW1Y 6QB. Prop: Chris Beetles. Tel: (020) 7839-7551. Website: www.chrisbeetles.com. E-mail: gallery@chrisbeetles.com. Est: 1981. Spec: Art; Art - History; Art - Reference; Artists; Dictionaries; Fine Art; Humour; Illustrated. PR: £5–500. CC: AE; MC; V. Mem: BA. [29/06/2003]

Bodyline Books, 150a Harbord Street, London, SW6 6PH. Prop: G.R. Lyon Esq. Tel: (020) 7385-2176. Fax: (020) 7610-3314. Website: www.bodylinebooks.com. E-mail: info@bodylinebooks.com. Est: 1996. Private premises. Internet and postal. Appointment necessary. Small general stock. Spec: Sport - Cricket. PR: £4–10,000. CC: MC; V. Cata: 3 a year. [Updated]

Bookseekers, 4 Manor Road, London, SW20 9AE. Prop: R. & J. Mernane. Tel: Withheld. Fax: (020) 8542-2448. Est: 1981. Private premises. Postal business only. Spec: Judaica; Religion - Jewish; Sport - Cricket; also Booksearch. Corresp: French, German, Hebrew. [20/05/2003]

Ron Chapman, 12 Bolton Gardens Mews, off Little Boltons, London, SW10 9LW. Tel: (020) 7373-8370. Est: 1970. Private premises. Appointment necessary. Large stock. Spec: Architecture; First Editions; Literature. PR: £5–1,000. Also at: Tindley & Chapman, London WC2N 4HE (q.v.). [01/07/2003]

Classic Bindings Ltd, ■ 61 Cambridge Street, Pimlico, London, SW1V 4PS. Prop: Mr. Sasha Poklewski–Koziell. Tel: (020) 7834-5554. Fax: (020) 7630-6632. Website: www.classicbindings.net. E-mail: info@classicbindings.net. Est: 1988. Shop open: **M:** 09:30–17:30; **T:** 09:30–17:30; **W:** 09:30–17:30; **Th:** 09:30–17:30; **F:** 09:30–17:30. Large stock. Spec: Architecture; Art; Bindings; Biography; Foreign Texts; History - General; Poetry; Religion - Christian; Topography - General; Topography - Local. PR: £10–5,000. CC: E; MC; V. Cata: on request. VAT No: GB 562 2080 66. [Updated]

Robin de Beaumont, 25 Park Walk, Chelsea, London, SW10 0AJ. Tel: (0207) 352-3440. Fax: (0207) 352-1260. Website: www.abebooks.com/home/RDEBOOKS. E-mail: rdebooks@aol.com. Est: 1980. Private premises. Internet and postal. Telephone first. Small stock. Spec: Architecture; Art; Bindings; Illustrated; Victoriana. PR: £20–3,000. CC: JCB; V. Corresp: French. Mem: ABA; ILAB. [15/07/2003]

Earlsfield Bookshop, ■ 513 Garratt Lane, Wandsworth, London, SW18 4SW. Prop: Charles Dixon. Tel: (020) 8946-3744. Est: 1995. Shop open: **M:** 16:00–18:00; **T:** 16:00–18:00; **W:** 16:00–18:00; **Th:** 16:00–18:00; **F:** 11:00–18:00; **S:** 10:00–17:00. Small general stock. Spec: PR: £1–50. [Updated]

Harfield Books of London, 81 Replingham Road, Southfields, London, SW18 5LU. Prop: P.V. Eastman. Tel: (020) 8871-0880. Fax: (020) 8871-0880. Website: www.harfieldbooks.com. E-mail: internet@harfieldbooks.com. Est: 1989. Warehouse; Internet and postal. Appointment necessary. Very large stock. Spec: Academic/Scholarly; also Booksearch & academic publishing. [Updated]

Europa Books, 15 Luttrell Avenue, Putney, London, SW15 6PD. Prop: Paul Hetherington PhD., F.S.A. Tel: (020) 8788-0312. Fax: (020) 8788-0312. E-mail: europabooks@ukonline.co.uk. Est: 1985. Private premises. Appointment necessary. Small stock. Spec: Antiquarian; Architecture; Art; Art - History; Art - Reference; Art - Technique; Art - Theory; Astrology; Decorative Art; Theatre. PR: £10–2,000. CC: MC; V. Note, appointments can be made at most times. Cata: occasionally. Corresp: French, German, Italian. Mem: PBFA. [Updated]

Exedra Booksearch Ltd., 40 Peterborough Road, London, SW6 3BN. Prop: Jonathan Tootell. Tel: (020) 7731-8500. Fax: (020) 7731-8400. Website: www.exedra.co.uk. E-mail: info@exedra.co.uk. Est: 1999. Postal business only. Contactable: **M:** 09:00–18:00; **T:** 09:00–18:00; **W:** 09:00–18:00; **Th:** 09:00–18:00; **F:** 09:00–18:00; **S:** 09:00–14:00. Very small general stock. Spec: Booksearch. CC: MC; V. Corresp: French. [Updated]

Paul Foster Bookshop, ■ 119 Sheen Lane, London, SW14 8AE. Tel: (020) 8876-7424. Fax: (020) 8876 7424. E-mail: paulfosterbooks@btinternet.com. Est: 1990. Internet and postal. Shop open: **W:** 10:30–18:00; **Th:** 10:30–18:00; **F:** 10:30–18:00; **S:** 10:30–18:00. Medium stock. Spec: Academic/Scholarly; Antiquarian; Art; Bindings; Children's - General; First Editions; Illustrated. PR: £5–10,000. CC: JCB; MC; V. Cata: 2 a year. Mem: ABA; PBFA; ILAB. [Updated]

Gloucester Road Bookshop, ■ 123 Gloucester Road, London, SW7 4TE. Prop: Nick Dennys. Tel: (020) 7370-3503. Fax: (020) 7373-0610. Website: www.gloucesterbooks.co.uk. E-mail: nick.dennys@ gloucesterbooks.co.uk. Est: 1983. Shop open: **M:** 09:30–22:30; **T:** 09:30–22:30; **W:** 09:30–22:30; **Th:** 09:30–22:30; **F:** 09:30–22:30; **S:** 10:30–18:30; **Su:** 10:30–18:30; Large stock. Spec: Antiques; Architecture; Art; Author - Greene, Graham; Children's - General; Fiction - General; History - General; Literature; Music - General; Natural History; Performing Arts; Philosophy; Poetry; Travel - General. PR: £1–5,000. CC: E; MC; V. Cata: 2 occasionally on modern first editions, literature,. [24/ 05/2003]

Michael Graves–Johnston, P. O. Box 532, 54 Stockwell Park Road, LONDON, SW9 0DR. Tel: (0207) 274-2069. Fax: (0207) 738-3747. Website: www.graves-johnston.com. E-mail: Books@ gravesjohnston.demon.co.uk. Est: 1978. Private premises. Appointment necessary. Large stock. Spec: Africana; Anthropology; Archaeology; Classical Studies; Colonial; Countries - Africa; Egyptology; Ethnography; Ethnology; Travel - Africa; Travel - Americas; Travel - Australasia/ Australia; Travel - Polar; Voyages & Discovery. PR: £10–10,000. CC: AE; E; MC; V. Cata: 4 a year. Mem: ABA; ILAB. VAT No: GB 238 2333 72. [15/07/2003]

Grays of Westminster, ■ 40 Churton Street, Pimlico, London, SW1V 2LP. Prop: Gray Levett & Nick Wynne. Tel: (020) 7828-4925. Fax: (020) 7976-5783. Website: www.graysofwestminster.co.uk. E-mail: info@graysofwestminster.co.uk. Est: 1985. Internet and postal. Shop open: **M:** 10:00–17:29; **T:** 10:00–17:30; **W:** 10:00–17:30; **Th:** 10:00–17:30; **F:** 10:00–17:30; **S:** 10:00–13:00. Spec: Photography. PR: £10–200. CC: AE; D; E; MC; V; Maestro. Also, new, secondhand and vintage Nikon cameras. VAT No: GB 503 1317 05. [Updated]

Robin Greer, 434 Fulham Palace Road, London, SW6 6HX. Prop: Robin Greer. Tel: (020) 7381-9113. Website: www.rarerobin.com. E-mail: rarities@rarerobin.com. Est: 1966. Private premises. Appointment necessary. Small stock. Spec: Arthurian; Author - Lang, Andrew; Children's - General; Children's - Illustrated; Illustrated. PR: £1–5,000. CC: MC; V. Cata: 5 a year. Corresp: Spanish. Mem: ABA; PBFA; ILAB. [Updated]

Peter Harrington Antiquarian B, ■ 100 Fulham Road, Chelsea, London, SW3 6HS. Tel: (020) 7591-0220. Fax: (020) 7225-7054. Website: www.peter-harrington-books.com. E-mail: mail@peter-harrington-books.com. Est: 1969. Shop open: **M:** 10:00–18:00; **T:** 10:00–18:00; **W:** 10:00–18:00; **Th:** 10:00–18:00; **F:** 10:00–18:00; **S:** 10:00–00:00. Very large general stock. Spec: Aeronautics; Antiquarian; Architecture; Atlases; Autographs; Bibles; Bindings; Botany; Children's - General; Churchilliana; Colour-Plate; Economics; Fine & Rare; First Editions; Fore-Edge Paintings; Geography; Illustrated; Literature; Maritime/Nautical. PR: £10–100,000. CC: AE; E; JCB; MC; V; SO, SW. Corresp: Polish, Spanish. Mem: ABA; PBFA; ILAB. VAT No: GB 701 5578 50. [Updated]

Searching for a title – and cannot find it on any Internet database?

Then try **www.sheppardsbooksearch.com**

By selecting the subject classification – the request goes to all dealers who major in that subject.

Thomas Heneage Art Books, ■ 42 Duke Street, St. James's, London, SW1Y 6DJ. Tel: (020) 7930-9223. Fax: (020) 7839-9223. Website: www.heneage.com. E-mail: artbooks@heneage.com. Est: 1977. Shop open: **M:** 09:30–18:00; **T:** 09:30–18:00; **W:** 09:30–18:00; **Th:** 09:30–18:00; **F:** 09:30–18:00. Spec: Antiques; Applied Art; Archaeology; Arms & Armour; Art; Art - History; Carpets; Catalogues Raisonnes; Ceramics; Collecting; Conservation; Decorative Art; Fine Art; Firearms/Guns; Furniture; Glass; Interior Design; Jewellery; Lace; Monographs; also Booksearch. PR: £2–30,000. CC: MC; V. Also, publishers of Art Book Survey. Open at other times by appointment. [17/09/2003]

Hesketh & Ward Ltd., 31 Britannia Road, London, SW6 2HJ. Prop: Viscount Bangor. Tel: (020) 7736-5705. Fax: (020) 7736-1089. E-mail: heskward@btinternet.com. Est: 1985. Private premises. Appointment necessary. Very small stock. Spec: Foreign Texts. PR: £80–5,000. Stock is mainly 16th century Continental, especially Italian. Cata: 2 a year. Corresp: French, Italian. Mem: ABA. VAT No: GB 394 8008 27. [Updated]

Hunersdorff Rare Books, P.O. Box 582, London, SW10 9RP. Prop: Richard von Hünersdorff. Tel: (020) 7373-3899. Fax: (020) 7370-1244. Website: www.abebooks.com/hunersdorff/home. E-mail: huner.rarebooks@dial.pipex.com. Est: 1969. Private premises. Appointment necessary. Spec: Architecture; Countries - South America; Gardening; Landscape; Languages - Foreign; Literature; Medicine; Science - General. PR: £25–100,000. CC: MC; V. Cata: 2 a year. Corresp: German, Spanish, French. Mem: ABA; ILAB. [Updated]

Andrew Hunter–Rare Books, Box 9, 34 Buckingham Palace Road, London, SW1W 0RH. Tel: (020) 7834-4924. Fax: (020) 7834-4924. Website: www.rarebookhunter.com. E-mail: andrew@rarebookhunter.com. Est: 2001. Private premises. Appointment necessary. Very small stock. Spec: Literature; Medicine; Science - General; Scottish Interest. PR: £200–25,000. Cata: 2 a year. Corresp: French, Spanish. VAT No: GB 782 2863 04. [Updated]

The Illustrated Book, 4 Haverhill Road, Balham, London, SW12 0HA. Prop: Mr J. Pearson. Tel: (020) 8675-5177. Fax: (020) 8675-5177. Website: www.theillustratedbook.co.uk. E-mail: joe@jpearson51.freeserve.co.uk. Est: 2000. Postal business only. Very small stock. Spec: Art - History; Art - Reference; Children's - General; Design; Illustrated; Printing; Private Press; Publishers - Curwen Press; Publishers - Penguin; Transatlantic arts; Typography; Vintage Paperbacks. PR: £1–1,000. [24/09/2003]

Romilly Leeper, 12 Bolton Garden Mews, London, SW10 9LW. Tel: (020) 7373-8370. Fax: (020) 7370-3226. Est: 1986. Private premises. Appointment necessary. Small stock. Spec: Sport - Horse Racing (all aspects); Travel - Asia, South East. PR: £6–100. Corresp: French, German, Portuguese. [Updated]

Mandalay Bookshop, 36c Sisters Avenue, London, SW11 5SQ. Prop: Nicholas Greenwood. Tel: (0207) 223-8987. Fax: (0207) 223-8987. Website: www.mandalaybookshop.com. E-mail: info@mandalaybookshop.biz. Est: 1994. Private premises. Internet and postal. Small stock. Spec: Animals and Birds; Anthropology; Botany; Colonial; Countries - Burma; Countries - China; Countries - India; Countries - South East Asia; Forestry; Gemmology; Military; Military History; Oriental; Plant Hunting; Travel - Asia, South East. PR: £5–1,500. CC: PayPal. WWII includes the Burma Campaign. Corresp: French, German, Burmese, Thai. [Updated]

Nicholas Meinertzhagen, 82 Ritherdon Road, London, SW17 8QG. Tel: (020) 8672-2288. Est: 1978. Private premises. Appointment necessary. Small stock. Spec: Countries - Europe; Countries - Hungary; Countries - Poland; Economics; Fine & Rare; Foreign Texts; History - European; Philosophy; Science - General. History of Eastern Europe; paintings drawings. Cata: occasionally. [updated]

My Back Pages, 8-10 Balham Station Road, London, SW16 6RT. Douglas Jeffers. Tel: 0208 675 9346. Fax: 0208 769 9741. E-mail: douglasjeffers@aol.com. Open: **M:** 10:10–20:00; **T:** 10:00–20:00; **W:** 10:00–20:00; **Th:** 10:00–20:00; **F:** 10:00–20:00; **S:** 10:00–19:00; **Su:** 11:00–18:00. Very large general stock. Spec: Academic/Scholarly; Architecture; Art; Cinema/Film; Countries - India; Egyptology; Fashion & Costume; Folio Society, The; Gardening; History - General; Irish Interest; Maritime/Nautical; Military History; Music - Jazz; Philosophy; Politics; Railways. CC: AE; JCB; MC. VAT No: GB 5620 221 84. [Updated]

Nibris Books, 14 Ryfold Road, Wimbledon Park, London, SW19 8BZ. Prop: Nigel Israel. Tel: (020) 8946-7207. Fax: (020) 8946-7207. E-mail: nibris_books@yahoo.com. Est: 1980. Private premises. Appointment necessary. Small stock. Spec: Gemmology; Horology; Jewellery; Mineralogy. PR: £10–500. Included in clasifications: jem stones, engraved gems, crown jewels regalia & ceremony. VAT No: GB 446 2021 80. [Updated]

Old World Books, 40 Peterboough Road, London, SW6 3BN. Prop: John Francis Phillimore. Tel: (020) 7352-3590. Website: www.oldworldbooks.com. E-mail: venicebooks@yahoo.co.uk. Est: 2003. Private premises. Shop at: Cannaregio 1190, Venezia 30121, Italy. Open: **M:** 10:00–19:00; **T:** 10:00–19:00; **W:** 10:00–19:00; **Th:** 10:00–19:00; **F:** 10:00–19:00; **Su:** 15:00–19:00; Closed for lunch: 13:00–15:00. Small stock. Spec: Literary Travel; Travel - Europe. PR: £5–1,500. CC: V. Also, books about Venice. Cata: occasionally. Corresp: Italian. Mem: PBFA. VAT No: GB 602 8936 37. [19/08/2003]

Paul Orssich, 2 St. Stephen's Terrace, South Lambeth, London, SW8 1DH. Tel: (020) 7787-0030. Fax: (020) 7735-9612. Website: www.orssich.com. E-mail: paulo@orssich.com. Est: 1980. Private premises. Internet and postal. Telephone first. Very large stock. Spec: Academic/Scholarly; Advertising; Author - Cervantes Saavedra, Miguel de; Bull Fighting; Countries - Andorra; Countries - Central America; Countries - Gibraltar; Countries - Mexico; Countries - Morocco; Countries - Portugal; Countries - Puerto Rico. PR: £25–5,000. CC: MC; V. Open any time by appointment. Cata: 4 – 3 months. Corresp: Spanish, Catalan, French, German, Italian. Mem: PBFA. VAT No: GB 442 4102 94. [Updated]

Hugh Pagan Limited, P.O. Box 4325, London, SW7 1DD. Tel: (020) 7589-6292. Fax: (020) 7589-6303. Website: www.hughpagan.com. E-mail: pagan@mistral.co.uk. Est: 1987. Spec: Architecture; Fine Art. [25/07/2003]

Petersham Books, Unit 67, 56 Gloucester Road, London, SW7 4UB. Prop: Kate Stewart. Tel: (020) 7581-9147. Fax: (020) 7581-9147. Website: www.modernfirsts.co.uk. E-mail: ks@modernfirsts.co.uk. Private premises. Internet and postal. Contactable. Small stock. Spec: Children's - General; Children's - Illustrated; Modern First Editions. PR: £15–5,000. CC: JCB; MC; V. Corresp: Italian, French. [14/03/2003]

Nigel Phillips, 5 Burleigh Place, Cambalt Road, Putney Hill, London, SW15 6ES. Tel: (020) 8788 2664. Fax: (020) 8780 1989. Website: www.nigelphillips.com. E-mail: nigel@nigelphillips.com. Est: 1981. Private premises. Appointment necessary. Open: Medium stock. Spec: Antiquarian; History of Ideas; Medicine; Science - General; Science - History of; Technology. PR: £15–50,000. CC: MC; V. Cata: 2 a year. Mem: ABA; ILAB. [Updated]

Philologus–Fine & Rare Books, 83 Stanthorpe Road, London, SW16 2EA. Prop: G. Frydberg & U.K.H. Polczynski. Tel: (020) 8677-2076. E-mail: Est: 1984. Postal business only. Spec: Antiquarian; Art - Reference; Bibliography; Foreign Texts; Languages - Foreign; Philosophy; Science - History of; also Booksearch. PR: £10–2,000. [24/09/2003]

Russell Rare Books, ■ 239A Fulham Road, Chelsea, London, SW3 6HY. Tel: (020) 7351-5119. Fax: (020) 7376-7227. Website: www.russellrarebooks.com. E-mail: c.russell@russellrarebooks.com. Est: 1977. Shop open: **M:** 14:00–18:00; **T:** 14:00–18:00; **W:** 14:00–18:00; **Th:** 14:00–18:00; **F:** 14:00–18:00. Very small stock. Spec: Atlases; Bindings; Natural History; Social History; Travel - General. PR: £200–10,000. CC: V. When closed: telephone (07768) 004152 for appointment. Also, large print books. Mem: ABA; PBFA. [Updated]

Sandpiper Books Ltd., 24 Langroyd Road, London, SW17 7PL. Prop: Robert Collie. Tel: (020) 8767-7421. Fax: (020) 8682-0280. Website: www.sandpiper.co.uk. E-mail: enquiries@sandpiper.co.uk. Est: 1983. Office &/or bookroom. Appointment necessary. Spec: Academic/Scholarly; Classical Studies; Medieval. PR: £2–20. CC: MC; V. Cata: 4 a year. [Updated]

Sims Reed Limited, 43a Duke Street, St. James's, London, SW1Y 6DD. Prop: Max Reed. Tel: (020) 7493-5660. Fax: (020) 7493-8468. Website: www.simsreed.com. E-mail: info@simsreed.com. Spec: Art; Artists; Illustrated. [01/08/2003]

John Thornton, ■ 455 Fulham Road, London, SW10 9UZ. Tel: (020) 7352-8810. Est: 1975. Shop open: **M:** 10:00–17:30; **T:** 10:00–17:30; **W:** 10:00–17:30; **Th:** 10:00–17:30; **F:** 10:00–17:30; **S:** 10:00–17:30. Medium stock. Spec: Religion - Roman Catholic. PR: £1–300. CC: MC; V; SW. [27/05/2003]

TSB Booksearch, 17 Gilbert Road, Wimbledon, London, SW19 1BP. Tel: (020) 8543-0898. E-mail: tsbbooks@hotmail.com. Est: 1989. Internet and postal. Small stock. Spec: Homosexuality & Lesbianism; also Booksearch. PR: £4–450. [Updated]

Mary Wells, 24 Minehead Road, London, SW16 2AW. Tel: (020) 8769-0778. Fax: (020) 8769-0778. Est: 1980. Market stand/stall. Book fairs only. Small stock. Spec: Also, Booksearch. PR: £1–500. Attends Bloomsbury Fair, Royal National. [Updated]

Worlds End Bookshop, ■ 357 Kings Rd, London, SW3 5ES. Prop: Stephen Dickson. Tel: (020) 7352 9376. E-mail: stevdcksn@btinternet.com. Est: 1990. Shop open: **M:** 10:00–18:30; **T:** 10:00–18:30; **W:** 10:00–18:30; **Th:** 10:00–18:30; **F:** 10:00–18:30; **S:** 10:00–18:30; **Su:** 10:00–18:30. Medium stock. Spec: Academic/Scholarly; Antiquarian; Applied Art; Art; Classical Studies; Decorative Art; Esoteric; Fashion & Costume; Fiction - General; History - General; Humanities; Literature; Military History; Modern First Editions; Mysticism; Oriental. CC: AE; JCB; MC; V; Switch. VAT No: GB 787 9773 37. [Updated]

Wykeham Books, 64 Ridgway, Wimbledon, London, SW19 4RA. Prop: H.S.G. Mather. Tel: (020) 8879-3721. Website: www.bibliographies.co.uk. E-mail: wykbooks@msn.com. Est: 1976. Private premises. Postal business only. Medium stock. Spec: Bibliography; Books about Books. PR: £5–15,000. Mem: PBFA. [Updated]

LONDON
(WEST POSTAL DISTRICTS)

Altea Gallery, ■ 35 Saint George St., London, W1S 2FN. Prop: Mr. Massimo De Martini. Tel: (020) 7491 0010. Fax: (020) 7491 0015. Website: www.alteamaps.com. E-mail: info@alteamaps.com. Est: 1993. Shop open: **M:** 10:00–18:00; **T:** 10:00–18:00; **W:** 10:00–18:00; **Th:** 10:00–18:00; **F:** 10:00–18:00. Medium stock. Spec: Astronomy; Atlases; Geography; Maritime/Nautical; Topography - General; Topography - Local; Travel - General; Voyages & Discovery. PR: £50–10,000. CC: AE; E; JCB; MC; V. Also, map search, colouring & restoration. Cata: quarterly. Corresp: Italian. Mem: ABA; PBFA; ILAB; IMCoS. VAT No: GB 649 5809 86. [Updated]

David Batterham, 36 Alexander Street, London, W2 5NU. Tel: (020) 7229-3845. E-mail: david.batterham@virgin.net. Est: 1966. Private premises. Appointment necessary. Small stock. Spec: Applied Art; Architecture; Caricature; Fashion & Costume; Illustrated; Journals - General; Technology; Typography. PR: £5–5,000. CC: MC; V. Cata: 6 a year. Corresp: French. [Updated]

Nicholas Bernstein, 2 Vaughan Avenue, London, W6 0XS. Prop: Nicholas Bernstein. Tel: (020) 874 17140. E-mail: nick.bernstein@excite.co.uk. Est: 1986. Private premises. Appointment necessary. Medium stock. Spec: Antiquarian; Bibles; Bindings; Curiosities; Dictionaries; Economics; Fiction - General; History of Ideas; Literature; Miniature Books; Sets of Books. PR: £25–5,000. Appointments: 7 days a week. Exhibits at monthly PBFA fairs at Hotel Russell. Corresp: French. Mem: PBFA. [Updated]

Biblion Ltd, ■ 1–7 Davies Mews, London, W1K 5AB. Director: Leo Harrison. Manager: Stephen Poole. Tel: (020) 7629-1374. Fax: (020) 7629-1374. Website: www.biblion.com. E-mail: info@biblion.co.uk. Est: 1999. Shop open: **M:** 10:00–18:00; **T:** 10:00–18:00; **W:** 10:00–18:00; **Th:** 10:00–18:00; **F:** 10:00–18:00; **S:** 10:00–18:00. Large stock. Spec: Alpinism/Mountaineering; Antiquarian; Applied Art; Architecture; Art; Bibles; Bibliography; Bindings; Books about Books; Children's - General; Colour-Plate; Fables; Fiction - Crime, Detective, Spy, Thrillers; Fine & Rare; Fine Printing; Illustrated. PR: £10–50,000. CC: E; JCB; MC; V. [Updated]

J. & S.L. Bonham, Flat 14, 84 Westbourne Terrace, London, W2 6QE. Prop: John & Suzanne Bonham. Tel: (020) 7402-7064. Fax: (020) 7402-0955. Website: www.bonbooks.dial.pipex.com. E-mail: bonbooks@dial.pipex.com. Est: 1976. Private premises. Internet and postal. Appointment necessary. Medium stock. Spec: Alpinism/Mountaineering; Countries - Africa; Countries - Australia; Countries - Polar; Topography - General; Travel - General; Travel - Africa; Travel - Americas; Travel - Asia; Travel - Australasia/Australia; Travel - Europe; Travel - Middle East. PR: £10–2,000. CC: MC; V; SW, SO. Valuations. Cata: 1 a year. occasionally. Corresp: German. Mem: ABA; PBFA; ILAB. VAT No: GB 362 1962 53. [Updated]

The Book Business, 90 Greenford Avenue, London, W7 3QS. Prop: Giles Levete. Tel: (020) 8840-1185. E-mail: bookbusiness@aol.com. Est: 1990. Private premises. Internet and postal. Appointment necessary. Very small stock. Spec: Academic/Scholarly; Children's - General; Literature; Modern First Editions; Odd & Unusual; Travel - General. PR: £10–2,000. CC: AE; E; JCB; MC. Mem: PBFA. [Updated]

Books & Things, P.O. Box 17768, London, W8 6ZD. Prop: M.M. Steenson. Tel: (020) 7370-5593. Fax: (020) 7370-5593. Website: www.booksandthings.co.uk. E-mail: martin@booksandthings.co.uk. Est: 1972. Warehouse; Internet and postal. Small stock. Spec: Advertising; Applied Art; Art - Reference; Children's - Illustrated; Decorative Art; Illustrated; Modern First Editions; Periodicals & Magazines; Photography; Private Press; Publishers - Studio, The; also Booksearch. PR: £20–1,000. CC: E; JCB; MC. Cata: 1 a year. on specialities. Mem: ABA; PBFA; ILAB. [Updated]

Julian Browning, P.O. Box 4005, London, W9 1XF. Tel: (020) 7286-6034. Fax: (020) 7286-1919. Website: www.jbautographs.com. Est: 1992. Private premises. Appointment necessary. Medium stock. Spec: Autographs; Documents - General; Manuscripts. PR: £20–2,000. CC: AE; MC; V. Cata: 1 a year on autograph letters, manuscripts & historical documents. [31/01/2003]

Chiltern Books, 9 York Mansions, 84 Chiltern Street, London, W1U 5AL. Prop: Georges Lannois. Tel: (020) 7935-8641. Est: 1965. Private premises. Appointment necessary. Small stock. Spec: Foreign Texts; Languages - Foreign; Modern First Editions; Publishers - Penguin; Travel - General. PR: £1–40. Corresp: French, Portuguese. [27/05/2003]

Cusack Books, P.O. Box 17696, London, W12 8WR. Prop: Elaine M. Cusack-O'Connell. Tel: (020) 8743-0517. Website: www.cusackbooks.com. E-mail: davidoconnell@tesco.net. Est: 1998. Private premises. Internet and postal. Contactable. Very small stock. Spec: Cinema/Film; Music - Popular; Music - Rock; Television. PR: £5–250. CC: D; E; JCB; MC; V. [18/08/2003]

Demetzy Books, ■ 29 Standlake Road, Ducklington, Oxfordshire, London, OX29 7UX. Prop: Paul & Marie Hutchinson. Tel: (01993) 702209. Fax: (01993) 702209. E-mail: demetzybooks@tiscali.co.uk. Est: 1971. Shop at: 113 Portobello Road, London W11. Open: **S:** 07:30–15:00; Medium stock. Spec: Antiquarian; Bibles; Bindings; Children's - General; Cookery/Gastronomy; Dogs; Illustrated; Literature; Medicine; Miniature Books; Natural History; Prayer Books; Travel - General. PR: £2–2,000. Exhibits at PBFA London Monthly and Oxford Fairs. Corresp: French. Mem: ABA; PBFA. VAT No: GB 208 5346 69. [Updated]

Marc–Antoine du Ry Medieval M, medievalmodern, 14 Bulstrode Street, London, W1U 2JG. Tel: 0044 (0)7770 888116. Fax: 0032 3 2381063. Website: www.medievalart.uk.com. E-mail: info@marcdury .co.uk. Est: 1995. Shop &/or gallery. Internet and postal. Appointment necessary. Open: **W:** 11:00–18:00; **Th:** 11:00–18:00; **F:** 11:00–18:00; **S:** 11:00–18:00. Spec: Book of Hours; Illuminated Manuscripts; Manuscripts; Medieval. PR: £100–100,000. Cata: 1 a year. Corresp: French; Italian. VAT No: GB 735 7640 1. [Updated]

Elton Engineering Books, 27 Mayfield Avenue, London, W4 1PN. Tel: (0208) 747 0967. E-mail: elton_engineering_books@compuserve.com. Est: 1985. Private premises. Internet and postal. Appointment necessary. Very small stock. Spec: Architecture; Building & Construction; Engineering; Naval; Railways; Transport. PR: £30–8,000. CC: MC; V. Cata: 1 a year. Corresp: French, German. Mem: ABA; ILAB. VAT No: GB 429 7966 90. [Updated]

James Fergusson Books & Manuscripts, 39 Melrose Gardens, London, W6 7RN. Tel: (020) 7602-3536. Fax: (020) 7602-0502. E-mail: jamesfergusson@btinternet.com. Est: 1986. Private premises. Postal business only. Appointment necessary. Very small stock. Spec: Letters; Manuscripts. Also, 19th & 20th century literary association copies, autographs and photographs. Cata: occasionally. [Updated]

Simon Finch Rare Books Ltd., 53 Maddox Street, London, W1S 2PN. Tel: (020) 7499-0974. Fax: (020) 7499-0799. Website: www.simonfinch.com. E-mail: rarebooks@simonfinch.com. Est: 1981. Spec: Art; Autographs; Bindings; Design; Early Imprints; Literature; Manuscripts; Medicine; Modern First Editions; Photography; Printing; Science - General. PR: £1–500,000. CC: AE; MC; V; SW. [05/09/2003]

First State Books, 35 Talbot Road, London, W2 5JG. Prop: Euan Stuart. Tel: (020) 7792-2672. Fax: (020) 7792-2672. Website: www.firststatebooks.com. E-mail: euan.stuart@firststatebooks.com. Est: 2001. Private premises. Internet and postal. Very small stock displayed at: Biblion, London W1K 5AB. Spec: Fiction - General; First Editions. PR: £15–100. [26/06/2003]

Sam Fogg Ltd, ■ 15d Clifford Street, London, W1S 4JZ. Tel: (020) 7534-2100. Fax: (020) 7534-2122. Website: www.samfogg.com. E-mail: info@samfogg.com. Est: 1978. Appointment necessary. Open: **M:** 09:29–17:30; **T:** 09:30–17:30; **W:** 09:30–17:30; **Th:** 09:30–17:30; **F:** 09:30–17:30. Small stock. Spec: Manuscripts. CC: MC; V. Cata: 1 a year. Corresp: French, German. Mem: ABA. VAT No: GB 467 6893 80. [09/10/2004]

Richard Ford, 70 Chaucer Road, London, W3 6DP. Tel: (020) 8993-1235. Fax: (020) 8752-1431. E-mail: richard.rmford@btopenworld.com. Est: 1982. Private premises. Appointment necessary. Open: Very small stock. Spec: Autographs; Bibliography; Documents - General; Manuscripts; Publishing. PR: £10–1,000. Also, historical documents. Cata: rarely on book history. Corresp: French, Italian. [Updated]

Fosters Bookshop, ■ 183 Chiswick High Road, London, W4 2DR. Prop: W.A. & M.A. Foster. Tel: (020) 8995-2768. Est: 1968. Shop open: **Th:** 10:30–17:00; **F:** 10:30–17:00; **S:** 10:30–17:00. Medium stock. Spec: Applied Art; Architecture; Art; Bindings; Children's - General; First Editions; Illustrated; Sets of Books; Signed Editions; Travel - General. PR: £2–1,000. Mem: PBFA. [Updated]

Fuller D'Arch Smith, 37b New Cavendish Street, London, W1G 8JR. Prop: Jean Overton Fuller & Timothy D'Arch Smith. Tel: (020) 7722-0063. Fax: (020) 7722-0063. Est: 1969. Private premises. Appointment necessary. Very small general stock. Spec: PR: £5–500. Cata: occasionally. Corresp: French, German, Italian, Russian. [Updated]

Hab Books, 35 Wellington Road, Ealing, London, W5 4UJ. Prop: T. Habraszewski. Tel: (020) 8932-5058. Fax: (020) 8932-5058. E-mail: tom@habbks.freeserve.co.uk. Est: 1981. Private premises. Postal business only. Spec: Biography; Countries - East Europe; Countries - Russia; Foreign Texts; Politics; Theology. Cata: occasionally. [Updated]

Adrian Harrington, 64a Kensington Church Street, Kensington, London, W8 4DB. Tel: (020) 7937-1465. Fax: (020) 7368-0912. Website: www.harringtonbooks.co.uk. E-mail: rare@harringtonbooks.co.uk. Est: 1971. Spec: Antiquarian; Art; Author - General; Author - Churchill, Sir Winston; Author - Conan Doyle, Sir Arthur; Author - Cornwell, Bernard; Author - Dickens, Charles; Author - Fleming, Ian; Author - Greene, Graham; Author - Johns, W.E.; Author - Kipling, R. PR: £10–50,000. CC: AE; MC; V. Also, bookbinding. Mem: ABA; PBFA. [17/09/2003]

Harrison's Books, ■ Biblion, 1–7 Davies Mews, London, W1K 5AB. Prop: Leo Harrison. Tel: (020) 7629-1374. Fax: (020) 7493-7158. Website: www.biblion.co.uk. E-mail: leo@ebiblion.co.uk. Est: 1967. Shop at: Biblion. Open: **M:** 10:00–18:00; **T:** 10:00–18:00; **W:** 10:00–18:00; **Th:** 10:00–18:00; **F:** 10:00–18:00; **S:** 10:00–18:00. Very small stock. Spec: Bindings; Children's - General; Illustrated; Sport - Angling/Fishing. PR: £20–5,000. CC: JCB; MC; V. Cata: 2 a year. [03/03/2003]

G. Heywood Hill Limited, ■ 10 Curzon Street, London, W1J 5HH. Tel: (020) 7629-0647. Fax: (020) 7408-0286. Website: www.gheywoodhill.com. E-mail: old@gheywoodhill.com. Est: 1936. Shop open: **M:** 09:00–17:30; **T:** 09:00–17:30; **W:** 09:00–17:30; **Th:** 09:00–17:30; **F:** 09:00–17:30; **S:** 09:00–12:30. Medium stock. Spec: Architecture; Children's - General; History - General; Illustrated; Literature; Natural History; also Booksearch. PR: £5–10,000. CC: MC; V; Switch. Also, new books. Cata: 4 occasionally. Corresp: French, German, Spanish, Italian. Mem: ABA; BA. VAT No: GB 239 4090 56. [Updated]

Judith Hodgson, 11 Stanwick Road, London, W14 8TL. Tel: (020) 7603-7414. Fax: (020) 7602-1431. E-mail: judithghodgson@supanet.com. Est: 1986. Private premises. Postal business only. Appointment necessary. Small stock. Spec: Antiquarian; Countries - Latin America; Countries - Portugal; Countries - Spain. Cata: 1 a year. Corresp: French, Spanish, Portuguese. Mem: ABA; ILAB. VAT No: GB 446 0649 44. [Updated]

Don Kelly Books, Admiral Vernon L16-20, 141-149 Portobello Rd, London, W11. Prop: Don Kelly. Tel: (020) 7731-0482. Fax: (020) 7731-0482. E-mail: donkellybooks@btinternet.com. Est: 1981. Market stand/stall. Mail to: P.O. Box 44132, London SW6 2WN. Open: **S:** 07:00–16:00. Medium stock. Spec: Antiques; Applied Art; Fine Art. PR: £5–1,000. CC: MC; V. International mail order, book search. Books may be viewed by appointment anytime. Also showing at Olympia Antique Fair 3 times yearly. VAT No: GB 563 2239 49. [Updated]

Robert J. Kirkpatrick, 6 Osterley Park View Road, London, W7 2HH. Tel: (020) 8567-4521. E-mail: rkirkpatrick .molesworth@virgin.net. Est: 1986. Private premises. Postal business only. Appointment necessary. Very small stock. Spec: Juvenile; Memoirs; Public Schools. PR: £1–100. Cata: 1 a year. [Updated]

Kitty Liebreich Antique Maps &, 5 Monk's Drive, London, W3 0EG. Tel: (020) 8992-5104. Fax: (020) 8992-5104. Website: www.kittyprint.com. E-mail: kitty@liebreich.co.uk. Est: 1972. Private premises. Internet and postal. Appointment necessary. Small stock. Spec: Animals and Birds; Antiquarian; Pacifism; Topography - General; Topography - Local. PR: £20–500. [24/09/2003]

Maggs Brothers Limited, ■ 50 Berkeley Square, London, W1J 5BA. Tel: (020) 7493-7160. Fax: (020) 7499-2007. Website: www.maggs.com. E-mail: postmaster@maggs.com. Est: 1853. Shop open: **M:** 09:30–17:00; **T:** 09:30–17:00; **W:** 09:30–17:00; **Th:** 09:30–17:00; **F:** 09:30–17:00. Very large stock. Spec: Author - Blake, N.; Autographs; Bibliography; Bindings; Early Imprints; Fine Printing; Geology; Illuminated Manuscripts; Letters; Literature; Manuscripts; Medicine - History of; Military History; Natural History; Travel - General. PR: £5–5,000,000. CC: V. Cata: 15 a year. Corresp: Japanese, Mandarin, German, French, Italian, Spanish. Mem: ABA; PBFA; BA; ILAB; BADA. [Updated]

Carol Manheim, 31 Ennismore Avenue, London, W4 1SE. Tel: (020) 8994-9740. Fax: (0709) 239 4665. E-mail: art.photo@lineone.net. Est: 1982. Spec: Art - History; Art - Reference; Artists; Fashion & Costume; Illustrated; Limited Editions; Photography; Private Press. PR: £20–1,000. CC: MC; V. [17/09/2003]

Marlborough Rare Books Ltd, ■ 144/146 New Bond Street, London, W1S 2TR. Prop: Jonathan Gestetner. Tel: (020) 7493-6993. Fax: (020) 7499-2479. E-mail: sales@mrb-books.co.uk. Est: 1948. Shop open: **M:** 09:30–17:30; **T:** 09:30–17:30; **W:** 09:30–17:30; **Th:** 09:30–17:30; **F:** 09:30–17:30; Medium stock. Spec: Architecture; Bibliography; Bindings; Colour-Plate; Country Houses; Fine Art; Illustrated; Landscape; Literature; Topography - General. PR: £50–50,000. CC: E; MC; V. Cata: 6 a year on art & architecture, travel & topography. Corresp: French, German. Mem: ABA; ILAB. [Updated]

Nineteenth Century Geological, 71a Oxford Gardens, London, W10 5UJ. John & Annie Henry. Tel: 020 8968 8647. Fax: 020 8968 8647. Website: n/a. E-mail: geol.maps@virgin.net. Est: 1998. Private premises. Internet and postal. Appointment necessary. Open: **M:** 09:00–18:00; **T:** 09:00–18:00; **W:** 09:00–18:00; **Th:** 09:00–18:00; **F:** 09:00–18:00; **S:** 09:00–23:00. Small stock. Spec: Atlases; Geology; Mining; Palaeontology. PR: £2–200. Also, geological consultancy. Corresp: French. Mem: IMC. [Updated]

Diana Parikian, Rare Books, 3 Caithness Road, London, W14 0JB. Tel: (020) 7603-8375. Fax: (020) 7602-1178. E-mail: dparikian@aol.com. Est: 1960. Private premises. Appointment necessary. Spec: Emblemata; Fine & Rare; Foreign Texts; Iconography. PR: £200–10,000. Cata: 2 a year. [30/06/2003]

Pickering & Chatto, ■ 36 St. George Street, London, W!S 2FA. Tel: (020) 7491-2656. Fax: (020) 7491-9161. Website: www.pickering-chatto.com. E-mail: j.hudson@pickering-chatto.com. Est: 1820. Shop open: **M:** 09:30–17:30; **T:** 09:30–17:30; **W:** 09:30–17:30; **Th:** 09:30–17:30; **F:** 09:30–17:30. Small stock. Spec: Chemistry; Early Imprints; Economics; Education & School; Health; Humanities; Incunabula; Literature; Manuscripts; Mathematics; Medicine; Pharmacy/Pharmacology; Philosophy; Science - General; Women. PR: £100–10,000. CC: MC; V. Cata: 10 a year. Corresp: French. Mem: ABA; PBFA; ILAB. VAT No: GB 691 3252 35. [Updated]

William Poole, 97 New Bond Street, London, W1S 1SL. Tel: (020) 7629-8738. Est: 1979. Private premises. Appointment necessary. Small stock. Spec: Academic/Scholarly; Classical Studies; Fine & Rare; Foreign Texts; Humanism; Publishers - General. Cata: 2 a year on European & British Books pre-1800, Classical Studies. [Updated]

Portobello Books, 328 Portobello Road, London, W10 5RU. Prop: Mr. L. Thompson. Tel: (020) 8964-3166. Fax: (020) 8266-1993. E-mail: sales@portobello-books.com. Est: 1992. PR: £1–100. [16/04/2003]

Jonathan Potter Ltd., 125 New Bond Street, London, W1S 1DY. Tel: (020) 7491-3520. Fax: (020) 7491-9754. Website: www.jpmaps.co.uk. E-mail: jpmaps@attglobal.net. Est: 1975. Shop &/or gallery. Open: **M:** 10:00–18:00; **T:** 10:00–18:00; **W:** 10:00–18:00; **Th:** 10:00–18:00; **F:** 10:00–18:00. Spec: Atlases; Cartography; Reference. PR: £30–30,000. CC: AE; D; MC; V. Also, reference books on the history of cartography & framing & paper restoration services. Cata: 1 a year. Mem: ABA; PBFA; ILAB. [Updated]

Quadrille at Delehar, ■ 146 Portobello Road, London, W11 2DZ. Prop: Valerie Jackson–Harris. Tel: (01923) 829079. Fax: (01923) 825207. E-mail: Est: 1965. Shop open: **S:** 09:00–16:00; Medium stock. Spec: Antiques; Dance; Performing Arts; Royalty - General. PR: £5–5,000. CC: AE; MC; V. Also, Valentines, Christmas cards. Mem: ABA; PBFA; ES. [26/08/2003]

Bernard Quaritch Ltd., ■ 8 Lower John Street, Golden Square, London, W1F 9AU. Prop: John Koh. Tel: (020) 7734-2983. Fax: (020) 7437-0967. Website: www.quaritch.com. E-mail: rarebooks@quaritch.com. Est: 1847. Shop open: **M:** 09:30–17:30; **T:** 09:30–17:30; **W:** 09:30–17:30; **Th:** 09:30–17:30; **F:** 09:30–17:30. Large stock. Spec: Alchemy; Antiquarian; Architecture; Art; Bibliography; Cookery/Gastronomy; Early Imprints; Economics; Incunabula; Literature; Manuscripts; Medicine; Philosophy; Photography; Religion - Islam; Science - General; Travel - General. PR: £100–500,000. CC: AE; MC; V; SW. Cata: 12 a year. Corresp: French, German, Italian, Spanish, Russian. Mem: ABA; PBFA; ILAB; SLAM, VDA, BADA. VAT No: GB GB840135854. [Updated]

A.F. Sephton, 16 Bloemfontein Avenue, Shepherds Bush, London, W12 7BL. Tel: (020) 8749-1454. Est: 1966. Private premises. Appointment necessary. Small general stock. Spec: Artists; Colour-Plate; Illustrated; Social History. PR: £10–100. [Updated]

Bernard J. Shapero Rare Books, ■ 32 St. George Street, London, W1S 2EA. Tel: (020) 7493-0876. Fax: (020) 7229-7860. Website: www.shapero.com. E-mail: info@shapero.com. Est: 1979. Internet and postal. Shop open: **M:** 09:30–18:30; **T:** 09:30–18:30; **W:** 09:30–18:30; **Th:** 09:30–18:30; **F:** 09:30–18:30; **S:** 11:00–17:00. Large stock. Spec: Academic/Scholarly; Africana; Alchemy; Alpinism/Mountaineering; American Indians; Americana; Animals and Birds; Anthropology; Antiquarian; Architecture; Arms & Armour; Art; Art - History; Astrology; Atlases; Author - 20th Century; Bibliography. PR: £50–100,000. CC: AE; D; E; JCB; MC; V; SW. Cata: 5 regularly on specialities. Corresp: French, German, Italian, Spanish, Dutch. Mem: ABA; PBFA; BA; ILAB. VAT No: GB 466 5294 16. [Updated]

Sokol Books Ltd, P.O. Box 2409, London, W1A 2SH. Prop: C.J. Sokol. Tel: (020) 7499-5571. Fax: (020) 7629-6536. E-mail: books@sokol.co.uk. Est: 1977. Appointment necessary. Spec: Antiquarian; Classical Studies; Early Imprints; Fine & Rare; History of Ideas; Incunabula; Literature; Science - History of; Travel - General. PR: £100–100,000. Mem: ABA; ILAB. [Updated]

Henry Sotheran Limited, ■ 2–5 Sackville Street, Piccadilly, London, W1S 3DP. Tel: (020) 7439-6151. Fax: (020) 7434-2019. Website: www.sotherans.co.uk. E-mail: sotherans@sotherans.co.uk. Est: 1761. Shop open: **M:** 09:30–06:00; **T:** 09:30–00:00; **W:** 09:30–00:00; **Th:** 09:30–00:00; **F:** 09:30–00:00; **S:** 10:00–04:00. Very large general stock. Spec: Architecture; Art; Bindings; Children's - General; Churchilliana; Illustrated; Literature; Natural History; Private Press; Sets of Books; Travel - General. PR: £20–100,000. CC: AE; D; MC; V. Cata: 15 a year. Mem: ABA; PBFA; ILAB. VAT No: GB 689 7172 69 [Updated]

Sue Lowell Natural History Books, 101 Cambridge Gardens, London, W10 6JE. Prop: Sue Lowell. Tel: (020) 8960-4382. Website: Abebooks.com. E-mail: sue4382@aol.com. Est: 1972. Private premises. Internet and postal. Telephone first. Open: **M:** 10:00–19:00; **T:** 10:00–19:00; **W:** 10:00–19:00; **Th:** 19:00–00:00; **F:** 19:00–00:00; **S:** 09:00–13:00; **Su:** 10:00–16:00. Medium stock. Spec: Academic/Scholarly; Animals and Birds; Art - Reference; Botany; Gardening; Medicine - History of; Natural History; New Naturalist; Ornithology; Science - History of; Travel - General; Zoology. PR: £10–4,000. CC: MC; V. Booksearch. Corresp: French. [Updated]

Melvin Tenner, 51 Gayford Road, London, W12 9BY. Tel: (020) 8740-6677. Fax: (020) 8740-6960. E-mail: tenner@abelgratis.com. Est: 1980. Private premises. Appointment necessary. Very small stock. Spec: International Affairs; also Booksearch. PR: £1–200. Corresp: French. [Updated]

Patrick Tuft, The Vicarage, Chiswick Mall, London, W4 2PJ. Tel: (withheld). Private premises. Postal business only. Very small stock. Spec: Bibles; Bibliography; History - General; Religion - Christian; Vatican and Papal History, The. [Updated]

C.R. White, 22 Denbigh Terrace, London, W11 2QJ. Tel: (020) 7228-7317. Fax: (020) 7598-1248. Postal business only. Very small stock. Spec: Travel - Africa; Travel - Polar. [22/04/2003]

Mrs. Teresa White, Flat 4, 79 St. Helen's Gardens, London, W10 6LJ. Tel: not disclosed. Private premises. Postal business only. Small stock. PR: £1–100. Cata: 52 – weekly. [Updated]

LONDON
(WEST CENTRAL POSTAL DISTRICTS)

Josephine Bacon, 179 Kings Cross Road, London, WC1X 9BX. Tel: (020) 7278 9490. Fax: (020) 7278 2447. E-mail: bacon@americanization.com. Private premises. Spec: Cookery/Gastronomy; Judaica; Languages - Foreign. [Updated]

Allsworth Rare Books, P.O.Box 134, 235 Earls Court Road, London, SW5 9FE. Tel: (020) 7377-0552. Fax: (020) 7377-0552. E-mail: jenny@allsworthbooks.com. Est: 2002. Office &/or bookroom. Appointment necessary. Spec: Africana; Photography; Sport - Big Game Hunting; Travel - General; Travel - Asia; Travel - Middle East; Voyages & Discovery. PR: £50–50,000. Valuations. Cata: 2 a year. Mem: ABA; PBFA; ILAB. Stock may be viewed (by appt.) at central London office. VAT No: GB 798 7327 57. [Updated]

Any Amount of Books, ■ 56 Charing Cross Road, London, WC2H 0QA. Tel: (020) 7836-3697. Fax: (020) 7240-1769. Website: www.anyamountofbooks.com. E-mail: charingx@ anyamountofbooks .com. Est: 1975. Shop open: **M:** 10:30–21:30; **T:** 10:30–21:30; **W:** 10:29–21:30; **Th:** 10:30–21:30; **F:** 10:30–21:30; **S:** 10:30–21:30; **Su:** 11:30–20:30. Academic/Scholarly; Antiquarian; Art - Reference. PR: £1–25,000. CC: AE; JCB; MC; PAYPAL. Also, books by the yard, i.e. for furnishing, film sets etc. & valuations. Cata: 1 a year. Mem: ABA; BA. [Updated]

Atlantis Bookshop, ■ 49a Museum Street, London, WC1A 1LY. Prop: Caroline Wise & Matthew Goulding. Tel: (020) 7405-2120. Website: www.atlantisbookshop.demon.co.uk. E-mail: atlantis@ theatlantisbookshop.com. Est: 1922. Shop open: **M:** 10:30–18:00; **T:** 10:30–18:00; **W:** 10:30–18:00; **Th:** 10:30–18:00; **F:** 10:30–18:00; **S:** 10:30–18:00. Small stock. Spec: Archaeology; Author - Crowley, A.; Author - Spare, A.O.; Mythology; Occult; Parapsychology. PR: £4–40. CC: AE; MC; V; SW. [updated]

Bertram Rota Ltd., ■ 31 Long Acre (First Floor), Covent Garden, London, WC2E 9LT. Tel: (020) 7836-0723. Fax: (020) 7497 9058. Website: www.bertramrota.co.uk. E-mail: bertramrota@ compuserve.com. Est: 1923. Shop open: **M:** 09:30–17:30; **T:** 09:30–17:30; **W:** 09:30–17:30; **Th:** 09:30–17:30; **F:** 09:30–17:30. Medium stock. Spec: Antiquarian; Autographs; First Editions; Literature; Modern First Editions; Private Press; also Booksearch. CC: D; E; JCB; MC; V. Mem: ABA; ILAB. [25/06/2003]

Steve Burak, ■ 18, Leigh Street, off Judd Street, London, WC1H 9EW. Prop: Steve Burak. Tel: (020) 7388-1153. E-mail: SteveBurakLondon@yahoo.com. Est: 2002. Telephone first. Shop at: Ground Floor, 18 Leigh Street, London WC1H 9EW. Open: **M:** 11:00–19:00; **T:** 11:00–19:00; **W:** 11:00–19:00; **Th:** 11:00–19:00; **F:** 11:00–19:00; **S:** 11:00–19:00. Medium stock. Spec: Academic/Scholarly; Antiquarian. PR: £5–1,000. [26/06/2003]

The Cinema Bookshop, ■ 13–14 Great Russell Street, London, WC1B 3NH. Prop: Fred Zentner. Tel: (020) 7637-0206. Fax: (020) 7436-9979. Est: 1969. Shop open: **M:** 10:30–17:30; **T:** 10:30–17:30; **W:** 10:30–17:29; **Th:** 10:30–17:30; **F:** 10:30–17:30; **S:** 10:30–17:30. Large stock. Spec: Cinema/Film. PR: £8–75. CC: E; JCB; MC; V. VAT No: GB 232 6938 54. [26/08/2003]

Collinge & Clark, ■ 13 Leigh Street, London, WC1H 9EW. Prop: Michael Collinge & Oliver Laurenson Clark. Tel: (020) 7387-7105. Fax: (020) 7388-1315. E-mail: collingeandclark@aol.com. Est: 1987. Shop open: **M:** 11:00–18:30; **T:** 11:00–18:30; **W:** 11:00–18:30; **Th:** 11:00–18:30; **F:** 11:00–18:30; **S:** 11:00–15:30; Medium stock. Spec: Fine Printing; History - British; Limited Editions; Papermaking; Private Press; Publishers - Curwen Press; Publishers - Incline Press; Typography. PR: £5–2,000. CC: AE; JCB; V. Also, pamphlets on British history. Corresp: French, Gerrman. Mem: PBFA. VAT No: GB 523 1738 64. [Updated]

Delectus Books, 27 Old Gloucester Street, London, WC1N 3XX. Prop: Michael R. Goss. Tel: (020) 8963-0979. Fax: (020) 8963-0502. Website: www.delectusbooks.co.uk. E-mail: mgdelectus@aol.com. Est: 1987. Private premises. Internet and postal. Very large stock. Spec: Academic/Scholarly; Aesthetic Movement; Anthropology; Astrology; Author - Blackwood, A.; Author - Huysmans, J.K.; Author - Machen, Arthur; Countries - Ireland; Countries - Latin America; Countries - Mexico; Countries - Middle East, The; Criminology. PR: £20–5,000. CC: E; JCB; MC; V; SW, So. Cata: 2 occasionally. Corresp: French, German, Spanish, Dutch. VAT No: GB 532 3080 82. [Updated]

David Drummond at Pleasures of Past Times, 11 Cecil Court, Charing Cross Road, London, WC2N 4EZ. Prop: David Drummond. Tel: (020) 7836-1142. Fax: (020) 7836-1142. E-mail: drummond@ popt.fsnet.co.uk. Est: 1967. Spec: Children's - General; Circus; Illustrated; Magic & Conjuring; Performing Arts. PR: £10–500. Also, juvenile illustrated. [Updated]

Francis Edwards (London) Limit, ■ 13 Great Newport Street, Charing Cross Road, London, WC2H 7JA. Tel: (020) 7379-7669. Fax: (020) 7836-5977. Website: www.francisedwards.co.uk. E-mail: sales@femilitary.demon.co.uk. Shop open: **M:** 10:00–19:00; **T:** 10:00–19:00; **W:** 10:00–19:00; **Th:** 10:00–19:00; **F:** 10:00–19:00; **S:** 10:00–19:00. Small general stock. Spec: Architecture; Art; Aviation; Bindings; Economics; Folklore; History - General; Law; Literature; Medicine; Military; Natural History; Naval; Philosophy; Theology; Voyages & Discovery. PR: £15–5,000. CC: AE; D; E; JCB; MC; V. Corresp: Spanish. Mem: ABA; PBFA; ILAB. VAT No: GB 594 2720 23. [Updated]

Fine Books Oriental Ltd., ■ 38 Museum Street, London, WC1A 1LP. Prop: Jeffrey Somers. Tel: (020) 7242-5288. Fax: (020) 7242-5344. Website: www.finebooks.demon.co.uk. E-mail: oriental@ finebooks.demon.co.uk. Est: 1977. Shop open: **M:** 09:30–17:30; **T:** 09:30–17:30; **W:** 09:30–17:30; **Th:** 09:30–17:30; **F:** 09:30–17:30; **S:** 11:00–17:00. Medium stock. Spec: Aviation; Canals/Inland Waterways; Cartoons; Countries - Asia; Countries - India; Countries - Japan; Psychic; Religion - Oriental; Spiritualism; Travel - Asia; Travel - Middle East. PR: £3–15,000. CC: AE; D; JCB; MC; V; Switch, Solo. Corresp: Japanese. Mem: PBFA. [Updated]

Michael Finney Antique Books &, ■ 31 Museum St., London, WC1A 1LG. Tel: (020) 7631-3533. Fax: (020) 7637-1813. Website: www.michaelfinney.co.uk. E-mail: prints@michaelfinney.co.uk. Est: 1979. Shop open: **M:** 10:00–18:00; **T:** 10:00–18:00; **W:** 10:00–18:00; **Th:** 10:00–18:00; **F:** 10:00–18:00; **S:** 10:00–18:00. Large general stock. Spec: Architecture; Illustrated; Natural History; Social History; Travel - General. PR: £20–5,000. CC: AE; MC; V. Cata: 6 a year. Corresp: Spanish, French, Italian. Mem: ABA; PBFA. VAT No: GB 577 8997 48. [21/07/2003]

Robert Frew Limited, ■ 106 Great Russell Street, London, WC1B 3NB. Tel: (020) 7580-2311. Fax: (020) 7580-2313. Website: www.robertfrew.com. E-mail: shop@robertfrew.com. Est: 1993. Shop open: **M:** 10:00–18:00; **T:** 10:00–18:00; **W:** 10:00–18:00; **Th:** 10:00–18:00; **F:** 10:00–18:00; **S:** 10:00–14:00. Spec: Antiquarian; Atlases; Author - Churchill, Sir Winston; Bindings; Cartography; Encyclopaedias; History - General; Illustrated; Literature; Sets of Books; Sport - Skiing; Travel - General. PR: £10–30,000. CC: AE; D; E; JCB; MC; V. Mem: ABA; PBFA; ILAB. VAT No: GB 625 8877 92. [Updated]

Gekoski Booksellers, ■ Pied Bull Yard, 15a Bloomsbury Square, London, WC1A 2LP. Prop: R.A. Gekoski, P.A. Grogan & J.A.M. Irvine. Tel: (020) 7404-6676. Fax: (020) 7404-6595. Website: www.gekoski.com. E-mail: rick@gekoski.com. Est: 1982. Shop open: **M:** 10:00–17:30; **T:** 10:00–17:30; **W:** 10:00–17:30; **Th:** 10:00–17:30; **F:** 10:00–17:30. Small stock. Spec: First Editions; Letters; Manuscripts. PR: £100–1,000. CC: MC; V. Cata: occasionally. Mem: ABA. VAT No: GB 418 5464 40. [Updated]

Grosvenor Prints, ■ 19 Shelton Street, Covent Garden, London, WC2H 9JN. Prop: Nigel Talbot. Tel: (020) 7836-1979. Fax: (020) 7379-6695. Website: www.grosvenorprints.com. E-mail: grosvenorprints @btinternet.com. Est: 1976. Shop open: **M:** 09:00–18:00; **T:** 09:00–18:00; **W:** 09:00–18:00; **Th:** 09:00–18:00; **F:** 09:00–18:00; **S:** 11:00–16:00. Large stock. Spec: Animals and Birds; Culture - National; Dogs; Maritime/Nautical; Military; Music - General; Royalty - General; Social History; Topography - General; Topography - Local; Travel - General. PR: £5–200. CC: AE; MC; V. Mem: ABA. [Updated]

Jarndyce Antiquarian Bookselle, 46 Great Russell Street, (opp. British Museum), London, WC1B 3PA. Prop: Brian Lake & Janet Nassau. Tel: (020) 7631-4220. Fax: (020) 7631-1882. Website: www.jarndyce.co.uk. E-mail: books@jarndyce.co.uk. Est: 1969. Shop &/or showroom. Internet and postal. Open: **M:** 10:30–17:30; **T:** 10:30–17:30; **W:** 10:30–17:30; **Th:** 10:30–17:30; **F:** 10:30–17:30. Large stock. Spec: Antiquarian; Author - Austen, Jane; Author - Byron, Lord; Author - Cobbett, William; Author - Dickens, Charles; Economics; Education & School; First Editions; Literature; Literature - Victorian; Manuscripts; Performing Arts; Plays; Politics; Social History; Theatre; Women. PR: £5–5,000. CC: AE; MC; V. Valuations and booksearch within our specialist areas. Cata: 6 on Literature & The Social Sciences pre. 1920. Corresp: French. Mem: ABA; PBFA; ILAB; BBA. VAT No: GB 524 0890 57. [Updated]

The Maghreb Bookshop, ■ 45 Burton Street, London, WC1H 9AL. Prop: Mohamed Ben Madani. Tel: (020) 7388-1840. Fax: (020) 7388-1840. Website: www.maghreview.com. E-mail: maghreb@ maghrebreview.com. Est: 1981. Shop open: **M:** 09:00–18:00; **T:** 09:00–18:00; **W:** 08:00–18:00; **Th:** 09:00–18:00; **F:** 09:00–18:00; **S:** 09:00–18:00. Spec: Academic/Scholarly; Anthropology; Archaeology; Architecture; Authors - Women; Colonial; Countries - Middle East, The; Countries - North Africa; Economics; Ethnography; Ethnology; Geography; Humanities; Literature; Social History; Social History. Corresp: Arabic, French. VAT No: GB 735 8794 81. [Updated]

Murder One, ■ 71–73 Charing Cross Road, London, WC2H 0AA. Prop: M. Jakubowski & N. Landau. Tel: (020) 7734-3483. Fax: (020) 7734-3429. Website: www.murderone.co.uk. E-mail: murder _london@compuserve.com. Est: 1989. Shop open: **M:** 10:00–19:00; **T:** 10:00–19:00; **W:** 10:00– 19:00; **Th:** 10:00–20:00; **F:** 10:00–20:00; **S:** 10:00–20:00. Very large stock. Spec: Crime (True); Fiction - Romantic; Fiction - crime, detective, spy, thrillers; Fiction - Science Fiction. PR: £1–500. CC: AE; E; JCB; MC; V. Corresp: French, Spanish, German & Italian. [06/08/2003]

Museum Bookshop, ■ 36 Great Russell Street, London, WC1B 3QB. Prop: Ashley Jones. Tel: (020) 7580-4086. Fax: (020) 7436-4364. Website: www.museumbookshop.org.uk/. Est: 1979. Internet and postal. Shop open: **M:** 10:00–17:30; **S:** 10:00–17:30. Spec: Antiquarian; Archaeology; Classical Studies; Countries - Egypt; Egyptology; History - Ancient; Travel - Middle East; also Booksearch. PR: £5–300. CC: AE; D; JCB; MC; V. Also, new books & back-numbers of journals. [29/07/2003]

Tim Bryars Ltd, ■ 8 Cecil Court, London, WC2N 4HE. Prop: Tim Bryars. Tel: (020) 7836-1901. Fax: (020) 7836-1910. Website: www.timbryars.co.uk. E-mail: tim@timbryars.co.uk. Est: 1997. Shop open: **M:** 11:00–18:00; **T:** 11:00–18:00; **W:** 11:00–18:00; **Th:** 11:00–18:00; **F:** 11:00–18:00; **S:** 12:00–17:00. Very large stock. Spec: Atlases; Cartography; Classical Studies; Early Imprints; Fine & Rare; Natural History; Topography - General. PR: £10–30,000. CC: MC; V. Mem: ABA; ILAB. VAT No: GB 839 6884 58. [Updated]

Pholiota Books, 179 Kings Cross Road, London, WC1X 9BZ. Prop: Josephine Bacon. Tel: (020) 7278-9490. Fax: (020) 7278-2447. Website: www.pholiota.cc. E-mail: bacon@pholiota.cc. Est: 1996. Storeroom. Internet and postal. Telephone first. Open: **M:** 09:00–18:00; Medium stock. Spec: Academic/Scholarly; Botany; Cookery/Gastronomy; Languages - Foreign; Literature in Translation; Travel - Middle East; Wine. PR: £1–60. Translations to and from any language. Corresp: French, Hebrew, Russian, German, Italian, Spanish. Mem: ATA, ITI. VAT No: GB 778 0611 12. [Updated]

Photo Books International, ■ 99 Judd Street, London, WC1H 9NE. Prop: Bill Herbert & Jasper Howard. Tel: (020) 7813-7363. Fax: (020) 7813-7363. Website: www.pbi-books.com. E-mail: pbi@britishlibrary.net. Est: 1998. Internet and postal. Shop open: **W:** 11:00–18:00; **Th:** 11:00– 18:00; **F:** 11:00–18:00; **S:** 11:00–18:00. Medium stock. Spec: Photography. PR: £5–200. CC: AE; MC; V. Mem: PBFA; BA. VAT No: GB 730 6914 40. [Updated]

Henry Pordes Books Ltd., ■ 58-60 Charing Cross Road, London, WC2H 0BB. Prop: Gino Della–Ragione. Tel: (020) 7836 9031. Fax: (020) 7240 4232. Website: www.henrypordesbooks.com. E-mail: info@henrypordesbooks.com. Est: 1980. Shop open: **M:** 10:00–19:00; **T:** 10:00–19:00; **W:** 10:00– 19:00; **Th:** 10:00–19:00; **F:** 10:00–19:00; **S:** 10:00–23:00. Spec: Academic/Scholarly; Advertising; Aeronautics; Africana; Antiques; Archaeology; Architecture; Art; Art - History; Arts, The; Bindings; Cinema/Film; Drama; Fashion & Costume; Fine Art; Fine Printing; History - General; Judaica; Literary Criticism. PR: £1–2,000. CC: AE; MC; V. Mem: PBFA. [Updated]

Arthur Probsthain, 41 Great Russell Street, London, WC1B 3PE. Tel: (020) 7636-1096. Fax: (020) 7636-1096. E-mail: ap@oriental-african-books.com. Est: 1902. Spec: Countries - Africa; Oriental. [08/07/2003]

Quinto of Charing Cross Road, ■ 48a Charing Cross Road, London, WC2H 0BB. Prop: Hay Cinema Bookshop Ltd. Tel: (0207) 379 7669. Fax: (0207) 836-5977. Website: www.haycinemabookshop.co.uk. E-mail: sales@femilitary.demon.co.uk. Est: 1905. Shop open: **M:** 09:00–21:00; **T:** 09:00–21:00; **W:** 09:00–21:00; **Th:** 09:00–21:00; **F:** 09:00–21:00; **S:** 09:00–21:00; **Su:** 12:00–08:00. Very large general stock. Spec: PR: £1–100. CC: AE; D; E; JCB; MC; V. Corresp: Spanish. VAT No: GB 594 2720 23. [Updated]

Quinto of Great Russell Street, ■ 63 Great Russell Street, London, WC1B 3BF. Tel: (0207) 430 2535. Fax: (0207) 430 2566. Website: www.haycinemabookshop.co.uk. E-mail: sales@quintogrs.co.uk. Est: 2002. Shop open: **M:** 10:00–19:00; **T:** 10:00–19:00; **W:** 10:00–19:00; **Th:** 10:00–19:00; **F:** 10:00–19:00; **S:** 10:00–19:00; **Su:** 10:00–19:00. Very large general stock. PR: £5–1,000. CC: AE; D; E; JCB; MC; V. Corresp: Spanish. VAT No: GB 594 2720 23. [Updated]

Red Snapper Books, ■ 22 Cecil Court, London, WC2N 4NE. Prop: James Allen. Tel: (020) 7240-2075. Fax: (01227) 277963. Website: www.redsnapperbooks.com. E-mail: james@redsnapperbooks.com. Est: 1996. Shop open: **M:** 10:00–17:30; **T:** 10:00–17:30; **W:** 10:00–17:30; **Th:** 10:00–17:30; **F:** 10:00–17:30; **S:** 10:00–17:30. Very small stock. Spec: Beat Writers; First Editions; Photography. PR: £10–20,000. CC: MC; V. Cata: 3 a year on beat/American, literature. [02/06/2003]

Rees & O'Neill Rare Books, ■ 27 Cecil Court, London, WC2N 4EZ. Prop: Angus O'Neill, David Rees. Tel: (020) 7836-3336. Website: www.rees-oneill.com. E-mail: books@rees-oneill.com. Est: 2002. Shop; Internet and postal. Open: **M:** 10:00–18:00; **T:** 10:00–18:00; **W:** 10:00–18:00; **Th:** 10:00–18:00; **F:** 10:00–18:00; **S:** 10:00–17:00. Spec: Antiques; Applied Art; Architecture; Art; Illustrated; Literature; Modern First Editions. CC: E; MC; V. Valuations. Cata: 5 – Modern First Editions. Mem: ABA; PBFA; ILAB. [Updated]

Roe and Moore, ■ 29 Museum Street, London, WC1A 1LH. Prop: Anthony and Deana Roe. Tel: (020) 7636-4787. Website: www.roeandmoore.co.uk. E-mail: roeandmoore@fsbdial.co.uk. Est: 1992. Shop open: M: 10:30–18:00; **T:** 10:30–18:00; **W:** 10:30–18:00; **Th:** 10:30–18:00; **F:** 10:30–18:00; **S:** 10:30–18:00. Medium stock. Spec: Art; Art Reference; Artists; Children's; Design; Fine Art; Illustrated; Juvenile; Pop-Up, Movable and Cut Out. PR: £1–3,000. CC: MC; V. [Updated]

Shipley Specialist Art Booksel, ■ 70 Charing Cross Road, London, WC2H 0BQ. Prop: Ian Shipley. Tel: (020) 7836-4872. Fax: (020) 7379-4358. Website: www.artbook.co.uk. E-mail: sales@artbook.co.uk. Est: 1979. Internet and postal. Shop open: **M:** 10:00–18:00; **T:** 10:00–18:00; **W:** 10:00–18:00; **Th:** 10:00–18:00; **F:** 10:00–18:00; **S:** 10:00–18:00. Spec: Advertising; Antiques; Applied Art; Architecture; Art; Art - History; Art - Reference; Artists; Book of Hours; Carpets; Catalogues Raisonnes; Ceramics; Conservation; Decorative Art; Ecclesiastical History & Architecture; Fashion & Costume. PR: £1–200. CC: AE; E; JCB; MC; V. Also, new books on the arts and a booksearch service. VAT No: GB 242 7752 54. [29/06/2003]

Skoob Russell Square, ■ 10 Brunswick Centre, (off Bernard Street), London, WC1N 1AE. Prop: C. Y. Loh. Tel: (020) 7278-8760. Fax: (020) 7278-3137. Website: www.skoob.com. E-mail: books@skoob.com. Est: 2001. Shop at: Will be moving, probably within the Brunswick Centre some time in 2005. Open: **M:** 11:00–19:00; **T:** 11:00–19:00; **W:** 11:00–19:00; **Th:** 11:00–19:00; **F:** 11:00–19:00; **S:** 11:00–22:00; **Su:** 12:00–17:00. Very large general stock. Spec: Academic/Scholarly; Anthropology; Architecture; Art; Aviation; Cinema/Film; Classical Studies; Computing; Drama; Economics; Esoteric; History - General; History - British; Law; Linguistics; Literary Criticism; Literature; Mathematics; Military. PR: £1–500. CC: AE; E; MC; V. [Updated]

Spink & Son Limited, 69 Southampton Row, Bloomsbury, London, WC1B 4ET. Tel: (020) 7563-4000. Fax: (020) 7563-4068. Website: www.spink-online.com. E-mail: info@spink.com. Est: 1666. Spec: Military; Numismatics. PR: £1–5,000. [14/07/2004]

Tindley & Chapman, ■ 4 Cecil Court, London, WC2N 4HE. Prop: James Tindley, Ron Chapman. Tel: (020) 7240-2161. Fax: (020) 7370-1062. Est: 1975. Shop open: **M:** 10:00–17:30; **T:** 10:00–17:30; **W:** 10:00–17:30; **Th:** 10:00–17:30; **F:** 10:00–17:30; **S:** 11:00–17:00. Medium stock. Spec: Fiction - General; Fiction - Crime, Detective, Spy, Thrillers; Fiction - Women; First Editions; Literature; Poetry. PR: £10–5,000. CC: MC; V. Cata: 4 – a year. Mem: PBFA. Also at: Ron Chapman, London SW10 9LW (q.v.). [Updated]

Travis & Emery Music Bookshop, ■ 17 Cecil Court, off Charing Cross Road, London, WC2N 4EZ. Tel: (020) 7240-2129. Fax: (020) 7497-0790. Website: www.travis-and-emery.com. E-mail: sheenq@travis-and-emery.com. Est: 1960. Shop open: **M:** 11:00–18:00; **T:** 11:00–18:00; **W:** 11:00–18:00; **Th:** 11:00–18:00; **F:** 11:00–18:00; **S:** 11:00–18:00; **Su:** 11:30–17:30; Closed for lunch: 14:00–14:30. Very large stock. Spec: Bell-Ringing (Campanology); Bibliography; Music - General; Music - Classical; Music - Composers; Music - Folk & Irish Folk; Music - Jazz; Music - Music Hall; Music - Musicians; Music - Opera; Music - Political Songs & Ballads; Music - Popular. PR: £1–5,000. CC: MC; V. Also, secondhand sheet music & new music books, plus prints. Cata: 4 a year.- Mem: ABA; PBFA; ILAB. VAT No: GB 239 5258 39. [Updated]

Ulysses, ■ 40 Museum Street, London, WC1 1LU. Prop: Peter Jolliffe. Tel: (020) 7831-1600. Fax: (020) 7419-0070. E-mail: ulyssesbooks@fsbdial.co.uk. Est: 1990. Shop open: **M:** 10:30–18:00; **T:** 10:30–18:00; **W:** 10:30–18:00; **Th:** 10:30–18:00; **F:** 10:30–18:00; **S:** 10:30–18:00. Large stock. Spec: Illustrated; Modern First Editions. PR: £5–1,000. CC: AE; MC; V. Cata: 5 a year. Mem: ABA; PBFA. [17/06/2003]

Unsworths Booksellers Ltd., ■ 12 Bloomsbury Street, London, WC1B 3QA. Prop: Charlie Unsworth & Sue Coe. Tel: (020) 7436-9836. Fax: (020) 7637-7334. Website: www.unsworths.com. E-mail: books@ unsworths.com. Est: 1986. Shop open: **M:** 10:30–20:00; **T:** 10:30–20:00; **W:** 10:30–20:00; **Th:** 10:30–20:00; **F:** 10:30–20:00; **S:** 10:30–20:00; **Su:** 11:00–19:00. Very large stock. Spec: Academic/Scholarly; Anthropology; Antiquarian; Archaeology; Architecture; Art; Bibliography; Bindings; Books about Books; Byzantium; Cinema/Film; Classical Studies; Early Imprints; Ecclesiastical History & Architecture; Egyptology; Fiction - General. PR: £1–5,000. CC: AE; D; E; JCB; MC; V; Maestro. Cata: 2 a year on Antiquarian and Rare. Mem: ABA; PBFA; BA; ILAB; Also at: 101 Euston Road, London NW1 2RA. VAT No: GB 480 1145 75. [Updated]

Waterstone's, ■ 82 Gower Street, London, WC1E 6EQ. Prop: HMV Media Group. Tel: (020) 7636-1577. Fax: (020) 7580-7680. Website: www.waterstones.co.uk/gowerst. E-mail: sh.gower .waterstones@lineone.net. Est: 1936. Shop open: **M:** 09:30–20:00; **T:** 10:00–20:00; **W:** 09:30–20:00; **Th:** 09:30–20:00; **F:** 09:30–20:00; **S:** 09:30–19:00; **Su:** 12:00–18:00. Medium stock. Spec: Academic/ Scholarly. CC: AE; D; MC; V. Also sells academic remainders and is situated within large, well-known bookshop. [Updated]

Nigel Williams Rare Books, ■ 25 Cecil Court, Charing Cross Road, London, WC2N 4EZ. Tel: (020) 7836-7757. Fax: (020) 7379-5918. Website: www.nigelwilliams.com. E-mail: sales@nigelwilliams.com. Est: 1989. Internet and postal. Shop open: **M:** 10:00–18:00; **T:** 10:00–18:00; **W:** 00:00–18:00; **Th:** 00:00–18:00; **F:** 00:00–18:00; **S:** 10:00–18:00. Large stock. Spec: Author - Christie, Agatha; Author - Fleming, Ian; Author - Greene, Graham; Author - Joyce, James; Author - Wodehouse, P.G.; Fables; Fiction - General; Fiction - Historical; First Editions; Literature; Manuscripts; Periodicals & Magazines. PR: £5–10,000. CC: AE; D; E; JCB; MC; V. Cata: 20 a year. Mem: ABA; PBFA; ILAB. VAT No: GB 574 3776 05. [Updated]

LONDON
(GREATER LONDON, OUTER)

BARKING

James Smith Booksellers, Vicarage Field Shopping Centre, Ripple Road, Barking, 1G11 8DQ. Prop: D.R. Bird. Tel: (020) 8591-9090. Fax: (020) 8591-9937. Website: www.jsbooks.co.uk. E-mail: op@jsb.org.uk. Est: 1926. Spec: Computing; Booksearch. PR: £5–50. Also, new titles export & schools book supply. [13/07/2003]

BEDDINGTON

Mrs. Patricia Clear, 33 Cedars Road, Beddington, CR0 4PU. Mrs Patricia Clear. Tel: (020) 8681-0251. E-mail: patandray@blueyonder.co.uk. Est: 1990. Private premises. Postal business only. Telephone first. Small general stock. Spec: Children's - General. PR: £1–100. Cata: 6 a year on Childrens. [Updated]

CARSHALTON

Croydon Bookshop, ■ 304 Carshalton Road, Carshalton, SM5 3QB. Prop: Mrs. P.F. Reding & P.J. Rogers. Tel: (020) 8643-6857. Est: 1954. Shop open: **T:** 10:30–17:30; **W:** 10:30–17:30; **Th:** 10:30–17:30; **F:** 10:30–17:30; **S:** 09:30–17:30. Medium stock. Spec: PR: £2–100. Corresp: French, German, Spanish. [Updated]

Japan Books (Y & S Company Ltd,) P.O. Box 693, Carshalton, SM5 3ZN. (*) Prop: Sammy I. Tsunematsu. Tel: Office (020) 8773-25. Fax: (020) 8286-8003. Website: www.yandscompany.co.uk/japanbooks.htm. E-mail: jbooksuk@aol.com. Est: 1975. Spec: Children's - General; Countries - Japan; Illustrated. PR: £20–7,500. Shop at: Biblion, 1–7 Davies Mews, London WC1Y 2LP. Tel: (020) 7629-1374. [28/08/2003]

Crosby Nethercott Books, 16 Kings Avenue, Carshalton, Surrey, SM5 4NX. (*) Prop: D.W. Beer. Tel: (020) 8643 4124. E-mail: crosbybooks@cwcom.net. Est: 1991. Private premises. Internet and postal. Appointment necessary. Small stock. Spec: Academic/Scholarly; Advertising; Aeronautics; Author - Rolt, L.T.C.; Canals/Inland Waterways; Churchilliana; Company History; History - Industrial; Railways; also Booksearch. PR: £5–100. Corresp: French, German. [Updated]

CROYDON

Steve Archer, 11 Bedford Place, Croydon, Surrey, CR0 2BS. (*). Tel: (020) 8686 3736. Website: www.ukbookworld.com/members/stevearcher. E-mail: stevearcher2000@yahoo.co.uk. Est: 2000. Private premises. Internet and postal. Small stock. Spec: Autobiography; Biography; Canals/Inland Waterways; Literary Travel; Literature; Modern First Editions; also Booksearch. PR: £2–200. CC: Paypal. [Updated]

Peter Howard (Books), 2 Park View Road, Addiscombe, Croydon, Surrey, CR0 7DE. (*). Tel: (020) 8656-8302. E-mail: barpeth@clara.co.uk. Est: 1979. Private premises. Appointment necessary. Very small stock. PR: £5–200. [14/04/2003]

EDGWARE

Two Jays Bookshop, ■ 119 High Street, Edgware, HA8 7DB. Prop: Joyce and Mark Matthews. Tel: (020) 8952-1349. Est: 1977. Shop open: **T:** 09:00–17:00; **W:** 09:00–17:00; **Th:** 09:00–17:00; **F:** 09:00–17:00; **S:** 09:00–17:00. Large general stock. PR: £2–100. [Updated]

ENFIELD

Terence J. McGee, 20 Slades Close, Enfield, Middlesex, EN2 7EB. Prop: T.J. & J.I. McGee. Tel: (020) 8366-5727. E-mail: tmcgee@globalnet.co.uk. Est: 1972. Private premises. Appointment necessary. Market stand. Open: **S:** 09:00–19:00; **Su:** 09:00–19:00. Small stock. Spec: Author - Betjeman, Sir John; Cinema/Film; Comics; Counterculture; Countries - Italy; Education & School; Music - General; Music - Music Hall; Nostalgia; Performing Arts; Science - General; Science - History of; Television; Theatre. PR: £1–500. Also, sound recordings & record tapes (inc. 16s, 33s, 45s,78s and CDs). Cata: occasionally. Corresp: French, German, Italian, Spanish. [Updated]

Oak Tree Books, 69 Landseer Road, Bush Hill Park, Enfield, Middlesex, EN1 1DP. Prop: Mr R.L. Conrich. [26/08/2003]

Felicity J. Warnes, ■ 82 Merryhills Drive, Enfield, Middlesex, EN2 7PD. Prop: F. J. Warnes. Tel: (020) 8367-1661. Fax: (020) 8372-1035. E-mail: felicity@fjwarnes.u-net.com. Est: 1978. Appointment necessary. Shop at: The Old Bookshop, 36 Gordon Road, Enfield. Large stock. Spec: Embroidery; Fashion & Costume; Jewellery; Knitting; Lace; Military; Social History; Textiles. PR: £5–200. CC: MC; V. Cata: 4 a year.Mem: PBFA; ES. [13/03/2003]

GREENFORD

Books B.C., 58 Elton Avenue, Greenford, Middlesex, UB6 0PP. (*) Prop: Martin McCrory. Tel: (020) 8864-0580. Est: 1987. Private premises. Appointment necessary. Very small stock. Spec: PR: £1–500. Cata: occasionally on Egyptology, Ancient History. [Updated]

HAMPTON HILL

Bates Books, 95 High Street, Hampton Hill, Middlesex, TW12 1NH. Prop: Garry and Jackie Bates. Tel: (020) 8941-6782. Private premises. Postal business only. Telephone first. Small stock. Spec: Children's - General; Education & School; First Editions; Illustrated. PR: £2–30. [19/05/2003]

HAMPTON

R. W. Clements, 114 High Street, Hampton, Middlesex, TW12 2ST. Prop: R. W. Clements. Tel: (020) 8979-3069. Est: 1992. Private premises. Appointment necessary. Large general stock. Spec: Archaeology; Art; Autobiography; Biography; Children's - General; Drama; Fiction - General; History - General; Irish Interest; Literature; Music - General; Poetry; Sport - General; Transport; Travel - General. PR: £5–1,000. All speciality subjects shown relate to Ireland. Also, ephemera and prints related to Ireland. Cata: 4 a year. [Updated]

R.S. and P.A. Scowen, 9 Birchwood Grove, Hampton, Middlesex, TW12 3DU. (*). Tel: (020) 8979-7429. Fax: (020) 8287-3810. E-mail: patscowen@waitrose.com. Est: 1978. Private premises. Appointment necessary. Small stock. Spec: Chess; Games; Sport - Billiards/Snooker/Pool. PR: £2–100. Also, back-numbers of relevant journals. [Updated]

HAMPTON–ON–THAMES

Ian Sheridan's Bookshop, ■ 34 Thames Street, Hampton–on–Thames, TW12 2DK. Prop: Ian Sheridan. Tel: (020) 8979-1704. Est: 1960. Shop open: **M:** 11:00–17:00; **T:** 11:00–17:00; **W:** 11:00–17:00; **Th:** 11:00–17:00; **F:** 11:00–17:00; **S:** 10:00–17:00; **Su:** 09:00–17:00. Very large general stock. PR: £2–500. Closes at dusk in winter. Corresp: French, German. [Updated]

HARROW

medievalbookshop, 118 Vaughan Road, West Harrow, Harrow, Middlesex, HA1 4ED. Prop: Nick Gorman. Tel: (07950) 147504. Website: www.medievalbookshop.co.uk. E-mail: admin@medievalbookshop.co.uk. Est: 2000. Private premises. Internet and postal. Shop at: PO Box 2082, Watford, WD18 0AD, U.K. Small stock. Spec: Academic/Scholarly; Archaeology; History - Middle Ages; History - Renaissance, The; Medieval; Religion - General. PR: £1–200. CC: Paypal. [Updated]

HATCH END

B. Heyman, 27 Sherington Avenue, Hatch End, Pinner, Middlesex, HA5 4DU. (*). Tel: Private premises. Postal business only. Small stock. Spec: Art; Drama; History - General; Literary Criticism; Theatre. [27/04/2003]

HAYES

The Churchill Book Specialist, 25a Station Road, Hayes, UB3 4BD. Tel: (020) 8573-6370. Website: www.wscbooks.com. E-mail: mark@wscbooks.com. Est: 1987. Private premises. Internet and postal. Appointment necessary. Medium stock. Spec: Author - Churchill, Sir Winston; Military; War - World War I; War - World War II. PR: £5–10,000. CC: MC; V. Cata: 8 a year. Mem: ABA. Also at: PO Box 90689, Tucson, AZ 85752 USA. [Updated]

ILFORD (SEE ALSO UNDER ESSEX)

Book Basket, 25a Meath Road, Ilford, Essex, IG1 1JA. (*) Prop: Peter Arnold. Tel: (0208) 514-5362. E-mail: peterarnoldiv@hotmail.com. Private premises. Postal business only. Spec: Academic/Scholarly; Africana; Almanacs; Alpinism/Mountaineering; Alternative Medicine; American Indians; Americana; Annuals; Anthologies; Anthropology; Antiquarian; Antiques; Archaeology; Architecture; Arms & Armour; Art; Art - History; Art - Reference. PR: £15–1,000. [29/06/2003]

Porcupine Books, 37 Coventry Road, Ilford, Essex, IG1 4QR. (*) Prop: Brian Ameringen. Tel: (0208) 554-3799. Website: www.porcupine.demon.co.uk. E-mail: brian@porcupine.demon.co.uk. Est: 1998. Private premises. Internet and postal. Appointment necessary. Open: **M:** 08:00–21:00; **T:** 08:00–21:00; **W:** 18:00–21:00; **Th:** 18:00–21:00; **F:** 20:00–21:00; **S:** 18:00–21:00; **Su:** 08:00–21:00. Medium stock. Spec: Fiction - Crime, Detective, Spy, Thrillers; Fiction - Fantasy, Horror; Fiction - Science Fiction. PR: £1–2,500. Cata: 4 a year. [Updated]

ISLEWORTH

Chaters Motoring Booksellers, 8 South Street, Isleworth, Middlesex, TW7 7DH. (*) Prop: F.P.A. Stroud. Tel: (020) 8568-9750. Fax: (020) 8569-8273. Website: www.chaters.co.uk. E-mail: books@chaters.co.uk. Est: 1957. Spec: Motorbikes; Motoring; also Booksearch. PR: £1–500. Also, new books in specialities. [17/07/2003]

KENLEY

David & Lynn Smith, The Hermitage, 21 Uplands Road, Kenley, Surrey, CR8 5EE. Tel: (020) 8660-9908. Fax: (020) 8660-9908. E-mail: smithbookskenley@tiscali.co.uk. Est: 1980. Storeroom. Appointment necessary. Small stock. Spec: Biology; Medicine; Medicine - History of; Pharmacy/Pharmacology; Science - General; Science - History of; Scientific Instruments. PR: £10–500. CC: JCB; MC; V. Cata: 1 a year. Mem: PBFA. [Updated]

KEW

Criterion Books, 6 Nylands Avenue, Kew, Richmond, TW9 4HH. (*) Prop: Terence Crimmings. Tel: and Fax: (020) 8876-1773. E-mail: terry.crimmings@tinyworld.co.uk. Est: 1992. Private premises. Postal business only. Appointment necessary. Very small stock. Spec: Academic/Scholarly; Advertising; Author - Durrell, Lawrence; Biography; Horizon Writers; Illustrated; Literary Travel; Literature; Modern First Editions; War - General. PR: £10–350. [Updated]

MORDEN

A. Burton–Garbett, 35 The Green, Morden, Surrey, SM4 4HJ. Tel: (020) 8540-2367. Fax: (020) 8540-4594. E-mail: Est: 1959. Private premises. Appointment necessary. Medium stock. Spec: Countries - Caribbean, The; Countries - Central America; Countries - Mexico; Countries - Portugal; Countries - South America; Countries - Spain. [19/02/2003]

NEW BARNET

ForensicSearch, 17 Greenacres, Glyn Avenue, New Barnet, EN4 9PJ. Prop: Nick Danks and Samantha Sproates. Tel: (020) 8440-8896. E-mail: forensicsearch@hotmail.com. Est: 1999. Private premises. Postal business only. Very small stock. Spec: Crime (True); Science - Forensic; also Booksearch. PR: £2–200. [Updated]

PINNER

The Eastcote Bookshop, ■ 156/160 Field End Road, Pinner, Middlesex, HA5 1RH. Prop: Eileen & David May. Tel: (020) 8866-9888. Fax: (020) 8905-9387. Est: 1993. Shop open: **T:** 12:00–16:00; **W:** 12:00–16:00; **F:** 10:30–17:00; **S:** 10:30–17:00. Very large stock. Spec: Alpinism/Mountaineering; American Indians; Annuals; Antiques; Art; Canals/Inland Waterways; Children's - General; Cinema/Film; Colour-Plate; Crime (True); Esoteric; Fiction - General; First Editions; Horticulture; Humour; Illustrated; Motoring. PR: £2–500. CC: MC; V. Occasional fairs. Mem: PBFA. [02/06/2003]

RICHMOND–UPON–THAMES

W. & A. Houben, 2 Church Court, Richmond–upon–Thames, TW9 1JL. (*) Prop: Mr. Chris Dunlop. Tel: (020) 8940-1055. E-mail: chrisdunlop1@aol.com. Est: 1963. PR: £1–500. Also, new books & secondhand CDs. [11/07/2003]

SUNBURY–ON–THAMES

Cecilia Marsden, 98 Manor Lane, Sunbury–on–Thames, Middlesex, TW16 6JB. (*). Tel: (01932) 785705. Fax: (01932) 785705. E-mail: maire@onetel.net.uk. Est: 1993. Private premises. Postal business only. Appointment necessary. Very small stock. Spec: Fiction - Crime, Detective, Spy, Thrillers. PR: £5–150. [Updated]

SUTTON (SEE ALSO UNDER SURREY)

Mike Park, 351 Sutton Common Road, Sutton, Surrey, SM3 9HZ. (*) Prop: Mike Park, Ian Smith & William To. Tel: (020) 8641-7796. Fax: (020) 8641-3330. E-mail: mikeparkbooks@aol.com. Est: 1974. Private premises. Appointment necessary. Open: **M:** 09:00–17:00; **T:** 09:00–17:00; **W:** 09:00–17:00; **Th:** 09:00–17:00; **F:** 09:00–17:00. Small stock. Spec: Botany; Flower Arranging; Forestry; Gardening; Herbalism; Horticulture; Landscape; Natural History; Plant Hunting; Rural Life; also Booksearch. PR: £1–1,000. CC: E; MC; V. Cata: 2 a year on specialities. Mem: PBFA. [Updated]

TEDDINGTON

Bill Luckman, 31 Grosvenor Court, Fairfax Road, Teddington, TW11 9BT. (*). Tel: (020) 8977 0609. E-mail: luckman@mailbox.co.uk. Est: 1984. Private premises. Postal business only. Appointment necessary. Small general stock. Also, Booksearch. PR: £3–400. [Updated]

TWICKENHAM

Books on Spain, P.O. Box 207, Twickenham, TW2 5BQ. (*) Prop: Keith Harris. Tel: (020) 8898-7789. Fax: (020) 8898-7789 (24 hours). E-mail: booksonspainplus@aol.com. Est: 1993. Private premises. Internet and postal. Large stock. Spec: Antiquarian; Bull Fighting; Countries - Andorra; Countries - Central America; Countries - Cuba; Countries - Gibraltar; Countries - Latin America; Countries - Mexico; Countries - Morocco; Countries - Portugal; Countries - South America; Countries - Spain. PR: £5–1,000. CC: AE; JCB; MC; V; Switch. Corresp: Spanish Portuguese French. Mem: PBFA. VAT No: GB 720 5623 63. [Updated]

Anthony C. Hall, Antiquarian B, ■ 30 Staines Road, Twickenham, TW2 5AH. Prop: Anthony C. Hall. Tel: (020) 8898-2638. Fax: (020) 8893-8855. Website: www.hallbooks.co.uk. E-mail: achallbooks@intonet.co.uk. Est: 1966. Shop open: **M:** 10:00–17:00; **Th:** 10:00–17:00; **F:** 10:00–17:00; Closed for lunch: 12:30–13:30. Small general stock. Spec: Countries - Africa; Countries - Asia; Countries - East Europe; Countries - Middle East, The; Countries - Russia; History - Industrial; Travel - Africa; Travel - Asia; Travel - Europe; Travel - Middle East. PR: £10–1,000. CC: MC; V. Large specialist stock seen by appointment only. Cata: occasionally on specialist subjects. Corresp: French, German, Russian, Spanish. Mem: ABA; PBFA. VAT No: GB 224 2699 61. [Updated]

John Ives Bookseller, 5 Normanhurst Drive, St. Margarets, Twickenham, TW1 1NA. (*). Tel: (020) 8892-6265. Fax: (020) 8744-3944. Website: www.ukbookworld.com/members/johnives. E-mail: jives@btconnect.com. Est: 1978. Private premises. Appointment necessary. Medium stock. Spec: Antiques; Architecture; Art - Reference; Ceramics; Collecting; Fashion & Costume; Glass; Jewellery; Needlework; Textiles. PR: £5–500. CC: JCB; MC; V. Cata: 3 a year. Mem: PBFA. VAT No: GB 409 8526 30. [Updated]

Marble Hill Books, 35 Napoleon Road, St. Margarets, Twickenham, TW1 3EW. (*). Tel: (020) 8892-0511. E-mail: philip@poppysplace.fsnet.co.uk. Est: 1993. Private premises. Internet and postal. Appointment necessary. Shop at: www.marblehillbooks.com. Open: **M:** 09:00–19:00; **T:** 09:00–19:00; **W:** 09:00–19:00; **Th:** 09:00–19:00; **F:** 09:00–19:00; **S:** 09:00–19:00; **Su:** 09:00–19:00. Medium stock. Spec: Africana; History - General; Literature; Modern First Editions; Natural History; Proof Copies; also Booksearch. PR: £10–18,000. CC: AE; E; JCB; MC; V. Corresp: French, German. Mem: Title Page Bookfairs. [Updated]

John Prescott - The Bookseller, ■ Paul Hoffmann House, 57 York Street, Twickenham, TW1 3LP. Prop: John Prescott. Tel: (020) 8940-3066. E-mail: johnprescott@avdv.demon.co.uk. Est: 1998. Shop open: **F:** 10:30–18:00; **S:** 10:30–18:00. Medium stock. Spec: Antiques; Archaeology; Architecture; Art; Art - History; Cinema/Film; Countries - South America; Fables; Fiction - General; First Editions; Folio Society, The; Health; Military History; Music - Classical; Photography; Poetry; Sport - Cricket; Theatre. PR: £1–100. Shop sales only. Corresp: German, French, Spanish, Dutch. [Updated]

Stephen Miller, 19 Clifden Road, Twickenham, Middlesex, TW1 4LU. Tel: (020) 8892-0331. Est: 1981. Private premises. Very small general stock. Spec: Antiquarian. PR: £1–500. Corresp: French. [Updated]

WELLING

Falconwood Transport & Military Bookshop, ■ 5 Falconwood Parade, The Green, Welling, DA16 2PL. (*) Prop: A.M. Doran. Tel: (020) 8303-8291. Fax: (020) 8303-8291. E-mail: falconw@globalnet.co.uk. Est: 1985. Shop open: **Th:** 09:30–17:30; **F:** 09:30–17:30; **S:** 09:30–17:30. Medium stock. Spec: Aviation; Engineering; Maritime/Nautical; Military; Motorbikes; Motoring; Railways; Traction Engines; Transport; Vintage Cars. PR: £5–50. CC: E; JCB; MC; V. Cata: 1 on aviation, road transport, military vehicles. VAT No: GB 427 0309 76. [Updated]

MERSEYSIDE

EASTHAM

Andrea Grieveson, 34 Pickmere Drive, Eastham, CH62 9EW. Prop: Andrea Grieveson. Tel: (0151) 328 0172. Website: golden.frog@lineone.net. E-mail: golden.frog@lineone.net. Est: 1983. Private premises. Internet and postal. Telephone first. Small stock. Spec: New Age. PR: £3–100. Corresp: French. [20/08/2003]

LIVERPOOL

Black Voices, 67 Hilberry Avenue, Liverpool, L13 7ET. Prop: T. Aitman. Tel: (0151) 228-1097. E-mail: tonyaitman@blackvoices.freeserve.co.uk. Est: 1992. Private premises. Internet and postal. Appointment necessary. Very small stock. Spec: Africana; Black Studies; also Booksearch in specialist subjects. PR: £3–2,000. [Updated]

Gradwell Concepts, 197 Brodie Avenue, Mossley Hill, Liverpool, L18 4RQ. Prop: Rev. Eric G. Davies. Tel: (0151) 724-1219. Est: 1987. Private premises. Appointment necessary. Small stock. Spec: Bibles; Ecclesiastical History & Architecture; Religion - Christian; Theology; also Booksearch. PR: £1–20. Cata: occasionally on specialities. Mem: ECBA. [17/06/2003]

Hylton Booksearch, 23 Chelsea Court, West Derby, Liverpool, L12 6RS. Prop: Mr. R.A. Hylton. Tel: (0151) 259-5163. Website: rahylton@btinternet.com. E-mail: hylton.booksearch@btinternet.com. Est: 1992. Postal business only. Very small stock. Spec: Author - General; Modern First Editions; also Booksearch. PR: £15–1,000. CC: V; PayPal. [Updated]

Modern Welsh Publications Ltd., 32 Garth Drive, Liverpool, L18 6HW. Prop: Professor D. Ben Rees. Tel: (0151) 724 1989. Fax: (0151) 724-5691. E-mail: ben@garthdrive.fsnet.co.uk. Est: 1962. Private premises. Postal business only. Medium stock. Spec: Countries - Wales; History - General; Literature in Translation; Politics; Theology. Corresp: Welsh. [03/07/2003]

Reid of Liverpool, ■ 105 Mount Pleasant, Liverpool, L3 5TB. Prop: Gerard Fitzpatrick. Tel: (0151) 709-2312. E-mail: reidofliverpool@yahoo.co.uk. Est: 1980. Shop open: **M:** 10:30–17:30; **T:** 10:30–17:30; **W:** 10:30–17:30; **Th:** 10:30–17:30; **F:** 10:30–17:30; **S:** 10:30–17:30. Spec: Academic/Scholarly; Culture - Popular; Esoteric; Fiction - General; Mind, Body & Spirit; Mysticism; Odd & Unusual; Psychology/Psychiatry; Religion - General; Social Sciences. PR: £1–1,000. [Updated]

PRESCOT

Nostalgia Unlimited, 19 Dunbeath Avenue, Rainhill, Prescot, L35 0QH. Tel: (0151) 426-2046. Est: 1988. Private premises. Postal business only. Small stock. Spec: Christmas; Collecting; Comic Books & Annuals; Comics; Newspapers - General; Nostalgia; Periodicals & Magazines. PR: £1–35. [Updated]

SOUTHPORT

Broadhurst of Southport Ltd., 5 & 7 Market Street, Southport, PR8 1HD. Prop: Laurens R. Hardman. Tel: (01704) 532064 & 534. Fax: (01704) 542009. Website: www.ckbroadhurst.com. E-mail: litereria@aol.com. Est: 1926. Spec: Architecture; Art; Bibliography; Biography; Children's - General; Fiction - General; Fine & Rare; History - General; Literary Criticism; Literature; Maritime/Nautical; Modern First Editions; Natural History; Private Press; Topography - General. PR: £5–5,000. Also, bookbinding & restoration service, new books on all subjects & a booksearch service. [21/05/2003]

Cover to Cover, 252 Balmoral Drive, Southport, PR9 8QA. Tel: (01704) 231443. Website: www.covers.freeuk.com. E-mail: covers@freeuk.com. Est: 1996. Private premises. Internet and postal. Telephone first. Spec: Applied Art; Architecture; Art; Ceramics; Cinema/Film; Circus; Crafts; Crochet; Decorative Art; Design; Dolls & Dolls' Houses; Embroidery; Fairgrounds; Gypsies; Knitting; Lace; Needlework; Performing Arts; Radio/Wireless; Rugs; Rural Life; Televisio PR: £1–300. [19/03/2003]

Kernaghans, ■ 57–65 Wayfarers Arcade, Lord Street, Southport, PR8 1NT. Prop: Alwyn & Bryan Kernaghan. Tel: (01704) 546329. Fax: (01704) 546329. E-mail: kernaghanbooks@hotmail.com. Est: 1972. Shop open: **M:** 10:00–17:00; **T:** 10:00–17:00; **W:** 10:00–17:00; **Th:** 10:00–17:00; **F:** 10:00–17:00; **S:** 10:00–17:00. Very large stock. Spec: Countries - Ireland; Fine & Rare; Irish Interest; Natural History; Pop-Up, 3D, Cut Out & Movable; Religion - Christian; Theology; Topography - Local; Travel - General. PR: £5–5,000. CC: AE; MC; V. Mem: PBFA. [Updated]

Don Mulyan, 48 Clairville, Lulworth Road, Southport, PR8 2FA. Don Mulyan. Tel: (01704) 568429. Fax: (01704) 568429. E-mail: don@mulryan.fsworld.co.uk. Est: 1970. Private premises. Appointment necessary. Open: **M:** 10:00–20:00; **T:** 10:00–20:00; **W:** 10:00–20:00; **Th:** 10:00–20:00; **F:** 10:00–20:00; **S:** 10:00–20:00. Very small stock. Spec: Countries - Isle of Man; Countries - Norway; Topography - Local. Specialist in Norway pre 1940. Cata: occasionally. [Updated]

Parkinsons, ■ Parkinson's Ginnel, 359–363 Lord Street, Southport, PR8 1NH. Prop: K.A. & J. Parkinson. Tel: (01704) 547016. Website: www.parki.com. E-mail: info@parki.com. Shop; Internet and postal. Open: **M:** 10:00–17:00; **T:** 10:00–17:00; **W:** 10:00–17:00; **Th:** 10:00–17:00; **F:** 10:00–17:00; **S:** 10:00–17:00; **Su:** 13:00–17:00. Large stock. Spec: Academic/Scholarly. [Updated]

Rosemary Books, 27 Cedar Street, Southport, PR8 6NQ. Prop: Eileen M. Golborn. Tel: (01704) 542134. Est: 1985. Private premises. Appointment necessary. Very small stock. Spec: Books about Books; Children's - General; Fiction - General; First Editions; Juvenile; Poetry; Religion - Christian. [Updated]

ST. HELENS

V. & C. Finn, 6 Knowsley View, Rainford, St. Helens, WA11 8SN. Tel: (01744) 883780. Est: 1992. Private premises. Appointment necessary. Small stock. Spec: Folio Society, The. PR: £1–200. Also, organiser of North West Book Fairs (see prelims). Cata: 3 a year. [Updated]

Harvest Books, 25, Thickwood Moss Lane, Rainford, St. Helens, WA11 8QL. Prop: Mrs. Janet Christie. Tel: (01744) 885747. E-mail: harvestbooks@btinternet.com. Est: 1998. Private premises. Internet and postal. Appointment necessary. Very small stock. Spec: Authors - Women; Cookery/Gastronomy; Food & Drink; Rural Life; Social History; also Booksearch. PR: £5–100. Cata: quarterly. Mem: PBFA. [28/08/2003]

WIRRAL

Thin Read Line, 11 St. Andrews Road, Claughton, Prenton, Wirral, CH43 1TB. Prop: Dr. R.A. Dutton. Tel: (0151) 652-4483. Fax: (0151) 652-4483. E-mail: richmond_dutton@hotmail.com. Est: 1999. Private premises. Postal business only. Medium stock. Spec: Aeronautics; Antiques; Arms & Armour; Aviation; Botany; Colonial; Firearms/Guns; Gardening; Horticulture; Maritime/Nautical; Military; Military History; Naval; War - General; War - World War II, also Booksearch. Attends military fairs. Cata: 1 on demand. Corresp: Dutch. [Updated]

NORFOLK

Abbey Books, Gothic House, 51 Hungate Street, Alysham, NR11 6AA. Prop: Bruce & Jill Tulloch. Tel: (01263) 732851. Fax: (01263) 732861. E-mail: abbey.books@btinternet.com. Est: 1978. Private premises. Book fairs only. Appointment necessary. Small stock. Spec: Academic/Scholarly; Art; Art - Reference; History - General; Social History. Corresp: French, German, Portuguese, Spanish. Mem: PBFA. VAT No: GB 322 2751 99. [27/02/2003]

Burebank Books, ■ 46 Red Lion Street, Aylsham, NR11 6ER. Prop: R. M. Crouch. Tel: (01263) 735710. Fax: (01263) 735703. E-mail: roger.crouch@freenet.co.uk. Est: 1993. Shop open: **M:** 10:00–17:00; **T:** 10:00–17:00; **W:** 10:00–13:00; **Th:** 10:00–17:00; **F:** 10:00–17:00; **S:** 09:00–17:00; Closed for lunch: 13:00–14:00. Small general stock. Spec: Archaeology; Cartography; Countries - Japan; History - General; History - Local; Maritime/Nautical; Military History; Social History; Travel - General. PR: £1–300. CC: JCB; MC; V; SW. Corresp: Italian, Japanese. [Updated]

Mayhew Books, 8 Sears Close, Aylsham, NR11 6JB. Prop: John & Linda Mayhew. Tel: (01263) 731305. Est: 1989. Private premises. Postal business only. Very small general stock. Spec: Booksearch. PR: £1–100. Cata: 1 a year on request. [Updated]

Brian Beighton, Garfield Villa, Garfield Terrace, Caister–on–Sea, NR30 5DQ. Tel: (withheld). Private premises. Appointment necessary. Small stock. Spec: Almanacs; Sport - Cricket. [08/07/2003]

Bookworms, ■ 9 New Street, Cromer, NR27 9HP. Prop: Susan & Ted Liddell & I.R. Petrie. Tel: (01263) 515078. Fax: (01263) 519008. Website: www.susanlid.freeserve.co.uk. E-mail: bookworms@susanlid.freeserve.co.uk. Est: 1987. Shop open: **M:** 10:00–17:00; **T:** 10:00–17:00; **W:** 10:00–17:00; **Th:** 10:00–17:00; **F:** 10:00–17:00; **S:** 10:00–17:00; **Su:** 10:00–17:00. Large stock. Spec: Art; Aviation; Biography; Children's - General; History - General; Literature; Music - General; Natural History; Sport - General; Topography - General; Transport; Travel - General; War - General. PR: £1–100. CC: AE. [24/07/2003]

Riderless Horse Books, Oakfields, Redgrave Road, Blo Norton, Diss, IP22 2JA. (*) Prop: Richard B. Hamburger. Tel: (01379) 898481. E-mail: rhbooks@dircon.co.uk. Est: 1991. Private premises. Internet and postal. Appointment necessary. Small stock. Spec: First Editions; Literary Criticism; Literature; Literature in Translation; Periodicals & Magazines; Poetry. PR: £2–1,000. CC: MC; V. Cata: 2 a year on Poetry, Modern literature. Corresp: French. Mem: PBFA. [29/06/2003]

Michael Taylor Rare Books, Hoblins, One Eyed Lane, Weybread, Diss, IP21 5TT. Tel: (01379) 853889. Fax: (01379) 853889. E-mail: michael@hoblins.demon.co.uk. Est: 1984. Private premises. Appointment necessary. Small stock. Spec: Bibliography; Calligraphy; Illustrated; Private Press; Typography. PR: £5–1,000. CC: MC; V. Cata: 4 a year. Mem: PBFA. [Updated]

DOWNHAM MARKET

Richard Everett, Sandfield House, 58 Lynn Road, Downham Market, PE38 9NN. Prop: Richard & Jenny Everett. Tel: (01366) 382074. Est: 1983. Office &/or bookroom; Appointment necessary. Large stock. Spec: Children's - General; Illustrated; Publishers - Warnes; Topography - Local. PR: £2–400. Mem: PBFA. Also at: Southwold Antiques Centre, Suffolk (q.v.). [Updated]

EAST RUDHAM

Victor Sutcliffe, Mulberry Coach House, East Rudham, PE31 8RD. Prop: Victor Sutcliffe. Tel: (01485) 528463. Website: www.victorsutcliffe.demon.co.uk. E-mail: vhs@victorsutcliffe.demon.co.uk. Est: 1970. Private premises. Internet and postal. Appointment necessary. Very small stock. Spec: Military History. PR: £15–5,000. CC: MC; V. Cata: occasionally. [Updated]

FAKENHAM

The Dancing Goat Bookshop, ■ 5 Oak Street, Fakenham, NR21 9DX. Prop: Michael Goss. Tel: (01328) 855757. E-mail: dancinggoatbooks@talk21.com. Est: 1998. Shop open: **M:** 10:00–16:00; **T:** 10:00–16:00; **W:** 10:00–16:00; **Th:** 10:00–16:00; **F:** 10:00–16:00; **S:** 10:00–16:00. Medium stock. Spec: American Indians; Americana; Folklore; Music - Folk & Irish Folk; Music - Popular; Music - Rock; Ornithology; Poetry; Vintage Paperbacks. PR: £1–100. CC: none. Also a coffee shop (coffee, tea, home made cakes & light lunches). [19/03/2003]

GREAT ELLINGHAM

John Knowles, Brick Kiln Farm, Hingham Road, Great Ellingham, Nr. Attleborough, NR17 1JE. Prop: John Knowles. Tel: (01953) 452257. Fax: (01953) 452733. Website: knowlesbooks.com. E-mail: enquire@johnknowlesbooks.com. Est: 1985. Private premises. Internet and postal. Appointment necessary. Small stock. Spec: Marque Histories (see also motoring); Motoring; Sport - Motor Racing; Transport. PR: £5–1,000. CC: E; JCB; MC; V; SW. Cata: 2 a year specialist subjects. Corresp: French, German. [Updated]

GREAT YARMOUTH

David Ferrow, ■ 77 Howard Street South, Great Yarmouth, NR30 1LN. Tel: (01493) 843800. Est: 1940. Shop open: **M:** 10:00–17:00; **T:** 10:00–17:00; **W:** 10:00–17:00; **F:** 10:00–17:00. Large stock. Spec: Topography - Local. PR: £1–10,000. CC: MC; V. Appointment required for Thursdays. Mem: ABA; PBFA. [18/06/2003]

HARLESTON

Black Cat Books, Meadow Cottage, High Road, Wortwell, Harleston, IP20 0EN. Prop: Ann Morgan–Hughes. Tel: (01986) 788826. Fax: (01986) 788826. Website: www.blackcatbooks.co.uk. E-mail: ann@blackcatbooks.co.uk. Est: 1984. Storeroom. Appointment necessary. Small stock. Spec: Cookery/Gastronomy; Embroidery; Fashion & Costume; Knitting; Lace; Needlework; Periodicals & Magazines; Social History; Textiles; Women. PR: £10–2,000. CC: MC; V. Cata: 4 a year on specialities. Corresp: French, German, Greek, Russian. Mem: ABA; PBFA. VAT No: GB 446 3847 25. [06/08/2003]

Riviera Books, ■ 9 Market Place, Harleston, IP20 9AD. Prop: David Chatten. Tel: (01379) 855123. E-mail: rivierabooks@fsmail.net. Est: 1999. Shop open: **T:** 10:00–16:30; **W:** 10:00–16:30; **Th:** 10:00–13:00; **F:** 10:00–16:30; **S:** 10:00–16:30. Large stock. PR: £2–200. CC: MC; V. Corresp: French. [Updated]

HINDRINGHAM

Fullerton's Booksearch, The Dukes House, 1 Moorgate Road, Hindringham, Fakenham, NR21 0PT. Prop: Humphrey Boon. Tel: 01328 87 87 81. Fax: (01328) 87 87 82. E-mail: fullertons .books@virgin.net. Est: 1991. Private premises. Postal business only. Appointment necessary. Open: **M:** 09:00–17:00; **T:** 09:00–17:00; **W:** 09:00–17:00; **Th:** 09:00–17:00; **F:** 09:00–17:00. Spec: Booksearch. PR: £18–7,000. CC: JCB; MC; V. VAT No: GB 631 8838 22. [Updated]

HINGHAM

K. Anthony Ward, ■ Fairland Bookshop, 2 Fairland Court, Hingham, NR9 4HN. Prop: K.A. & V.J. Ward. Tel: (01953) 850006. E-mail: wardbooks@castleacre.fsbusiness.co.uk. Est: 1963. Shop open: **T:** 11:00–16:00; **W:** 11:00–16:00; **Th:** 11:00–16:00; **F:** 11:00–16:00; **S:** 11:00–16:00. Small general stock. Spec: Bibliography; Books about Books; Limited Editions; Literature; Modern First Editions. PR: £5–500. CC: MC; V. Mem: PBFA. [22/07/2003]

HOLT

Jackdaw Books, ■ 10 New Street, Holt, NR25 6JJ. Prop: Mick & Eleanor Finn. Tel: (01263) 711658. Fax: (01263) 710056. Website: www.jackdawbooks.co.uk. E-mail: eleanor.finn@btopenworld.com. Est: 1997. Internet and postal. Shop open: **M:** 09:00–16:00; **T:** 09:00–16:00; **W:** 09:00–16:00; **F:** 09:00–16:00; **S:** 09:00–16:00. Large general stock. Spec: Academic/Scholarly; Animals and Birds; Antiquarian; Archaeology; History - General; History - British. PR: £5–2,000. CC: MC; V; SW. VAT No: GB 784 6478 72. [Updated]

HUNSTANTON

Musicalania, 8B Melton Drive, Hunstanton, PE36 5DD. Prop: David Burkett. Tel: 01485 534282. E-mail: musicalania@btinternet.com. Est: 1973. Private premises. Internet and postal. Telephone first. Small stock. Spec: Music - General; Music - Composers; Music - Popular. PR: £1–50. Cata: 5 – Bi-monthly. Corresp: French and German. [Updated]

KING'S LYNN

Brazenhead Ltd., Greenside, Market Place, Burnham Market, King's Lynn, PE31 8HD. Prop: H.S. Kenyon. Tel: (01328) 730700. Fax: (01328) 730929. Website: www.brazenhead.co.uk. E-mail: brazenheadbook@aol.com. Est: 1996. Shop &/or gallery; Internet and postal. Open: **M:** 09:30–17:00; **T:** 09:30–17:00; **W:** 09:30–17:00; **Th:** 09:30–17:00; **F:** 09:30–17:00; **S:** 09:30–17:00. Very large stock. Spec: Architecture; Art; Children's - General; History - Local; Military. PR: £1–10,000. CC: MC; V; switch. [Updated]

John Lowe, 7 Orchard Grove, West Lynn, King's Lynn, PE34 3LE. Tel: (01553) 661271. E-mail: john@lowebooks.fsnet.co.uk. Est: 1982. Spec: Academic/Scholarly; Advertising; Aeronautics; Alternative Medicine; Archaeology; Folklore; History - British; Topography - General. PR: £2–200. Mem: PBFA. [Updated]

Torc Books, ■ 9 Hall Road, Snettisham, King's Lynn, PE31 7LU. Prop: Heather Shepperd. Tel: (01485) 541188. Est: 1977. Shop open: **F:** 10:00–16:00; **S:** 10:00–16:00. Medium stock. PR: £1–100. Open other times by appointment. [Updated]

NORTH WALSHAM

Angel Books, ■ 4 Aylsham Road, North Walsham, NR28 OBH. Prop: Mr. W., Ms. M. & Mrs. O.D. Green. Tel: (01692) 404054. E-mail: angelbooks@onetel.net.uk. Est: 1989. Shop open: **Th:** 09:00–17:00; **F:** 09:00–17:00; **S:** 09:00–16:00. Medium stock. Spec: History - Local; Sport - Cycling; Topography - Local; also Booksearch. PR: £1–500. Cata: 1 a year. Mem: PBFA. [15/05/2003]

C.J. Murphy, 5 Burton Avenue, North Walsham, NR28 0EW. Tel: (01692) 402831. Fax: none. Website: www.abebooks.com/home/CHRISMURPHY. E-mail: chris@cmurphy6.fsnet.co.uk. Est: 1999. Private premises. Postal business only. Telephone first. Medium stock. Spec: Academic/Scholarly; Annuals; Antiquarian; Art - Reference; Atlases; Author - General; Autobiography; Children's - General; Comic Books & Annuals; Dictionaries; Espionage; Ex-Libris; Fiction - General; First Editions; History - General; Literature; also Booksearch. PR: £1–1,000. [Updated]

NORWICH

Carlton Books, 44 Langley Road, Chedgrave, Norwich, NR14 6HD. Prop: A.P. Goodfellow. Tel: (01508) 520124. Est: 1974. Private premises. Appointment necessary. Open: Small stock. Spec: History - Local; Natural History; Ornithology; Topography - Local. PR: £1–500. Mem: PBFA. [Updated]

J. & D. Clarke, The Elms, 19 Heigham Grove, Norwich, NR2 3DQ. Tel: (01603) 619226. E-mail: jonddclarke@norwichnorfolk.freeserve.co.uk. Est: 2004. Private premises. Postal business only. Very small stock. Spec: Topography - General; Topography - Local. PR: £1–500. Attends local PBFA fairs. Mem: PBFA. [Updated]

John Debbage, 28 Carterford Drive, Norwich, NR3 4DW. Tel: (01603) 488015. Fax: (01603) 788933. E-mail: norvicsales@btopenworld.com. Spec: Topography - Local. [15/05/2003]

J.R. & R.K. Ellis, ■ 53 St. Giles Street, Norwich, NR2 1JR. Tel: (01603) 623679. Est: 1960. Shop open: **M:** 08:30–18:00; **T:** 08:30–18:00; **W:** 08:30–18:00; **Th:** 08:30–18:00; **F:** 08:30–18:00; **S:** 08:30–18:00. Large general stock. PR: £1–100. Also, Market Stalls. [Updated]

Freya Books & Antiques, St. Mary's Farm, Cheney's Lane, Tacolneston, Norwich, NR16 1DB. (*) Prop: Colin Lewsey. Tel: (01508) 489252. Website: www.freyaantiques.co.uk. E-mail: freyaantiques@ic24.net. Est: 1971. Storeroom. Medium stock. Spec: Fiction - General; Juvenile, also Booksearch. PR: £1–50. CC: MC; V. Also, 3,000sq ft antique furniture. Corresp: French, Danish. [09/07/2003]

Hawes Books, 8 Keswick Road, Cringleford, Norwich, NR4 6UG. Prop: T.L.M. & H.J. Hawes. Tel: (01603) 452043. Est: 1980. Private premises. Appointment necessary. Large stock. Spec: Genealogy; History - Local; History - National; Topography - General. PR: £2–200. VAT No: GB 342 4870 57. [Updated]

Katnap Arts, 1 Whitefields, Norwich Road, Saxlingham Nethergate, Norwich, NR15 1TP. Prop: Margaret Blake. Tel: (01508) 498323. Fax: (01508) 498323. Website: http://www.katnap.co.uk. E-mail: mail@katnap.co.uk. Est: 1999. Private premises. Internet and postal. Contactable. Medium stock. Spec: Annuals; Architecture; Art; Art - History; Art - Reference; Children's - General; Entertainment - General; First Editions; History - General; Literature; Natural History; Typography; Vintage Paperbacks, also Booksearch. PR: £5–250. CC: MC; V. [Updated]

David Lake, 36 Colney Lane, Cringleford, Norwich, NR4 7RE. Tel: 07909 896 809. E-mail: djl@netcom.co.uk. Est: 1990. Private premises. Postal business only. Small stock. Spec: Antiquarian; Children's - Illustrated; Colour-Plate; Topography - Local. PR: £5–500. [Updated]

LyngHeath Books, 51 Pightle Way, Lyng, Norwich, NR9 5RL. Prop: Tim Holt. Tel: (01603) 879037. Website: www.lyngheathbooks.co.uk. E-mail: lyngheathbooks@hotmail.com. Est: 1999. Private premises. Internet and postal. Appointment necessary. Open: **M:** 08:00–20:00; **T:** 08:00–20:00; **W:** 08:00–20:00; **Th:** 08:00–20:00; **F:** 08:00–20:00; **S:** 08:00–20:00; **Su:** 10:00–17:00. Small stock. Spec: Sport - Football (Soccer); also Booksearch. PR: £2–300. Corresp: French. [Updated]

Saint Michael at Plea Bookshop, Antiques Centre, St. Michael at Plea Church, Bank Plain, Norwich, NR2 4SN. Prop: Joy Clarke. Tel: (01603) 617700. E-mail: Est: 1990. Spec: Children's - General; Fiction - General; Topography - General; Topography - Local. PR: £1–200. [14/09/2003]

Tasburgh Books, 20 Henry Preston Road, Tasburgh, Norwich, NR15 1NU. Prop: Janet Lamb & David Newton. Tel: (01508) 471921. E-mail: tasburgh@dircon.co.uk. Est: 1995. Private premises. Internet and postal. Telephone first. Small stock. Spec: Applied Art; Architecture; Art - History; Art - Reference; Decorative Art; Fine Art; Folio Society, The. CC: AE; MC; V. Cata: 4 a year. Mem: ABA. [14/04/2003]

Tombland Bookshop, ■ 8 Tombland, Norwich, NR3 1HF. Prop: J.G. & A.H. Freeman. Tel: (01603) 490000. Fax: (01603) 760610. Website: abe.com. E-mail: tombland.bookshop@virgin.net. Est: 1975. Internet and postal. Shop open: **M:** 09:30–17:00; **T:** 09:30–17:17; **W:** 09:30–00:17; **Th:** 09:30–00:17; **F:** 09:30–17:00; **S:** 09:30–16:30. Very large general stock. Spec: Architecture; Art; Topography - Local; also Booksearch. PR: £1–5,000. CC: MC; V. Corresp: French/German/Italian. Also at: Freeman's Corner Bookshop, Norwich. [Updated]

Touchstone Books, 1 Fairstead Road, Sprowston, Norwich, NR7 8XG. Prop: Robert Illsley. Tel: (01603) 401284. Est: 1985. Private premises. Postal business only. Very small stock. Spec: Literature; Modern First Editions. [25/06/2002]

Michael Watson Books, Sea Mere, Hingham, Norwich, NR9 4LP. Tel: (01953) 850217. Est: 1995. Postal business only. [26/08/2003]

SALTHOUSE

John Hart, Salt Barn, Bard Hill, Salthouse, NR25 7XB. Tel: (01263) 741380. Fax: (01263) 741700. E-mail: johnhartbks@btopenworld.com. Est: 1987. Private premises. Appointment necessary. Small stock. Spec: Literature. PR: £20–2,000. CC: MC; V. Cata: 5 a year. Corresp: French. Mem: ABA, PBFA. VAT No: GB 529 2455 28. [Updated]

SHERINGHAM

R.L. Cook, 12 Sycamore Grove, Sheringham, NR26 8PG. Tel: (01263) 822050. Est: 1950. Private premises. Appointment necessary. Very small stock. Spec: Antiquarian; Juvenile; Literature; Travel - General. PR: £20–250. [27/04/2003]

Peter Pan Bookshop, ■ 5 The Courtyard, Station Road, Sheringham, NR26 8RF. Prop: Peter Cox. Tel: (01263) 824411. Est: 1994. Shop open: **M:** 10:30–17:00; **T:** 10:30–17:00; **W:** 10:30–17:00; **Th:** 10:30–17:00; **F:** 10:30–17:00; **S:** 10:30–17:00; **Su:** 12:00–16:00; Small general stock. PR: £1–20. Secondhand books published after 1980. Also at: Peter's Bookshop, 19 St Peter's Road (q.v.). [Updated]

Peter's Bookshop, ■ 19 St. Peter's Road, Sheringham, NR26 8QY. Prop: Peter Cox. Tel: (01263) 823008. Est: 1984. Shop open: **M:** 10:00–17:30; **T:** 10:00–17:30; **W:** 10:00–17:30; **Th:** 10:00–17:30; **F:** 10:00–17:30; **S:** 10:00–17:30; **Su:** 13:00–17:00. Very large stock. Spec: Children's - General; Fiction - General; Literature. PR: £1–100. CC: E; MC; V. Winter hours: (Nov. to Mar.) Mon./Tue. & Thurs. to Sat. 10:30–16:30. Corresp: French. Also at: The Peter Pan Bookshop, Sheringham, Norfolk (q.v.). [Updated]

SWANTON ABBOT

Hamish Riley–Smith, Swanton Abbot Hall, Swanton Abbot, NR10 5DJ. Prop: Hamish Riley-Smith. Tel: (01692) 538244. Fax: (01692) 538696. Website: www.riley-smith.com. E-mail: hamish@riley-smith.co.uk. Est: 1974. Private premises. Internet and postal. Telephone first. Very small stock. Spec: Academic/Scholarly; Antiquarian; Economics; Fine & Rare; Foreign Texts; Letters; Literature; Manuscripts; Philosophy; Science - General; Scottish Interest. PR: £100–20,000. Also, manuscripts & signed autograph letters. Cata: 1 a year, infrequent. VAT No: GB 342 4732 69. [Updated]

WELLS–NEXT–THE–SEA

The Old Station Pottery & Book, 2/4 Maryland, Wells–Next–The–Sea, NR23 1LX. Prop: Thomas Borthwick. Tel: (01328) 710847. Fax: (01328) 711566. E-mail: oldstation.books@btinternet.com. Est: 1996. Spec: Children's - General; Topography - General. PR: £1–50. [05/03/2003]

WYMONDHAM

The Bookshop, ■ 1 Town Green, Wymondham, NR18 OPN. Prop: M. & A.C. Thompson. Tel: (01953) 602244. E-mail: mac.thompson@btopenworld.com. Est: 1975. Shop open: **M:** 10:45–16:45; **T:** 10:30–16:45; **Th:** 10:30–16:45; **F:** 10:30–16:45; **S:** 10:00–17:00. Large general stock. Spec: Comics; Entertainment - General; Music - General; Topography - General. PR: £1–300. [Updated]

Turret House, ■ 27 Middleton Street, Wymondham, NR18 0AB. Prop: Dr. D.H. & R.A. Morgan. Tel: (01953) 603462. E-mail: hughmorgan@turrethouse.demon.co.uk. Est: 1972. Shop. Telephone first. Very small general stock. Spec: Astronomy; Mathematics; Medicine; Microscopy; Natural Sciences; Science - General; Science - History of; Scientific Instruments. PR: £1–1,000. CC: MC; V. Open usually open Monday – Saturday 09:00–18:00 but telephone first to save a wasted journey. Mem: PBFA. VAT No: GB 282 1349 63. [Updated]

NORTH YORKSHIRE

AUSTWICK

Austwick Hall Books, Austwick Hall, Austwick, Near Settle, Lancaster, LA2 8BS. Tel: (015242) 51794. E-mail: austwickhall@btinternet.com. Medium stock. Spec: Animals and Birds; Anthropology; Biology; Botany; Conservation; Countries - Iceland; Entomology; Evolution; Farriers; Fine & Rare; First Editions; Medicine; Natural History; Phrenology; Science - General; Voyages & Discovery. PR: £5–2,000. [Updated]

BEDALE

Sugen & Co., Southwood House, Well, Bedale, DL8 2RL. Prop: K. Sugen. Tel: (01677) 470079. Website: http://www.film-tvtieins.co.uk. E-mail: sugenbooks@ukf.net. Est: 1993. Private premises. Internet and postal. Medium stock. PR: £3–100. Cata: 5 – 2 months approx. [29/06/2003]

CATTERICK VILLAGE

Brock Books, 43 High Street, Catterick Village, DL10 7LL. Prop: Jude Haslam. Tel: (01748) 818729. Website: www.brockbooks.com. E-mail: judehaslam@hotmail.com. Est: 2002. Private premises. Internet and postal. Appointment necessary. Open: **M:** 09:00–17:30; **T:** 09:00–17:30; **W:** 09:00–17:30; **Th:** 15:00–18:00; **F:** 11:00–17:00; **S:** 09:00–17:00; **Su:** 10:00–16:00. Very small stock. Spec: Animals and Birds; Annuals; Art; Author - Johns, W.E.; Author - Kipling, Rudyard; Author - Morton, H.V.; Author - Ratcliffe, Dorothy Una; Author - Ruskin, John; Author - Shaw, George Bernard; Author - Stevenson, Robert Louis; Author - Wells, H.G. PR: £5–500. CC: PayPal. Illustrations. Cata: 1 a year. Corresp: Espanol. [Updated]

DACRE

Theatreshire Books, Dacre Hall, Dacre, HG3 4ET. Prop: Catherine Shire. Tel: (01423) 780497. Fax: (01423) 781957. E-mail: theatreshire@theatresearch.co.uk. Est: 2000. Private premises. Internet and postal. Appointment necessary. Open: **F:** 04:00–00:00. Small stock. Spec: Engineering; Fire & Firefighters; Performing Arts; Theatre. PR: £1–3,000. Cata: 1 a year. [Updated]

FILEY

Professional Book Services, 10 Hope St., Filey, YO14 9DL. Prop: Peter Jacques. Tel: (01723) 515170. Fax: No Fax. Website: www.bookspluspictures.com. E-mail: books@bookspluspictures.com. Est: 1996. Private premises. Internet and postal. Very small general stock. Spec: Booksearch. PR: £2–50. CC: PayPal. Cata: on request. VAT No: GB 758 7448 73. [Updated]

GIGGLESWICK

Post Horn Books, ■ Belle Hill, Giggleswick, BD24 0BA. Prop: Patricia & Edward Saunders. Tel: (01729) 823438. Website: www.abebooks.com/home/posthorn. E-mail: posthornbooks@btinternet.com. Est: 1979. Shop open: **T:** 10:30–17:30; **W:** 09:30–17:30; **Th:** 10:30–17:30; **F:** 10:30–17:30; **S:** 10:30–17:30; Closed for lunch: 12:00–14:00. Medium stock. Spec: Alpinism/Mountaineering; Countries - Africa; Countries - Asia; Environment, The; Religion - Quakers; Sport - Caving (Spelaeology); Topography - Local. PR: £1–200. [14/04/2003]

GUISBOROUGH

K.A. McCaughtrie, 7 Grosvenor Square, Guisborough, TS14 6PB. Tel: (01287) 633663. Est: 1986. Private premises. Postal business only. Appointment necessary. Very small stock. Spec: Biography; Crime (True); Fiction - Crime, Detective, Spy, Thrillers. PR: £1–50. [Updated]

HARROGATE

Books (For All), ■ 23a Commercial Street, Harrogate, HG1 1UB. Prop: Jenny Todd. Tel: (01423) 561982. E-mail: booksforall@amserve.net. Est: 1998. Shop open: **M:** 10:30–17:00; **T:** 10:30–17:00; **W:** 10:30–17:00; **Th:** 10:30–17:00; **F:** 10:30–17:00; **S:** 10:30–17:00. Large stock. Spec: Art - History; Biography; Children's - General; Cookery/Gastronomy; Esoteric; Fiction - Science Fiction; History - General; Horticulture; Literature; Music - General; Natural History; Religion - General; Topography - General. PR: £1–100. CC: MC; V; SW. [Updated]

Books at the Warehouse, 32 Glebe Avenue, Harrogate, HG2 0LT. Prop: Jo Lunt. Tel: (01423) 523656. E-mail: jolunt@amserve.net. Est: 1993. Private premises. Postal business only. Appointment necessary. Open: **M:** 10:00–17:00; **T:** 10:00–17:00; **W:** 10:00–17:00; **Th:** 10:00–17:00; **F:** 10:00–17:00; **S:** 10:00–17:00; **Su:** 10:00–16:00. Medium stock. Spec: Art - Reference; Ceramics; Publishers - Penguin. PR: £1–100. Corresp: French, German. [Updated]

Bookstop Bookshop, 28 Mayfield Grove, Harrogate, HG1 5HB. Prop: J.K. Shackleton. Tel: (01423) 505817. E-mail: bookstopbookshop@aol.com. Est: 1986. Spec: History - General; Military History. PR: £1–100. Also, board games. [26/06/2003]

Oval Books, 7 Chantry Court, Ripley, Harrogate, HG3 3AD. Prop: M.S. Spark. Tel: (01423) 772346. Est: 1985. Private premises. Appointment necessary. Very small stock. Spec: Sport - Rugby. PR: £1–150. Cata: 3 a year. Corresp: French. [27/05/2003]

HELMSLEY

Helmsley Antiquarian & Secondh, ■ The Old Fire Station, Borogate, Helmsley, YO62 5BN. Prop: Myles Moorby. Tel: (01439) 770014. Est: 1985. Shop open: **M:** 10:00–17:00; **T:** 10:00–17:00; **W:** 09:00–17:00; **Th:** 10:00–17:00; **F:** 10:00–17:00; **S:** 10:00–17:00; **Su:** 12:00–17:00. Medium stock. Spec: Architecture; Art; Topography - Local. PR: £1–100. CC: MC; V. VAT No: GB 390 4976 18. [Updated]

INGLETON

John Killeen, 16 Main Street, Ingleton, LA6 3HF. Tel: (015242) 41021. Est: 1974. Private premises. Appointment necessary. Medium stock. Spec: Literature; Marxism; Philosophy; Religion - Roman Catholic; Topography - Local; Travel - General. PR: £1–300. Attends fairs in Northern England. Corresp: French. Mem: PBFA. [Updated]

KNARESBOROUGH

Pennymead Books, 1 Brewerton Street, Knaresborough, HG5 8AZ. Prop: David Druett. Tel: (01423) 865962. Fax: (01423) 547057. Website: www.pennymead.com. E-mail: pennymead@aol.com. Est: 1984. Private premises. Internet and postal. Telephone first. Small stock. Spec: Carriages & Driving; Colonial; Countries - Bermuda; Countries - Caribbean, The; Countries - Cuba; Countries - Puerto Rico; Countries - Dominican Republic (Santo Domingo); Countries - West Indies, The; Philately; Sport - Badminton; Sport - Hockey. PR: £5–5,000. CC: JCB; MC; V. Also, postage stamp auctioneer. Cata: 1 a year. Mem: PBFA. VAT No: GB 387 9262 94. [Updated]

LEALHOLM

Stepping Stones Bookshop, ■ Stepping Stones, Lealholm, near Whitby. Prop: Judith & Lawrence Davies. Tel: (01947) 897382. Est: 1970. Shop open: **M:** 10:00–17:00; **T:** 10:00–17:00; **W:** 10:00–17:00; **Th:** 09:00–17:00; **F:** 10:00–17:00; **S:** 10:00–17:00; **Su:** 10:00–17:00. Medium stock. PR: £1–100. [26/09/2003]

PICKERING

Alan Avery, 15 Middleton Road, Pickering, YO18 8AL. Prop: Alan Avery. Tel: (01751) 476863. Website: www.abebooks.com/home/avery. E-mail: avery_uk@yahoo.com. Est: 1988. Private premises. Postal business only. Appointment necessary. Open: **M:** 09:00–17:00; **T:** 09:09–17:17; **W:** 09:00–17:00; **Th:** 09:00–17:00; **F:** 09:00–17:00; **S:** 09:00–13:00. Small stock. Spec: Folio Society, The. PR: £5–60. CC: AE; JCB; V. [Updated]

Sybil Buckley, ■ Pickering Antique Centre, Southgate, Pickering, YO18 8BN. Tel: (01751) 477210. E-mail: buckleysbooks@lineone.net. Est: 1998. Shop at: 37a Westgate, Pickering, North Yorkshire, YO18 8BA. Open: **M:** 10:00–17:00; **T:** 10:00–17:00; **W:** 10:00–17:00; **Th:** 10:00–17:00; **F:** 10:00–17:00; **S:** 10:00–17:00; **Su:** 10:00–17:00. Small general stock. PR: £1–200. CC: MC; V; DELTA. [Updated]

Cobweb Books, ■ Ye Olde Corner Shoppe, 1 Pickering Road, Thornton–Le–Dale, Pickering, YO18 7LG. Prop: Robin & Sue Buckler. Tel: (01751) 476638. Website: www.cobwebbooks.co.uk. E-mail: robin@cobweb-books-yorks.fsnet.co.uk. Est: 17. Shop open: **M:** 10:00–17:00; **T:** 10:00–17:00; **W:** 10:00–17:00; **Th:** 10:00–17:00; **F:** 10:00–17:00; **S:** 10:00–17:00; **Su:** 10:00–17:00. Very large stock. Spec: Antiquarian; Aviation; First Editions; Illustrated; Military; Motoring; Railways; Topography - General; Transport. PR: £1–1,000. CC: AE; E; JCB; MC; V; SW. [Updated]

Inch's Books, 6 Westgate, Pickering, YO18 8BA. Prop: Peter & Eleanor Inch. Tel: (01751) 474928. Fax: (01751) 475939. Website: www.inchsbooks.co.uk. E-mail: inchs.books@dial.pipex.com. Est: 1986. Office &/or bookroom. Telephone first. Open: **M:** 09:00–17:00; **T:** 09:00–17:00; **W:** 09:00–17:00; **Th:** 09:00–17:00; **F:** 09:00–17:00. Medium stock. Spec: Architecture; Building & Construction; Cities; Design; History - Design; Landscape; Town Planning; Urban History. PR: £10–1,500. CC: JCB; MC. Cata: 8 – 1-2 months. Corresp: French. Mem: ABA; PBFA; ILAB. VAT No: GB 412 1286 94. [Updated]

RICHMOND

Ian Dyer Cricket Books, 29 High Street, Gilling West, Richmond, DL10 5JG. Prop: Michael & Jennie Gauntlett. Tel: (01748) 822786. Fax: (0870) 7051561. Website: www.cricketbooks.co.uk. E-mail: iandyer@cricketbooks.co.uk. Est: 1979. Private premises. Internet and postal. Telephone first. Medium stock. Spec: Sport - Cricket. PR: £2–3,500. CC: MC; V; Maestro. Mem: Cricket Society/CMA/MCC. VAT No: GB 698 9620 57. [Updated]

Richmond Books, ■ 25 Silver Meadows, Barton, Richmond, DL10 4QN. Prop: Bob & Gail Ions. Tel: (01325) 377332. E-mail: richmondbooks@ions.ndo.co.uk. Est: 1995. Internet and postal. Shop open: **M:** 09:30–16:30; **T:** 09:30–16:30; **W:** 09:30–16:30; **Th:** 09:30–16:30; **F:** 09:30–16:30; **S:** 09:30–16:30; **Su:** 10:00–16:30. Medium stock. Spec: Academic/Scholarly; Advertising; Aeronautics; Africana; Agriculture; Alchemy; Almanacs; Art; Biography; History - General; Literature; Military History; Poetry; Topography - Local. PR: £1–200. [Updated]

RIPON

Hornseys', ■ 3 Kirkgate, Ripon, HG4 1PA. Prop: Bruce, Susan & Daniel Hornsey. Tel: (01765) 602878. Fax: (01765) 601692. Est: 1990. Shop open: **M:** 09:00–17:30; **T:** 09:00–17:30; **W:** 09:00–17:30; **Th:** 09:00–17:30; **F:** 09:00–17:30; **S:** 09:00–17:30; **Su:** 09:00–17:30. Medium stock. Spec: Alpinism/Mountaineering; Architecture; Aviation; Children's - General; Fashion & Costume; History - General; Military History; Motoring; Sport - General; Topography - General; Topography - Local. PR: £1–1,500. CC: MC; V; Switch. We stock prints and engravings on a variety of subjects. daniel@rarebooks.freeserve.co.uk. [08/03/2003]

SALTBURN–BY–THE–SEA

Saltburn Bookshop, ■ 3 Amber Street, Saltburn–by–the–Sea, TS12 1DT. Prop: Jösef Thompson. Tel: (01287) 623335. E-mail: josefthompson@freeuk.com. Est: 1978. Shop open: **M:** 11:00–17:00; **T:** 11:00–17:00; **W:** 11:00–17:00; **Th:** 11:00–17:00; **F:** 11:00–17:00; **S:** 11:00–17:00; Closed for lunch: 13:00–14:00. Medium stock. Spec: Booksearch. PR: £1–100. Winter opening hours: Mon to Sat 11–4 (Closed for lunch 1-2). [Updated]

SCARBOROUGH

Antiquary Ltd., (Bar Bookstore), ■ 4 Swanhill Road, Scarborough, YO11 1BW. Prop: Michael Chaddock. Tel: (01723) 500141. Website: www.ukbookworld.com/members/Barbooks. E-mail: antiquary@btinternet.com. Est: 1976. Shop open: **T:** 10:30–17:00; **W:** 10:30–17:00; **Th:** 10:30–17:00; **F:** 10:30–17:00; **S:** 10:30–18:00. Medium stock. Spec: Academic/Scholarly; Art; Author - Housman, A.E.; History - General; Literature; Topography - General; Topography - Local; also Booksearch. PR: £1–450. Mem: PBFA. [Updated]

The Bookshelf, ■ 6 Victoria Road, Scarborough, YO11 1SD. Prop: Mrs. Leslie Anne Stones. Tel: (01723) 381677. Website: www.bookshelf.scarborough.co.uk. E-mail: bookshelf@scarborough.co.uk. Est: 2000. Shop open: **M:** 10:00–17:00; **T:** 10:00–17:00; **W:** 10:00–17:00; **Th:** 10:00–17:00; **F:** 10:00–17:00; **S:** 10:00–17:00. Small general stock. PR: £1–100. Corresp: Some French. [Updated]

Richard Dalby, 4 Westbourne Park, Scarborough, YO12 4AT. Tel: (01723) 377049. Est: 1976. Private premises. Postal business only. Very small stock. Spec: Fiction - Fantasy, Horror; Fiction - Supernatural; Literature. Cata: 2 a year. Mem: PBFA. [Updated]

SELBY

Anthony Vickers, 23 Baffam Gardens, Selby, YO8 9AY. Tel: (01757) 705949. E-mail: anthonyvickers@bun.com. Est: 1993. Private premises. Internet and postal. Telephone first. Open: Small stock. Spec: Academic/Scholarly; Advertising; Aeronautics; Alpinism/Mountaineering; Archaeology; Architecture; History - Industrial; Mining; Topography - Local; Topology; Windmills & Watermills. PR: £5–500. Mem: PBFA. [Updated]

SETTLE

Anderson Slater Antiques, ■ 6 Duke Street, Settle, BD24 9DW. Prop: Kenneth C. Slater. Tel: (01729) 822051. Fax: (01969) 663751. Est: 1998. Shop open: **M:** 10:00–17:00; **T:** 10:00–17:00; **W:** 10:00–17:00; **Th:** 10:00–17:00; **F:** 10:00–17:00; **S:** 10:00–17:00. Medium stock. Spec: Animals and Birds; Antiques; Art; Arts, The; Biography; Fiction - General; First Editions; Literary Criticism; Music - General; Poetry; Travel - General. PR: £3–60. VAT No: GB 160 0763 92. [Updated]

Peter M. Thornber, 3 School Hill, Settle, BD24 9HB. Tel: (01729) 824067. E-mail: hastathas@ hotmail.com. Est: 1997. Private premises. Appointment necessary. Small stock. Spec: Agriculture; Antiquarian; Ecclesiastical History & Architecture; Farming & Livestock; Modern First Editions; Religion - Christian; Theology. PR: £5–500. Also, valuations, consultancy and researcher, commissions at auctions. Corresp: French. [Updated]

SKIPTON

Grove Rare Books, ■ The Old Post Office, Bolton Abbey, Skipton, BD23 6EX. Prop: Andrew & Janet Sharpe. Tel: (01756) 710717. Fax: (01756) 711098. Website: www.grovebookshop.co.uk. E-mail: antiquarian@groverarebooks.co.uk. Est: 1984. Shop open: **T:** 10:00–17:00; **W:** 10:00–17:00; **Th:** 10:00–17:00; **F:** 10:00–17:00; **S:** 10:00–17:00; Closed for lunch: 13:00–14:00. Medium stock. Spec: Bindings; Fiction - General; Illustrated; Literature; Rural Life; Sets of Books; Sport - Angling/ Fishing; Sport - Field Sports; Sport - Hunting; Topography - General; Topography - Local. PR: £10–3,000. CC: JCB; MC; V; SW, SO. Cata: 2 a year. Mem: ABA; PBFA; BA. VAT No: GB 756 1269 18. [Updated]

C.L. Hawley, 26 Belgrave Street, Skipton, BD23 1QB. (*) Prop: Catherine Hawley. Tel: (01756) 792380. Website: www.clhawley.co.uk. E-mail: clh@clhawley.co.uk. Est: 2000. Private premises. Postal business only. Small general stock. Spec: Academic/Scholarly; Arts, The; Biography; Children's - General; History - General; History - Local; Humanities; Literary Criticism; also Booksearch. PR: £2–250. CC: JCB; MC; V; debit cds. Also on Ibooknet. [Updated]

Skipton Antiques Centre, ■ Cavendish Square, Skipton, BD23 2AB. Tel: (01756) 797667. Shop open: **M:** 11:00–16:30; **T:** 11:00–16:30; **W:** 11:00–16:30; **Th:** 11:00–16:30; **F:** 11:00–16:30; **S:** 11:00–16:30; **Su:** 11:00–16:30. Spec: PR: £1–5,000. Display stock from Seabreeze, for details see under Thornton Cleveleys, Lancs. (q.v.). [Updated]

STAITHES

John L. Capes (Books, Maps & Prints), Church Street, Staithes, Cleveland, TS13 5DB. Tel: (01947) 840 790. Website: www.johncapes.co.uk. E-mail: capes@staithes.fsbusiness.co.uk. Est: 1969. Private premises. Appointment necessary. Very small general stock. Spec: Academic/Scholarly; Antiquarian; Fine Art; Topography - Local. PR: £10–2,000. Mem: PBFA. [Updated]

STAMFORD BRIDGE

Batterdale Books, 32 Godwin's Way, Stamford Bridge, YO41 1DB. Prop: Gordon B. & Fleur L. Steven. Tel: (01759) 372616. Website: http://hometown.aol.com/GBSteven. E-mail: GBSteven@aol.com. Est: 1994. Private premises. Postal business only. Small stock. Spec: Banking & Insurance; Canals/Inland Waterways; Company History; Industry; Railways; Steam Engines. PR: £1–100. Cata: 4 a year on railways. [25/06/2003]

TADCASTER

Roy Allport, Bramblings, 120 Wighill Lane, Tadcaster, LS24 8HE. Tel: (01937) 834176. Fax: (01937) 834176. E-mail: royport@clara.co.uk. Est: 1991. Private premises. Internet and postal. Appointment necessary. Very small stock. Spec: Academic/Scholarly; Folklore; Gypsies; Rural Life; Social History; Traction Engines; Windmills & Watermills. PR: £2–200. [Updated]

THIRSK

Potterton Books, The Old Rectory, Sessay, Thirsk, YO7 3LZ. Prop: Clare Jameson. Tel: (01845) 501218. Fax: (01845) 501439. Website: www.pottertonbooks.co.uk. E-mail: enquiries@pottertonbooks.co.uk. Est: 1982. Spec: Antiquarian; Antiques; Applied Art; Architecture; Art - Reference; Carpets; Ceramics; Decorative Art; Fine Art; Gardening; Interior Design; Jewellery; Textiles; also Booksearch. PR: £5–5,000. CC: AE; D; MC; V. [Updated]

WHITBY

Endeavour Books, ■ 1 Grape Lane, Whitby, YO22 4BA. Tel: 01947 821331. Website: www.enbooks .co.uk. E-mail: linda@enbooks.co.uk. Est: 1989. Internet and postal. Shop open: **M:** 10:30–17:00; **T:** 10:30–17:00; **W:** 10:30–17:00; **Th:** 10:30–17:00; **F:** 10:30–17:00; **S:** 10:30–17:00; **Su:** 10:30–17:00. PR: £3–50. CC: MC; V. [Updated]

John R. Hoggarth, Thorneywaite House, Glaisdale, Whitby, YO21 2QU. Tel: (01947) 897338. Website: www.johnrhoggarth.co.uk. E-mail: john@johnrhoggarth.co.uk. Est: 1978. Private premises. Internet and postal. Appointment necessary. Small stock. Spec: Author - Baden-Powell, Lord Robert; Children's - General; History - General; Scouts & Guides. PR: £1–100. CC: PayPal. [Updated]

YARM

Richard J. Hodgson (Books), Manor Farm, Kirklevington, Yarm, TS15 9PY. Tel: (01642) 780445. E-mail: rjhodgsonbooks@clara.co.uk. Private premises. Appointment necessary. Medium stock. Spec: Agriculture; Colour-Plate; Ex-Libris; Farming & Livestock; Guide Books; Illustrated; Magic & Conjuring; Natural History; Philately; Poultry; Sheep/Shepherding; Travel - General. PR: £1–1,000. Mem: PBFA. [Updated]

YORK

Barbican Bookshop, ■ 24 Fossgate, York, YO1 9TA. Prop: Christian Literature Stalls Ltd. Tel: (01904) 653643. Fax: (01904) 653643. Website: barbicanbookshop.co.uk. E-mail: mail@barbicanbookshop .co.uk. Est: 1960. Shop open: **M:** 09:00–17:30; **T:** 09:15–17:30; **W:** 09:00–17:30; **Th:** 09:00–17:30; **F:** 09:15–17:30; **S:** 09:00–17:30. Large general stock. Spec: Aeronautics; Bibles; Buses/Trams; Canals/ Inland Waterways; Ecclesiastical History & Architecture; Folio Society, The; History - General; History - British; History - Industrial; History - Local; Literature; Maritime/Nautical; Military; Military History. PR: £1–500. CC: E; JCB; MC; V. Also, new books, remainders, cards & videos. Cata: 2 a year on Theology & Yorkshire. Mem: PBFA; BA. VAT No: GB 169 3696 12. [Updated]

Boer War Books, 8 Mill Lane, Heworth, York, YO31 7TE. Prop: E.A. Hackett. Tel: (01904) 415829. Fax: (01904) 415829. Est: 1969. Private premises. Postal business only. Very small stock. Spec: Countries - South Africa; Military; Military History. PR: £20–2,000. [Updated]

Fossgate Books, ■ 36 Fossgate, York, YO1 9TF. Prop: Alex Helstrip. Tel: (01904) 641389. E-mail: alexhelstrip@hotmail.com. Est: 1992. Shop open: **M:** 10:00–17:30; **T:** 10:00–17:30; **W:** 10:00–17:30; **Th:** 10:00–17:30; **F:** 10:00–17:30; **S:** 10:00–17:30. Very large stock. Spec: Academic/Scholarly; Antiquarian; Folio Society, The; History - General. PR: £2–300. CC: MC; V. Cata: 1 a year. [Updated]

Empire Books, 12 Queens Staith Mews, York, YO1 6HH. Prop: Colin Hinchcliffe. Tel: (01904) 610679. Fax: (01904) 641664. E-mail: colin@empires.demon.co.uk. Est: 1990. Private premises. Internet and postal. Appointment necessary. Large stock. Spec: Travel - General; Travel - Africa; Travel - Americas; Travel - Asia; Travel - Australasia/Australia; Travel - Europe; Travel - Middle East; Travel - Polar. PR: £3–1,000. CC: MC; V. Cata: quarterly. VAT No: GB 647 2977 92. [Updated]

Lucius Books Ltd, 15 Main Street, Wilberfoss, York, YO41 5NN. (*) Prop: James Hallgate. Tel: (0759) 380960. E-mail: james@luciusbooks.fsnet.co.uk. Est: 1993. Private premises. Appointment necessary. Very small stock. Spec: Author - Christie, Agatha; Author - Fleming, Ian; Author - Johns, W.E.; Children's - General; Children's - Illustrated; Fine & Rare; First Editions; Illustrated. PR: £30–20,000. CC: JCB; MC; V. Cata: 3 a year. Mem: ABA; PBFA; ILAB. VAT No: GB 766 9110 08. [29/06/2003]

Minster Gate Bookshop, ■ 8 Minster Gates, York, YO1 7HL. Prop: Nigel Wallace. Tel: (01904) 621812. Fax: (01904) 622960. Website: www.minstergatebooks.co.uk. E-mail: rarebooks@ minstergatebooks.co.uk. Est: 1970. Internet and postal. Shop open: **M:** 10:00–17:30; **T:** 10:00– 17:30; **W:** 10:00–17:30; **Th:** 10:00–17:30; **F:** 10:00–17:30; **S:** 10:00–17:30; **Su:** 11:00–19:00. Large general stock. Spec: Arthurian; Children's - General; Folklore; Illustrated; Literature; also Booksearch. PR: £1–500. CC: MC; V. Corresp: French. Mem: PBFA. VAT No: GB 450 7122 78. [Updated]

Nostalgia Publications Ltd., ■ 91–93 Nunnery Lane, York, YO23 1AH. Prop: Jim Barker. Tel: (01904) 624901. Fax: (01904) 654925. Website: www.nostalgia-publications.co.uk. E-mail: jim@products .demon.co.uk. Est: 1983. Internet and postal. Shop at: 1 Victoria Street, off Nunnery Lane, York (side of the office). Open: **T:** 11:00–17:30; **W:** 11:00–17:30; **Th:** 11:00–17:30; **F:** 11:00–17:30; **S:** 11:00–17:30. Medium stock. Spec: Glamour; Periodicals & Magazines. PR: £1–100. CC: MC; V. Mailorder. Cata: bi-monthly. [21/07/2003]

Oblong Books, ■ 36 Fossgate, York, YO19TF. Prop: Alex Helstrip. Tel: (01904) 641389. E-mail: alexhelstrip@hotmail.com. Est: 1992. Shop open: **M:** 10:00–17:30; **T:** 10:00–17:30; **W:** 10:00–17:30; **Th:** 10:00–17:30; **F:** 10:00–17:30; **S:** 10:00–17:30. Large stock. Spec: Academic/Scholarly; Antiquarian; Arts, The; Aviation; Biography; Children's - General; Cinema/Film; Fiction - General; First Editions; Folio Society, The; History - General; Literary Criticism; Literature; Maritime/Nautical; Military; Music - General. PR: £2–500. CC: MC; V. Cata: 2 a year on the Folio Society. Corresp: Spanish. [29/06/2003]

Ken Spelman, ■ 70 Micklegate, York, YO1 6LF. Prop: Peter Miller & Tony Fothergill. Tel: (01904) 624414. Fax: (01904) 626276. Website: www.kenspelman.com. E-mail: rarebooks@kenspelman.com. Est: 1948. Shop open: **M:** 09:00–17:30; **T:** 09:00–17:30; **W:** 09:00–17:30; **Th:** 09:00–17:30; **F:** 09:00–17:30; **S:** 09:00–17:30. Very large general stock. Spec: Academic/Scholarly; Antiquarian; Fine Art; History - General; Horticulture; Literature, also Booksearch. PR: £1–10,000. CC: E; MC; V; SW. Also, valuations & on-line search and ordering. Cata: 3 a year. Mem: ABA; PBFA; ILAB. [25/06/2003]

Stone Trough Books, ■ 38 Fossgate, York, YO1 9TF. Prop: George Ramsden. Tel: (01904) 670323. Fax: (01944) 768465. E-mail: george@stonetrough.demon.co.uk. Est: 1981. Shop open: **T:** 10:00–17:30; **W:** 10:00–17:30; **Th:** 10:00–17:30; **F:** 10:00–17:30; **S:** 10:00–17:30. Small general stock. Spec: Literature. PR: £2–200. CC: V. Cata: 2 a year on Literature. Corresp: French, German. VAT No: GB 237 5500 70. [18/07/2003]

WestField Books, 28 Easthorpe Drive, York, YO26 6NR. Prop: Arthur Cunningham. Tel: (01904) 794711. E-mail: westfieldbooks@btopenworld.com. Est: 1990. Private premises. Internet and postal. Contactable. Medium stock. Spec: Antiquarian. PR: £10–5,000. Mem: PBFA. [Updated]

NORTHAMPTONSHIRE

BRACKLEY

The Old Hall Bookshop, ■ 32 Market Place, Brackley, NN13 7DP. Prop: John & Lady Juliet Townsend. Tel: (01280) 704146. Website: http://www.oldhallbooks.com. E-mail: books@oldhallbooks.com. Est: 1977. Shop. Spec: Children's - General; Topography - Local; Travel - General, also Booksearch. PR: £1–100. CC: AE; JCB; MC; V; Maestro. Mem: ABA; PBFA; BA. [Updated]

GEDDINGTON

Cooksweb, Dukes Farm, 39 Queen Street, Geddington, NN14 1AZ. Prop: Natalie Miller. Tel: (01536) 460991. Fax: (01536) 741704. Website: www.cooksweb.co.uk. Est: 1999. Private premises. Internet and postal. Appointment necessary. Open: **M:** 09:30–15:00; **T:** 09:30–15:00; **W:** 09:30–15:00; **Th:** 09:30–15:00; **F:** 09:30–15:00. Small stock. Spec: Brewing; Christmas; Cookery/Gastronomy; Crafts; Embroidery; Etiquette; Fashion & Costume; Flower Arranging; Food & Drink; Gardening; Horticulture; Viticulture; Whisky; Wine, also Booksearch. CC: MC; V; Debit. Cata: 6 a year on Food & Drink. Corresp: French, German. VAT No: GB 745 8304 20. [25/06/2003]

NORTHAMPTON

Occultique, 30 St. Michael's Avenue, Northampton, NN1 4JQ. Prop: Michael John Lovett. Tel: (01604) 627727. Fax: (01604) 603860. Website: www.occultique.co.uk. E-mail: enquiries@occultique.co.uk. Est: 1973. Private premises. Internet and postal. Appointment necessary. Shop at: www.mantic-arts.co.uk. Medium stock. Spec: Alchemy; Alternative Medicine; American Indians; Astrology; Author - Crowley, Aleister; Author - Spare, Austin Osman; Earth Mysteries; Egyptology; Erotica; Esoteric; Fiction - Fantasy, Horror; Folklore; Freemasonry & Anti-Masonry; Ghosts; Herbalism. PR: £1–1,000. CC: PayPal. Also, new books, essential oils, herbs & occult paraphernalia. Cata: 2 a year, fairly frequently. [Updated]

Roosterbooks, 7 Elysium Terrace, Northampton, NN2 6EN. Prop: Roy Sheffield. Tel: (01604) 720983. Fax: (01604) 720983. E-mail: roosterbooks@aol.com. Est: 1997. Private premises. Internet and postal. Large general stock. Spec: Biography; History - General; Mind, Body & Spirit; Modern First Editions; also Booksearch. PR: £1–4,000. CC: JCB; MC. VAT No: GB 655 1461 40. [Updated]

Ryeland Books, 18 St. George's Place, Northampton, NN2 6EP. Prop: Alan & Joy Riley. Tel: (01604) 716901. E-mail: amriley@ryeland.demon.co.uk. Est: 1998. Private premises. Appointment necessary. Small stock. Spec: Architecture; Art - History; History - General; Literary Criticism; Literature; Natural History; Theology. PR: £3–1,000. Cata: 3 a year. Mem: PBFA. [Updated]

OUNDLE

Geraldine Waddington Books & P, ■ 3 West Street, Oundle, PE8 4EJ. Tel: (01832) 275028. Fax: (01832) 275028. Website: www.geraldinewaddington.com. E-mail: g.waddington@dial.pipex.com. Est: 1984. Internet and postal. Shop open: **M:** 10:00–17:00; **T:** 10:00–17:00; **Th:** 10:00–17:00; **F:** 10:00–17:00; **S:** 10:00–17:00. Medium stock. Spec: Art - Reference; Engraving; Ex-Libris; Folio Society, The; Illustrated; Private Press. PR: £2–500. CC: MC; V. Cata: 4 a year on wood engraving. Mem: PBFA. VAT No: GB 745 9396 81. [Updated]

RUSHDEN

Booksmart, 4 Manning Rise, Rushden, NN10 0LY. Prop: Andy Wagstaff. Tel: (01933) 357416. Website: www.booksmart.co.uk. E-mail: wagstaa@hotmail.com. Est: 1990. Postal business only. PR: £1–10. [Updated]

SILVERSTONE

Collectors Carbooks, ■ 2210 Silverstone Technolgy Park, Silverstone Circuit, Silverstone, NN12 8TN. Prop: Chris Knapman. Tel: (01327) 855888. Fax: (01327) 855999. Website: www.collectorscarbooks. com. E-mail: sales@collectorscarbooks.com. Est: 1993. Internet and postal. Shop open: **M:** 09:00–17:00; **T:** 09:00–17:00; **W:** 09:00–17:00; **Th:** 09:00–17:00; **F:** 09:00–17:00; **S:** 08:30–14:30. Large stock. Spec: Marque Histories (see also motoring); Motorbikes; Motoring; Sport - Motor Racing; Transport; Vintage Cars; also Booksearch. PR: £1–1,200. CC: MC; V. Open certain race Saturdays 08:30–14:30. Attends historic motor racing events. VAT No: GB 649 2588 91. [Updated]

TOWCESTER

Mr. Pickwick of Towcester, Lavender Cottage, Shutlanger, Towcester, NN12 7RR. Prop: William Mayes. Tel: (01604) 862006. Fax: (01604) 862006. Website: www.yell.co.uk.sites/pickwickbookfinders. Est: 1963. Private premises. Internet and postal. Very large stock. Spec: Author - Dickens, Charles; Biography; Books about Books; Fiction - General; Literature; Memoirs; Newspapers - General; Periodicals & Magazines; Sport - General; Television; also Booksearch. PR: £3–300. Cata: occasionally. [Updated]

WELLINGBOROUGH

R.C. Brett, 32 Abbots Way, Wellingborough, NN8 2AG. Tel: (01933) 224502. E-mail: joe.brett@ btinternet.com. Private premises. Postal business only. Appointment necessary. Very small stock. Spec: Sport - Athletics; Sport - Olympic Games, The. PR: £1–75. Cata: occasionally. [24/07/2003]

Lost Books, 103 Leyland Trading Estate, Wellingborough, NN8 1RT. Prop: Meisterco Limited. Tel: (01933) 228828. Fax: (01933) 228828. Website: www.lostbooks.net. E-mail: gareth@lostbooks.net. Est: 2000. Warehouse; Internet and postal. Appointment necessary. Open: **M:** 09:00–17:30; **T:** 09:00– 17:30; **W:** 09:00–17:30; **Th:** 09:00–17:30; **F:** 09:00–17:30; **S:** 09:00–17:00. Very large stock. Spec: Arms & Armour; History - General; Military; Military History; Naval; War - General; War - Napoleonic; War - World War I; War - World War II; also Booksearch. PR: £5–5,000. CC: AE; MC; V. Cata: Subject Catalogues. Corresp: German, French. VAT No: GB 818746887. [Updated]

The Park Gallery & Bookshop, ■ 16 Cannon Street, Wellingborough, NN8 4DJ. Prop: J.A. Foster. Tel: (01933) 222592. Website: www.ukbookworld.com/members/parkbookshop. E-mail: judy@ parkbookshop.freeserve.co.uk. Est: 1979. Internet and postal. Shop open: **M:** 10:00–17:30; **T:** 10:00–17:30; **W:** 10:00–17:30; **Th:** 10:00–14:30; **F:** 10:00–17:30; **S:** 10:00–18:00. Medium stock. Spec: Antiquarian; Antiques; Author - Bates, H.E.; Biography; Children's - General; Fiction - General; Military; Railways; Topography - General; Topography - Local, also Booksearch. PR: £1–500. Also, collectables, ephemera, prints & maps, plus picture framing. [Updated]

NORTHUMBERLAND

ALNWICK

Barter Books, ■ Alnwick Station, Alnwick, NE66 2NP. Prop: Stuart & Mary Manley. Tel: (01665) 604888. Fax: (01665) 604444. Website: www.barterbooks.co.uk. E-mail: bb@barterbooks.co.uk. Est: 1991. Shop open: **M:** 09:00–19:00; **T:** 09:00–19:00; **W:** 09:00–19:00; **Th:** 09:00–19:00; **F:** 09:00–19:00; **S:** 09:00–19:00; **Su:** 09:00–19:00. Very large general stock. PR: £1–6,000. CC: AE; D; E; MC; V. open rest of the year, Mon-Sun 09:00–17.00. Corresp: French. Mem: IOBA. Also at: Barter Books, Seahouses, Northumberland. VAT No: GB 414 3504 88. [Updated]

BEADNELL

Shearwater Bed & Books, Shearwater, 78 Harbour Road, Beadnell, Northumberland, NE67 5BE. Prop: John Lumby. Tel: (01665) 720654. E-mail: shearwaterbooks@yahoo.co.uk. Private premises. Internet and postal. Appointment necessary. Small stock. Spec: Lepidopterology / Lepidoptery; Natural History; New Naturalist; Ornithology; also Booksearch. PR: £10–500. Also, bookbinding + B&B Attends British Bird Watching Fair. Cata: 1 a year in Febuary. [Updated]

BERWICK–UPON–TWEED

Bridge Street Bookshop, ■ 41 Bridge Street, Berwick–upon–Tweed, TD15 1ES. Prop: Christopher & Do Shaw. Tel: (01289) 304986. Fax: (01289) 304986. Est: 1993. Shop open: **M:** 09:15–17:00; **T:** 09:15–17:00; **W:** 09:15–17:00; **Th:** 09:15–13:00; **F:** 09:15–17:00; **S:** 08:00–17:00. Small general stock. Spec: History - Local; Rural Life. PR: £1–150. CC: MC; V. [18/06/2003]

Anne Hattle, 31 Church Street, Berwick–upon–Tweed, TD15 1EE. Tel: (01289) 331502. E-mail: Est: 1984. Spec: History - General; Scottish Interest; Topography - General. PR: £1–100. [26/08/2003]

HALTWHISTLE

Newcastle Bookshop@Haltwhistle, ■ Market Square, Haltwhistle, NE49 0BG. Prop: Valerie Levitt. Tel: (01434) 320 103. Website: www.newcastlebookshop.com. E-mail: newcstlbk@aol.com. Est: 1975. Shop open: **Th:** 11:00–16:00; **F:** 11:00–16:00; **S:** 11:00–16:00. Medium stock. Spec: Art; Art - History; Art - Reference; Illustrated; Photography. PR: £1–500. CC: AE; JCB; MC; V; SW. Also, old prints. [Updated]

HEXHAM

Alex Fotheringham, East Chesterhope, West Woodburn, Hexham, NE48 2RQ. Tel: (01434) 270046. Fax: (01434) 632931. Private premises. Appointment necessary. Very small stock. Spec: Antiquarian; Architecture; Art; Bibliography; Literature; Theology. PR: £20–2,500. Cata: 6 a year. Mem: ABA; PBFA. VAT No: GB 646 1882 17. [Updated]

Hencotes Books & Prints, ■ 8 Hencotes, Hexham, NE46 2EJ. Prop: Penny Pearce. Tel: (01434) 605971. E-mail: enquiries@hencotesbooks.onyxnet.co.uk. Est: 1981. Shop open: **M:** 10:30–17:00; **T:** 10:30–17:00; **W:** 10:30–17:00; **F:** 10:30–17:00; **S:** 10:30–17:00. Medium stock. Spec: Booksearch. PR: £1–1,000. CC: JCB; MC; V; SW. Also attends P.B.F.A. and local fairs. Mem: PBFA. VAT No: GB 796 9893 26. [Updated]

Newgate Books and Translations, 3 Quatre Bras, Hexham, NE46 3JY. Prop: Davina and John Dwyer. Tel: (01434) 607650. Fax: (01434) 607650. E-mail: newgate.books@virgin.net. Est: 1987. Private premises. Postal business only. Contactable. Open: **M:** 09:00–18:00; **T:** 09:00–18:00; **W:** 09:00–18:00; **Th:** 09:00–18:00; **F:** 09:00–18:00; **S:** 09:00–12:00; Closed for lunch: 12:45–14:15. Small general stock. Spec: Conservation; Environment, The; Fiction - Crime, Detective, Spy, Thrillers; Music - Classical. PR: £5–250. French - English Translation. Corresp: French, German. [Updated]

Priestpopple Books, ■ 9b Priestpopple, Hexham, NE46 1PF. Prop: John B. Patterson. Tel: (01434) 607773. E-mail: priestpopple.books@tinyworld.co.uk. Est: 1997. Shop open: **M:** 09:00–17:00; **T:** 09:00–17:00; **W:** 09:00–17:00; **Th:** 09:00–17:00; **F:** 09:00–17:00; **S:** 09:00–17:00. Very large stock. Spec: Academic/Scholarly; Art - Reference; Author - General; Author - Carlyle, Thomas; Children's - General; Cinema/Film; Crafts; Dogs; Education & School; Languages - Foreign; Medieval; Military History; Music - General; Natural History; Religion - General. PR: £1–500. Also, sheet music and used LPs. [Updated]

MORPETH

Intech Books, 14 Bracken Ridge, Morpeth, NE61 3SY. Prop: Mr. D. J. Wilkinson. Tel: (01670) 519102. Fax: (01670) 515815. E-mail: djwintech@talk21.com. Est: 1981. Private premises. Internet and postal. Appointment necessary. Small stock. Spec: Children's - General; Comic Books & Annuals; Fiction - General; First Editions; Sport - Golf; Topography - Local, also Booksearch. PR: £1–100. [29/06/2003]

STOCKSFIELD

Leaf Ends, Ridley Mill, Stocksfield, NE43 7QU. Prop: Mrs Moira Tait. Tel: (01661) 844261. Fax: (01661) 844261. Website: www.abebooks.com. E-mail: alexander.tait@virgin.net. Est: 1995. Storeroom. Internet and postal. Appointment necessary. Large general stock. PR: £1–1,000. CC: MC; V. VAT No: GB 747 2468 08. [Updated]

WOOLER

Hamish Dunn Antiques & Books, ■ 17 High Street, Wooler, NE71 6BU. Tel: (01668) 281341. Est: 1986. Shop open: **M:** 09:00–16:00; **T:** 09:00–16:00; **W:** 09:00–16:00; **Th:** 09:00–12:00; **F:** 09:00–16:00; **S:** 09:00–16:00. Small general stock. PR: £1–100. CC: AE; D; V. [Updated]

NOTTINGHAMSHIRE

GUNTHORPE

Letterbox Books, The Coach House, Gunthorpe, NG14 7ES. Prop: Bob Dakin. Tel: (0115) 966-4349. E-mail: b@bobdakin.plus.com. Est: 1993. Postal business only. Spec: Alpinism/Mountaineering; History - Local; Sport - Caving (Spelaeology); Sport - Potholing; Topography - General; Topography - Local, also Booksearch. PR: £1–200. [Updated]

KIRKBY–IN–ASHFIELD

Kyrios Books, ■ 11 Kingsway, Kirkby–in–Ashfield, NG17 7BB. Prop: Keith Parr. Tel: (01623) 452556 answe. Website: www.kyriosbooks.co.uk. E-mail: keith@kyriosbooks.co.uk. Est: 1989. Shop; Internet and postal. Telephone first. Open: **M:** 09:00–16:30; **T:** 09:00–16:30; **W:** 09:00–16:00; **Th:** 09:00–16:30; **F:** 09:00–16:30; **S:** 09:00–16:30. Closed for lunch: 12:00–13:00. Large stock. Spec: Autobiography; Ecclesiastical History & Architecture; Philosophy; Prayer Books; Religion - General; Religion - Christian; Theology. PR: £1–100. Cata: quarterly. Mem: FSB. [Updated]

MANSFIELD

R. W. Price, 19 Park Avenue, Mansfield, NG18 2AU. Prop: Mr G.D. Price. Tel: (01623) 629858. Website: www.snap.to/uk. E-mail: gdp@gdprice.freeserve.co.uk. Est: 1986. Private premises. Internet and postal. Very large general stock. Spec: Beat Writers; Children's - General; Comedy; Erotica; Espionage; Fiction - General; Fiction - Crime, Detective, Spy, Thrillers; Fiction - Fantasy, Horror; Fiction - Romantic; Fiction - Science Fiction; Fiction - Westerns; First Editions; Modern Firsts. PR: £1–100. Cata: 4 a year. [Updated]

NEWARK–ON–TRENT

Lawrence Books, Newark Antiques Centre, Lombard Street, Newark–on–Trent, NG24 1XP. Prop: Arthur Lawrence. Tel: (01636) 605865. Est: 1987. Market stand/stall. Open: **M:** 09:00–16:30; **T:** 09:00–16:30; **W:** 09:00–16:30; **Th:** 09:00–16:30; **F:** 09:00–16:30; **S:** 09:00–16:30; **Su:** 11:00–16:00. Small stock. Spec: Aviation; Diaries; History - General; Letters; Maritime/Nautical; Military; Poetry; Topography - Local. PR: £1–200. Exhibits at book fairs, bookbinding. Alternative tel: (01636) 701619. [Updated]

Jandee Books, Melrose, Old Hall Lane, East Markham, Newark-on-Trent, NG22 0RF. Tel: (01777) 871759. Website: www.ukbookworld.com/members/jandee. Private premises. Internet and postal. Very small general stock. PR: £1–500. [15/03/2003]

NOTTINGHAM

Artco, 6 Grantham Road, Radcliffe on Trent, Nottingham, NG12 2HD. Prop: Mr. H. Boehm. Tel: (0115) 933-3530. Fax: (0115) 911-9746. Est: 1970. Private premises. Appointment necessary. Small stock. Spec: Applied Art; Art; Art - Reference; Artists; Arts, The; Colour-Plate; Foreign Texts; Illustrated; Limited Editions; Literature; Private Press. PR: £10–1,000. CC: MC; V. Cata: occasional lists. Corresp: German. [Updated]

Geoffrey Blore's Bookshop, ■ 484 Mansfield Road, Sherwood, Nottingham, NG5 2BF. Tel: (0115) 969-1441. Est: 1987. Shop open: **M:** 10:30–17:00; **T:** 10:30–17:00; **W:** 10:30–17:00; **Th:** 10:30–17:00; **F:** 10:30–17:00; **S:** 10:30–17:00. Very large general stock. [Updated]

Caron Books, 29 Clarence Road, Attenborough, Nottingham, NG9 5HY. Prop: Steve Caron. Tel: (0115) 925 4851. Website: www.caronbooks.co.uk. E-mail: caronbooks@btclick.com. Est: 2000. Spec: Fiction - General. PR: £3–150. [15/05/2003]

A. Holmes, 82 Highbury Avenue, Nottingham, NG6 9DB. Prop: A .Holmes. Tel: (0115) 979-5603. E-mail: aholmesbooks@ntlworld.com. Est: 1997. Private premises. Postal business only. Telephone first. Very large general stock. Spec: Biography; Gypsies; History - General; Military; Travel - General. PR: £5–1,000. [Updated]

Jermy & Westerman, ■ 203 Mansfield Road, Sherwood, Nottingham, NG1 3FS. Prop: G.T. Blore. Tel: (0115) 947-4522. Est: 1977. Shop open: **M:** 11:00–17:00; **T:** 11:00–17:00; **W:** 11:00–17:00; **Th:** 11:00–17:00; **F:** 11:00–17:00; **S:** 11:00–17:00. Medium stock. Spec: Illustrated; Literature; Topography - Local. Also at: Geoffrey Blore's Bookshop, Nottingham. [Updated]

Frances Wakeman Books, PO Box 8039, , Nottingham, NG5 2WN. Prop: Frances & Paul Wakeman. Tel: (0115) 875 3944. Fax: none. Website: www.fwbooks.com. E-mail: info@fwbooks.com. Est: 1970. Private premises. Internet and postal. Appointment necessary. Very small stock. Spec: Bibliography; Books about Books; Papermaking; Printing; Private Press; Publishing; Typography. PR: £100–6,000. CC: AE; E; JCB; MC; V. Also, publishing books about books. Cata: 1 a year. Mem: PBFA. VAT No: GB 685 4226 14. [Updated]

PLEASLEY VALE

Caroline Hartley Books, Mill 3, Unit J2, Pleasley Vale Business Park, Outgang Lane, Pleasley Vale, NG19 8RL. Prop: Caroline Hartley. Tel: (01246) 558481. Website: www.abebooks.com/home/ carolinehartley. E-mail: hartleybooks@ntlworld.com. Est: 1992. Warehouse; Internet and postal. Very large general stock. Spec: Odd & Unusual. PR: £1–100. CC: MC; V. [Updated]

REDMILE

Forest Books, Overfields, 1, Belvoir Road, Redmile, NG13 0GL. Tel: (01949) 842360. Fax: (01949) 844196. Website: www.forestbooks.co.uk. E-mail: bib@forestbooks.co.uk. Est: 1979. Private premises. Internet and postal. Appointment necessary. Medium stock. Spec: Bibliography; Bindings; Bookbinding; Books about Books; Papermaking; Printing; Typography. PR: £5–5,000. CC: MC; V. Cata: 4 a year. Mem: PBFA. [Updated]

SANDIACRE

A.E. Beardsley, 14 York Avenue, Sandiacre, NG10 5HB. Prop: Tony and Irene Beardsley. Tel: (0115) 917-0082. Website: www.ukbookworld.com/members/aebbooks. E-mail: aebbooks@ntlworld.com. Est: 1991. Private premises. Appointment necessary. Small general stock. Spec: Countries - Malaysia; Topography - General; Travel - General; also Booksearch. PR: £4–400. Exhibits at Buxton Book Fair and 1,000 books on www.abebooks.com. [Updated]

SUTTON IN ASHFIELD

Ashfield Books and Records, ■ 110 Outram Street, Sutton in Ashfield, NG17 4FS. Prop: Stephen & Susan Cooke. Tel: daytime (01623) 5536. Est: 1990. Shop open: **M:** 10:00–17:00; **T:** 10:00–17:00; **W:** 10:00–17:00; **Th:** 10:00–17:00; **F:** 10:00–17:00; **S:** 10:00–17:00. Small general stock. Spec: Art; Cinema/ Film; History - General; Medicine; Music - General; Politics; Psychology/Psychiatry; Theatre; Topography - General; Transport; Travel - General; War - General; also Booksearch. CC: JCB; MC; SW. Naxos CDs, Sheet Music, Cassette Tapes, Vinyl Records. VAT No: GB 797 2060 05. [23/07/ 2003]

Kingfisher Book Service, 6 Ash Grove, Skegby, Sutton in Ashfield, NG17 3FH. Prop: Malcolm Walters. Tel: (01623) 552530. Fax: (01623) 552530. Website: www.kingfisher-books.co.uk. E-mail: quotes@ kingfisher-books.co.uk. Est: 1991. Private premises. Postal business only. Very small general stock. Spec: Fiction - General; Military; War - General; also Booksearch. PR: £3–100. CC: AE; E; JCB; MC; V. [Updated]

OXFORDSHIRE

ABINGDON

Bennett & Kerr Books, Millhill Warehouse, Church Lane, Steventon, Abingdon, OX13 6SW. (*) Prop: Edmund Bennett & Andrew Kerr. Tel: (01235) 820604. Fax: (01235) 821047. Website: www.abebooks .com/home/bennettkerr. E-mail: bennettkerr@aol.com. Est: 1982. Storeroom. Internet and postal. Telephone first. Open: **M:** 09:30–17:30; **T:** 09:30–17:30; **W:** 09:30–17:30; **Th:** 09:30–17:30; **F:** 09:30–17:30; **S:** 10:00–13:00; Closed for lunch: 13:15–14:15. Medium stock. Spec: Academic/Scholarly; Art - History; Ecclesiastical History & Architecture; History - General; Iconography; Literary Criticism; Medieval; Palaeography; Philology. PR: £5–500. CC: MC; V; Switch. Cata: 6 a year on Medieval & Renaissance studies, English studies. Corresp: French, Italian. Mem: ABA; PBFA; ILAB. Also at: Oxbow Books, Park End Place, Oxford. VAT No: GB 348 7058 28. [Updated]

Mary Mason, 55 Winterborne Road, Abingdon, OX14 1AL. Prop: Mary Mason. Tel: (01235) 559929. Website: www.masonpeett.co.uk. E-mail: marymason@mmbooks.freeserve.co.uk. Est: 1988. Private premises. Internet and postal. Appointment necessary. Medium stock. Spec: Art; Author - Ardizzone, Edward; Children's - General; Comic Books & Annuals; Illustrated; Juvenile. PR: £1–1,000. CC: PayPal. Booksearch. Cata: occasionally. Corresp: French. [Updated]

BICESTER

The Bookshop Down The Lane, ■ 14 Wesley Lane, Bicester, OX26 6JU. Prop: Tony Simcock. Tel: (01869) 360085 or 34. Est: 2000. Shop open: **M:** 10:00–17:00; **T:** 10:00–17:00; **W:** 10:00–17:00; **Th:** 10:00–17:00; **F:** 10:00–16:00; Closed for lunch: 13:00–14:00. Medium stock. PR: £1–100. CC: E; JCB; MC; V. [03/07/2003]

DaSilva Puppet Books, 63 Kennedy Road, Bicester, OX26 8BE. Prop: Ray DaSilva. Tel: (01869) 245793. Fax: (01869) 245793. Website: www.puppetbooks.co.uk. E-mail: dasilva@puppetbooks.co.uk. Est: 1986. Private premises. Internet and postal. Appointment necessary. Very small stock. Spec: Entertainment - General; Performing Arts; Puppets & Marionettes; Theatre. PR: £1–200. CC: MC; V; SW. Also, new specialist books & consultancy on Puppet Theatre. Cata: 2 a year. Corresp: French. VAT No: GB 119 7586 34. [Updated]

BLEWBURY

Blewbury Antiques, ■ London Road, Blewbury, OX11 9NX. Prop: Eric Richardson. Tel: (01235) 850366. Est: 1971. Shop open: **M:** 10:00–18:00; **Th:** 10:00–18:00; **F:** 10:00–18:00; **S:** 10:00–18:00; **Su:** 10:00–18:00. Very small general stock. Also, collectables, garden ornaments. [Updated]

BURFORD

The Classics Bookshop, 23 Sheep Street, Burford, OX18 4LS. C.P. & A.V. Powell-Jones. Tel: 0199 3822969. Fax: 0199 3822969. Website: www.classicsbookshop.co.uk. E-mail: sales@ classicsbookshop.com. Est: 1975. Office &/or bookroom. Internet and postal. Appointment necessary. Open: **S:** 10:00–17:00; Closed for lunch: 13:00–14:00. Medium stock. Spec: Classical Studies; Languages - Foreign. PR: £5–1,500. CC: AE; MC; V. Stock includes Latin and Greek classic. Also offers a framing service. Cata: 3 a year on Latin and Greek classics. Corresp: French. Mem: PBFA. Also at: 3 Turl Street, Oxford OX1 3DQ. VAT No: GB 298 2963 94. [Updated]

The Classics Bookshop, 23 Sheep Street, Burford, OX18 4LS. Prop: C.P. & A.V. Powell–Jones. Tel: (01993) 822969. Fax: (01993) 822969. Website: www.classicsbookshop.co.uk. E-mail: classicsbookshop@hotmail.com. Est: 1976. Office &/or bookroom. Internet and postal. Appointment necessary. Open: **W:** 10:00–17:00; **S:** 10:00–17:00; Closed for lunch: 13:00–14:00. Medium stock. Spec: Archaeology; Classical Studies; History - Ancient. PR: £10–1,000. CC: AE; JCB; MC; V. Framing service. Cata: 4 a year – classics only. Mem: PBFA. VAT No: GB 298 2933 94. [Updated]

CHIPPING NORTON

Greensleeves, P.O. Box 156, Chipping Norton, OX7 3XT. Prop: P.R. & C. Seers. Tel: (01608) 676140. Fax: (01608) 676140. Website: www.greensleevesbooks.co.uk. E-mail: greensleeves@v21mail.co.uk. Est: 1982. Private premises. Postal business only. Medium stock. Spec: Alternative Medicine; Anthroposophy; Astrology; Esoteric; Health; Herbalism; Homeopathy; Metaphysics; Mysticism; Mythology; Natural Health; New Age; Occult; Parapsychology; Psychic; Psychology/Psychiatry; Psychotherapy; Religion - Christian; Religion. PR: £1–500. CC: MC; V; Switch. Also, new books and booksearch service. Cata: 8 – specialities. Mem: BA. VAT No: GB 596 3357 96. [Updated]

Kellow Books, ■ 6 Market Place, Chipping Norton, OX7 5NA. Prop: Peter & Jan Combellack. Tel: (01608) 644293. Est: 1998. Shop open: **M:** 10:00–16:30; **T:** 10:00–16:30; **W:** 10:00–16:30; **Th:** 10:00–16:30; **F:** 10:00–16:30. Medium stock. Spec: Children's - General; Company History; Fiction - General; Maritime/Nautical; Military History; Natural History; Ornithology; Topography - General; Topography - Local. PR: £2–800. CC: AE; D; E; JCB; MC; V. [Updated]

COWLEY

Thornton's Bookshop, 65 St Luke's Road, Cowley, Oxford, OX4 3JE. Prop: W.A. Meeuws. Tel: (01865) 779832. Fax: (01865) 321126. Website: www.thorntonsbooks.co.uk. E-mail: thorntons@booknews.demon.co.uk. Est: 1835. Private premises. Internet and postal. Contactable. Medium stock. Spec: Classical Studies; Fine & Rare; History - General; History - Ancient; Languages - Foreign; Philosophy; Theology; Topography - General; Travel - General, also Booksearch. PR: £15–1,000. CC: E; JCB; MC; V; Maestro. Corresp: French, Dutch, German, Spanish, Italian. Mem: ABA; BA; ILAB; BASEES. VAT No: GB GB 194 4663. [Updated]

DEDDINGTON

Brian Carter, 13 High Street, Deddington, OX15 0SJ. Prop: Brian Carter. Tel: (01869) 337341. E-mail: carterbe@lineone.net. Est: 1974. Private premises. Postal business only. Contactable. Small stock. Spec: Ecclesiastical History & Architecture; Oxford Movement; Philosophy; Theology. PR: £5–500. CC: MC; V. We take telephone calls from 09:00 to 21:00 all week. [Updated]

K.R. Clark, Manor Flat, Deddington Manor, New Street, Deddington, OX15 0SS. Tel: (01869) 338543. Market stand/stall. Shop at: Oxford Antique & Craft Market, Gloucester Green, Oxford. Open: **Th:** 08:00–15:00. Spec: Art; Bindings; Literature; Topography - Local. Mem: PBFA. Also at: Oxford Antique & Craft Mkt, Gloucester Green. [19/02/2003]

DIDCOT

The Parlour Bookshop, ■ 30 Wantage Road, Didcot, OX11 0BT. Prop: Roy Frank Burton. Tel: (01235) 818989. Fax: (01235) 814494. Est: 1995. Shop open: **T:** 10:00–16:00; **W:** 10:00–16:00; **Th:** 10:00–16:00; **F:** 10:00–16:00; **S:** 10:00–00:00; Closed for lunch: 12:45–13:45. Medium stock. Spec: Military; Railways; Topography - General. PR: £1–50. Closed Bank Holidays, Good Friday, Easter Monday, Christmas Eve to 4 January. [Updated]

Wayside Books & Cards, Wayside Wellshead, Harwell, Didcot, OX11 0HD. Prop: J.A.B. & J.L. Gibson. Tel: (01235) 835256. E-mail: gibsonjab@aol.com. Est: 1985. Private premises. Postal business only. Open in summer. Medium stock. Spec: Arms & Armour; Astronomy; Biography; Countries - Melanesia; Fiction - Science Fiction; Journals - General; Law; Physics; Religion - General; Science - General; Science - History of. PR: £1–100. [Updated]

DORCHESTER ON THAMES

Pablo Butcher, Overy Mill, Dorchester on Thames, OX10 7JU. Tel: (01865) 341445. Fax: (01865) 340180. Est: 1974. Private premises. Appointment necessary. Small stock. Spec: Art; Ethnography; Photography; Travel - Africa; Travel - Americas; Travel - Asia, South East; Travel - India; Travel - Islamic World. Cata: occasionally. Mem: ABA; PBFA; ILAB. [Updated]

EAST HAGBOURNE

E.M. Lawson & Company, Kingsholm, East Hagbourne, OX11 9LN. Prop: W.J. & K.M. Lawson. Tel: (01235) 812033. Est: 1919. Private premises. Appointment necessary. Very small stock. Spec: Antiquarian; Countries - Africa; Countries - Americas, The; Countries - Australasia; Economics; Literature; Medicine; Science - General; Voyages & Discovery. Cata: occasionally. Mem: ABA. [27/04/2003]

FARINGDON

E.W. Classey Limited, 9 Regal Way, Faringdon, SN7 7BX. Prop: Peter & E.W. Classey. Tel: (01367) 244700. Fax: (01367) 244800. Website: www.classeybooks.com. E-mail: bugbooks@classey .demon.co.uk. Est: 1949. Office &/or bookroom. Internet and postal. Open: **M:** 09:00–16:00; **T:** 09:00–16:00; **W:** 09:00–16:00; **Th:** 09:00–16:00; **F:** 09:00–15:00. Large stock. Spec: Entomology; Natural History; also Booksearch. PR: £1–15,000. CC: E; MC; V. Also, natural history publisher & new books. Cata: 4 a year. [Updated]

N.W. Jobson, 8 Weston Cottages, Buscot Wick, Faringdon, SN7 8DN. Prop: Nigel Jobson. Tel: (01367) 252240. E-mail: jobbobookfinder@tiscali.co.uk. Est: 1981. Private premises. Postal business only. Small stock. Spec: Booksearch. PR: £1–100. [Updated]

GORING–ON–THAMES

Nevis Railway Books, ■ Barbara's, The Orchard, Goring–on–Thames, RG8 9HB. Prop: N.J. Bridger. Tel: (01491) 873032. Website: www.nevis-railway-bookshops.co.uk. Est: 1992. Shop open: **M:** 10:00–17:00; **T:** 10:00–17:00; **W:** 10:00–17:00; **Th:** 10:00–17:00; **F:** 10:00–17:00; **S:** 10:00–17:00; Closed for lunch: 13:00–14:15. Very small stock. Spec: Railways. PR: £1–50. Also at: Railway Book & Magazine Search, Newbury, Berks. (qv.) and Nevis railway Bookshops, Marlborough, Wilts (q.v). [Updated]

HENLEY–ON–THAMES

Bromlea Rare Books, PO Box 4623, Henley on Thames, RG9 4WH. Tel: (0033) 563264558. Website: www.bromlea.com. E-mail: finebooks@bromlea.com. Est: 1988. Private premises. Internet and postal. Shop at: Le Presbytere, St Vincent, 82330, Varen, France. Small stock. Spec: Children's - Illustrated; Literature; Modern First Editions. PR: £25–50,000. CC: AE; E; MC; V. Cata: 2 a year. Corresp: French, German, Spanish, Italian. Mem: ABA; ILAB. [08/08/2003]

Jonkers Rare Books, ■ 24 Hart Street, Henley–on–Thames, RG9 2AU. Prop: Christiaan & Sam Jonkers. Tel: (01491) 576427. Fax: (01491) 573805. Website: www.jonkers.co.uk. Est: 1990. Shop open: **M:** 10:00–17:30; **T:** 10:00–17:30; **W:** 10:00–17:30; **Th:** 10:00–17:30; **F:** 10:00–17:30; **S:** 10:00–17:30. Small stock. Spec: Author - Fleming, Ian; Author - Potter, Beatrix; Children's - General; Illustrated; Literature; Modern First Editions; Topography - Local. PR: £20–5,000,000. CC: AE; MC; V. Cata: 4 – occasionally, on modern firsts, illustrated, children's. Corresp: French, Italian, Spanish. Mem: ABA; PBFA; ILAB. [22/07/2003]

Richard J. Kingston, ■ 95 Bell Street, Henley–on–Thames, RG9 2BD. Tel: (01491) 574535. Est: 1911. Shop open: **M:** 09:30–17:00; **T:** 09:30–17:00; **W:** 09:30–17:00; **Th:** 09:30–17:00; **F:** 09:30–17:00; **S:** 09:30–17:00. Small stock. Spec: Maritime/Nautical; Navigation; Topography - General; Travel - General. [27/05/2003]

Richard Way Booksellers, ■ 54 Friday Street, Henley–on–Thames, RG9 1AH. Prop: Richard Way & Diana Cook. Tel: (01491) 576663. Fax: (01491) 576663. Est: 1978. Shop open: **M:** 10:00–17:30; **T:** 10:00–17:30; **W:** 10:00–17:30; **Th:** 10:00–17:30; **F:** 10:00–17:30; **S:** 10:00–17:30. Small general stock. Spec: Sport - Rowing. PR: £1–200. CC: JCB; V. Mem: ABA. [Updated]

HOOK NORTON

Orangeberry Books, Rowan House, Queens Street, Hook Norton, Banbury, OX15 5PH. Prop: Paul Tranter. Tel: (01608) 737928. Fax: (01608) 730810. Website: www.orangeberry.co.uk. E-mail: books@orangeberry.co.uk. Est: 1995. Private premises. Internet and postal. Telephone first. Medium stock. Spec: Literature; Poetry; Science - General; Technology; Travel - General. PR: £5–1,000. CC: E; MC; V; Maestro. Corresp: French. Mem: IBN. VAT No: GB 800 0734 85. [Updated]

OXFORD

Antiques on High, ■ 85 High Street, Oxford, OX1 4BG. Prop: Paul Lipson amd Sally Young. Tel: (01865) 251075. Est: 1997. Shop open: **M:** 10:00–17:00; **T:** 10:00–17:00; **W:** 10:00–17:00; **Th:** 10:00–17:00; **F:** 10:00–17:00; **S:** 10:00–17:00; **Su:** 11:00–17:00. Medium stock. Spec: Antiques; Architecture; Art; Art - History; Autobiography; Biography; Children's - General; Collecting; Decorative Art; Fiction - General; First Editions; History - General; Illustrated; Military History; Music - General; Natural History; Poetry. PR: £1–200. CC: AE; E; JCB; MC; V. Has stock for 'Books on High' and 'Music Bookshop'. [Updated]

Arcadia, ■ 4 St. Michael's Street, Oxford, OX1 2DU. Tel: (01865) 241757. Est: 1975. Shop open: **M:** 10:00–17:30; **T:** 10:00–17:30; **W:** 10:00–17:30; **Th:** 10:00–17:30; **F:** 10:00–17:30; **S:** 10:00–18:00. Very small general stock. PR: £1–50. CC: AE; D; E; JCB; MC; V. Mainly prints and postcards. Mem: PBFA. [Updated]

Ars Artis, 31 Abberbury Road, Oxford, OX4 4ET. Prop: G.B. & H.J. Lowe. Tel: (01865) 770714. Est: 1976. Private premises. Appointment necessary. Large stock. Spec: Applied Art; Architecture; Art - History; Art - Reference; Artists; Catalogues Raisonnes; Fine Art; Photography. PR: £1–5,000. Corresp: French, German. VAT No: GB 119 1785 58. [Updated]

Blackwell's Music Shop, ■ 23-25 Broad Street, Oxford, OX1 3AX. Tel: (01865) 333580. Fax: (01865) 728020. Website: www.music.blackwell.co.uk. E-mail: books.music@blackwell.co.uk. Est: 1955. Internet and postal. Shop open: **M:** 09:00–18:00; **T:** 09:30–18:00; **W:** 09:00–18:00; **Th:** 09:00–18:00; **F:** 09:00–18:00; **S:** 09:00–18:00; **Su:** 11:00–17:00. Medium stock. Spec: Music - General; Music - Classical; Music - Composers; Music - Musicians; Music - Opera. PR: £2–100. CC: MC; V. [Updated]

Blackwell's Rare Books, ■ 48 - 51 Broad Street, Oxford, OX1 3BQ. Tel: (01865) 333555. Fax: (01865) 794143. Website: www.rarebooks.blackwell.co.uk. E-mail: rarebooks@blackwell.co.uk. Est: 1879. Internet and postal. Shop open: **M:** 09:00–18:00; **T:** 09:30–18:00; **W:** 09:00–18:00; **Th:** 09:00–18:00; **F:** 09:00–18:00; **S:** 09:00–20:00. Small stock. Spec: Classical Studies; Juvenile; Literature; Modern First Editions; Private Press; Travel - General. PR: £20–20,000. CC: MC; V. Vast range of new books, particularly in academic subjects. Cata: 4 a year. Corresp: French, German, Russian. Mem: ABA; PBFA; ILAB. [Updated]

Roy Davids Ltd., The Old Forge, Rectory Road, Great Haseley, Oxford, OX44 7JG. Prop: Roy Davids. Tel: (01844) 279154. Fax: (01844) 278221. Website: www.roydavids.com. E-mail: manuscripts@ roydavids.com. Est: 1994. Private premises. Spec: Autographs; History - General; Letters; Manuscripts; Music - General. PR: £50–100,000. CC: MC; V. Also, portraits and related artefacts. Cata: occasionally. Mem: ABA; ILAB. [08/07/2003]

Game Advice, 71 Rose Hill, Oxford, OX4 4JR. Prop: Alick Elithorn & Karen Stevenson. Tel: (01865) 777317. Fax: (01865) 433050. Website: www.game-advice.com. E-mail: a.elithorn@ntlworld.com. Est: 1975. Private premises. Internet and postal. Telephone first. Large general stock. Spec: Academic/ Scholarly; Anthropology; Children's - General; Computing; Education & School; Fore-Edge Paintings; Games; History of Ideas; Juvenile; Linguistics; Magic & Conjuring; Medicine; Medicine - History of; Neurology; Philosophy; Psychoanalysis. PR: £3–9,000. Also, chess sets, antique games & puzzles, chess prints, educational software, computer & personal consultancy, booksearch & loan. Cata: 2 – biannual. Corresp: French. [29/06/2003]

Hanborough Books, The Foundry, Church Hanborough, Nr. Witney, Oxford, OX29 8AB. Prop: Dennis Hall. Tel: (01993) 881260. Fax: (01993) 883080. Website: www.parrotpress.co.uk. E-mail: dennis@parrotpress.co.uk. Est: 1970. Private premises. Appointment necessary. Small stock. Spec: Antiquarian; Illustrated; Limited Editions; Private Press; Typography. PR: £5–650. CC: MC; V. Cata: 4 a year. VAT No: GB 490 6827 17. [Updated]

The Inner Bookshop, ■ 111 Magdalen Road, Oxford, OX4 1RQ. Prop: R.E. Ashcroft & A.S. Cheke. Tel: (01865) 245301. Fax: (01865) 245521. Website: www.innerbookshop.com. E-mail: mail@innerbookshop.com. Est: 1982. Internet and postal. Shop open: **M:** 10:00–17:45; **T:** 10:00–17:45; **W:** 10:00–17:45; **Th:** 10:00–17:45; **F:** 10:00–17:45; **S:** 10:00–17:45. Large stock. Spec: Alchemy; Alternative Medicine; American Indians; Anthroposophy; Arthurian; Astrology; Cryptozoology; Earth Mysteries; Esoteric; Folklore; Fore-Edge Paintings; Freemasonry & Anti-Masonry; Ghosts; Health; Herbalism; Hermeticism; Judaica; Magic & Conjuring. PR: £1–1,000. CC: E; MC; V; SW; SO. Also, new books on specialities & tarot cards, New Age music, bargain books and a passive booksearch service. Mem: PBFA. [29/06/2003]

Jericho Books, ■ 48 Walton Street, Oxford, OX2 6AD. Prop: Frank Stringer. Tel: (01865) 511992. Fax: (0870) 1315166. Website: www.jerichobooks.com. E-mail: shop@jerichobooks.com. Est: 1997. Shop open: **M:** 10:30–18:00; **T:** 10:30–18:00; **W:** 10:30–18:00; **Th:** 10:30–18:00; **F:** 10:30–18:00; **S:** 10:30–18:00; **Su:** 11:00–17:30; Large stock. Spec: Academic/Scholarly; Antiquarian; Art; Cinema/Film; Classical Studies; Fiction - Fantasy, Horror; Fine & Rare; First Editions; History - General; Literature; Mind, Body & Spirit; Odd & Unusual; Philosophy; Politics; Religion - General; Theology. PR: £2–1,000. CC: MC; V. Also, a booksearch service. Cata: occasionally. Corresp: French. Italian. Mem: ABA; PBFA. VAT No: GB 717 9092 13. [09/05/2003]

Leabeck Books, Meadowbrook Farm, Sheepwash Lane, Steventon, Oxford, OX13 6SD. Prop: Tony Sloggett. Tel: (01235) 820914. E-mail: tony.sloggett@britishlibrary.net. Est: 1993. Private premises. Internet and postal. Appointment necessary. Small stock. Spec: Antiques; Art; Children's - General; First Editions; History - General; Literature. PR: £5–200. Corresp: French, German. Also at: Antiques on High, 85 High Street, Oxford, OX1 1BG. [Updated]

Magna Gallery, ■ 85 High Street, Oxford, OX1 4BG. Prop: Martin Blant. Tel: (01285) 750753. Fax: (01285) 750753. Website: www.magna-gallery.com. E-mail: info@magna-gallery.com. Est: 1969. Shop open: **M:** 10:00–17:00; **T:** 10:00–17:00; **W:** 10:00–17:00; **Th:** 10:00–17:00; **F:** 10:00–17:00; **S:** 10:00–17:00; **Su:** 11:00–17:00. Small stock. PR: £5–1,000. CC: AE; MC; V. Corresp: French. [10/07/2003]

Chris Morris, 67 Home Close, Wolvercote, Oxford, OX2 8PT. Tel: (01865) 557806. E-mail: chrisandbarbara@yahoo.com. Est: 1992. Private premises. Internet and postal. Small general stock. Spec: Cinema/Film; Motoring; Music - General; Sport - Motor Racing; Television; also Booksearch. PR: £1–75. [Updated]

St Philip's Books, ■ 82 St. Aldates, Oxford, OX1 1RA. Prop: Christopher James Zealley. Tel: (01865) 202182. Fax: (01865) 202184. Website: www.stphilipsbooks.co.uk. E-mail: sales@ stphilipsbooks.co.uk. Est: 1995. Internet and postal. Shop open: **M:** 10:00–17:00; **T:** 10:00–17:00; **W:** 10:00–17:00; **Th:** 10:00–17:00; **F:** 10:00–17:00; **S:** 10:00–17:00; Large stock. Spec: Academic/ Scholarly; Antiquarian; Art - History; Author - Inklings, The; Author - Lewis, C.S.; Author - Newman, Cardinal; Bibles; Ecclesiastical History & Architecture; History - General; History - British; History - European; Literature; Religion - General; Religion - Christian; Religion - Roman Catholic; Theology. PR: £1–2,000. CC: MC; V; SO, SW. Religious books bought nationwide. Cata: 4 a year. Mem: PBFA. VAT No: GB 717 925 021. [Updated]

Tooley, Adams & Co., PO Box 174, Wallingford D.O., Oxford, OX10 0YT. Prop: Stephen Luck. Tel: (01491) 838298. Fax: (01491) 834616. Website: www.tooleys.co.uk. E-mail: steve@tooleys.co.uk. Est: 1982. Private premises. Postal business only. Spec: Atlases. PR: £10–10,000. CC: AE; D; MC; V. Mem: ABA; I.A.M.A. [Updated]

Waterfield's, ■ 52 High Street, Oxford, OX1 4AS. Prop: Robin Waterfield Ltd. Tel: (01865) 721809. Est: 1973. Shop open: **M:** 09:45–17:45; **T:** 09:45–17:45; **W:** 09:45–17:44; **Th:** 08:45–17:45; **F:** 09:45–17:45; **S:** 09:45–17:45. Large stock. Spec: Academic/Scholarly; Antiquarian; Arts, The; First Editions; History - General; Humanities; Literary Criticism; Literature; Philosophy. PR: £1–5,000. CC: E; MC; V. Catalogues also on 17th and 18thC books. Cata: 4 a year on Eng Lit, history, philosophy. Corresp: French. Mem: ABA; PBFA. VAT No: GB 195 8007 39. [Updated]

STONESFIELD

Austin Sherlaw-Johnson, Woodland View, Churchfields, Stonesfield, OX29 8PP. Tel: (01993) 898223. E-mail: austin.sherlaw-johnson@virgin.net. Est: 2001. Private premises. Appointment necessary. Open: **M:** 09:00–17:00; **T:** 09:00–17:00; **W:** 09:00–17:00; **Th:** 09:00–17:00; **F:** 09:00–17:00. Medium stock. Spec: Music - General; Music - Composers; Music - Opera; Musical Instruments. PR: £1–500. Cata: 4 – occasionally. Also at: Malvern Bookshop, Malvern, Worcestershire (q.v.) and Antiques on High, 85 High Street, Oxford. [Updated]

WALLINGFORD

Toby English, ■ 10 St. Mary's Street, Wallingford, OX10 0EL. Tel: (01491) 836389. Fax: (01491) 836389. Website: www.tobyenglish.com. E-mail: toby@tobyenglish.com. Est: 1981. Shop open: **M:** 09:30–16:45; **T:** 09:30–16:45; **W:** 09:30–17:00; **Th:** 09:30–16:45; **F:** 09:30–16:45; **S:** 09:30–17:00. Large stock. Spec: Academic/Scholarly; Architecture; Art; Author - Inklings, The; First Editions; Private Press; Topography - Local; Typography, also Booksearch. PR: £1–500. CC: AE; JCB; MC; V; SW. Cata: 2 – Art and Architecture, Renaissance Studies. Mem: PBFA. [10/07/2003]

WANTAGE

Parrott Books, ■ Regent Mall, Town Centre, Wantage, OX12 8BU. Tel: (01367) 820251. Fax: (01367) 820210. E-mail: parrottbooks@aol.com. Est: 1997. Shop open: **M:** 08:30–17:30; **T:** 08:30–17:30; **W:** 08:30–17:30; **Th:** 08:30–17:30; **F:** 08:30–17:30; **S:** 08:30–17:00.Very large stock. PR: £2–50. [Updated]

WARBOROUGH

Nineteenth Century Books, St. Mary's Cottage, 61 Thame Road, Warborough, Wallingford, OX10 7EA. Prop: Dr. Ann M. Ridler. Tel: (01865) 858379. Fax: (01865) 858575. Website: www.ukbookworld .com/members/papageno. E-mail: annridlersoutter@warboro.fsnet.co.uk. Est: 1984. Private premises. Internet and postal. Small stock. Spec: Biography; Books about Books; History - General; Literature; Natural History; Philology; Poetry; Topography - General; also Booksearch. PR: £5–500. CC: MC; V. Cata: 2 a year on 19th century. Corresp: French, Spanish. Mem: PBFA. [Updated]

WITNEY

Church Green Books, ■ 46 Market Square, Witney, OX28 6AL. Prop: Roger & Margaret Barnes. Tel: (01993) 700822. Website: www.churchgreen.co.uk. E-mail: books@churchgreen.co.uk. Est: 1992. Shop open: **M:** 10:00–16:00; **T:** 10:00–16:00; **W:** 10:00–16:00; **Th:** 10:00–16:00; **F:** 10:00–16:00; Medium stock. Spec: Bell-Ringing (Campanology); Music - Folk & Irish Folk; Rural Life; Topography - Local; also Booksearch. PR: £1–300. CC: MC; V. Valuations of Bell-ringing books. Cata: 2 a year. Also, church bells & bell-ringing. Mem: PBFA. [Updated]

RUTLAND

The Rutland Bookshop, ■ 13 High Street West, Uppingham, LE15 9QB. Prop: Mr & Mrs Edward Baines. Tel: (01572) 823450. Est: 1979. Shop open: **T:** 11:00–17:00; **W:** 11:00–17:00; **Th:** 11:00–17:00; **F:** 11:00–17:00; **S:** 11:00–17:00. Medium stock. Spec: Education & School; Farming & Livestock; Farriers; Fiction - General; Gardening; Literary Criticism; Natural History; Odd & Unusual; Ornithology; Poetry; Public Schools; Rural Life; Sport - General; Topography - Local. PR: £1–500. Attends: Burghley Horse Trials, Rutland Water Bird Fair and Rutland & Leicester Agricultural Show. Corresp: French, German. Mem: PBFA. [Updated]

SHROPSHIRE

BISHOP'S CASTLE

Autolycus, ■ 10 Market Square, Bishop's Castle, SY95DN. David & Jay Wilkinson. Tel: (01588) 630078. Fax: (01588) 630078. Website: www.booksonline.uk.com. E-mail: Autolycusbc@aol.com. Est: 1996. Internet and postal. Shop open: **M:** 11:00–16:30; **T:** 11:00–16:30; **W:** 11:00–16:30; **Th:** 11:00–16:30; **F:** 11:00–16:30; **S:** 10:30–17:00. Medium stock. Spec: Children's - Early Titles; Children's - General; Children's - Illustrated; First Editions; Literature; Travel - General, also Booksearch. CC: MC; V; Paypal, Maestro. Cata: infrequently. Corresp: French, German. VAT No: GB 771 9717 90. [Updated]

Yarborough House Bookshop, ■ Yarborough House, The Square, Bishop's Castle, SY9 5BN. Prop: Carol Wright. Tel: (01588) 638318. Est: 1980. Shop open: **T:** 10:00–17:30; **Th:** 10:00–17:30; **F:** 10:00–17:30; **S:** 09:00–17:30. Medium stock. PR: £1–20. Also, secondhand classic records. [28/04/2003]

BRIDGNORTH

The Bookpassage, ■ 57a High Street, Bridgnorth, WV16 4DX. Prop: David Lamont. Tel: (01746) 768767. E-mail: bookman@btconnect.com. Est: 1990. Shop open: **M:** 09:00–17:15; **T:** 09:00–17:15; **W:** 08:00–17:15; **Th:** 09:00–17:15; **F:** 09:00–17:15; **S:** 09:00–17:15. Large general stock. PR: £1–500. Open occasionally on Sundays. [Updated]

Bookstack & D.J. Creece (Bookb, The Bindery Book Store, 3 Castle Terrace, Bridgnorth, WV16 4AH. Prop: Elizabeth Anderton (Books), Dermott Creece (Binder). Tel: (01746) 768008. Fax: (01756) 768008. E-mail: djcbookbinder@onetel.com. Est: 1975. Storeroom. Appointment necessary. Open: **M:** 09:00–17:00; **T:** 09:00–17:00; **W:** 09:00–17:00; **Th:** 13:00–17:00; **F:** 09:00–15:00; **S:** 10:00–12:00; Very small stock. Spec: Pre-Raphaelite. PR: £1–200. [Updated]

LUDLOW

Judith Adams, ■ The Art Bookshop, 3 Quality Square, off Castle Sq., Ludlow, SY8 1AR. Tel: (01584) 872758. Shop open: **F:** 10:00–17:00; **S:** 10:00–17:00. Medium stock. Spec: Architecture; Art; Art - History; Art - Reference; Artists; Decorative Art; Fine Art; Gardening; Textiles. PR: £3–300. CC: MC; V. Mem: PBFA. [25/09/2004]

Ampersand Books, Ludford Mill, Ludlow, SY8 1PR. Prop: Michael Dawson. Tel: (01584) 877813. Fax: (01584) 877519. Website: www.ampersandbooks.co.uk. E-mail: popups@ampersandbooks.co.uk. Est: 1982. Private premises. Appointment necessary. Small stock. Spec: Children's - General; Judaica; Pop-Up, 3D, Cut Out & Movable. PR: £5–1,000. Also, repairing of pop-ups & moveables. Cata: 1 a year on website. [Updated]

M. & M. Baldwin, ■ 24 High Street, Cleobury Mortimer, Kidderminster, Ludlow, DY14 8BY. (*). Tel: (01299) 270110. Fax: (01299) 270110. E-mail: mb@mbaldwin.free-online.co.uk. Est: 1978. Shop open: **W:** 14:00–18:00; **S:** 10:14–13:18; Closed for lunch: 13:00–14:00. Medium stock. Spec: Author - Rolt, L.T.C.; Aviation; Canals/Inland Waterways; Crafts; Cryptography; Espionage; Maritime/Nautical; Military; Military History; Motoring; Railways; Sport - Canoeing/Kayaks; Sport - Yachting; Transport; Vintage Cars; War - World War II. PR: £1–500. CC: AE; MC; V. Also, publisher of books. Corresp: French. Mem: F.S.B. VAT No: GB 547 6638 05. [Updated]

Lyndon Barnes - Books, 3 Mortimer Drive, Ludlow, SY8 4JW. Prop: Lyndon Barnes. Tel: (01568) 780641. Fax: (01568) 780641. Website: www.abebooks.com. E-mail: lyndonbarnes@clara.co.uk. Est: 1988. Private premises. Postal business only. Contactable. Open: **M:** 09:00–17:00; **T:** 09:00–17:00; **W:** 09:00–17:00; **Th:** 09:00–17:00; **F:** 09:00–17:00; **S:** 09:00–17:00; **Su:** 09:00–17:00. Very small stock. Spec: Music - Classical; Music - Country & Western; Music - Jazz; Music - Popular; Music - Rock. PR: £2–100. CC: PayPal. All stock on abebooks. Cata: 4 a year on general non fiction, 1 on music. [Updated]

Innes Books, 22 Julian Road, Ludlow, SY8 1HA. Prop: Pat Innes. Tel: (01584) 878146. Website: www.innesbooks.co.uk. E-mail: patricia@innesbooks.fsnet.co.uk. Est: 1997. Private premises. Internet and postal. Appointment necessary. Open: **M:** 09:00–10:00; **T:** 09:00–10:00; **W:** 09:00–10:00; **Th:** 09:00–10:00; **F:** 09:00–10:00; **S:** 10:00–06:00; **Su:** 10:00–05:00. Small general stock. Spec: Academic/Scholarly; Children's - General; Fiction - General; Illustrated; Literature; Modern First Editions. PR: £3–600. CC: PayPal. VAT No: GB 812 5174 53. [Updated]

Offa's Dyke Books, Old School House, Downton-on-the Rock, Ludlow, SY8 2HX. Prop: S.R. Bainbridge. Tel: (01584) 856212. Fax: (01584) 856757. E-mail: books@offas-dyke.fsnet.co.uk. Est: 1974. Private premises. Appointment necessary. Spec: Antiquarian; Architecture; Art; Bindings; Fine & Rare; Literature. CC: MC; V; Paypal. Cata: 2 a year. VAT No: GB 393 9270 15. [Updated]

Olynthiacs, 19 Castle View Terrace, Ludlow, SY8 2NG. Prop: Neil MacGregor. Tel: (01584) 872671. Website: www.ukbookworld.com/members/olynthiacs. E-mail: juvenal@martial.fsnet.co.uk. Est: 1735. Storeroom. Postal business only. Contactable. Open: **M:** 09:00–18:00; **T:** 09:00–18:00; **W:** 09:00–18:00; **Th:** 09:00–18:00; **F:** 09:00–18:00; **S:** 09:00–18:00; Closed for lunch: 13:00–14:00. Medium stock. Spec: Author - Wodehouse, P.G.; Biography; Classical Studies; Ecclesiastical History & Architecture; Fiction - General; History - General; Linguistics; Philology; Theology. PR: £5–500. [Updated]

MUCH WENLOCK

P.J. Mead, 6 Blakeway Hollow, Much Wenlock, TF13 6AR. Tel: (01952) 727591. Fax: (01952) 727591. E-mail: meadbooks@yahoo.com. Est: 1976. Private premises. Postal business only. Spec: Antiquarian; Bibliography; Bindings; Books about Books; Juvenile; Miniature Books; Sport - General. PR: £10–1,000. Mem: PBFA. VAT No: GB 349 3412 50. [29/06/2003]

Wenlock Books, ■ 12 High Street, Much Wenlock, TF13 6AA. Prop: Anna Dreda. Tel: (01952) 727877. Fax: (01952) 727877. Website: www.wenlockbooks.co.uk. E-mail: info@wenlockbooks.co.uk. Est: 1985. Shop open: **M:** 10:00–17:00; **T:** 10:00–17:00; **W:** 10:00–17:00; **Th:** 10:00–17:00; **F:** 10:00–17:00; **S:** 10:00–17:00. Medium stock. PR: £10–25. CC: MC; V. Mem: BA. VAT No: GB 823 8745 08. [Updated]

ORLETON

P Rulton Books, 3 Hallets Well, Orleton, SY8 4HH. Prop: Peter Rulton. Tel: (01568) 780860. E-mail: pjrulton@hotmail.com. Est: 1994. Private premises. Internet and postal. Telephone first. Open: Small stock. Spec: Fiction - General; Fiction - Crime, Detective, Spy, Thrillers; Fiction - Science Fiction; Illustrated; Literature; Modern First Editions. PR: £5–10,000. CC: JCB; V. [19/03/2003]

OSWESTRY

Arcadia, 6 Upper Brook Street, Oswestry, SY10 2TB. Prop: Joyce & Rod Whitehead. Tel: (01691) 655622. E-mail: Est: 1997. Spec: Antiquarian; Arts, The; History of Ideas; Illustrated; Literary Criticism; Literature; Needlework; Philosophy; Poetry; Topography - General. PR: £1–25. [26/08/2003]

Bookworld, ■ 32 Beatrice Street, Oswestry, SY11 1QG. Prop: John Cranwell. Tel: (01691) 657112. Fax: (01691) 657112. Website: www.tgal.co.uk/bookworld. E-mail: jc.bookworld@arrowweb.co.uk. Est: 1993. Shop open: **M:** 09:00–17:00; **T:** 09:00–17:00; **W:** 09:00–17:00; **Th:** 08:00–17:00; **F:** 09:00–17:00; **S:** 09:00–17:00. Medium stock. Spec: Alpinism/Mountaineering; Antiques; Autobiography; Children's - General; Cookery/Gastronomy; Crafts; Dictionaries; Gardening; Guide Books; Humour; Maritime/Nautical; Sport - Hockey; Travel - General; also Booksearch. PR: £1–1,000. CC: E; JCB; MC; V. Cata: See our website. [Updated]

SHREWSBURY

Candle Lane Books, ■ 28 & 29, Princess Street, Shrewsbury, SY1 1LW. Prop: John & Margaret Thornhill. Tel: (01743) 365301. Est: 1974. Shop open: **M:** 09:30–17:00; **T:** 09:00–17:00; **W:** 09:00–17:00; **Th:** 09:00–17:00; **F:** 09:00–17:00; **S:** 09:00–17:00. Very large stock. Spec: Booksearch. PR: £1–3,000. CC: MC; V. Updated]

Gemini–Books, 66 Oakfield Road, Copthorne, Shrewsbury, SY3 8AE. Prop: Geoff and Rosalie Davies. Tel: (01743) 343750. E-mail: enquiries@gemini-books.co.uk. Est: 2000. Storeroom. Appointment necessary. M: 10:00–16:00; **T:** 10:00–16:00; **W:** 10:00–16:00; **Th:** 10:00–16:00; **F:** 10:00–16:00; **S:** 10:00–16:00; **Su:** 10:00–16:00. Medium stock. Spec: Children's - General; Fiction - General. PR: £4–300. CC: AE; JCB; MC; V. Exhibits at Kinver Book Fair in Staffordshire (3rd Sunday every month). [Updated]

Oriental and African Books, 33 Whitehall Street, Shrewsbury, SY2 5AD. Prop: Paul D. Wilson. Tel: (01743) 352575. Fax: (01743) 363432. Website: www.africana.co.uk. E-mail: paul@africana.co.uk. Est: 1982. Office &/or bookroom. Internet and postal. Telephone first. Large stock. Spec: Academic/Scholarly; Africana; Black Studies; Countries - Africa; Countries - Middle East, The; Travel - Africa; Travel - Middle East. PR: £25–2,000. CC: E; JCB; MC; V. Cata: 3 a year. Corresp: French, Arabic. VAT No: GB 434 0550 82. [Updated]

Roundwood Books, ■ 24 Claremont Hill, Shrewsbury, SY1 1RD. Prop: Andrew Cork. Tel: (01743) 244833. E-mail: roundwoodbooks@btinternet.com. Est: 1995. Shop open: **T:** 10:00–17:00; **W:** 10:00–17:00; **Th:** 10:00–17:00; **F:** 10:00–17:00; **S:** 10:00–17:00. Medium stock. Spec: PR: £1–50. CC: MC; V. Mem: DTMFC. [19/08/2003]

TELFORD

Andrew Cox, 16, Garbett Road Aquaduct, Telford, TF4 3RX. Prop: Andrew Cox. Tel: (01952) 590630. E-mail: andyaituk@aol.com. Est: 2000. Private premises. Postal business only. Telephone first. Small stock. Spec: Antiquarian; Author - Verne, Jules; Author - Wells, H.G.; Children's - Illustrated; Fiction - Historical; Fiction - Science Fiction. PR: £1–10. Updated]

Fin Rare Books, 27 Deepfield Road, Dawley, Telford, TF4 3EH. Prop: Stephen H. Dawes (Sam). Tel: (01952) 591711. E-mail: finrb@blueyonder.co.uk. Est: 1984. Private premises. Appointment necessary. Medium stock. PR: £15–200. CC: PayPal. [06/06/2003]

WEM

Black Five Books, ■ 54 High Street, Wem, SY4 5DW. Prop: Ken Simpson. Tel: 0845 166 4084. Website: www.black5books.co.uk. E-mail: black5books@wemshropshire.freeserve.co.uk. Est: 1984. Shop; Telephone first. Very large stock. Spec: Aviation; Biography; Children's - General; Education & School; Fiction - General; Fiction - Historical; History - General; History - Ancient; History - British; History - Local; Horticulture; Humour; Literature; Military History; Railways. PR: £1–200. CC: MC; V; Maestro. Mem: BA. VAT No: GB 701 2786 58. [Updated]

Booksets.com Ltd, Unit 5 & 6, Wem Business Park, New Street, Wem, SY4 5JX. Tel: (01948) 710345. Fax: 0870 0521838. Website: www.booksets.com. E-mail: sales@booksets.com. Est: 1974. Warehouse; Internet. Contactable. Very large general stock. Spec: Academic/Scholarly; Computing; Periodicals & Magazines; Reference; Special collections; University Texts. PR: £5–5,000. CC: AE; MC; V; Maestro. VAT No: GB 696131125. [Updated]

Kabristan Archives, 19 Foxleigh Grove, Wem, SY4 5BS. Prop: Eileen Hewson FRGS. Tel: (01939) 234061. E-mail: kabristan@talk21.com. Est: 2004. Private premises. Internet and postal. Very small stock. Spec: Countries - India; Countries - Ireland; Geography; Publishing. PR: £5–100. [Updated]

WHITCHURCH

Barn Books, ■ Pear Tree Farm, Norbury, Whitchurch, SY13 4HZ. Prop: Mary Perry. Tel: (01948) 663742. Fax: (01948) 663742. Website: www.barnbooks.co.uk. E-mail: barnbooks@barnbooks.co.uk. Est: 1985. Shop open: **F:** 10:00–17:30; **S:** 10:00–17:30; **Su:** 10:00–17:30. Spec: Agriculture; Farming & Livestock; Gardening; History - Local; Horticulture; Rural Life; Topography - Local. PR: £1–500. Also, open on Bank Holidays. [Updated]

SOMERSET

BATH

Bath Book Exchange, ■ 35 Broad Street, Bath, BA1 5LP. Mr. L.M. Turner. Tel: (01225) 466214. E-mail:
Est: 1959. Shop open: **M:** 09:30–17:00; **T:** 09:30–17:00; **W:** 09:30–17:00; **Th:** 09:30–17:00; **F:** 09:30–
17:00; **S:** 09:30–17:00; Closed for lunch: 12:00–13:00. Medium stock. Spec: Booksearch. PR: £1–10.
[26/08/2003]

Bath Old Books, ■ 9c Margarets Buildings, Bath, BA1 2LP. Tel: (01225) 422244. E-mail: batholdbooks
@yahoo.co.uk. Est: 1990. Shop open: **M:** 10:00–17:00; **T:** 10:00–17:00; **W:** 10:00–17:00; **Th:** 10:00–
17:00; **F:** 10:00–17:00; **S:** 10:00–17:00; **Su:** 00:00–17:00. Large stock. Spec: Antiquarian; Art;
Children's - Illustrated; Literature; Topography - Local; also Booksearch. CC: JCB; MC; V. Also,
valuations. Corresp: French. Mem: PBFA. [Updated]

George Bayntun, ■ Manvers Street, Bath, BA1 1JW. Prop: E.W.G. Bayntun–Coward. Tel: (01225)
466000. Fax: (01225) 482122. Website: www.georgebayntun.com. E-mail: ebc@georgebayntun.com.
Est: 1894. Shop open: **M:** 09:00–17:29; **T:** 09:00–17:30; **W:** 09:00–17:30; **Th:** 09:00–17:30; **F:** 09:00–
17:30; **S:** 09:30–13:00; Closed for lunch: 13:00–14:00. Small stock. Spec: Bindings; Children's -
General; Children's - Illustrated; Fine & Rare; First Editions; Illustrated; Literature; Poetry. PR: £10–
5,000. CC: MC; V; SW, SO. Also, bindery incorporating the famous binding firm of Robert Riviere &
Son, est. 1829. Corresp: French. Mem: ABA; PBFA. VAT No: GB 137 5073 71. [14/07/2004]

Camden Books, ■ 146 Walcot Street, Bath, BA1 5BL. Prop: Victor & Elizabeth Suchar. Tel: (01225)
461606. Fax: (01225) 461606. Website: www.camdenbooks.com. E-mail: suchcam@msn.com. Est:
1984. Internet and postal. Shop open: **M:** 11:00–16:00; **T:** 11:00–16:00; **W:** 11:00–16:00; **Th:** 11:00–
16:00; **F:** 11:00–16:00; **S:** 11:00–16:00. Large general stock. Spec: Academic/Scholarly; Architecture;
Art - History; Biography; Civil Engineering; Classical Studies; Company History; Diaries;
Economics; History - Byzantine; History - Middle Ages; History of Civilisation; Letters;
Literature; Mathematics; Philosophy. PR: £10–2,000. CC: JCB; MC. Mem: PBFA. [17/06/2003]

Janet Clarke, 3 Woodside Cottages, Freshford, Bath, BA2 7WJ. Tel: (01225) 723186. Fax: (01225)
722063. E-mail: janetclarke@ukgateway.net. Est: 1973. Private premises. Postal business only. Small
stock. Spec: Cookery/Gastronomy; Food & Drink; Wine. PR: £5–3,000. Cata: 1 a year. [29/06/2003]

Peter Goodden Books Ltd, 7 Clarendon Villas, Widcombe Hill, Bath, BA2 6AG. Tel: (01225) 310986. E-
mail: peter.goodden@ukonline.co.uk. Est: 1976. Internet and postal. Small stock. Spec: Music -
General; Musical Instruments. PR: £5–1,500. CC: JCB; MC; V. Corresp: Simple French. Mem:
PBFA. VAT No: GB 195 9854 90. [Updated]

George Gregory, Manvers Street, Bath, BA1 1JW. Prop: Charlotte Bayntun-Coward. Tel: (01225)
466000. Fax: (01225) 482122. E-mail: isabelle@georgebayntun.com. Est: 1846. Shop &/or gallery.
Open: **M:** 09:00–17:30; **T:** 09:00–17:30; **W:** 09:00–17:30; **Th:** 09:00–17:30; **F:** 09:00–17:30; **S:** 08:30–
13:00; Closed for lunch: 13:00–14:00. Large general stock. Spec: Literature. PR: £1–200. CC: MC; V.
Engraved portraits and views. [Updated]

Patterson Liddle, ■ 10 Margaret's Buildings, Brock Street, Bath, BA1 2LP. John Patterson & Steve
Liddle. Tel: (01225) 426722. Fax: (01225) 426722. Website: www.pattersonliddle.com. E-mail:
mail@pattersonliddle.com. Est: 1982. Shop open: **M:** 10:00–17:30; **T:** 10:00–17:30; **W:** 10:00–17:30;
Th: 10:00–17:30; **F:** 10:00–17:30; **S:** 10:00–17:30. Medium stock. Spec: Architecture; Art; Aviation;
Bindings; Canals/Inland Waterways; History - Local; Illustrated; Railways; Topography - General;
Travel - General. PR: £1–5,000. CC: MC; V. Cata: occasionally on aviation, canals & British railways.
Mem: ABA; PBFA; ILAB. VAT No: GB 358 0633 48. [Updated]

Robert & Susan Pyke, 2 Beaufort Villas, Claremont Road, Bath, BA1 6LY. Robert & Susan Pyke. Tel: (01225) 311710. Fax: (01225) 311710. Website: www.abebooks.com/home/pykemaritime. E-mail: robert.pyke@virgin.net. Est: 1974. Private premises. Appointment necessary. Medium stock. Spec: Maritime/Nautical; Sport - Yachting. PR: £7–2,000. CC: MC; V; SW. Cata: 2 a year. Mem: PBFA. VAT No: GB 328 20 8270. [Updated]

Hugh Ashley Rayner, 4 Malvern Buildings, Fairfield Park, Bath, BA1 6JX. Prop: Hugh A. Rayner. Tel: (01225) 463552. Fax: (01225) 463552. Website: www.indiabooks.co.uk. E-mail: hughrayner@ indiabooks.co.uk. Private premises. Internet and postal. Appointment necessary. Open: **M:** 10:00–19:00; **T:** 10:00–19:00; **W:** 10:00–19:00; **Th:** 10:00–19:00; **F:** 10:00–19:00; **S:** 10:00–19:00; **Su:** 12:00–18:00. Small stock. Spec: Countries - Asia; Countries - Burma; Countries - Central Asia; Countries - Himalayas, The; Countries - India; Countries - Sri Lanka; Photography; Travel - Asia. PR: £35–500. CC: AE; D; JCB; MC; V. Valuations, Library Cataloguing. Cata: 1 a year on India & The Orient. Corresp: German. Mem: PBFA. [Updated]

Solitaire Books, Holly Lawn, Prospect Place, Beechen Cliff, Bath, BA2 4QP. Prop: Martyn Thomas. Tel: (01225) 469441. E-mail: solitaire@hollylawn.org. Est: 1994. Private premises. Postal business only. Very small stock. Spec: Books about Books; Printing; Private Press; Typography. PR: £30–300. CC: PayPal. Cata: occasionally on Printing and private press. Corresp: Dutch, French, Spanish. [Updated]

The Traveller's Bookshelf, Canal House, Murhill, Limpley Stoke, Bath, BA2 7FQ. Prop: Jenny Steadman. Tel: (01225) 722589. E-mail: jenny@travellersbookshelf.co.uk. Est: 1991. Private premises. Internet and postal. Spec: Countries - Afghanistan; Countries - Albania; Countries - Arabia; Countries - Armenia; Countries - Asia Minor; Countries - Balkans, The; Countries - Central Asia; Countries - China; Countries - Ethiopia; Countries - Far East, The; Countries - Greece. PR: £20–5,000. CC: MC; V; Switch. Cata: 4 – Mem: ABA; PBFA; ILAB. VAT No: GB 779 2193 85. [Updated]

CASTLE CARY

Bailey Hill Bookshop, Fore Street, Castle Cary, BA7 7BG. Prop: Peter Booth. Tel: (01963) 350917. Fax: (01963) 351230. Website: www.baileyhillbookshop.co.uk. E-mail: books@baileyhillbookshop.co.uk. Est: 1978. Open: **M:** 09:30–18:00; **T:** 09:30–18:00; **W:** 09:30–18:00; **Th:** 09:30–18:00; **F:** 09:30–18:00; **S:** 09:30–17:00. Small general stock. PR: £1–100. CC: AE; JCB; MC; Also, new books and greetings cards. Mem: PBFA. VAT No: GB 501 6633 79. [25/06/2003]

CHARD

P.J. Baron - Scientific Book S, Lakewood, Chard, TA20 4AJ. Prop: Dr. P. Baron. Tel: (01460) 66319. Fax: (01460) 66319. Website: www.barons.clara.net. Est: 1975. Private premises. Internet and postal. Open: Small stock. Spec: Biology; Botany; Chemistry; Computing; Ecology; Engineering; Mathematics; Medicine; Natural History; Science - General; Zoology. PR: £5–150. CC: MC; V; SW. Cata: 6 – on science; computing/medicine; separate catalogue. Corresp: French. VAT No: GB 549 4779 82. [15/03/2003]

CLAPTON–IN–GORDANO

Avonworld Books, 1 Swancombe, Clapton–in–Gordano, BS20 7RR. Prop: Michael C. Ross. Tel: (01275) 842531. Fax: (01275) 849221. Website: www.avonworld-booksource.co.uk. E-mail: books@avonworld.demon.co.uk. Est: 1984. Office &/or bookroom. Internet and postal. Appointment necessary. Open: **M:** 09:00–18:00; **T:** 09:00–18:00; **W:** 09:00–18:00; **Th:** 09:00–18:00; **F:** 09:00–18:00; Closed for lunch: 13:00–14:00. Small stock. Spec: Art; Author - Buchan, John; Author - Coward, Noel; Author - Graves, Robert; Author - Kipling, Rudyard; Author - Sayers, Dorothy; Literature; Modern First Editions. PR: £1–500. CC: MC; V. Valuations for insurance or probate of private collections in our author specialities. Cata: Author or Category stock print-outs on request. Corresp: German (post only, not e-mail). Mem: PBFA. VAT No: GB 496 6867 66. [Updated]

CLEVEDON

Clevedon Books, Canbourne Cottage, 6 Seavale Road, Clevedon, BS21 7QB. Prop: George & Wendy Douthwaite. Tel: (01275) 872304. Fax: (01275) 342817. E-mail: clevedonbooks@globalnet.co.uk. Est: 1970. Private premises. Internet and postal. Appointment necessary. Shop at: Shop at 27 Copse road, Clevedon. Open: **Th:** 11:00–16:30; **F:** 11:00–16:30; **S:** 11:05–16:30; Closed for lunch: 13:00–14:15. Very large stock. Spec: Architecture; Art - History; Geology; History - Industrial; History of Ideas; Science - History of; Transport; Travel - General. PR: £10–3,000. CC: JCB; MC; V; Debit. Also, colouring & mounting service. Cata: 6 a year. Mem: PBFA. Also at: 27 Copse Road, Clevedon. (q.v.). [Updated]

K.W. Cowley, Bookdealer, Trinity Cottage, 153 Old Church Road, Clevedon, BS21 7TU. Tel: (01275) 872247. E-mail: kencowley@blueyonder.co.uk. Est: 1987. Private premises. Postal business only. Telephone first. Spec: Academic/Scholarly; Anthologies; Books about Books; Cinema/Film; Fiction - Crime, Detective, Spy, Thrillers; Fiction - Fantasy, Horror; Fiction - Science Fiction; Ghosts; Pulps; Supernatural; Vintage Paperbacks. PR: £1–100. Cata: 2 occasionally. [Updated]

CREWKERNE

Books Galore, ■ 1 The Old Warehouse, North Street, Crewkerne, TA18 7AJ. Prop: Bryan & Helen Hall. Tel: (01460) 74465. Fax: (01460) 74465. E-mail: hallbook@aol.com. Est: 1968. Shop open: **M:** 10:00–17:00; **T:** 10:00–17:00; **W:** 10:00–17:00; **Th:** 10:00–17:00; **F:** 10:00–17:00; **S:** 10:00–17:00; Closed for lunch: 12:00–13:00. Large stock. Spec: Art; Biography; Children's - General; Natural History; Rural Life; Sport - General; Topography - General. PR: £1–50. [17/08/2003]

Gresham Books, ■ 31 Market Street, Crewkerne, TA18 7JU. Prop: James Hine. Tel: (01460) 77726. Fax: (01460) 52479. Website: www.greshambooks.co.uk. E-mail: jameshine@gresham-books. demon.co.uk. Est: 1972. Shop open: **M:** 10:00–17:00; **T:** 10:00–17:00; **W:** 10:00–17:00; **Th:** 10:00–17:00; **F:** 10:00–17:00; **S:** 10:00–17:00. Medium stock. Spec: Antiquarian; Antiques; Architecture; Cookery/Gastronomy; Fashion & Costume; Food & Drink; Needlework; Sport - Golf; Wine. PR: £1–1,000. CC: AE; MC; V; Switch. Mem: ABA; PBFA. [Updated]

Anne Hine / Gresham Books, ■ 31 Market Street, Crewkerne, TA18 7JU. Tel: (01460) 77726. Fax: (01460) 52479. E-mail: annehine@gresham-books.demon.co.uk. Est: 1994. Shop open: **M:** 10:00–17:00; **T:** 10:00–17:00; **W:** 10:00–17:00; **Th:** 10:00–17:00; **F:** 10:00–17:00; **S:** 10:00–17:00. Very small stock. Spec: Publishers - Warnes. CC: AE; MC; V. [Updated]

DULVERTON

Rothwell & Dunworth Ltd, ■ 2 Bridge Street, Dulverton, TA22 9HJ. Tel: (01398) 323169. E-mail: rothwellm@aol.com. Est: 1975. Shop. Book fairs only. Open: **M:** 10:30–17:15; **T:** 10:30–17:15; **W:** 10:30–17:15; **Th:** 10:30–17:15; **F:** 10:30–17:15; **S:** 10:30–17:15; **Su:** 11:00–16:00; Large stock. Spec: Academic/Scholarly; Art; Literature; Sport - Angling/Fishing; Sport - Big Game Hunting; Sport - Hunting. PR: £1–5,000. CC: MC; V. Cata: 2 a year on Sporting Books Military History. Mem: ABA; PBFA. [Updated]

FROME

Upper–Room Books, ■ Above Antiques & Country Living, Vallis Way, Babcox, Frome, BA11 3BA. Prop: Victor Adams. Tel: (01373) 467125. Fax: (01373) 467125. Website: www.vabooks.com. E-mail: victoradams@vabooks.co.uk. Est: 1990. Internet and postal. Shop open: **M:** 09:30–17:30; **T:** 09:30–17:30; **W:** 09:30–17:30; **Th:** 09:30–17:30; **F:** 09:30–17:30; **S:** 09:30–17:30. Medium stock. Spec: Art; Artists; Author - Morris, William; Crafts; Furniture; Woodwork. PR: £5–1,000. CC: JCB; MC; V. Mem: PBFA. [Updated]

GLASTONBURY

Book Barn Ltd., 17-18 Market Place, Glastonbury, BA6 9HL. Prop: Derek Bolton. Tel: (01458) 835698. Website: www.bookbarn.co.uk. E-mail: bookbarn@netcomuk.co.uk. Spec: [26/08/2003]

ILMINSTER

David Clarke Books, P.O. Box 24, Ilminster, TA19 0YU. Prop: David Clarke. Tel: (01460) 242330. Fax: (01460) 241547. E-mail: dclarke@lineone.net. Est: 1999. Private premises. Internet and postal. Appointment necessary. Medium stock. Spec: Aeronautics; Farming & Livestock; Fiction - General; Gardening; History - British; Horticulture; Natural History; Railways; Rural Life; Topography - General; Topography - Local; Travel - Islamic World; Travel - Middle East; also Booksearch. PR: £4–300. Cata: occasionally. Corresp: French. [Updated]

Ile Valley Bookshop, ■ 10 Silver Street, Ilminster, TA19 0DJ. Prop: Chris Chapman. Tel: (01460) 57663. Fax: (01460) 57188. E-mail: ilevalley@aol.com. Est: 1985. Shop open: Very small general stock. [Updated]

LANGPORT

The Old Bookshop, ■ Bow Street, Langport, TA10 9PQ. Prop: Heather Ridgway. Tel: (01458) 252644. Est: 1984. Shop open: **W:** 09:00–17:00; **Th:** 09:00–17:00; **F:** 09:00–17:00; **S:** 09:00–17:00. Medium stock. Spec: Autobiography; Biography; Crafts; Literature; Natural History; Ornithology; Rural Life; Social History; Topography - Local; Travel - General, also Booksearch.PR: £1–100. [03/02/2003]

MERRIOTT

Richard Budd, The Coach House, Glebelands, Merriott, TA16 5RE. Prop: Richard Budd. Tel: (01460) 78297. E-mail: richardbudd@btconnect.com. Est: 1972. Private premises. Postal business only. Appointment necessary. Small stock. Spec: Author - Beckett, S.; First Editions; Limited Editions; Literary Criticism; Literature; Poetry. PR: £10–5,000. CC: E; MC; V. Also, attends 50 bookfairs a year. Cata: 6 every two months. Corresp: French. Mem: ABA; PBFA; ILAB. [Updated]

MIDSOMER NORTON

Tom Randall, Welton Hill Cottage, Welton Grove, Midsomer Norton, Radstock, BA3 2TS. (*). Tel: (01761) 418926. E-mail: Est: 1987. Spec: Ethnology; Folklore; Mythology; Topography - Local; Traction Engines; Transport; also Booksearch. PR: £2–500. [Updated]

MILVERTON

Cat Lit, Loundshay Manor Cottage, Preston Bowyer, Milverton, TA4 1QF. Tel: (01823) 401527. Fax: (01823) 401527. E-mail: amolibros@aol.com. Est: 2002. Private premises. Postal business only. Open in summer. Spec: Cats; Dogs; Sport - Field Sports. [Updated]

MINEHEAD

Rare Books & Berry, ■ High Street, Porlock, Minehead, TA24 8PT. Prop: Mike Berry and Christopher Ondaatje. Tel: (01643) 863255. Fax: (01643) 863092. Website: www.rarebooksandberry.co.uk. E-mail: search@rarebooksandberry.co.uk. Est: 1992. Shop open: **M:** 09:30–17:00; **T:** 09:30–17:00; **W:** 09:30–17:00; **Th:** 09:30–17:00; **F:** 09:30–17:00; **S:** 09:30–17:00; Closed for lunch: 13:00–14:00. Medium stock. Spec: Author - Edwards, Lionel; Sport - Angling/Fishing; Sport - Hunting; Topography - Local. PR: £1–1,000. CC: MC; V; S, SW. Cata: occasionally. VAT No: GB 801 1222 04. [Updated]

MOORLYNCH

Arnold Desmond, Polden, Moor Road, Moorlynch, TA7 9BU. Tel: (01458) 210911. Fax: (01458) 210911. Postal business only. Open: Small general stock. Spec: Academic/Scholarly; Author - Arnold, Matthew. PR: £4–100. [13/03/2003]

NORTH CHERITON

Paper Pleasures, Holt Farm, North Cheriton, BA8 0AQ. Lesley Tyson. Tel: (01963) 33718. Website: www.paperpleasures.com. E-mail: books@paperpleasures.com. Est: 1998. Private premises. Postal business only. Appointment necessary. Small stock. Spec: Art; Erotica; Ex-Libris; Glamour; Homosexuality & Lesbianism; Literature; Periodicals & Magazines; Photography; Sexology. PR: £5–2,000. CC: MC; V; SW. Cata: 3 a year on Erotica. Mem: PBFA. [Updated]

PEASEDOWN ST. JOHN

BookLovers, The Post Office, 12 Bath Road, Peasedown St. John, BA2 8DH. Prop: Heather Spence. Tel: 0870 1200 970. Fax: 0870 1200 980. Website: www.booklovers.co.uk. E-mail: dgs@booklovers.co.uk. Est: 1998. Shop &/or showroom; Internet and postal. Telephone first. Large stock. Spec: Biography; Gambling; History - General; Modern First Editions. PR: £1–100. CC: AE; D; E; JCB; MC; SW, DE. Cata: occasional. [Updated]

QUEEN CAMEL

Steven Ferdinando, The Old Vicarage, Queen Camel, Nr. Yeovil, BA22 7NG. Tel: (01935) 850210. E-mail: stevenferdinando@onetel.com. Est: 1977. Office &/or bookroom. Telephone first. Open: Medium stock. Spec: Agriculture; Author - Hardy, Thomas; Author - Powys Family, The; Illustrated; Irish Interest; Literature; Topography - Local; Travel - General. PR: £10–800. CC: MC; V. Mem: PBFA. Also at: Bath Old Books, Bath. (q.v.). [Updated]

SIMONSBATH

Spooner & Co., Mead Cottage, Honeymead, Simonsbath, TA24 7JX. Prop: Brian John Spooner. Tel: (01643) 831562. Fax: (01643) 831562. E-mail: spoonerb@supanet.com. Est: 1985. Private premises. Appointment necessary. Small stock. Spec: Antiquarian; Archaeology; Architecture; Bibliography; Ecclesiastical History & Architecture; Genealogy; Heraldry; History - Local; Theology; Topography - Local; also Booksearch. PR: £3–230. Also, bookbinding and repairs. [Updated]

SOMERTON

Simon's Books, ■ Broad Street, Somerton, Prop: Bryan Ives. Tel: (01458) 272313. Est: 1978. Shop open: **M:** 10:00–16:30; **T:** 10:00–16:30; **W:** 09:00–16:30; **Th:** 09:00–16:30; **F:** 10:00–16:30; **S:** 10:00–16:30. Large general stock. PR: £1–100. [Updated]

STOKE SUB HAMDON

R.G. Watkins, Book and Print Room, 9 North Street Farm Workshops, Stoke Sub Hamdon, TA14 6QR. Tel: (01935) 822891. Fax: (01935) 822891. Website: www.rgw.eurobell.co.uk/. E-mail: rgw@eurobell .co.uk. Est: 1985. Office &/or bookroom. Appointment necessary. Open: **F:** 10:00–05:00. Small stock. Spec: Arts, The; Author - Lawrence, T.E.; Collecting; History - General, also Booksearch. PR: £1–500. CC: AE; MC; V. Cata: 4 a year. Corresp: French. Mem: PBFA. [Updated]

TAUNTON

Badger Books, 11 Salisbury Street, Taunton, TA2 6NA. Prop: Janet & Nic Tall. Tel: (01823) 323180. Website: www.badgerbooks.co.uk. E-mail: janetnic@badgerbooks.co.uk. Est: 2002. Private premises. Internet and postal. Appointment necessary. Small stock. Spec: Author - Blyton, Enid; Author - Brent-Dyer, Elinor M.; Author - Forest, A; Children's - General. PR: £1–200. Corresp: German. [Updated]

Dene Barn Books & Prints, Brackenbury, Ash Priors, Taunton, TA4 3NF. Tel: (01823) 433103. Est: 1990. Private premises. Appointment necessary. Very small general stock. Spec: Botany; Natural History; Topography - Local. PR: £10–500. Picture Framing. [Updated]

The Eastern Traveller, 52 Mountway Road, Bishops Hull, Taunton, TA1 5LS. Prop: Geoffrey Mullett. Tel: (01823) 327012. E-mail: Est: 1979. Postal business only. Spec: History - General; Military; Military History; Travel - General; Travel - Africa; Travel - Asia; Travel - Middle East; Voyages & Discovery. PR: £5–50. [26/08/2003]

Russell Needham Books, 5 Silver St., Milverton, Taunton, TA4 1LA. (*). Tel: (01823) 400470. Fax: (0870) 0561167. Website: www.needhambooks.demon.co.uk. E-mail: russell@needhambooks.demon.co.uk. Private premises. Internet and postal. Very small stock. Spec: Academic/Scholarly; Alchemy; Author - Bennett, J.G.; Foreign Texts; Fourth Way; Literature; Modern First Editions; Mysticism; Occult; Religion - General; Spiritualism. PR: £5–300. [Updated]

Russell Books, 2 Mount Nebo, Taunton, TA1 4HG. Prop: D.R. & E.M. Kerr. Tel: (01823) 330887. E-mail: russellbooks@ukonline.co.uk. Est: 1997. Private premises. Internet and postal. Contactable. Spec: Art; Children's - General; Fiction - General; Fiction - Science Fiction; First Editions; History - General; Humour; Military; Poetry; Religion - General; Topography - General; War - General; also Booksearch. PR: £1–100. CC: JCB; MC. Corresp: French, Japanese, Latin. [16/09/2003]

WEDMORE

Max Gate Books, Max Gate, Theale, Wedmore, BS28 4SN. Prop: Mrs. J.M. Dupont. Tel: (01934) 712267. E-mail: Est: 1983. Postal business only. Spec: Cookery/Gastronomy; Crafts; Embroidery; Gardening; Needlework; Women. PR: £5–100. [26/08/2003]

WELLINGTON

Peter J. Ayre, Greenham Hall, Greenham, Wellington, TA21 0JJ. Tel: (01823) 672603. Fax: (01823) 672307. E-mail: peterjayre@aol.com. Est: 1980. Private premises. Internet and postal. Appointment necessary. Small stock. Spec: Academic/Scholarly; Countries - Africa; Countries - Kenya; Countries - Tanzania; Natural History; Sport - Big Game Hunting; Travel - Africa; also Booksearch. PR: £10–1,000. CC: JCB; MC; V. Cata: quarterly. Mem: PBFA. [Updated]

Mary Sharpe, 55 Twitchen, Holcombe Rogus, Wellington, TA21 0PS. Tel: (01823) 672304. Est: 1995. Private premises. Postal business only. Small general stock. Spec: Author - Austen, Jane; Author - Brontes, The; Author - Burney, Fanny; Author - Eliot, G.; Author - Gaskell, E.; Author - Hardy, Thomas; Children's - General; Illustrated; Literature; Topography - General. PR: £5–200. Exhibits at bookfairs. Cata: 2 a year. Mem: PBFA. [Updated]

WEST PENNARD

Eddie Baxter - Books, The Old Mill House, West Pennard, BA6 8ND. Prop: Josie Matthews. Tel: (01749) 890369. Fax: (01749) 890369. Est: 1956. Private premises. Postal business only. Very small stock. Spec: Dance; Music - General; Music - Jazz; also Booksearch. Cata: occasionally on specialities. [Updated]

WESTON–SUPER–MARE

Chris Crook, ■ P.O. Box 180, Weston–Super–Mare, BS22 9SS. Prop: Chris Crook. Tel: (01225) 422244. Fax: (01963) 33718.　Est: 1980. Shop at: Bath Old Books, Margarets Buildings, Brock Street, Bath. Open: **M:** 10:00–17:00; **T:** 10:00–17:00; **W:** 10:00–17:00; **Th:** 10:00–17:00; **F:** 10:00–17:00; **S:** 10:00–17:00. Small stock. Spec: Architecture; Art; Art - History; Art - Reference; Natural History. PR: £8–300. Mem: PBFA. [19/05/2003]

Manna Bookshop, ■ 30 Orchard Street, Weston–Super–Mare, BS23 1RQ. Prop: Peter Fairnington. Tel: (01934) 636228.　Est: 1981. Shop open: **M:** 10:00–17:00; **T:** 10:00–17:00; **W:** 10:00–17:00; **Th:** 10:00–17:00; **F:** 10:00–17:00; **S:** 10:00–17:00. Large general stock. PR: £1–100.　(Sometimes closed on Thursday). [Updated]

Sterling Books, ■ 43a Locking Road, Weston-Super-Mare, BS23 3DG. Prop: David Nisbet. Tel: (01934) 625056. Website: www.abe.com. E-mail: sterling.books@talk21.com. Est: 1966. Shop open: **T:** 10:00–17:30; **W:** 10:00–17:30; **Th:** 10:00–13:00; **F:** 10:00–17:30; **S:** 10:00–17:30. Very large general stock. Spec: Academic/Scholarly; Advertising; Aeronautics; Antiquarian; Art; Bindings; Crafts; History - General; Theology; Topography - General; Travel - General; also Booksearch. PR: £1–1,500. CC: AE; D; E; JCB; MC; V. Also, bookbinding & restoration, picture-framing service. Mem: ABA; ILAB; ABA. [Updated]

SOUTH YORKSHIRE

DONCASTER

Hedgerow Books, 10 Whitbeck Close, Wadworth, Doncaster, DN11 9DZ. Prop: Peter & Elizabeth Hedge. Tel: (01302) 856311. Fax: (01302) 856311. Website: www.hedgerowbooks.com. E-mail: info@hedgerowbooks.com. Est: 1988. Private premises. Internet and postal. Appointment necessary. Open: **M:** 09:00–21:00; **T:** 09:00–21:00; **W:** 09:00–21:00; **Th:** 09:00–21:00; **F:** 09:00–21:00; **S:** 09:00–12:30; Closed for lunch: 12:30–14:00. Small stock. Spec: Ecclesiastical History & Architecture; History - Industrial; Sport - Boxing; Sport - Football (Soccer). PR: £1–500. CC: MC; V; Switch. Cata: 4 a year on Boxing & Football Mem: PBFA. VAT No: GB 657 8581 80. [Updated]

Saxton Books Ltd, 18 Saxton Avenue, Doncaster, DN4 7AX. Tel: 01302 371071. Fax: 01302 371071. E-mail: john-webb@altair.co.uk. Est: 1997. Private premises. Internet and postal. Very small stock. Spec: Author - Austen, Jane; Author - Bates, H.E.; Author - Bramah, Ernest.; Author - Flint, William Russell; Author - Rand, Ayn; Author - Shute, Neville; Economics; Engraving; Fine Art; First Editions; Free Thought; Modern First Editions; Naval; Palaeont PR: £10–1,000. [Updated]

ECKINGTON

The Bibliophile, 42 Fern Close, Eckington, S21 4HE. Prop: Michael P. Russell. Tel: (01246) 434025. Fax: (01246) 434025. E-mail: mpr@supanet.com. Est: 1997. Spec: Freemasonry & Anti-Masonry; Medicine; Printing. PR: £1–50. [updated]

SHEFFIELD

Annie's Books, 7 Spout Copse, Sheffield, S6 6FB. Prop: Christine Wren. Tel: (0114) 234 0199. Fax: (0114) 232 0866. Website: www.abebooks.com/home/chriswren. E-mail: wrentrading@talk21.com. Est: 1999. Private premises. Postal business only. Appointment necessary. Open: **M:** 09:00–17:00; **T:** 09:00–17:00; **W:** 09:00–17:00; **Th:** 09:00–17:00; **F:** 09:00–17:00. Small stock. Spec: Animals and Birds; Cats; Children's - General; D.I.Y (Do It Yourself); Modern First Editions; also Booksearch. PR: £1–200. CC: AE; MC; V; SW. Cata: 2 a year. [Updated]

Baedekers & Murray Guides, 11 St. Quentin Drive, Sheffield, S17 4PN. Prop: Dr. R.H. Hickley. Tel: (0114) 236-6306. Website: roger_hickley@dial.Pipex.com. E-mail: roger_hickley@dial.pipex.com. Est: 1991. Private premises. Appointment necessary. Very small stock. Spec: Guide Books; Travel - General. PR: £10–500. Cata: 1 a year. Corresp: French, German, Swedish, Finnish. [Updated]

Chantrey Books, 24 Cobnar Road, Sheffield, S8 8QB. Prop: Clare Brightman. Tel: (0114) 274-8958. E-mail: chantrey.24@btinternet.com. Est: 1981. Spec: Botany; Cookery/Gastronomy; Food & Drink; Gardening; Herbalism; Illustrated; Plant Hunting; Rural Life. PR: £5–500. Mem: PBFA. [Updated]

Alan Hill Books, Unit 4, Meersbrook Works, Sheffield, S8 9FT. Prop: Alan Hill. Tel: (01142) 556242. E-mail: alanhillbooks@supanet.com. Est: 1980. Shop &/or showroom; Internet and postal. Telephone first. Open: **M:** 10:30–14:30; **T:** 10:30–14:30; **W:** 10:30–14:30; **Th:** 10:30–14:30; **F:** 10:30–14:30. Large stock. Spec: Academic/Scholarly; Genealogy; Topography - Local. PR: £5–500. CC: MC; V. VAT No: GB 533 9950 19. [Updated]

The Porter Bookshop, ■ 227 Sharrowvale Road, Sheffield, S11 8ZE. Prop: Margot Armitage. Tel: (0114) 266-7762. Est: 1988. Shop; Telephone first. Medium stock. Spec: Academic/Scholarly; Crime (True); Humanities; Literature. [27/05/2003]

Margaret Riccetti, 303 Uperthorpe, Sheffield, S6 3NG. Prop: Margaret Riccetti. Tel: (0114) 266-6305. Website: www.riccetti.freeserve.co.uk. Est: 1997. Private premises. Internet. Appointment necessary. Small stock. Spec: Antiquarian; Art; Art - History; Atlases; Collecting. PR: £5–500. CC: Paypal. maggie@riccetti.freeserve.co.uk. Corresp: Italian, French. Mem: Also at: Court House Antiques, 2-6 Town End Road, Ecclesfield. [07/06/2003]

Tilleys Vintage Magazine Shop, ■ 281 Shoreham Street, Sheffield, S1 4SS. Prop: Antonius & Albertus Tilley. Tel: (0114) 275-2442. Website: www.tilleysmagazines.com. E-mail: tilleys281@aol.com. Est: 1978. Shop open: **T:** 10:00–16:30; **W:** 10:00–16:30; **Th:** 10:00–16:30; **F:** 10:00–16:30; **S:** 10:00–16:30; Very large stock. Spec: Comic Books & Annuals; Comics; Periodicals & Magazines; Spiritualism. PR: £1–200. CC: AE; MC; V. Also at: 21 Derby Road, Chesterfield (q.v.). [updated]

YSF Books, ■ 365 Sharrowvale Road, Hunters Bar, Sheffield, S11 8ZG. Prop: J. & R. Eldridge. Tel: (0114) 268-0687. Website: www.ysfbooks.com. E-mail: ysfbooks@ysfbooks.com. Est: 1986. Internet and postal. Shop open: **M:** 09:30–17:00; **T:** 09:30–17:00; **W:** 09:30–17:00; **Th:** 09:30–17:00; **F:** 09:30–17:00; **S:** 09:30–17:00. Large general stock. Spec: Aeronautics; Alpinism/Mountaineering; Applied Art; Art - History; Arts, The; Aviation; Food & Drink; Gardening; Maritime/Nautical; Military; Music - General; Natural History; Photography; Religion - General; Social History; Topography - General. PR: £1–300. [01/07/2003]

WOMBWELL

Bijou Books, Nimrod, 55 Aldham House Lane, Wombwell, S73 8RG. Prop: Maureen Firth, Dr. Gregory Firth (Assistant). Tel: (01226) 755012. Fax: (01226) 755012. E-mail: maureenfirth@blueyonder.co.uk. Est: 1982. Private premises. Postal business only. Small stock. Spec: Art - Reference; Arts, The; Biography; Ceramics; Cookery/Gastronomy; Illustrated; Limited Editions; Literature; Memoirs; Philosophy; Photography; Private Press; Travel - General; also Booksearch. PR: £1–500. [Updated]

STAFFORDSHIRE

BURTON UPON TRENT

Michael Morris, Weavers Green, Tutbury Road. Needham, Burton upon Trent, DE13 9PQ. Tel: (01283) 575344. Est: 1993. Private premises. Postal business only. Spec: Antiquarian; Atlases; Cartography; Country Houses; Documents - General; Illustrated; Topography - General. PR: £5–1,500. Also, charts and plans. VAT No: GB 694 6934 73. [08/07/2003]

Ian J. Sherratt, Rhoslyn, Victoria St. Yoxall, Burton upon Trent, DE13 8NG. Tel: Not supplied. Est: 1989. Private premises. Postal business only. Small general stock. PR: £1–20. [Updated]

LICHFIELD

Mike Abrahams, 9 Burton Old Road, Streethay, Lichfield, WS13 8LJ. Tel: (01543) 256200. E-mail: Est: 1979. Spec: Antiques; Banking & Insurance; Canals/Inland Waterways; Children's - General; Collecting; Comic Books & Annuals; Cookery/Gastronomy; Crime (True); Earth Mysteries; Fashion & Costume; Guide Books; Gypsies; History - Local; Magic & Conjuring; Motoring PR: £1–500. [26/08/2003]

Steve Brown (Books), 2 Curborough Cottages, Watery Lane, Lichfield, WS13 8ER. Prop: Steve Brown. Tel: (01543) 264498. Website: www.abebooks.com/home/sbbooks. E-mail: steve.brown26@virgin.net. Est: 1992. Private premises. Internet and postal. Appointment necessary. Small general stock. Spec: Sport - Horse Racing (all aspects). PR: £5–500. Cata: on Horse racing continuous online Corresp: French. Mem: PBFA. Also at: Curborough Hall Antiques Centre, Watery Lane, Lichfield. [Updated]

David Clegg, 6 Longbridge Road, Lichfield, WS14 9EL. Tel: (01543) 252117. Est: 1984. Private premises. Postal business only. Very small general stock. Spec: Occult; Religion - General; Travel - General. PR: £5–20. [Updated]

Terry W. Coupland, 15 Harwood Road, Lichfield, WS13 7PP. Tel: (01543) 256599. Est: 1980. Private premises. Appointment necessary. Small stock. Spec: Bookbinding; Children's - General; Illustrated; Juvenile; Papermaking; Printing; Private Press; Publishing; Sport - Golf. PR: £5–1,500. Attends PBFA fairs. Cata: 3 a year on printing, typography, private press. Mem: PBFA. [02/07/2003]

Colin Shakespeare Books, 3 Chestnut Drive, Shenstone, Lichfield, WS14 OJH. Prop: Colin & Lilian Shakespeare. Tel: (01543) 480978. Est: 1991. Private premises. Postal business only. Contactable. Open: **M:** 09:00–21:00; **T:** 09:00–21:00; **W:** 09:00–21:00; **Th:** 09:00–21:00; **F:** 09:00–21:00. Small stock. Spec: Topography - General. PR: £3–1,500. [Updated]

The Staffs Bookshop, 4 and 6 Dam Street, Lichfield, WS13 6AA. Prop: Miss Hawkins. Tel: (01543) 264093. Fax: (01543) 264093. Website: http://www.staffsbookshop.co.uk. E-mail: contact@staffsbookshop.co.uk. Est: 1938. Shop &/or gallery. Internet and postal. Open: **M:** 09:30–17:30; **T:** 09:30–17:30; **W:** 09:30–17:30; **Th:** 09:30–17:30; **F:** 09:30–17:30; **S:** 09:30–17:30; **Su:** 13:00–16:00. Very large stock. Spec: Author - Johnson, Samuel; Children's - General; Dolls & Dolls' Houses; History - General; Literature; Theology; Topography - Local. PR: £1–1,000. CC: MC; V; Switch. Prints, Sheet Music, Ephemera. VAT No: GB 784 5011 28. [Updated]

NEWCASTLE–UNDER–LYME

Pomes Penyeach, 25 Curzon Street, Basford, Newcastle–under–Lyme, ST5 0PD. Prop: Paul Robinson. Tel: (01782) 630729. Website: www.abebooks.com. E-mail: books@pomes-penyeach.co.uk. Est: 1985. Private premises. Appointment necessary. Small general stock. Spec: Academic/Scholarly; Children's - General; First Editions; History - General; Literary Criticism; Literature; Modern First Editions; Philosophy; Poetry; Psychology/Psychiatry; Science - General; University Texts, also Booksearch. PR: £1–500. CC: AE; MC; V; Delta. Mem: PBFA. [Updated]

Keith Twigg Toy Books, 27 Lansdell Avenue, Porthill, Newcastle-under-Lyme, ST5 8ET. Tel: (01782) 642932. Est: 1970. Postal business only. Spec: Dolls & Dolls' Houses; Toys. PR: £20–200. [Updated]

STAFFORD

Ray Roberts (Booksellers), Whiston Hall Mews, Whiston Hall, Whiston, Nr. Penkridge, Stafford, ST19 5QH. Tel: (01785) 712232. Fax: (01785) 712232. Est: 1980. Private premises. Appointment necessary. Small stock. Spec: Aviation; Motorbikes; Motoring; Sport - Ballooning; Sport - Cycling; Steam Engines; Traction Engines; Transport; Travel - General; Vintage Cars. PR: £1–500. CC: AE; MC; V. Also: publisher – Bentley Motoring. Cata: 1 a year on motoring. [Updated]

STOKE–ON–TRENT

Abacas Books & Cards, ■ 56–60 Millrise Road, Milton, Stoke–on–Trent, ST2 7BW. Prop: Dave & Margaret Mycock. Tel: (01782) 543005. Est: 1980. Shop open: **M:** 09:00–17:00; **T:** 09:00–17:00; **Th:** 09:00–17:00; **F:** 09:00–17:00; **S:** 09:00–13:00. Medium stock. Spec: Art; Autobiography; Bindings; Biography; Ceramics; Cookery/Gastronomy; Fiction - General; Gardening; History - General; Military; Music - General; Natural History; New Age; Photography; Poetry; Railways; Sport - General; Topography - General. PR: £1–200. Also, attends Buxton Book Fairs. VAT No: GB 478 7684 71. [Updated]

Acumen Books, Rushton House, 167 Nantwich Road, Audley, Stoke-on-Trent, ST7 8DL. Managing Director: C.B. Pearson. Tel: (01782) 720753. Fax: (01782) 720798. Website: www.acumenbooks .co.uk. E-mail: shop@acumenbooks.co.uk. Est: 1978. Open: **M:** 02:00–15:00 or **Th:** 02:00–15:00. Spec: Sport - Cricket. PR: £1–20. CC: MC; V. Cata: 1 a year on Cricket Umpiring and Scoring. Mem: ACU&S MCIArb. [02/08/2003]

Cartographics, 49 Grange Road, Biddulph, Stoke–on–Trent, ST8 7RY. Prop: R.J. & S.W. Dean. Tel: (01782) 513449. Website: www.cartographics.co.uk. E-mail: carto@tesco.net. Est: 1969. Private premises. Internet and postal. Appointment necessary. Very large stock. Spec: Canals/Inland Waterways; Cartography. PR: £1–500. Also, map drawing-repair-mounting-conservation. Historical research from cartographic sources. Corresp: French (limited!). VAT No: GB 318 9820 32. [Updated]

TAMWORTH

G. & J. Chesters, ■ 14 Market Street, Polesworth, Tamworth, B78 1HW. Prop: Geoff & Jean Chester. Tel: (01827) 894743. Website: www.abebooks.com/home/geoffchesters. E-mail: gandjchesters@ tiscali.co.uk. Est: 1970. Shop open: **M:** 10:10–17:17; **T:** 10:10–17:17; **W:** 10:10–21:21; **Th:** 10:10– 17:17; **F:** 10:10–17:17; **S:** 10:10–17:17. Very large general stock. Spec: Academic/Scholarly; Anthropology; Criminology; Economics; Education & School; Geography; Geology; History - General; Linguistics; Literary Criticism; Mathematics; Medicine - History of; Music - Classical; Philosophy; Politics; Psychology/Psychiatry. PR: £1–1,000. CC: AE; MC; V; SW. Mem: PBFA. VAT No: GB 112 6448 93. [Updated]

UTTOXETER

J.O. Goodwin, Woodcrofts Farm, Highwood, Uttoxeter, ST14 8PS. Tel: (01889) 562792. Est: 1965. Private premises. Appointment necessary. Small general stock. PR: £1–200. VAT No: GB 125 9041 83. [Updated]

WALSALL (SEE ALSO UNDER WEST MIDLANDS)

SETI Books, 3C, Kingswood Drive, Walsall, WS6 6NX. David J Ward. Tel: 01922 413277. Fax: 01922 413277. E-mail: davidjward@setibooks.freeserve.co.uk. Est: 2002. Private premises. Internet and postal. Telephone first. Very small stock. Spec: Cryptozoology; Earth Mysteries; Esoteric; Ghosts; Metaphysics; Mind, Body & Spirit; New Age; Occult; Psychic; U.F.O.s; Unexplained, The; Witchcraft. PR: £1–175. [Updated]

WOMBOURN

Rookery Bookery, 39 Rookery Road, Wombourn, WV5 0JH. Prop: Colin Hardwick. Tel: (01902) 895983. E-mail: rookerybookery@hotmail.com. Est: 1987. Private premises. Appointment necessary. Very small general stock. Spec: PR: £1–250. Cata: occasionally. Corresp: French. [Updated]

YOXALL

Ray Sparkes (Books), The Hollies, Bond End, Yoxall, DE13 8NH. (*). Tel: (01543) 472274. Fax: (01543) 472274. E-mail: Est: 1987. Private premises. Appointment necessary. Small stock. Spec: History - Local; Reference; Topography - General. PR: £2–3,000. Cata: 4 a year on British directories. Mem: PBFA. VAT No: GB 478 2190 24. [28/04/2003]

SUFFOLK

BECCLES

Besleys Books, ■ 4 Blyburgate, Beccles, NR34 9TA. Prop: Piers & Gabby Besley. Tel: (01502) 715762. Fax: {01502) 675649. Website: www.besleysbooks.demon.co.uk. E-mail: piers@besleysbooks .demon.co.uk. Shop open: **M:** 09:30–17:00; **T:** 09:30–17:00; **Th:** 09:30–17:00; **F:** 09:30–17:00; **S:** 09:30–17:00. Large stock. Spec: Gardening; Illustrated; Natural History. PR: £1–1,000. CC: JCB; MC; V. Cata: 2 biennial. Mem: ABA; PBFA. [Updated]

BOXFORD

Dolphin Books, Old Coach House, Broad Street, Boxford, CO10 5DX. Prop: Rita Watts. Tel: (01787) 211630. Website: wwwukbookworld.com/members/dolphinbooks. E-mail: rwdolphinbooks@ aol.com. Est: 1988. Private premises. Internet and postal. Appointment necessary. Small general stock. Spec: Arts, The; Authors - Women; Autobiography; Biography; History - General; History - Women; Literature; Memoirs; Performing Arts; Politics; Rural Life; also Booksearch. PR: £5–50. Stock also on biblion.com and alibris.com. [Updated]

BUNGAY

Bardsley's Books, ■ 22 Upper Olland Street, Bungay, NR35 1BH. Prop: W.N.A. & D.H. Bardsley. Tel: (01986) 892077. Website: www.bardsleysbooks.co.uk. E-mail: antonybardsley@easynet.co.uk. Est: 1998. Shop open: **M:** 10:00–17:30; **T:** 10:00–17:30; **Th:** 10:00–17:30; **F:** 10:00–17:30; **S:** 10:00–17:30. Very large general stock. Spec: Antiquarian; Art; Bibles; Books about Books; Cinema/Film; Countries - Mexico; Countries - Poland; Ecclesiastical History & Architecture; Fine Printing; History - General; Iconography; Illuminated Manuscripts; Music - General; Mysticism; Religion - General. PR: £1–250. Also, cards, O.S. Maps, CDs & new books to order. [25/06/2003]

Beaver Booksearch, 33 Hillside Road East, Bungay, NR35 1JU. Sarah Coulthurst & Nicholas Watts. Tel: (01986) 896698. Fax: (01986) 896698. Website: www.beaverbooksearch.co.uk. E-mail: nick@ beaverbooksearch.co.uk. Est: 1995. Private premises. Postal business only. Small stock. Spec: Bridge; also Booksearch. PR: £1–50. CC: AE; MC; V; SW. VAT No: GB 638 1296 25. [Updated]

Scorpio Books, Autumn Cottage, Low Street, Ilketshall St. Margaret, Bungay, NR35 1QZ. Prop: Lorna & Patrick Quorn. Tel: (01986) 781721. Fax: (01986) 781721. Website: www.booksatpbfa.com. E-mail: scorpiobooks@clara.co.uk. Est: 1979. Private premises. Internet and postal. Appointment necessary. Medium stock. Spec: Art; Aviation; Military; Music - Jazz; War - General; Women. PR: £1–500. CC: E; JCB; MC; V. Corresp: French, Spanish. Mem: PBFA. [Updated]

BURES

Major Iain Grahame, Daws Hall, Lamarsh, Bures, CO8 5EX. Prop: Iain Grahame. Tel: (01787) 269213. Fax: (01787) 269634. Website: www.IainGrahameRareBooks.com. E-mail: majorbooks@ compuserve.com. Est: 1979. Private premises. Internet and postal. Telephone first. Open: M: 09:00–21:00; **T:** 09:00–21:00; **W:** 09:00–21:00; **Th:** 09:00–21:00; **F:** 09:00–21:00; **S:** 09:00–17:00; **Su:** 09:00–17:00. Medium stock. Spec: Natural History; Sport - Field Sports; also Booksearch. PR: £5–50,000. CC: AE; MC; V; Access. Cata: 2 a year on Sporting, Natural History & Africana. Corresp: French and Italian. Mem: ABA. VAT No: GB 341 7566 51. [03/08/2003]

BURY ST EDMUNDS

Sally Smith Books, 13 Manor Garth, Pakenham, Bury St Edmunds, IP31 2LB. Tel: (01359) 230431. Website: www.sallysmithbooks.co.uk. E-mail: sally@sallysmithbooks.co.uk. Est: 1989. Private premises. Internet. Appointment necessary. Medium stock. Spec: Antiques; Art - Reference; Bibliography; Biography; Children's - General; Crafts; Fiction - General; Literature - Victorian; Natural History; Publishing; Travel - General; War - General. PR: £1–1,000. Corresp: French. [Updated]

Bury Bookshop, ■ 28a Hatter Street, Bury St. Edmunds, IP33 1NE. Prop: Joe & Sheila Wakerley. Tel: (01284) 703107. Fax: (01284) 755936. E-mail: burybooks@btconnect.com. Est: 1980. Shop open: **M:** 09:00–17:30; **T:** 08:00–17:30; **W:** 09:00–17:30; **Th:** 08:00–17:30; **F:** 09:00–17:30; **S:** 09:00–17:30. Medium stock. PR: £1–300. CC: AE; MC; V. [Updated]

Janet Carters, 40 Church Lane, Barton Mills, Bury St. Edmunds, IP28 6AY. Tel: (01638) 717619. Fax: (01638) 717619. E-mail: cartersbooks@aol.com. Est: 1978. Private premises. Appointment necessary. Small stock. Spec: Sport - Horse Racing (all aspects). PR: £2–500. Cata: occasionally on horse racing. VAT No: GB 334 0238 92. [Updated]

CLARE

Trinders' Fine Tools, ■ Malting Lane, Clare, Sudbury, CO10 8NW. Prop: Peter and Rosemary Trinder. Tel: (01787) 277130. Fax: (01787) 277677. Website: www.trindersfinetools.co.uk/. E-mail: peter@ trindersfinetools.co.uk. Est: 1975. Internet and postal. Shop open: **M:** 10:00–17:00; **T:** 10:00–17:00; **W:** 10:00–12:00; **Th:** 10:00–17:00; **F:** 10:00–17:00; **S:** 10:00–17:00; Closed for lunch: 13:00–14:00. Small stock. Spec: Antiques; Applied Art; Architecture; Art; Art - Reference; Artists; Arts, The; Building & Construction; Carpets; Collecting; Conservation; Crafts; Decorative Art; Design; Embroidery; Engineering; Fashion & Costume; Fine Art; Firearms/Guns; Furniture. PR: £2–500. CC: AE; JCB; MC; V. NB. Please phone before travelling lest we be closed! Mem: PBFA. VAT No: GB 299 6575 77. [Updated]

DEBENHAM

David Shacklock (Books), ■ 27 High St., Debenham, IP14 6QN. Prop: David Shacklock. Tel: (01728) 861286. E-mail: riley01@globalnet.co.uk. Est: 1986. Shop open: **T:** 10:00–17:00; **F:** 14:00–20:00; **S:** 10:00–16:00. Medium stock. Spec: Annuals; Anthologies; Author - Baring-Gould, S.; Author - Henty, G.A.; Biography; Fiction - General; Guide Books; History - General; Juvenile; Military; Reference; Royalty - General; Theology; Topography - General; Victoriana. PR: £1–150. Closed Tuesday 13:00–14:00. Also at: Townsend Mill, Halstead. [Updated]

EYE

Elizabeth Nelson, Owl Cottage, 153 The Street, Stoke Ash, Eye, IP23 7EW. Tel: (01379) 678481. Fax: (01379) 678481. E-mail: eliznelson@owlcot.demon.co.uk. Est: 1982. Private premises. Appointment necessary. Small stock. Spec: Antiques; Art; Aviation; Maritime/Nautical; Military. PR: £5–1,500. CC: MC; V. Cata: 3 a year on fine & applied art, antiques reference. Mem: PBFA. VAT No: GB 428 0755 47. [Updated]

Robin Doughty - Fine Books, 3 Ash Tree Close, Fressingfield, Eye, IP21 5RT. Prop: Robin Doughty. Tel: (01379) 586809. E-mail: robin.doughty@btinternet.com. Est: 1994. Postal business only. Small general stock. Spec: Antiquarian; Art; Illustrated; Literature; Private Press; Religion - General; Religion - Quakers; Topography - General; Topography - Local. PR: £1–2,500. All details valid from 1 July 2005. Mem: PBFA. [Updated]

Thomas Rare Books, Valley Farm House, Yaxley, Eye, IP23 8BX. Prop: G.L. Thomas. Tel: (01379) 783288. Fax: (01379) 783288. Website: www.abebooks.com. E-mail: thomasrarebooks@ btinternet.com. Est: 1978. Private premises. Postal business only. Shop at: www.booksatpbfa.com. Spec: Antiquarian. PR: £10–10,000. CC: JCB; V. Mem: PBFA. [Updated]

FELIXSTOWE

Books Only, 84 Garrison Lane, Felixstowe, IP11 7RQ. Prop: Colin E. Sharman. Tel: (01394) 285546. Website: www.ukbookworld.com/members.shac. E-mail: colin.sharman@btopenworld.com. Est: 1980. Private premises. Internet and postal. Small stock. Spec: Comedy; Cookery/Gastronomy; Photography; Politics; Topography - Local. PR: £1–100. [Updated]

Poor Richard's Books, ■ 17 Orwell Road, Felixstowe, IP11 7EP. Prop: Dick Moffat. Tel: (01394) 283138. E-mail: moffatsfx@aol.com. Est: 1997. Shop open: **M:** 09:00–17:00; **T:** 09:00–17:00; **W:** 09:00–17:00; **Th:** 09:00–17:00; **F:** 09:00–17:00; **S:** 09:00–17:00. Very large general stock. PR: £1–500. CC: MC; V; SW, Solo. Also, searches and book repair. Corresp: French. Mem: PBFA. [Updated]

Treasure Chest Books, ■ 61 Cobbold Road, Felixstowe, IP11 7BH. Prop: R. & R. Green. Tel: (01394) 270717. Shop open: **M:** 09:30–17:30; **T:** 09:30–17:30; **W:** 09:30–17:30; **Th:** 09:30–17:30; **F:** 09:30–17:30; **S:** 09:30–17:30. Very large general stock. Spec: Art; Aviation; Cinema/Film; Occult; Topography - Local; Transport. CC: E; JCB; MC. Mem: PBFA. [Updated]

FRAMLINGHAM

Mrs. V.S. Bell (Books), ■ 19 Market Hill, Framlingham, Nr. Woodbridge, IP13 9BB. Tel: (01728) 723046. E-mail: rvbell@breathe.com. Est: 1974. Shop open: **M:** 10:00–16:00; **T:** 10:00–16:00; **W:** 10:00–12:00; **Th:** 10:00–16:00; **F:** 10:00–16:00; **S:** 09:00–16:00. Medium stock. Spec: Fiction - Crime, Detective, Spy, Thrillers; also Booksearch. PR: £2–75. [Updated]

Mrs. A. Kent (Books), ■ 19 Market Hill, Framlingham, Nr. Woodbridge, IP13 9BB. Tel: (01728) 723046. Est: 1974. Shop open: **M:** 10:00–16:00; **T:** 10:00–16:00; **W:** 10:00–12:00; **Th:** 10:00–14:00; **F:** 10:00–14:00; **S:** 09:00–16:00; Closed for lunch: 13:00–14:00. Medium stock. Spec: Fiction - Crime, Detective, Spy, Thrillers; also Booksearch. PR: £1–100. [Updated]

HALESWORTH

Andrew Jones, 25 Rectory Street, Halesworth, IP19 8AE. Tel: (01986) 835944. Fax: (01869) 337146. E-mail: andrewjones.history@dsl.pipex.com. Est: 1977. Private premises. Postal business only. Open: Very small general stock. Spec: Academic/Scholarly; Fine & Rare; History - General. PR: £5–1,000. Cata: 5 – or 6 a year. [Updated]

IPSWICH

Roy Arnold, ■ 77 High Street, Needham Market, Ipswich, IP6 8AN. Tel: (01449) 720110. Fax: (01449) 722498. Website: www.royarnold.com. E-mail: ra@royarnold.com. Est: 1976. Internet and postal. Shop open: **M:** 10:10–17:17; **T:** 10:10–17:17; **W:** 10:10–17:17; **Th:** 10:10–17:17; **F:** 10:10–17:17; **S:** 10:00–17:00. Medium stock. Spec: Antiquarian; Antiques; Applied Art; Rural Life; Scientific Instruments; Windmills & Watermills; Woodwork, also Booksearch. PR: £4–3,000. CC: MC; V. Also, new books on specialities. Cata: 1 – Mem: PBFA; TATHS, SOT, EAIA, MWTCA. VAT No: GB 334 0169 85. [Updated]

Claude Cox Old & Rare Books, ■ College Gateway Bookshop, 3 & 5 Silent Street, Ipswich, IP1 1TF. Prop: Anthony Brian Cox. Tel: (01473) 254776. Fax: (01473) 254776. Website: www.claudecox.co.uk. E-mail: books@claudecox.co.uk. Est: 1944. Shop open: **W:** 10:00–17:00; **Th:** 10:00–17:00; **F:** 10:00–17:00; **S:** 10:00–17:00; Medium stock. Spec: Antiquarian; Art - Reference; Bibliography; Bindings; Books about Books; Ex-Libris; Fine Printing; Fore-Edge Paintings; History - General; Illuminated Manuscripts; Illustrated; Limited Editions; Literature; Military; Natural History; Papermaking. CC: E; JCB; MC; V; SW. Binding Repairs Suffolk Prints & Maps. Cata: 6 a year on Antiquarian and Printing & the Art of the Book. Mem: ABA; PBFA; ILAB; PLA, PHS. VAT No: GB 304 7952 56. [Updated]

Footrope Knots, 501 Wherstead Road, Ipswich, IP2 8LL. Prop: Des & Liz Pawson. Tel: (01473) 690090. E-mail: knots@footrope.fsnet.co.uk. Est: 1981. Private premises. Postal business only. Appointment necessary. Very small stock. Spec: Crafts; Maritime/Nautical; Sport - Yachting. PR: £1–100. [Updated]

Gippeswic Books, 21 Belmont Road, Ipswich, IP2 9RJ. Prop: Martin L. Crook. Tel: (01473) 682302. Fax: (01473) 682302. Est: 1991. Private premises. Postal business only. Small general stock. Spec: History - General; Military History; Topography - Local; Travel - General. PR: £2–300. Attends bookfairs. Mem: PBFA. [Updated]

The Idler, ■ 37 High Street, Hadleigh, Ipswich, Prop: Bryan & Jane Haylock. Tel: (01473) 827752. Est: 1980. Shop open: **M:** 09:30–17:00; **T:** 09:30–17:00; **W:** 09:30–12:00; **Th:** 09:30–17:00; **F:** 09:30–17:00; **S:** 09:30–17:00. Medium stock. Spec: Art; also Booksearch. PR: £1–100. Also, new books, publisher's remainders, art materials, greetings cards. VAT No: GB 410 6933 74. [Updated]

LAVENHAM

R.G. Archer, ■ 7 Water Street, Lavenham, Sudbury, CO10 9RW. Tel: (01787) 247229. Est: 1970. Shop open: **M:** 10:00–17:00; **T:** 10:00–17:00; **Th:** 09:00–17:00; **F:** 10:00–17:00; **S:** 10:00–17:00; **Su:** 10:00–00:00. Medium stock. PR: £1–1,000. Open all bank holidays. [26/02/2003]

LONG MELFORD

Lime Tree Books, Hall Street, Long Melford, CO10 9JF. Prop: Bryan Marsh. Tel: (01787) 311532. Est: 1992. Spec: Antiquarian; Art; Colour-Plate; Countries - Poland; Fiction - General; First Editions; History - General; Natural History; Topography - General; Topography - Local. PR: £1–500. [Updated]

LOWESTOFT

A Book for All Reasons, Rockville House, 6 Pakefield Road, Lowestoft, NR33 0HS. Prop: G.A. Michael Sims. Tel: (01502) 581011. Fax: (01502) 574891. Website: www.abfar.co.uk. E-mail: books@abfar.co.uk. Est: 1994. Private premises. Internet and postal. Medium stock. Spec: Author - Heyer, Georgette; Author - Yates, Dornford; Fiction - General; Fiction - Historical; Fiction - Romantic; History - Local; Naval; Topography - Local; War - World War II. PR: £5–500. CC: MC; V; SW. Also on ibooknet. VAT No: GB 770 1056 57. [Updated]

R. W. Lamb, Talbot House, 158 Denmark Road, Lowestoft, NR32 2EL. Tel: (01502) 564306. Fax: (01502) 564306. E-mail: talbot@rwlamb.co.uk. Est: 1972. Private premises. Internet and postal. Appointment necessary. Classical Studies. Cata: 2 a year. [Updated]

John Rolph, ■ Manor House, Pakefield Street, Lowestoft, NR33 0JT. Tel: (01502) 572039. Est: 1952. Shop open: **T:** 11:00–17:00; **W:** 11:00–17:00; **F:** 11:00–17:00; **S:** 11:00–17:00. Closed for lunch: 13:00–14:30. Medium stock. Spec: PR: £1–100. [Updated]

NEWMARKET

C.D. Paramor, 25 St. Mary's Square, Newmarket, CB8 0HZ. Tel: (01638) 664416. Fax: (01638) 664416. E-mail: cdparamor@btopenworld.com. Est: 1974. Private premises. Appointment necessary. Medium stock. Spec: Cinema/Film; Dance; Entertainment - General; Music - General; Performing Arts; Television; Theatre; also Booksearch. PR: £1–350. Cata: 60 a year. [Updated]

R.E. & G.B. Way, Brettons, Burrough Green, Newmarket, CB8 9NA. Tel: (01638) 507217. Fax: (01638) 508058. Website: http://www.geocities.com/regbway. E-mail: waybks@msn.com. Est: 1958. Private premises. Telephone first. Open: **M:** 08:30–17:30; **T:** 08:30–17:30; **W:** 08:30–17:30; **Th:** 08:30–17:30; **F:** 08:30–17:30; **S:** 08:30–12:00. Spec: Animals and Birds; Natural History; Private Press; Sport - Big Game Hunting; Sport - Field Sports. CC: MC; V. Mem: ABA; PBFA; BA. VAT No: GB 103 4378 02. [Updated]

SAXMUNDHAM

Roger Ballantyne–Way, Kiln House, Benhall Low Street, Saxmundham, IPI7 1JQ. Prop: Roger Ballantyne-Way. Tel: (01728) 604711. E-mail: ballantyne.way@virgin.net. Est: 1979. Private premises. Internet and postal. Appointment necessary. Medium stock. Spec: Architecture; Art; Art - History; Art - Reference; Artists; Arts, The; Decorative Art; Design; Fashion & Costume; Illustrated; Printing; Private Press; also Booksearch. PR: £5–1,000. CC: AE; MC; V. NB. Booksearch is on Suffolk writers. Cata: 1 a year on art. Mem: PBFA. [01/08/2003]

Chapel Books, ■ Westleton, Saxmundham, IP17 3AA. Prop: Robert Jackson. Tel: (01728) 648616. Website: www.chapelbooks.com. E-mail: bob.thechapel@virgin.net. Est: 1982. Shop open: **M:** 12:00–17:00; **T:** 12:00–17:00; **W:** 12:00–17:00; **Th:** 12:00–17:00; **F:** 12:00–17:00; **S:** 12:00–17:00; **Su:** 12:00–17:00. Large general stock. PR: £1–500. CC: AE; MC; V; maestro. VAT No: GB 811 7652 39. [Updated]

Keith A. Savage, ■ 35 High Street, Saxmundham, IP17 1AJ. Tel: 01728 604538. Fax: 01986 872231(answerphone). Est: 1992. Shop open: **M:** 10:30–13:00; **T:** 10:30–17:00; **W:** 10:30–17:00; **F:** 10:30–17:00; **S:** 10:30–13:00. Small general stock. Spec: Children's - General; Comic Books & Annuals; Comics. PR: £1–150. [Updated]

Sax Books, ■ 4a High St., Saxmundham, IP17 1DF. Prop: Richard W.L. Smith, M.V.O. Tel: (01728) 605775. E-mail: richard@saxbooks.co.uk. Est: 2000. Shop open: **W:** 10:00–16:00; **Th:** 10:00–16:00; **F:** 10:00–16:00; **S:** 10:00–16:00. Medium stock. Spec: Art; Autobiography; Biography; Churchilliana; Cookery/Gastronomy; Fiction - General; Fiction - Crime, Detective, Spy, Thrillers; History - General; Military History; Publishers - Penguin; Railways; Religion - General; Royalty - General; Sport - Cricket. PR: £1–200. Also Tuesday opening 10.00-16.00: summer months only. Mem: PBFA. [Updated]

SOUTHWOLD

Southwold Antiques Centre, ■ Buckenham Mews, 83 High Street, Southwold, IP18 6DS. Tel: (01502) 723060. Shop open: **M:** 10:00–17:00; **T:** 10:00–17:00; **W:** 10:00–17:00; **Th:** 10:00–17:00; **F:** 10:00–17:00. **S:** 11:00–17:00; **Su:** 09:00–17:00. Small stock. Spec: Children's - General; Publishers - Warnes; Topography - Local. PR: £2–50. Local topography includes Adrian Bell. Mem: PBFA. Also at: Richard Everett at Downham Market, Norfolk (q.v.). [Updated]

STOWMARKET

H.G. Pratt, Harvesters, Rectory Road, Wyverstone, Stowmarket, IP14 4SH. Tel: (01449) 781372. Fax: (01449) 781872. E-mail: guypratt@harvesters99.fsnet.co.uk. Private premises. Postal business only. Contactable. Open: **M:** 09:00–17:00; **T:** 09:00–17:00; **W:** 09:00–17:00; **Th:** 09:00–17:00; **F:** 09:00–17:00; Small stock. Spec: History - Local; Photography; Religion - Christian; Rural Life; Topography - Local; also Booksearch. PR: £10–200. Also, valuations for probate, family division and insurance. Cata: 1 a year on photography. VAT No: GB 496 7023 16. [Updated]

SUDBURY

Beckham Books Ltd., Chilton Mount, Newton Road, Sudbury, CO10 2RS. Prop: Mrs. J.E. Beckham. Tel: (01787) 373683. Fax: (01787) 375441. Website: www.beckhambooks.com. E-mail: sales@ beckhambooks.co.uk. Est: 1994. Private premises. Internet and postal. Telephone first. Open: **M:** 09:00–18:00; **T:** 09:00–18:00; **W:** 09:00–18:00; **Th:** 09:00–18:00; **F:** 09:00–18:00; **S:** 09:00–18:00; **Su:** 10:00–17:00. Large general stock. Spec: Antiquarian; Bibles; Bindings; Biography; Ecclesiastical History & Architecture; History - General; Languages - Foreign; Prayer Books; Religion - General; Religion - Methodism; Religious Texts; Theology, also Booksearch. PR: £1–4,000. CC: AE; E; JCB; MC; V. Booksearch is free. Mem: PBFA. VAT No: GB 750 9305 36. [Updated]

Derek Vanstone - Aviation Book, Tymperley Farm, Great Henny, Sudbury, CO10 7LX. Tel: (01787) 269291. Fax: (01787) 269291. Website: www.aircraftbooks.com. E-mail: derek.vanstone@lineone.net. Est: 1996. Private premises. Internet and postal. Contactable. Open: **M:** 09:00–18:00; **T:** 09:00–18:00; **W:** 09:00–18:00; **Th:** 09:00–18:00; **F:** 09:00–18:00; **S:** 09:00–13:00. Small stock. Spec: Aviation; Maritime/Nautical; Military. PR: £1–200. CC: AE; MC; V. Cata: 3 a year. Mem: PBFA. VAT No: GB 711 3364 72. [10/05/2003]

WOODBRIDGE

Blakes Books, ■ 88 The Thoroughfare, Woodbridge, IP12 1AL. Prop: Robert Green. Tel: (01394) 380302. Est: 1983. Shop open: **M:** 09:30–17:00; **T:** 09:30–17:00; **W:** 09:30–17:00; **Th:** 09:30–17:00; **F:** 09:30–17:00; **S:** 09:30–17:00. Large general stock. PR: £1–100. CC: MC; V. Mem: PBFA. [26/09/2004]

W.H. Collectables, 24 Ipswich Road, Woodbridge, IP12 4BU. Prop: Michael Wheeler. Tel: (01394) 385021. Fax: (01394) 385021. Est: 1981. Storeroom. Appointment necessary. Open: **M:** 09:00–20:00; **T:** 09:00–20:00; **W:** 09:00–20:00; **Th:** 09:00–20:00; **F:** 09:00–20:00. Large stock. Spec: Aeronautics; Alpinism/Mountaineering; Americana; Banking & Insurance; Children's - General; Colonial; Comics; Documents - General; Guide Books; Illuminated Manuscripts; Literary Travel; Maritime/Nautical; Mining; Ottoman Empire; Photography; Railways; Scouts & Guides; Transport; Travel - General. PR: £10–500. CC: D; MC; V. Stock also covers Australia, Canada and New Zealand. Cata: 3 a year on specialities. Corresp: German. Mem: ES. Also at: [Updated]

SURREY

ASHTEAD

Nigel Smith Books, 2 Bagot Close, Ashtead, KT21 1NS. Tel: (01372) 272517. Fax: (01372) 272517. Website: www.abebooks.com/home/nigelsmyth. E-mail: nigels.myth@ukgateway.net. Est: 1999. Postal business only. PR: £2–300. [Updated]

BYFLEET

Joppa Books Ltd., ■ 68 High Road, Byfleet, KT14 7QL. Prop: Nadeem M. Elissa. Tel: (01932) 336777. Fax: (01932) 348881. Website: www.joppabooks.com. E-mail: joppa@joppabooks.com. Est: 1989. Internet and postal. Shop open: **M:** 10:00–14:00; **T:** 10:00–16:00; **W:** 10:00–16:00; **Th:** 10:00–16:00; **F:** 10:00–16:00; Closed for lunch: 12:00–14:00. Large stock. Spec: Academic/Scholarly; Antiquarian; Archaeology; Canals/Inland Waterways; Carriages & Driving; Countries - Middle East, The; Egyptology; History - National; Military; Oriental; Politics; Religion - Islam; Travel - Africa; Travel - Asia; Travel - Middle PR: £5–5,000. CC: AE; MC; V; SW. Cata: 24 – every two weeks. Corresp: Arabic, French. Mem: PBFA. VAT No: GB 493 7403 24. [Updated]

CATERHAM

Chaldon Books & Records, 1 High Street, Caterham, CR3 5UE. Prop: K. Chesson. Tel: (01883) 348583. E-mail: Est: 1994. Booksearch. PR: £1–200. [26/08/2003]

COBHAM

Nectar Books, P.O. Box 263, Cobham, KT11 2YZ. Prop: T.G. Kent. Tel: (01932) 865637. E-mail: sales@nectarbooks.co.uk. Est: 1976. Private premises. Postal business only. Appointment necessary. Very small general stock. Spec: Broadcasting; Cinema/Film; Drama; Entertainment - General; Erotica; Genealogy; Memorabilia; Music - General; Performing Arts; also Booksearch. PR: £5–200. [14/04/2003]

DORKING

A.J. Coombes, 24 Horsham Road, Dorking, RH4 2JA. Prop: John Coombes. Tel: (01306) 880736. Fax: (01306) 743641. E-mail: john.coombes@ukgateway.net. Est: 1967. Private premises. Appointment necessary. Small stock. Spec: Architecture; History - General; History - British; History - Local; Topography - General; Topography - Local. Cata: 1a year on British local history & topography. Corresp: German. Mem: ABA. VAT No: GB 210 5273 14. [Updated]

T.S. Hill Books, ■ 9 Falkland Road, Dorking, RH4 3AB. Prop: Tim Hill. Tel: (01306) 886468. E-mail: Est: 1987. Shop. Appointment necessary. Open: **M:** 09:00–17:00; **T:** 09:00–17:00; **W:** 09:00–17:00; **Th:** 09:00–17:00; **F:** 09:00–17:00. Very small general stock. PR: £5–500. [26/08/2003]

C.C. Kohler, 12 Horsham Road, Dorking, RH4 2JL. Tel: (01306) 881532. Fax: (01306) 742438. E-mail: cornflwr@cornflwr.demon.co.uk. Est: 1963. Storeroom. Appointment necessary. Medium stock. Spec: Special collections. Corresp: German. Mem: ABA; ILAB. VAT No: GB 293 7862 08. [Updated]

EAST HORSLEY

Emjay Books, Ashdene, High Park Avenue, East Horsley, KT24 5DF. Prop: M. Gardner. Tel: (01483) 283373. E-mail: emjaybooks@lineone.net. Est: 1990. Private premises. Internet and postal. Appointment necessary. Large stock. Spec: American Indians; Author - Bates, H.E.; Author - Byron, Lord; Author - Christie, Agatha; Author - Francis, Dick; Author - Tangye, D.; Motoring; Private Press; Reference; also Booksearch. PR: £5–3,000. CC: V. [01/07/2003]

Rowan House Books, Rowans, Norrels Ride, East Horsley, KT24 5EH. Prop: George Spranklins. Tel: (01483) 282482. Fax: (01483) 285924. Website: www.abeooks.com. E-mail: gsprankling@aol.com. Est: 1995. Private premises. Internet and postal. Appointment necessary. Medium stock. Spec: Children's - General; First Editions; Illustrated. PR: £10–500. CC: MC; V. [Updated]

EAST MOLESEY

Books Bought & Sold Ltd, ■ 68 Walton Road, East Molesey, KT8 ODL. Prop: P.J. Sheridan & W.J. Collyer. Tel: (020) 8224-3609. Fax: (020) 8224-3576. Website: www.books.keyuk.com. E-mail: sheridan@books.keyuk.com. Est: 1985. Shop open: **T:** 10:00–17:00; **W:** 10:00–17:00; **Th:** 10:00–17:00; **F:** 10:00–17:00; **S:** 10:00–17:00. Medium stock. Spec: Aeronautics; Aviation; Children's - General; History - General; Illustrated; Military; Motoring; Railways; Topography - Local; also Booksearch. PR: £1–900. CC: D; E; JCB; MC; V. Organisers of HD Book Fairs. VAT No: GB 644 1831 46. [Updated]

Cecil Books, ■ Nostradamus II Antiques Centre, 53 Bridge Road, East Molesey, KT8 9ER. Prop: Desmond & Ruth Cecil. Tel: Shop: (020) 8783 059. Fax: (020) 8224-5856. E-mail: ruthcecil@dial.pipex.com. Est: 1996. Shop open: **T:** 10:00–17:00; **W:** 10:00–17:00; **Th:** 10:00–17:00; **F:** 10:00–17:00; **S:** 10:00–17:00; **Su:** 11:00–17:00. Small general stock. Spec: Antiquarian; Biography; Poetry; Travel - General; also Booksearch. PR: £5–500. Corresp: French, German, Italian. [12/05/2003]

EGHAM

Blacklock's, ■ 8 Victoria Street, Englefield Green, Egham, TW20 0QY. Prop: Graham Dennis. Tel: (01784) 438025. Est: 1988. Shop open: **M:** 09:00–17:00; **T:** 09:00–17:00; **W:** 09:00–17:00; **Th:** 09:00–17:00; **F:** 09:00–17:00; **S:** 09:00–13:00; Closed for lunch: 13:00–14:00. Small general stock. Spec: Sport - Polo. PR: £2–250. CC: MC; V. Cata: 2 a year on polo. [Updated]

Corfe Books, ■ 'Corfe', Mount Lee, Egham, TW20 9PD. Prop: Mark Hayhoe. Tel: (01932) 850674. Est: 2001. Shop at: 163 Station Road, Adlestone, Surrey KT15 2BA. Open: **T:** 10:00–16:00; **W:** 10:00–16:00; **Th:** 10:00–16:00; **F:** 10:00–17:45; **S:** 10:00–17:45. Large stock. Spec: Aeronautics; Animals and Birds; Antiques; Archaeology; Architecture; Espionage; Fiction - General; History - General; Military History; Modern First Editions; Motoring; Naval; Railways; Signed Editions, also Booksearch. PR: £1–300. [Updated]

EPSOM

Vandeleur Antiquarian Books, 6 Seaforth Gardens, Stoneleigh, Epsom, KT19 0NR. Prop: E.H. Bryant. Tel: (020) 8393-7752 (24hrs). Fax: (020) 8393-7752 (24hrs). Est: 1971. Private premises. Appointment necessary. Small stock. Spec: Alpinism/Mountaineering; Antiquarian; Bindings; Sport - Big Game Hunting; Sport - Rowing; Travel - Africa; Travel - Americas; Travel - Asia; Travel - Europe; Travel - Polar; Voyages & Discovery. PR: £5–2,000. Exhibits at bookfairs. Also, rowing prints and Indian Mogul-style paintings. Mem: PBFA. [Updated]

ESHER

Elizabeth Gant, 8 Sandon Close, Esher, KT10 8JE. Prop: Elizabeth Gant. Tel: (020) 8398-0962. Fax: (020) 8398-5107. Website: www.bookline.co.uk. E-mail: egant@bookline.co.uk. Est: 1982. Private premises. Appointment necessary. Small stock. Spec: Children's - General; Illustrated. PR: £1–800. CC: JCB; V. Cata: 3 a year, every four months. Mem: ABA; PBFA. [Updated]

EWELL

Ewell Bookshop, ■ 9A High Street, Ewell, Epsom, KT17 1SG. Prop: Patrick Hillman. Tel: (020) 8383 1283. E-mail: ewellbookshop@hotmail.com. Est: 2002. Shop open: **T:** 09:30–17:00; **W:** 09:30–17:00; **Th:** 09:30–17:00; **F:** 13:00–19:00; **S:** 09:00–17:00. Medium stock. Spec: Aviation; Military History; Naval; Railways; Topography - General; Topography - Local; Transport; also Booksearch. PR: £1–200. [Updated]

New dealers in the British Isles can register their business on
www.sheppardsdirectories.com

J.W. McKenzie Ltd, ■ 12 Stoneleigh Park Road, Ewell, Epsom, KT19 0QT. (*). Tel: (0208) 3937700. Website: www.mckenzie-cricket.co.uk. E-mail: jwmck@netcomuk.co.uk. Est: 1971. Internet and postal. Shop open: **M:** 09:00–17:00; **T:** 09:00–17:00; **W:** 09:00–17:00; **Th:** 09:00–17:00; **F:** 09:00–17:00; **S:** 10:00–13:00; Closed for lunch: 13:00–14:00. Medium stock. Spec: Sport - Cricket. CC: E; JCB; MC; V. Cata: 4 occasionally. [Updated]

FARNHAM

Derek Burden, 1 Boundstone Road, Wrecclesham, Farnham, GU10 4TH. Prop: Derek Burden. Tel: (01252) 793615. Fax: (01252) 794789. E-mail: dweburden@aol.com. Est: 1967. Private premises. Internet and postal. Appointment necessary. Large stock. Spec: Graphics; Illustrated. PR: £1–1,000. [Updated]

Oxfam, ■ 3 The Woolmead, Farnham, GU7 9TX. Tel: (01252) 726951. Fax: (01252) 726951. Est: 1943. Shop open: **M:** 09:30–16:30; **T:** 09:30–16:30; **W:** 09:30–16:30; **Th:** 09:30–16:30; **F:** 09:30–16:30; **S:** 09:30–16:29. Very small general stock. PR: £1–3. CC: MC; V; SW. [09/07/2003]

GODALMING

Catalyst Booksearch Services, 1 Weston House, Ballfield Road, Godalming, GU7 2HB. Prop: Patrick Blosse. Tel: 01483 428500. Website: www.abebooks.com/home/PATBLOSSE/. E-mail: books@catalystbs.com. Est: 1997. Private premises. Internet and postal. Appointment necessary. Large stock. Spec: Animals and Birds; Annuals; Author - General; Biography; Children's - General; Children's - Illustrated; Cinema/Film; Crime (True); Drama; Fiction - General; Fiction - Crime, Detective, Spy, Thrillers; First Editions; History - General; Natural History. PR: £2–250. [Updated]

Crouch Rare Books, Syringa, Tuesley Lane, Godalming, GU7 1SB. Prop: A.S. Crouch. Tel: (01483) 420390. Fax: (01483) 421371. Website: www.crbooks.co.uk. E-mail: tcrouch@crbooks.co.uk. Est: 1970. Storeroom. Internet and postal. Telephone first. Open: **M:** 09:00–17:30; **T:** 09:00–17:30; **W:** 09:00–17:30; **F:** 09:00–17:30; **S:** 09:00–17:30; Closed for lunch: 13:00–14:00. Medium stock. Spec: Academic/Scholarly; Antiquarian; Archaeology; Canals/Inland Waterways; Classical Studies; Countries - Greece; Crafts; Ecclesiastical History & Architecture; Egyptology; Embroidery; Foreign Texts; History - General; History of Civilisation; Lace; Languages - Foreign; Literature; Medieval; Religion - Christian; Religion - Jewish; Textiles; Theology. PR: £2–1,000. CC: AE; JCB; MC; V; Switch. Also, publishers. Cata: 3 a year. Corresp: French, Greek, Latin. VAT No: GB 417 6129 55. [Updated]

HASLEMERE

Anglo-American Rare Books, Galleons Lap, P.O. Box 71, Haslemere, GU27 1YT. Prop: Jack Laurence and David Purt. Tel: (01428) 606462. Fax: (01428) 606462. E-mail: anglobooks@aol.com. Est: 1995. Private premises. Postal business only. Small stock. Spec: Americana; Author - General; Author - Eliot, T.S.; Author - Greene, Graham; Author - Hemingway, Ernest; Author - James, Henry; Author - Mailer, Norman; Author - Murdoch, I.; Author - Sassoon, Siegfried; Fiction - General; Journalism; Literature. PR: £5–2,000. Also, a booksearch service. Mem: PBFA. [20/08/2003]

HINDHEAD

Beacon Hill Bookshop, ■ Beacon Hill Road, Hindhead, GU26 6QL. Prop: Stan & Cherie Jenks. Tel: (01428) 606783. Est: 1970. Shop open: **M:** 09:00–16:00; **T:** 09:00–16:00; **Th:** 09:00–16:00; **F:** 09:00–16:00; **S:** 09:00–16:00. Large general stock. Cata: 52 a year to trade only. [Updated]

HORLEY

Reigate Galleries, Cedar Cottage, Haroldslea Drive, Horley, RH6 9PH. Prop: K. & J. Morrish. Tel: (01293) 773426. Est: 1960. Private premises. Postal business only. Contactable. Open: **M:** 09:00–17:00; **T:** 09:00–17:00; **W:** 09:00–12:00; **Th:** 09:00–17:00; **F:** 09:00–17:00. Small general stock. PR: £5–300. CC: MC; V. Mem: PBFA. [Updated]

LEATHERHEAD

Dandy Lion Editions, ■ 63, High Street, Leatherhead, KT22 8AQ. Prop: Angela McCarthy. Tel: (01372) 377785. Website: www.dandylioneditions.co.uk. E-mail: angela@dandylioneditions.co.uk. Est: 1995. Internet and postal. Shop open: **T:** 10:00–16:30; **W:** 10:00–16:30; **Th:** 10:00–16:30; **F:** 10:00–16:30; **S:** 09:00–17:00. Medium stock. Spec: Academic/Scholarly; Art; Biography; Children's - General; Children's - Illustrated; Early Imprints; Entertainment - General; Folio Society, The; History - General; Lace; Military History; Natural Health; Natural History; New Age; Occult; Pacifism. PR: £1–100. CC: JCB; MC; Internet & Postal sales. [Updated]

MITCHAM

J.G. Natural History Books, 149 Sherwood Park Road, Mitcham, CR4 1NJ. Prop: J. Greatwood. Tel: (020) 8764-4669. Fax: (020) 8764-4669. Website: www.reptilebooks.com. E-mail: jgbooks@ btinternet.com. Est: 1969. Spec: Gemmology; Herpetology. PR: £10–500. CC: MC; V. Also, new books. Cata: 12 a year on new herpetological books only. [26/05/2003]

Kay Books Ltd., 88 Glebe Court, Mitcham, CR4 3NG. Tel: (020) 8640-7779. Fax: (020) 8640-7779. Est: 1968. Telephone first. Spec: Bindings; Topography - General; Travel - General. jacqui@ degnanj.fsnet.co.uk. Mem: PBFA. [01/07/2003]

NEW MALDEN

Steve Baxter, 13 Westbury Road, New Malden, KT3 5BE. Tel: (020) 8942-4431. Fax: (020) 8942-2249. E-mail: baxterfinebooks@aol.com. Private premises. Postal business only. Small stock. Spec: Antiquarian; Bindings; Churchilliana; Fine & Rare; First Editions; History - General; Literature; Sets of Books; also Booksearch. CC: AE; JCB; MC; V. Mem: ABA; PBFA; ILAB. VAT No: GB 711 1425 88. [Updated]

OXTED

Postings, P.O. Box 1, Oxted, RH8 0FD. Prop: R.N. Haffner. Tel: (01883) 722646. Fax: (01883) 722646. Est: 1992. Private premises. Postal business only. Very small stock. Spec: Aviation; Philately; Railways; Sport - Ballooning; Topography - Local; Transport. PR: £5–300. CC: E; JCB; MC; V. Also, postcards. Cata: 2 a year on postal history, memorabilia, civil aviation. Mem: PTS. [Updated]

Secondhand Bookshop, ■ 56 Station Road West, Oxted, RH8 9EU. Prop: David Neal. Tel: (01883) 715755. Est: 1993. Shop open: **M:** 10:00–17:00; **T:** 10:00–17:00; **W:** 10:00–17:00; **Th:** 10:00–17:00; **F:** 10:00–17:00; **S:** 10:00–17:00. Medium stock. PR: £1–400. Also, at home, by appointment. Also at: Books in the Basement, Oxted (q.v.) and Browsers's Coffee Shop, Lingfield, Surrey. VAT No: GB 725 4573 27. [Updated]

SHAMLEY GREEN

Eric Thompson, Hullhatch, Shamley Green, Guildford, GU5 0TG. Tel: (01483) 893694. Fax: (01483) 892219. Est: 1978. Private premises. Appointment necessary. Large stock. Spec: Motoring; also Booksearch. PR: £5–750. Cata: 1 a year on motoring. [Updated]

SURBITON

The Bookroom, ■ 146 Chiltern Drive, Surbiton, KT5 9HF. Prop: Keith Alexander. Tel: (020) 8404-6644. Fax: (020) 8399-8168. E-mail: kmabooks@aol.com. Est: 2002. Shop open: **W:** 11:00–18:00; **Th:** 11:00–18:00; **F:** 11:00–18:00; **S:** 11:00–18:00; Large stock. Spec: Academic/Scholarly; Advertising; Aeronautics; Agriculture; Antiques; Architecture; Art; Biography; Children's - General; Cinema/ Film; Fiction - General; Health; History - General; Modern First Editions; Music - General; Plays; Poetry. PR: £1–30. Fair organiser: see Title Page Book Fairs in prelims. [19/05/2003]

Caissa Books, 5 Pembroke Avenue, Berrylands, Surbiton, KT5 8HN. Prop: Mike Sheehan. Tel: (020) 8399 6591. Fax: (020) 8399 6591. E-mail: caissa.books@tinyworld.co.uk. Est: 1980. Postal business only. Contactable. Open: **M:** 14:00–20:00; **T:** 14:00–20:00; **W:** 14:00–20:00; **Th:** 14:00–20:00; **F:** 14:00–20:00. Small stock. Spec: Chess. PR: £3–3,000. CC: MC; V. Cata: 1 a year. Corresp: French and German. [Updated]

SUTTON

Nonsuch Books, 176 Mulgrave Road, Cheam, Sutton, SM2 6JS. Prop: Robert and Lynette Gleeson. Tel: (020) 8770 7875. E-mail: nonsuch.books@virgin.net. Est: 1990. Private premises. Postal business only. Appointment necessary. Open: **M:** 09:00–17:00; **T:** 09:00–17:00; **W:** 09:00–17:00; **Th:** 09:00–17:00; **F:** 09:00–17:00; **S:** 09:00–17:00. Small stock. Spec: Archaeology; Architecture; Art; Art - History; Art - Reference; History - General; Illustrated; Literature. PR: £5–200. [Updated]

WALLINGTON

RGS Books, 3 Dower Street, Wallington, SM6 0RG. Tel: (0208) 647 2003. Fax: (0208) 647 2003. E-mail: rgsbooks@btinternet.com. Est: 1960. Private premises. Internet and postal. Large general stock. Spec: Academic/Scholarly; Antiquarian; Antiques; Architecture; Art; Artists; Arts, The; Author - Wells, H.G.; Bibliography; Books about Books; Children's - General; Churchilliana; Drama; Ex-Libris; Fiction - General; Heraldry; History - General; Miniature Books; Oriental; Painting; Scottish Interest; Theatre. PR: £2–500. Stocks titles on history of London. Mem: PLA; SB. [Updated]

WALTON–ON–THAMES

Grey House Books, 2 Wilton Lodge, 35 Rydens Road, Walton–on–Thames, KT12 3DX. Prop: Camille Wolff. Tel: (01932) 245610. Est: 1972. Spec: Crime (True); Criminology. [26/08/2003]

Fred Lake, 104 Kings Road, Walton–on–Thames, KT12 2RE. Tel: (01932) 227824. Private premises. Postal business only. Very small stock. Spec: Periodicals & Magazines; Sport - Archery; Sport - Field Sports. PR: £1–150. [Updated]

WEYBRIDGE

Fun in Books, 5 Abbey Lands, Cobbetts Hill, Weybridge, KT13 0UB. Prop: Michael J. White. Tel: (01932) 852626. E-mail: mail@melitzer.freeserve.co.uk. Est: 1994. Storeroom. Postal business only. Spec: Freemasonry & Anti-Masonry; Glamour; Humour. PR: £5–1,000. CC: MC; V. Cata: 1 a year freemasonry. [Updated]

Mrs. D.M. Green, 7 Tower Grove, Weybridge, KT13 9LX. Tel: (01932) 241105. Est: 1974. Private premises. Appointment necessary. Very small stock. Spec: Atlases; Topography - General. PR: £1–3,500. Cata: Lists sent on request. Mem: IMCos. [Updated]

WOKING

Goldsworth Books & Prints Ltd, ■ 47 Goldsworth Road, Woking, GU21 6JY. Prop: Brian & Joyce Hartles. Tel: (01483) 767670. Fax: (01483) 767670. Website: goldsworthbooks.com. E-mail: brian@goldsworthbooks.com. Est: 1986. Internet and postal. Shop open: **T:** 10:00–17:00; **W:** 10:00–17:00; **Th:** 10:00–17:00; **F:** 10:00–17:00; **S:** 09:30–16:30. Very large stock. PR: £1–5,000. CC: JCB; V. Mem: PBFA. VAT No: GB 641 2513 73. [Updated]

Peter Kennedy, ■ 2 Shirley Place, Knaphill, Woking, GU21 2PL. Tel: (01483) 797293. Fax: (01483) 488006. E-mail: peter@peterkennedy.com. Est: 1972. Shop open. Shop at: at 87 Portobello Road, London W11. Open: **S:** 08:00–16:00. Spec: Atlases; Botany; Illustrated; Natural History. CC: V. Also, antique prints. Appointment necessary Mon-Friday. Mem: ABA. [Updated]

TYNE AND WEAR

LIVERSEDGE

Heckmondwike Book Shop, ■ 66 Union Road, Liversedge, WF15 7JF. Prop: David Sheard. Tel: (01924) 505666. E-mail: david.sheard@ntlworld.com. Est: 1984. Shop; Internet and postal. Open. Shop at: 21 Milton Road Norristhorpe West Yorkshire WF15 7BB. Open: **S:** 10:00–17:00. Large stock. Spec: Author - Wheatley, Dennis; Fiction - General; Fiction - Crime, Detective, Spy, Thrillers; Fiction - Science Fiction; Publishers - Pan; Publishers - Penguin; Publishers - Puffin; Vintage Paperbacks. PR: £1–100. Will open shop at other times by arrangement. VAT No: GB 427 5900 45. [Updated]

NEWCASTLE UPON TYNE

Frank Smith Maritime Aviation, ■ 92 Heaton Road, Newcastle upon Tyne, NE6 5HL. Prop: Alan Parker. Tel: (0191) 265-6333. Fax: (0191) 224-2620. E-mail: books@franksmith.freeserve.co.uk. Est: 1981. Internet and postal. Shop open: **M:** 10:00–16:00; **T:** 10:00–16:00; **W:** 10:00–16:00; **Th:** 10:00–16:00; **F:** 09:00–16:00. Large stock. Spec: Aviation; Maritime/Nautical; Motoring; Shipbuilding; Sport - Yachting. PR: £4–1,000. CC: AE; E; JCB; MC; V. Cata: 24 monthly on Aviation & Maritime. Corresp: German, French, Dutch. Mem: PBFA. VAT No: GB 297 9302 12. [Updated]

Robert D. Steedman, ■ 9 Grey Street, Newcastle upon Tyne, NE1 6EE. Prop: D.J. Steedman. Tel: (0191) 232-6561. Est: 1907. Shop open: **M:** 09:00–17:00; **T:** 09:00–17:00; **W:** 09:00–17:00; **Th:** 09:00–17:00; **F:** 09:00–17:00; **S:** 09:00–12:30. Large general stock. PR: £1–5,000. CC: JCB; MC; V; S, SW. Cata: occasionally. Mem: ABA; BA. VAT No: GB 177 1638 41. [Updated]

NORTH SHIELDS

Keel Row Books, ■ 11 Fenwick Terrace, Preston Road, North Shields, NE29 0LU. Tel: Withheld. Est: 1980. Shop open: **M:** 10:30–17:00; **T:** 10:30–17:00; **Th:** 10:30–17:00; **F:** 10:30–17:00; **S:** 10:30–17:00; **Su:** 11:00–16:00. Very large stock. Spec: Alpinism/Mountaineering; Art; Children's - General; Cinema/Film; Comic Books & Annuals; Crime (True); Military; Military History; Politics; Railways; Theatre; Voyages & Discovery; War - General. PR: £1–700. [Updated]

WHITLEY BAY

Olivers Bookshop, ■ 48a Whitley Road, Whitley Bay, NE26 2NF. Prop: John Oliver. Tel: (0191) 251-3552. Est: 1987. Shop open: **M:** 11:00–17:00; **Th:** 11:00–17:00; **F:** 11:00–17:00. Medium stock. PR: £1–500. Mobile (0771) 8392830. [17/09/2003]

The Rider Haggard Society, 27 Deneholm, Monkseaton, Whitley Bay, NE25 9AU. Tel: (0191) 252-4516. Fax: (0191) 252-4516. E-mail: rb27allen@aol.com. Very small stock. Spec: Author - Haggard, Sir Henry Rider; Author - Heyer, Georgette; Author - Stoker, B.; also Booksearch. PR: £2–300. Also, Editor for the Rider Haggard Society. Cata: on request. Corresp: French, Spanish. [Updated]

WARWICKSHIRE

ALCESTER

Home Farm Books, 44 Evesham Road, Cookhill, Alcester, B49 5LJ. Prop: Tony Read. Tel: (01789) 763115. Fax: (01789) 766086. E-mail: readbk@globalnet.co.uk. Est: 1979. Private premises. Postal business only. Small stock. Spec: Cockfighting; Dogs; Firearms/Guns; Natural History; Rural Life; Sport - Angling/Fishing; Sport - Big Game Hunting; Sport - Falconry; Sport - Field Sports; Taxidermy; also Booksearch. PR: £2–400. Cata: 4 a year on specialities. [29/07/2003]

HENLEY–IN–ARDEN

Arden Books & Cosmographia, 11 Pound Field, Wootton Wawen, Henley–in–Arden, B95 6AQ. Prop: David Daymond. Tel: (01564) 793476. Est: 1998. Private premises. Postal business only. Small general stock. Spec: Antiques; Art; Biography; Canals/Inland Waterways; Children's - General; Crafts; Food & Drink; Gardening; Guide Books; History - General; History - Local; Maritime/Nautical; Natural History; Needlework; Poetry; Railways; Rural Life; Topography - General. PR: £1–50. Corresp: French, German. [Updated]

KENILWORTH

LSA Books, 45 Randall Road, Kenilworth, CV8 1JX. Prop: Les Anscombe. Tel: (01926) 850580. Website: www.ukbookworld.com/members/lesanscombe. E-mail: lesanscombe@lineone.net. Est: 1998. Private premises. Internet. Appointment necessary. Small general stock. Spec: Biography; Literature; Performing Arts. PR: £10–50. [11/05/2003]

KINETON

Kineton Books, ■ Bookshop, Southam Street, Kineton, CV35 0LP. Prop: J Neal. Tel: (01926) 640700. Website: www.kinetonbooks.co.uk. E-mail: josie@kinetonbooks.co.uk. Est: 1998. Shop at: 25 Shortacres, Kineton, Warwickshire, CV35 0LH. Open: **W:** 10:00–17:00; **Th:** 10:00–17:00; **F:** 10:00–17:00; **S:** 10:00–16:00. Medium stock. Spec: Annuals; Author - Milligan, Spike; Children's - General; Illustrated; Publishers - Ladybird Books. PR: £1–200. [Updated]

RUGBY

Central Bookshop, ■ 4 Central Buildings, Railway Terrace, Rugby, CV21 3EL. Prop: Jonathan & Amanda Sewell. Tel: (01788) 577853. E-mail: centralbookshop@aol.com. Est: 1998. Internet and postal. Shop open: **M:** 09:30–05:00; **Th:** 09:30–05:00; **F:** 09:30–05:00; **S:** 09:30–05:00. Very large stock. Spec: Architecture; Art; Autobiography; Crime (True); Fiction - General; History - General; Military; Modern First Editions; Travel - General; War - General. PR: £2–2,000. CC: AE; E; MC; V; Switch. [Updated]

STRATFORD–UPON–AVON

Chaucer Head Bookshop, ■ 21 Chapel Street, Stratford–upon–Avon, CV37 6EP. Prop: Richard & Vanessa James. Tel: (01789) 415691. Website: www.stratford-upon-avonbooks.co.uk. E-mail: books@stratford-upon-avonbooks.co.uk. Shop open: **M:** 10:00–18:00; **T:** 10:00–18:00; **W:** 10:00–18:00; **Th:** 10:10–18:00; **F:** 10:00–18:00; **S:** 10:00–18:00. Medium stock. Spec: Author - Corelli, Marie; Author - Shakespeare, William; Topography - Local. PR: £2–600. CC: MC; V; SW. Corresp: French. [Updated]

Paul Meekins Books, Valentines, Long Marston, Stratford–upon–Avon, CV37 8RG. Prop: Paul Meekins. Tel: (01789) 722434. Fax: (01789) 722434. Website: www.paulmeekins.co.uk. E-mail: paul@paulmeekins.co.uk. Est: 1989. Private premises. Internet and postal. Appointment necessary. See website for details of shows we attend. Large stock. Spec: Arms & Armour; Fashion & Costume; Firearms/Guns; History - General; History - Ancient; History - British; History - Middle Ages; Medicine - History of; Medieval; Military; Military History; Publishers - Roundwood Press; Rural Life; War - General. PR: £2–200. CC: MC; V. Cata: by subject, and listed on website. [Updated]

STUDLEY

Brewin Books Ltd., Doric House, 56 Alcester Road, Studley, B80 7NP. Director: K.A.F. Brewin. Tel: (01527) 854228. Fax: (01527) 852746. Website: www.brewinbooks.com. E-mail: admin@ brewinbooks.com. Est: 1973. Office &/or bookroom. Internet and postal. Telephone first. Open: **M:** 09:00–17:00; **T:** 09:00–17:00; **W:** 09:00–17:00; **Th:** 09:00–17:00; **F:** 09:00–17:00. Closed for lunch: 13:00–13:30. Medium stock. Spec: Aviation; Genealogy; Motoring; Railways; Steam Engines; Topography - Local; Transport; Vintage Cars.   Also, publishers of local history books. Cata: annually. VAT No: GB 705 0077 73. [Updated]

WARWICK

Duncan M. Allsop, ■ 68 Smith Street, Warwick, CV34 4HU. Tel: (01926) 493266. Fax: (01926) 493266. Website: www.clique.co.uk/abe.htm. E-mail: duncan.allsop@btopenworld.com. Est: 1966. Shop open: **M:** 09:30–17:30; **T:** 09:30–17:30; **W:** 09:30–17:30; **Th:** 09:30–17:30; **F:** 09:30–17:30; **S:** 09:30–17:30. Large stock. Spec: Antiquarian; Bindings; Fine & Rare. PR: £5–3,000. CC: MC; V; SW, SO. Mem: ABA. [16/06/2003]

Phillip Robbins, 3 Normandy Close, Hampton Magna, Warwick, CV35 8UB. Prop: Phillip John Robbins. Tel: (01926) 494368. E-mail: phillrobbins@yahoo.co.uk. Est: 1990. Private premises. Internet and postal. Contactable. Small stock. Spec: Author - Moore, John; Conservation; Entomology; Magic & Conjuring; Manuals - General; Manuals - Seamanship; Manuscripts; Marine Sciences; Maritime/Nautical; Natural History; also Booksearch. PR: £3–50. Mem: PBFA. [29/06/2003]

WEST MIDLANDS

BILSTON

Christine M. Chalk (Old & Out, 17 Regent Street, Bilston, WV14 6AP. Tel: (01902) 403978. Fax: (01902) 403978. E-mail: ChristineMChalk@aol.com. Est: 1996. Private premises. Postal business only. Very small stock. Spec: Art; Artists; Literature. PR: £1–200. Cata: occasonally. [Updated]

BIRMINGHAM

Afar Books International, 11 Church Place, 135 Edward Road, Balsall Heath, Birmingham, B12 9JQ. Prop: Alf Richardson. Tel: (0121) 440-3918. Est: 1990. Private premises. Postal business only. Medium stock. Spec: Anthropology; Black Studies; Colonial; Countries - Africa; Countries - Caribbean, The; Countries - Egypt; Egyptology; Voyages & Discovery; also Booksearch. PR: £1–300. Cata: 1 a year. Only telephone evenings or Sunday. [Updated]

Armchair Books, 26 Lysander Way, Castle Vale, Birmingham, B35 7JN. Prop: I.M. & L.E. Loader. Tel: (0121) 748-1710. Fax: (0121) 748 1710. Est: 1988. Private premises. Postal business only. Small general stock. Spec: Booksearch. PR: £1–150. Cata: 2 a year. [26/09/2004]

Birmingham Books, 202 Witton Lodge Road, Birmingham, B23 5BW. Prop: Mike Attree. Tel: (0121) 3845318. E-mail: mike.attree@blueyonder.co.uk. Est: 2004. Private premises. Internet and postal. Appointment necessary. Spec: Alpinism/Mountaineering; Author - Fleming, Ian; Author - Greene, Graham; Children's - Illustrated; Fiction - Crime, Detective, Spy, Thrillers; Fiction - Fantasy, Horror; Fiction - Science Fiction; Folio Society, The. [Updated]

Robin Doughty Fine Books, 100a Frederick Road, Stechford, Birmingham, B33 8AE. Tel: (0121) 783-7289. E-mail: robin.doughty@btinternet.com. Est: 1994. Private premises. Postal business only. Appointment necessary. Small general stock. Spec: Antiquarian; Art; Illustrated; Literature; Private Press; Religion - General; Religion - Quakers; Topography - General; Topography - Local. PR: £1–2,500. Mem: PBFA. [Updated]

Elmfield Books, 24 Elmfield Crescent, Moseley, Birmingham, B13 9TN. Prop: Liz Palmer. Tel: (0121) 689-6246. Website: www.elmfieldbooks.co.uk. E-mail: elmfieldbooks@blueyonder.co.uk. Est: 1999. Private premises. Internet and postal. Appointment necessary. Small stock. Spec: Cookery/Gastronomy; Food & Drink; Illustrated; Natural History; Topography - General; Topography - Local. PR: £5–500. Attend bookfairs and other events. Cata: 1 a year. Mem: PBFA. [Updated]

Heritage, P.O. Box 3075, Edgbaston, Birmingham, B15 2EW. Prop: Gill & Jem Wilyman. Tel: (0121) 440-2734. E-mail: heritagebook@aol.com. Est: 1985. Private premises. Book fairs only. Appointment necessary. Medium stock. Spec: Antiquarian; Atlases; Cartography; Ex-Libris; Heraldry; Illustrated; Motoring; Private Press; Royalty - General; Topography - Local. PR: £10–2,500. Mem: PBFA. [Updated]

Mood Indigo Books, 22 Sterling Court, 48 Newhall Hill, Birmingham, B1 3JN. Prop: K. Rajput. Tel: (07817) 225345. E-mail: moodindigobooks@hotmail.com. Private premises. Postal business only. Very small stock. Spec: Languages - Foreign; Literature; Religion - Islam. PR: £15–200. Also, Internet booksellers. Corresp: Farsi, French. Mem: Also at: Maryland, USA. [14/04/2003]

Moseley Books, 7 Cornerstone, Birmingham, B13 8EN. Tel: (0121) 442 6062. Website: www.moseleybooks.co.uk. E-mail: john@moseleybooks.co.uk. Est: 2002. Storeroom. Internet and postal. Small stock. Spec: Classical Studies; Humanities; Philosophy; Politics. PR: £2–50. [Updated]

Kelvin Watson, 616 Pershore Road, Birmingham, B29 7HG. Tel: (0121) 472-8556. E-mail: kelvin39endpaper@aol.com. Est: 1980. Spec: Philosophy; Poetry. [14/04/2003]

Stephen Wycherley, ■ 508 Bristol Road, Selly Oak, Birmingham, B29 6BD. Prop: Stephen & Elizabeth Wycherley. Tel: (0121) 471-1006. Est: 1971. Shop open: **M:** 10:00–17:00; **T:** 10:00–17:00; **Th:** 10:00–17:00; **F:** 10:00–17:00; **S:** 10:00–17:00. Large general stock. PR: £1–500. Summer (July-August) open on Thursdays and Fridays only. Cata: occasional short single lists. Corresp: French, Dutch. Mem: PBFA. [Updated]

COVENTRY

Armstrongs Books & Collectable, ■ 178 Albany Road, Earlsdon, Coventry, CV5 6NG. Prop: Colin Rowe Armstrong. Tel: (024) 7671-4344. Est: 1983. Shop open: **M:** 10:00–18:00; **T:** 10:00–18:00; **W:** 10:00–18:00; **Th:** 10:00–18:00; **F:** 10:00–18:00; **S:** 10:00–18:00. Medium stock. Spec: Comic Books & Annuals; Comics; Fiction - Science Fiction; First Editions; Publishers - Penguin. PR: £1–100. [20/05/2003]

Malcolm Harris (Books), 154 Avon Street, Coventry, CV2 3GP. Tel: (withheld). Private premises. Postal business only. Very small stock. Spec: Autobiography; Fiction - Crime, Detective, Spy, Thrillers; Modern First Editions; Signed Editions; Theatre, also Booksearch. Cata: as requested. [Updated]

Silver Trees Books, Silver Trees Farm, Balsall St., Balsall Common, Coventry, CV7 7AR. Prop: Brian and Elaine Hitchens. Tel: (01676) 533143. Fax: (01676) 533143. Website: www.abebooks.com. E-mail: brian.hitchens@tesco.net. Private premises. Postal business only. Telephone first. Small stock. Spec: Ceramics; Children's - General; Gardening; Military; Modern First Editions. PR: £3–1,500. CC: AE; JCB; MC; V; Switch. Corresp: French. [Updated]

HALESOWEN

Anvil Books, ■ 52 Summer Hill, Halesowen, B63 3BU. Prop: J.K. Maddison & C.J. Murtagh. Tel: (0121) 550-0600. Website: www.anvilbookshalesowen.co.uk. E-mail: jkm@anvilbookshalesowen. co.uk. Est: 1997. Shop; Internet and postal. Telephone first. Open: **T:** 10:00–17:00. **Th:** 10:00–17:00. **S:** 10:00–17:00. Medium stock. Spec: Art; Canals/Inland Waterways; History - Industrial; Industry; Maritime/Nautical; Navigation; Railways; Shipbuilding; Topography - Local; Transport; also Booksearch. PR: £1–200. [updated]

Janus Books / Waverley Fairs, Newlands, 9 Hayley Park, Hayley Green, Halesowen, B61 1EJ. Prop: Royston Thomas Slim. Tel: (0121) 550-4123. Est: 1968. Private premises. Postal business only. Open: Small stock. Spec: Motoring; Topography - General; Topography - Local; War - General. PR: £1–500. Also, book fair organiser – see prelims: Kinver, Powick (Malvern) and Bromsgrove Antique Fairs. [Updated]

KINGSWINFORD

Wright Trace Books, 70 Ash Crescent, Kingswinford, DY6 8DH. Prop: Colin Micklewright and Pam Wright. Tel: (01384) 341211. Est: 2001. Postal business only. Spec: Animals and Birds; Annuals; Dogs; Modern First Editions; also Booksearch. [02/02/2003]

OLDBURY

Anthony Dyson, 57 St John's Road, Oldbury, B68 9SA. Tel: (0121) 544-5386. Est: 1973. Private premises. Appointment necessary. Small stock. Spec: Fashion & Costume; Fiction - Crime, Detective, Spy, Thrillers; Literary Criticism; Literature. Cata: frequently. [Updated]

SALTLEY

Albion Books, Beechcroft, 15 Woodlands Road, Saltley, Birmingham, B8 3AG. Prop: John Bentley. Tel: (0121) 328 2878. Est: 1999. Private premises. Postal business only. Small stock. Spec: Military; Military History; War - General; War - World War I; also Booksearch. PR: £1–100. Other subjects: origins of the Great War; international politics. [Updated]

SOLIHULL

Fifth Element, 15 St. Lawrence Close, Knowle, Solihull, B93 0EU. Prop: Michael Rogers. Tel: (01564) 773106. E-mail: fifthelement@postmaster.co.uk. Est: 1996. Postal business only. Spec: Author - Wilson, Colin; Beat Writers; Counterculture; Drugs; Esoteric. [Updated]

Helion & Company Ltd, 26 Willow Road, Solihull, B91 1UE. Tel: (0121) 705-3393. Fax: (0121) 711-4075. Website: www.helion.co.uk. E-mail: books@helion.co.uk. Est: 1992. Private premises. Postal business only. Very large stock. Spec: Academic/Scholarly; Archaeology; Arms & Armour; Aviation; Countries - Germany; Firearms/Guns; History - General; History - 19th Century; History - American; History - Anarchism; History - Ancient; History - British; History - Byzantine; also free Booksearch. PR: £1–3,500. CC: AE; E; JCB; MC; V; Switch. Cata: quarterly. Corresp: German, French, Spanish. VAT No: GB 797 4185 72. [14/04/2003]

SUTTON COLDFIELD

Patrick Walcot, 60 Sunnybank Road, Sutton Coldfield, B73 5RJ. Patrick Walcot. Tel: (0121) 382-6381. Fax: 0870 0511 418. Website: www.walcot.demon.co.uk. E-mail: patrick@walcot.demon.co.uk. Est: 1980. Private premises. Postal business only. Appointment necessary. Very small stock. Spec: Travel - Polar. PR: £10–5,000. Cata: 2 a year on Polar Exploration. Mem: ABA. [Updated]

WALSALL (ALSO SEE UNDER STAFFORDSHIRE)

Margaret & Geoff Adkins, 7 Boscobel Road, Walsall, WS1 2PL. * Prop: Margaret Adkins. Tel: (01922) 622641 (answerphone). Est: 1995. Private premises. Postal business only. Small stock. Spec: Rural Life; Transport. PR: £1–100. Also attends book fairs. [30/06/2003]

A.J. Mobbs, 65 Broadstone Avenue, Walsall, WS3 1JA. Tel: (01922) 477281. Fax: (01922) 477281. Website: www.mobbs.birdbooks.btinternet.co.uk. E-mail: mobbs.birdbooks@btinternet.com. Est: 1982. Private premises. Internet and postal. Appointment necessary. Small stock. Spec: Academic/ Scholarly; Entomology; Herpetology; Natural Health; Natural History; Ornithology. PR: £1–200. [Updated]

J. & M.A. Worrallo, 29 Trees Road, The Delves, Walsall, WS1 3JU. Prop: John & Mark Anthony Worrallo. Tel: (01922) 721224. Website: www.ukbookworld.com/members/worras. E-mail: jworrallo@aol.com. Est: 1980. Private premises. Postal business only. Appointment necessary. Small general stock. Spec: Also, booksearch. PR: £1–100. [Updated]

WOLVERHAMPTON

Books & Bygones (Pam Taylor), ■ 19 Hollybush Lane, Penn, Wolverhampton, WV4 4JJ. Tel: (01902) 334020. Fax: (01902) 334747. Est: 1987. Shop open: **S:** 08:30–17:00; **Su:** 08:30–17:00. Medium stock. Spec: Authors - Women; Autographs; Dictionaries; Fiction - Science Fiction; History - General; History - Industrial; Magic & Conjuring; Performing Arts; Poetry; Scouts & Guides; Transport; Women. Open other times by appointment only. [Updated]

R. & S. Crombie, 73 Griffiths Drive, Wednesfield, Wolverhampton, WV11 2JN. Tel: (01902) 733462. E-mail: royandsheila@rcrombie.freeserve.co.uk. Est: 1995. Private premises. Book fairs only. Telephone first. PR: £1–100. [Updated]

Mogul Diamonds, 17 High Street, Albrighton, Wolverhampton, WV7 3JT. Prop: Gerald Leach. Tel: (01902) 372288. Website: www.ukbookworld.com/members/mogul. E-mail: moguldiamonds@ btopenworld.comk. Est: 1999. Spec: Biography; Biology; History - Local; Music - General; Topography - Local. PR: £1–200. Specialises in books about Shropshire. [Updated]

The Old Bookshop, ■ 53 Bath Road, Wolverhampton, WV1 4EL. Prop: Kate Lee. Tel: (01902) 421055. E-mail: theoldbookshop@btopenworld.com. Est: 1967. Shop open: **M:** 13:00–15:00; **T:** 10:10–15:15; **W:** 10:00–15:00; **Th:** 10:00–15:00; **F:** 10:00–15:00; **S:** 10:00–17:00. Very large stock. Spec: Art; Embroidery; History - General; Literature; Needlework; Theology; Topography - Local. PR: £1–200. CC: MC; V. [03/08/2003]

WEST SUSSEX

ARUNDEL

Kims Bookshop, ■ 10 High Street, Arundel, BN18 9AB. Prop: Mrs L.L Flowers. Tel: (01903) 882680. Website: www.kimsbookshop.com. E-mail: kimsbookshop@hotmail.com. Est: 1977. Shop open: **M:** 10:00–17:00; **T:** 10:00–17:00; **W:** 10:00–17:00; **Th:** 10:00–17:00; **F:** 10:00–17:00; **S:** 10:00–17:30; **Su:** 10:30–17:00. Large stock. Spec: Aeronautics; Archaeology; Artists; Astrology; Author - General; Books about Books; Comics; Company History; Diaries; Folio Society, The; Food & Drink; Gardening; History - General; Letters; Literary Criticism; Literature; Music - General; Needlework. PR: £1–1,000. CC: V. Also at: Worthing and Chichester. VAT No: GB 193 1791 43. [Updated]

Baynton–Williams Gallery, 37a High Street, Arundel, BN18 9AB. Prop: Sarah & Roger Baynton–Williams. Tel: (01903) 883588. Fax: (01903) 883588. Website: www.baynton-williams.com. E-mail: gallery@baynton-williams.freeserve.co.uk. Est: 1946. Spec: Atlases; Travel - General. PR: £100–15,000. Also, prints & maps. [Updated]

BILLINGSHURST

Books and Things, 58–62 High Street, Billingshurst, RH14 9NY. Prop: Jean Lawson. Tel: (01403) 785131. E-mail: Est: 1976. Spec: Booksearch. PR: £1–100. [28/08/2003]

BOGNOR REGIS

Meadowcroft Books, 21 Upper Bognor Road, Bognor Regis, PO21 1JA. Prop: Emma Laing & Anthony Parry. Tel: (01243) 868614 (24hr. Fax: (01243) 868714 (24hr). Website: www.meadowcroftbooks .demon.co.uk. E-mail: quotes@meadowcroftbooks.demon.co.uk. Est: 1996. Private premises. Appointment necessary. Very small stock. Spec: Primarily Booksearch. PR: £1–50. CC: MC; V; SW. VAT No: GB 699 0227 01. [14/04/2003]

CHICHESTER

The Chichester Bookshop, ■ 39 Southgate, Chichester, PO19 1DP. Prop: Nicholas Howell. Tel: (01243) 785473. E-mail: chibooks@fsbdial.co.uk. Est: 1994. Shop open: **M:** 09:30–17:00; **T:** 09:30–17:00; **W:** 09:30–17:00; **Th:** 09:30–17:00; **F:** 09:30–17:00; **S:** 09:30–17:00. Large stock. Spec: Railways; Topography - Local; also Booksearch and valuations. Mem: PBFA. [Updated]

Peter Hancock, ■ 40–41 West Street, Chichester, PO19 1RP. Tel: (01243) 786173. Fax: (01243) 778865. Est: 1965. Shop open: **T:** 10:00–17:30; **W:** 10:00–17:30; **Th:** 10:00–17:30; **F:** 10:00–17:30; **S:** 10:30–17:30. Small general stock. Spec: Aeronautics; Alpinism/Mountaineering; Americana; Antiquarian. PR: £5–500. CC: AE; E; JCB; MC; V. VAT No: GB 192 8554 28. [Updated]

Kims Bookshop, ■ 28 South Street, Chichester, PO19 1EL. Tel: (01243) 778477. Website: www.kimsbookshop.com. E-mail: kimsbookshop@hotmail.com. Est: 1972. Shop open: **M:** 10:00–17:00; **T:** 10:00–17:00; **W:** 10:00–17:00; **Th:** 10:00–17:00; **F:** 10:00–17:00; **S:** 09:30–17:30. Very large stock. PR: £1–10. Also at: Worthing and Arundel. [Updated]

Stride & Son, Southdown House, St. John's Street, Chichester, PO19 1XQ. Prop: Mark Hewitt & others. Tel: (01243) 780207. Fax: (01243) 786713. Website: www.stridesauctions.co.uk. E-mail: enquiries@ stridesauctions.co.uk. Est: 1890. Office &/or bookroom. Internet and postal. Appointment necessary. Open: **W:** 09:30–13:00. Spec: Advertising; Anthropology; Antiquarian; Archaeology; Architecture; Arms & Armour; Art; Atlases; Author - General; Autobiography; Churchilliana. PR: £10–10,000. CC: MC; V. Cata: 3 sales per year. Mem: RICS. VAT No: GB 193 0045 83. [29/06/2003]

COWFOLD

Michael Phelps, Allfreys House, Bolney Road, Cowfold, RH13 8AZ. Tel: (01403) 864049. Fax: (01403) 864730. E-mail: phelobooks@tiscali.co.uk. Est: 1974. Spec: Aeronautics; Alchemy; Astronomy; Aviation; Botany; Brewing; Chemistry; Engineering; Geology; Herbalism; Homeopathy; Hydrography; Mathematics; Medicine; Medicine - History of; Microscopy; Mineralogy; Mining; Natural History; Natural Sciences. PR: £10–100. [17/07/2003]

EAST GRINSTEAD

The Bookshop, ■ Tudor House, 22 High Street, East Grinstead, RH19 3AW. Prop: J. & H. Pye. Tel: (01342) 322669. Shop open: **M:** 09:00–17:30; **T:** 09:00–17:30; **W:** 09:00–17:30; **Th:** 09:00–17:30; **F:** 09:00–17:30; **S:** 09:00–17:30. Medium stock. Spec: History - General; also Booksearch. CC: AE; MC; V. Mem: BA. VAT No: GB 472 9663 08. [Updated]

GORING–BY–SEA

Barry Jones, Daymer Cottage, 28 Marine Crescent, Goring–by–Sea, BN12 4JF. Tel: (01903) 244655. Fax: (01903) 244655. Est: 1990. Private premises. Appointment necessary. Medium stock. Spec: Railways; Traction Engines; Transport. PR: £1–500. Appointments only between 09:00 and 21:00. Railway Collectors Fairs Organiser. Cata: 1 a year on railways. [Updated]

HASSOCKS

Doro Books, Lower Sands, Brighton Road, Hassocks, BN6 9LY. Prop: D. & R. Franklin. Tel: (01273) 843293. Est: 1985. Private premises. Postal business only. Very large stock. Spec: Company History; Illustrated; Industry; Juvenile. PR: £1–500. Cata: occasionally. Corresp: Most European. Mem: PBFA. [Updated]

Post Mortem Books, 58 Stanford Ave, Hassocks, BN6 8JH. Prop: Ralph Spurrier. Tel: (01273) 843066. Fax: (0870) 161-7332. Website: www.postmortembooks.com. E-mail: ralph@pmbooks.demon.co.uk. Est: 1979. Private premises. Internet and postal. Appointment necessary. Open: **M:** 08:00–18:00; **T:** 08:10–18:18; **Th:** 08:00–18:00; **F:** 10:00–16:00; **S:** 01:00–00:00. Medium stock. Spec: Fiction - Crime, Detective, Spy, Thrillers. PR: £5–1,000. CC: AE; MC; V; Maestro. Cata: 2 a year. [Updated]

B. & C. Seago, Flat 2, 107 Keymer Road, Keymer, Hassocks, BN68 8QL. Prop: Brian and Chris Seago. Tel: (01273) 841429. Est: 1974. Private premises. Appointment necessary. Small general stock. PR: £20–1,000. Also, prints and maps. [28/04/2003]

HORSHAM

Horsham Bookshop, ■ 4 Park Place, Horsham, RH12 1DG. Prop: Nick, Tom & Christine Costin. Tel: (01403) 252187. Website: www.horshambookshop.com. E-mail: sales@horshambookshop.com. Est: 1986. Shop open: **T:** 09:30–17:00; **W:** 09:30–17:00; **Th:** 09:30–17:00; **F:** 09:30–17:00; **S:** 09:30–17:00. Very large general stock. Spec: Antiquarian; Art; Aviation; Bindings; Biography; History - General; History - Local; Military; Motoring; Topography - Local. PR: £1–20,000. CC: AE; MC; V; Maestro. Mem: PBFA. [Updated]

Merlin Books, P.O. Box 153, Horsham, RH12 2YG. Prop: Mike Husband. Tel: (01403) 257626. Fax: (01403) 257626. Website: www.merlinbooks.com. E-mail: info@merlinbooks.com. Est: 1990. Private premises. Internet and postal. Telephone first. Very small stock. Spec: Motorbikes; also Booksearch. PR: £2–60. CC: E; JCB; MC; V. Cata: 8 a year. [Updated]

LANCING

Paul Evans Books, 13 Berriedale Drive, Sompting, Lancing, BN15 OLE. Tel: (01903) 764655. Fax: (01903) 764655. Website: www.paulevansbooks.com. E-mail: paulevans@paulevansbooks.com. Est: 1991. Private premises. Postal business only. Appointment necessary. Small stock. Spec: Art; Author - Bloomsbury Group, The; Author - Sackville-West, Vita; Author - Woolf, Virginia; Publishers - Hogarth Press. PR: £5–50,000. Cata: 3 – or 4 on specialities. [Updated]

LITTLEHAMPTON

Buckland Books, Holly Tree House, 18 Woodlands Road, Littlehampton, BN17 5PP. Prop: Mr. Chris Blanchett. Tel: (01903) 717648. Fax: (01903) 717648. Website: www.tiles.org/pages/bookshlf.htm. E-mail: cblanchett@lineone.net. Est: 1991. Private premises. Postal business only. Appointment necessary. Small stock. Spec: Antiques; Architecture; Building & Construction; Ceramics; Collecting; Decorative Art; Interior Design. PR: £2–300. CC: MC; V; Switch. Also, new books from around the world. Cata: 2 – 6 monthly. VAT No: GB 630 8660 43. [14/04/2003]

JB Books & Collectables, 14 Kingsmead, Thornlea Park, Littlehampton, BN17 7QS. Prop: Mrs J. Brittain. Tel: (01903) 725819. Fax: (01903) 725819. Website: www.jbbooks.co.uk. E-mail: jan@jbbooks.co.uk. Est: 1997. Private premises. Internet and postal. Telephone first. Open: **M:** 09:00–17:30; **T:** 09:00–17:30; **W:** 09:00–17:30; **Th:** 09:00–17:30; **F:** 09:00–17:30; **S:** 09:00–17:00; Closed for lunch: 13:00–14:00. Small general stock. Spec: Children's - General; Illustrated. PR: £1–500. CC: JCB; MC; V; Maestro. Mem: PBFA. [Updated]

Chris Adam Smith Modern First, 9 Western Road, Littlehampton, BN17 5NP. Tel: (01903) 722392. Website: www.adamsmithbooks.com. E-mail: chrisadamsmith@btinternet.com. Est: 1993. Private premises. Internet and postal. Appointment necessary. Small stock. Spec: Children's - General; Fiction - Crime, Detective, Spy, Thrillers; Fiction - Historical; Fiction - Science Fiction; Maritime/ Nautical; Modern First Editions. PR: £10–4,000. CC: AE; E; JCB; MC; SW. [Updated]

South Downs Book Service, Garden Cottage, 39c Arundel Road, Littlehampton, BN17 7BY. Prop: Ms. J.A. Bristow. Tel: (01903) 723401. Fax: (01903) 726318. Est: 1994. Private premises. Postal business only. Appointment necessary. Small stock. Spec: Academic/Scholarly; Antiquarian; Diaries; Ecclesiastical History & Architecture; Economics; History - Industrial; History - Local; History - National; Maritime/Nautical; Social History. PR: £4–400. [Updated]

MIDHURST

Wheeler's Bookshop, ■ Red Lion Street, Midhurst, GU29 9PB. Prop: Mr. Simon Wheeler. Tel: (01730) 817666. Website: www.abebooks.com/home/SIMONWHEELER. E-mail: info@ wheelersbookshop.co.uk. Shop open: **M:** 10:00–17:00; **T:** 10:00–17:00; **W:** 10:00–17:00; **Th:** 10:10– 17:17; **F:** 10:00–17:00; **S:** 10:00–17:00. Medium stock. Spec: Booksearch. CC: E; MC; V. [Updated]

PETWORTH

Tim Boss, North Street, Petworth, GU28 0DD. Prop: Tim Boss. Tel: (01798) 343170. Est: 1993. Private premises. Postal business only. Small stock. PR: £1–350. Also, 10,000 inexpensive prints; some maps. Exhibits at bookfairs. [Updated]

Muttonchop Manuscripts, ■ The Playhouse Gallery, Lombard Street, Petworth, GU28 0AG. Prop: Roger Clarke. Tel: (01798) 344471. Fax: (01798) 344471. E-mail: rogmutton@aol.com. Est: 1992. Shop open: **T:** 10:00–16:00; **W:** 10:00–16:00; **Th:** 10:00–16:00; **F:** 10:00–16:00; **S:** 10:00–17:00. Medium stock. Spec: Agriculture; Antiquarian; Bibliography; Bindings; Books about Books; Erotica; Fables; Farming & Livestock; Firearms/Guns; Glamour; Manuscripts; Odd & Unusual; Traction Engines; Transport. PR: £5–5,000. CC: D; E; JCB; MC; V; SW, S. Corresp: French. Mem: PBFA. VAT No: GB 704 6864 26. [17/04/2003]

PLAISTOW

Explorer Books, Fallow Chase, Durfold Wood, Plaistow, RH14 OPL. Prop: J.I. & S.J. Simper. Tel: (01483) 200286. Fax: (01483) 200286. E-mail: explbooks@aol.com. Est: 1985. Private premises. Appointment necessary. Very small stock. Spec: Countries - Antarctic, The; Countries - Arctic, The; Countries - Greenland; Countries - Polar; Travel - Polar; Voyages & Discovery. PR: £10–1,000. Cata: 3 A YEAR. [Updated]

SHOREHAM–BY–SEA

Sansovino Books, 9 Mill Lane, Shoreham–By–Sea, BN43 5AG. Prop: Q. & R. Barry. Tel: (01273) 455753. Est: 1991. Storeroom. Appointment necessary. Medium stock. Spec: First Editions; Literature; Maritime/Nautical; Military; Private Press; also Booksearch. PR: £5–200. Cata: 3 a year, general. Also at: Sansovino, Stokelsy, Cleveland. [Updated]

A.C. Seddon, 53 Old Fort Road, Shoreham–by–Sea, BN43 5RL. Tel: (01273) 461501. Est: 1978. Private premises. Appointment necessary. Small stock. Spec: Author - Swinburne, A.C.; Literature; Modern First Editions; Vintage Paperbacks. [01/07/2003]

STEYNING

dgbbooks, 15 Ingram Road, Steyning, BN44 3PF. Prop: Denise Bennett. Tel: (01903) 814895. E-mail: dgbbooks@talk21.com. Internet. Spec: Authors - Women; Biography; Fiction - General. PR: £5–50. [Updated]

WALDERTON

John Henly, 1 Brooklands, Walderton, Chichester, PO18 9EE. Tel: (023) 9263-1426. Fax: (023) 9263-1544. E-mail: johnhenly1@compuserve.com. Est: 1986. Private premises. Postal business only. Appointment necessary. Spec: Geology; Mineralogy; Natural History; Palaeontology. CC: MC; V. Cata: 4 a year. Mem: PBFA. VAT No: GB 582 5689 92. [Updated]

WORTHING

Badgers Books, ■ 8–10 Gratwicke Road, Worthing, BN11 4BH. Prop: Ray Potter & Meriel Cocks. Tel: (01903) 211816.   Est: 1982. Shop open: **M:** 09:00–17:30; **T:** 09:00–17:30; **W:** 09:00–17:30; **Th:** 09:00–17:30; **F:** 09:00–17:30; **S:** 09:00–18:00. Large general stock. CC: E; JCB; MC; V; SW, EL, SO.   VAT No: GB 587 5552 89. [Updated]

Kim's Bookshop, ■ 19 Crescent Road, Worthing, BN11 1RL. Prop: Mrs. M.L. Francombe & Mrs. L.L. Flowers. Tel: (01903) 206282.   Website: www.kimsbookshop.com. E-mail: kimsbookshop@hotmail.com. Est: 1972. Shop open: **M:** 09:30–17:30; **T:** 09:30–17:30; **W:** 09:30–17:30; **Th:** 09:30–17:30; **F:** 09:30–17:30; **S:** 09:30–17:30. Very large stock. Spec: Antiques; Arts, The; Music - General; Natural History; Transport. PR: £1–1,000. CC: V. Book stock approx 50,000 titles.   Also at: 10 High St., Arundel, West Sussex BN18 9AB (q.v.) and 28 South St., Chichester, West Sussex PO19 1EL (q.v.). [Updated]

Optimus Books Ltd, ■ 8 Ann Street, Worthing, BN11 1NX. Tel: (01903) 205895. Fax: (01903) 213438. E-mail: optimusbooks@easynet.co.uk. Est: 1975. Shop. Internet and postal. Open: **M:** 09:00–17:30; **T:** 09:00–17:30; **W:** 09:00–17:30; **Th:** 09:00–17:30; **F:** 09:00–17:30; **S:** 09:00–17:30. Medium stock. CC: AE; MC; V. Mem: PBFA. VAT No: GB 193 7839 11. [25/06/2003]

Satara Books, 105 Hayling Rise, High Salvington, Worthing, BN13 3AQ. Prop: Phyl Tate. Tel: (01903) 267173. Est: 1987. Private premises.   Postal business only. Very small stock. Spec: Autobiography; Children's - General; Cinema/Film; First Editions; Guide Books; Modern First Editions; Topography - General; Topography - Local; Windmills & Watermills. PR: £10–200. Attends Southampton Book Fairs. [27/05/2003]

Jamie Sturgeon, 14 Longlands, Worthing, BN14 9NT. Tel: (01903) 201910. Private premises. Appointment necessary. Small stock. Spec: Fiction - Crime, Detective, Spy, Thrillers; also Booksearch. PR: £1–100. Cata: 4 a year.   [15/04/2003]

WEST YORKSHIRE

BATLEY

Vintage Motorshop, ■ 749 Bradford Road, Batley, WF17 8HZ. Prop: R. & C. Hunt. Tel: (01924) 470773. Fax: (01924) 470773. Website: www.vintagemotorshop.co.uk. E-mail: books@ vintagemotorshop.co.uk. Est: 1976. Shop open: **Th:** 11:00–17:00; **F:** 11:00–17:00; **S:** 11:00–17:00. Medium stock. Spec: Motorbikes; Motoring; Traction Engines; Transport; Vintage Cars. PR: £1–30. CC: MC; V. [Updated]

BRADFORD

The Idle Booksellers, 7 Town Lane, Idle, Bradford, BD10 8PR. Prop: Ros Stinton & Michael Compton. Tel: (01274) 613737. E-mail: idlebooks@bd108pr.freeserve.co.uk. Est: 1990. Private premises. Telephone first. Small stock. Spec: Author - Brontes, The; Author - Gissing, George; Genealogy; Topography - Local. PR: £1–600. [Updated]

Woodbine Books, 15 Stone Street, Bradford, BD15 9JR. Prop: Colin Neville. Tel: (01274) 824759. Website: www.abebooks.com/home/woodbine. E-mail: woodbine@blueyonder.co.uk. Private premises. Internet and postal. Appointment necessary. Very small stock. Spec: Artists; Author - Webb, Mary; Bindings; Engraving; Fine & Rare; First Editions; Illustrated; Natural History; Poetry; Private Press; Rural Life; Signed Editions. PR: £5–1,300. Mem: PBFA; FPBA, PLA. [Updated]

BRIGHOUSE

Northern Herald Books, 5 Close Lea, Rastrick, Brighouse, HD6 3AR. Prop: R.W. Jones. Tel: (01484) 721845. E-mail: bobjones_nhb@talk21.com. Est: 1985. Private premises. Postal business only. Large stock. Spec: Academic/Scholarly; Economics; Free Thought; Politics; Social History; Social Sciences; Socialism; Trade Unions; Women. PR: £1–100. Corresp: French. Mem: PBFA. [Updated]

CLECKHEATON

Sparrow Books, 10 Peaseland Close, Cleckheaton, BD19 3HA. Prop: Andrew Pinnock. Tel: and Fax: (01274) 876995. E-mail: apinnock@cix.co.uk. Est: 1992. Private premises. Internet and postal only. Medium stock. Spec: Academic/Scholarly; Geography, Geology; Politics; Topography - General; Topography - Local; also Booksearch. PR: £1–80. Exhibits at Leeds Book Fairs.

HALIFAX

M.R. Clark, 18 Balmoral Place, Halifax, HX1 2BG. Tel: (01422) 357475. Est: 1981. Private premises. Appointment necessary. Medium stock. Spec: Gardening; Natural History; also Booksearch. Cata: 1 – or 2 a year on gardening. [Updated]

Bruce Holdsworth Books, 26 Lane Ends Green, Hipperholme, Halifax, HX3 8EZ. Prop: Bruce Holdsworth. Tel: (01422) 203307. Website: www.bruceholdsworthbooks.com. E-mail: Bruce@ bruceholdsworthbooks.com. Est: 1993. Private premises. Internet and postal. Medium stock. Spec: Art; Art - History; Art - Reference; Arts, The; Crafts; Decorative Art; Fine Art; Sculpture; also Booksearch. PR: £15–5,000. CC: AE; JCB; MC; V; Maestro. Cata: 12 monthly. Mem: PBFA. VAT No: GB 686 9604 74. [Updated]

HEBDEN BRIDGE

Christopher I. Browne, Hawdon Hall, Hebden Bridge, HX7 7AL. Prop: C.I. .Browne. Tel: (01422) 844744. Fax: (01422) 844744. Website: www.gilbertandsullivanonline.com. E-mail: sales@ gilbertandsullivanonline.com. Est: 1998. Private premises. Internet and postal. Telephone first. Medium stock. Spec: Music - Classical; Music - Music Hall; Music - Opera; Music - Printed; Performing Arts. CC: AE; MC; V. Mem: SASS/G&S Society. [Updated]

The Glass Key, ■ 16 Market Street, Hebden Bridge, HX7 6AA. Prop: James Fraser. Tel: (01422) 846265. E-mail: jfraser@glasskey.prestel.co.uk. Est: 1991. Shop open: **F:** 11:30–17:30; **S:** 11:30–17:30; **Su:** 11:30–17:30. Small stock. Spec: Fiction - Crime, Detective, Spy, Thrillers; First Editions; Literature; also Booksearch. PR: £1–100. Cata: 2 on specialities. Corresp: French. [18/06/2003]

HOLMFIRTH

Beardsell Books, ■ Toll House Bookshop, 32–34 Huddersfield Road, Holmfirth, HD9 2JS. Prop: Elaine V. Beardsell. Tel: (01484) 686541. Fax: (01484) 688406. Website: www.toll-house.co.uk. E-mail: tollhouse.bookshop@virgin.net. Est: 1977. Internet and postal. Shop open: **M:** 09:00–17:00; **T:** 09:00–17:00; **W:** 09:00–17:00; **Th:** 09:00–17:00; **F:** 09:00–17:00; **S:** 09:00–17:30; **Su:** 13:00–17:00. Very large general stock. Spec: Antiquarian; History - General; History - Local. PR: £1–1,000. CC: MC; V. Mem: PBFA; BA. [09/06/2003]

Daisy Lane Books, ■ Towngate, Holmfirth, HD9 1HA. Prop: J. & B. Townsend–Cardew. Tel: (01484) 688409. Website: www.area5.co.uk/daisy-lane-books. Shop open: **M:** 09:00–17:00; **T:** 09:00–17:00; **W:** 09:00–17:00; **Th:** 09:00–17:00; **F:** 09:00–17:00; **S:** 09:00–17:00; **Su:** 09:00–17:00. Very large general stock. Winter open: 09:30–16:30 Monday to Sunday. [09/04/2003]

Madalyn S. Jones, Horsegate Hill House, 3 Town End Road, Wooldale, Holmfirth, HD9 1AH. Prop: Madalyn S. Jones. Tel: (01484) 681580. Fax: (01484) 681580. Website: www.madalynjonesbooks .co.uk. E-mail: madalynjonesbooks@yahoo.co.uk. Est: 1978. Private premises. Appointment necessary. Very small stock. Spec: Arts, The; Sculpture; also Booksearch. PR: £1–250. Mem: PBFA. [Updated]

HUDDERSFIELD

Childrens Bookshop, ■ 37/39 Lidget Street, Lindley, Huddersfield, HD3 3JF. Prop: Sonia & Barry Benster. Tel: (01484) 658013. Fax: (01484) 460020. E-mail: barry@hudbooks.demon.co.uk. Est: 1975. Shop open: **M:** 09:00–17:30; **T:** 09:00–17:30; **W:** 09:00–17:30; **Th:** 09:00–17:30; **F:** 09:00–17:30; **S:** 09:00–17:00. Small stock. Spec: Author - Dickens, Charles; Children's - General; Medicine; Medicine - History of. CC: JCB; MC. Mem: BA. [Updated]

Elaine Lonsdale Books, 4 Scar Top, Golcar, Huddersfield, HD7 4DT. Prop: Elaine Lonsdale. Tel: 01484 644193. E-mail: Lainelonsdale@yahoo.co.uk. Est: 1990. Spec: Author - Alcotts, The; Authors - Women; Literary Criticism; Literature; Poetry; Social History; Topography - General; Women. PR: £1–100. Also, bookbinder. [Updated]

William H. Roberts, The Crease, 113 Hill Grove, Salendine Nook, Huddersfield, HD3 3TL. Tel: (01484) 654463. Fax: (01484) 654463. Website: www.williamroberts-cricket.com. E-mail: william.roberts2@ virgin.net. Est: 1997. Private premises. Internet and postal. Telephone first. Spec: Sport - Cricket. CC: V. Mem: PBFA. [Updated]

Susan Taylor Books, Briar Cottage, 2 Top of the Hill, Thurstonland, Huddersfield, HD4 6XZ. Tel: (01484) 662120. E-mail: richard@mosleyr.freeserve.co.uk. Est: 1986. Private premises. Postal business only. Appointment necessary. Small stock. Spec: Women; also Booksearch. PR: £1–150. Corresp: French, German. Also at: these premises - Aphra Books (q.v.). [18/09/2003]

Nick Tozer Railway Books, 62 Parkgate, Huddersfield, HD4 7NG. Prop: Nick Tozer. Tel: (01484) 663811. Fax: (01484) 663811. Website: www.railwaybook.com. E-mail: nick@railwaybook.com. Est: 1997. Postal business only. Medium stock. Spec: Railways; also Booksearch. PR: £1–50. [Updated]

ILKLEY

Rupert Cavendish Books, 10 Elmete Grange, Main Street, Menston, Ilkley, LS29 6LA. Tel: (01943) 884228. E-mail: rcavendish@aol.com. Est: 1994. Private premises. Postal business only. Small stock. Spec: Sport - General. PR: £5–500. [13/03/2003]

Greenroom Books, 9 St. James Road, Ilkley, LS29 9PY. Prop: Geoff Oldham. Tel: (01943) 607662. E-mail: greenroombooks@blueyonder.co.uk. Est: 1991. Private premises. Contactable. Small stock. Spec: Academic/Scholarly; Cinema/Film; Comedy; Dance; Drama; Entertainment - General; Fashion & Costume; Performing Arts; Radio/Wireless; Television; Theatre. PR: £8–30. CC: PayPal. Cata: occasionally on performing arts. Corresp: French. [Updated]

Skyrack Books, ■ 20 Skipton Road, Ilkley, LS29 9EJ. Prop: Steven Dyke. Tel: (01943) 601598. Fax: (01943) 601598. Est: 2000. Shop open: **T:** 10:00–17:00; **W:** 10:00–17:00; **Th:** 10:00–17:00; **F:** 10:00–17:00; **S:** 10:00–17:00; Closed for lunch: 13:00–14:00. Medium stock. Spec: Canals/Inland Waterways; History - Industrial; History - Local; Railways; Topography - Local; also Booksearch. PR: £1–100. And stocks on Yorkshire, new books, book tokens. Cata: occasionally on Yorkshire & transport/industries. Mem: BA. [Updated]

Mark Sutcliffe, 14 St. John's Avenue, Addingham, Ilkley, LS29 0QB. Tel: (01943) 830117. Fax: (01943) 830117. Website: www.abebooks.com/home/marksutcliffe/. E-mail: msfe@btinternet.com. Est: 1996. Private premises. Internet and postal. Appointment necessary. Very small stock. Spec: Author - Blake, N.; Author - Chandler, Raymond; Author - Crofts, Freeman Wills; Author - Hammett, Dashiell; Fiction - Crime, Detective, Spy, Thrillers; First Editions; Publishers - Collins (Crime Club, The). PR: £5–3,000. CC: JCB; MC; V. Cata: on detective fiction, some modern firsts and children's. Mem: PBFA. [Updated]

KEIGHLEY

Birchwood Books, ■ 39 Church Street, Keighley, BD22 0QA. Tel: (01535) 692349. E-mail: andrew .darling@tesco.net. Est: 2001. Shop open: **Th:** 10:00–17:00; **F:** 10:00–17:00; **S:** 10:00–16:00. Large stock. Spec: Music - General; Music - Folk & Irish Folk. [24/04/2004]

KIRKSTALL

The Bookshop, Kirkstall, ■ 10 Commercial Road, Kirkstall, Leeds, LS5 3AQ. Prop: R.A. & P.P. Brook. Tel: (0113) 278-0937. Fax: (0113) 278-0937. E-mail: book.shop@btinternet.com. Est: 1982. Shop open: **M:** 10:15–17:30; **T:** 10:15–17:30; **W:** 10:15–16:30; **Th:** 10:15–16:30; **F:** 10:15–17:30; **S:** 10:15– 17:30. Large general stock. Spec: Antiquarian. PR: £1–2,000. CC: MC; V. [Updated]

LEEDS

Bates & Hindmarch, 2 Cumberland Road, Headingley, Leeds, LS6 2EF. Prop: Jeffery Bates. Tel: (0113) 278-3306. Website: www.abebooks.com. E-mail: jefferybates@aol.com. Est: 1987. Private premises. Appointment necessary. Small stock. Spec: Antiquarian; Bindings; Cartoons; Countries - Afghanistan; Countries - Asia; Countries - Central Asia; Countries - India; Countries - Tibet; Sport - Big Game Hunting; Travel - Asia. PR: £20–1,000. CC: AE; JCB; MC. Cata: 6 a year. Mem: PBFA. VAT No: GB 417 9947 06. [02/06/2003]

John Blanchfield, 5 Stanmore Place, Leeds, LS4 2RR. Prop: John Blanchfield. Tel: (0113) 274-2406. E-mail: john@blanchfield.demon.co.uk. Est: 1984. Private premises. Internet and postal. Appointment necessary. Medium stock. Spec: Academic/Scholarly; History - Industrial; Industry. PR: £5–500. CC: JCB; V. Cata: 1 issued october. Mem: PBFA. VAT No: GB 405 5743 61. [29/06/2003]

John Bonner, 82a Allerton Grange Rise, Moortown, Leeds, LS17 6LH. Tel: (0113) 269-0213. E-mail: johnbonner@btinternet.com. Est: 1990. Private premises. Postal business only. Small stock. Spec: Aviation; Biography; Military. PR: £1–100. [Updated]

Bryony Books, 11 Woodhall Avenue, Leeds, LS5 3LH. Prop: Joan & Bill Martin. Tel: (0113) 258-7283. E-mail: Est: 1976. Private premises. Appointment necessary. Very small stock. Spec: Children's - General. PR: £2–100. [09/04/2003]

Coracle Books, 88 Ash Road, Leeds, LS6 3HD. Prop: Paul Hudson. Tel: (0113) 278-2531. Fax: (0113) 278-2531. E-mail: madmountaineer@madasafish.com. Est: 1980. Private premises. Postal business only. Appointment necessary. Very small stock. Spec: Alpinism/Mountaineering; Poetry; Sport - Climbing & Trekking. PR: £5–80. Cata: 1 a year. [Updated]

Old Cathay Fine Books, 80 Lovell Park Grange, Sheepscar, Leeds, LS7 1DT. Prop: Ian Edwards. Tel: (0113) 248-1421. E-mail: ianedwards@ntlworld.com. Est: 1986. Private premises. Internet and postal. Small stock. Spec: Banking & Insurance; Children's - Illustrated; Colour-Plate; Economics; Politics; Social Sciences; Socialism; Topography - General. PR: £5–1,000. Business incorporates 'Academic and Scholarly Fine Books'. Cata: 1 a year on children's & colour, illustrated; academic & economics. [Updated]

Elephant Books, ■ off Midland Road, Nr. Hyde Park Corner, Leeds, LS6 1BQ. Prop: Neil Whitworth. Tel: (0113) 274-4021. Est: 1987. Shop open: **M:** 10:00–18:00; **T:** 10:00–18:00; **W:** 10:00–18:00; **Th:** 10:00–18:00; **F:** 10:00–18:00; **S:** 10:00–18:00. Large stock. Spec: Arts, The; Philosophy; Psychology/ Psychiatry. PR: £1–100. CC: AE; D; E; JCB; MC; V; SO. [08/07/2003]

Find That Book, 74 Oxford Avenue, Guiseley, Leeds, LS20 9BX. Prop: David Herries. Tel: (01943) 872699. Website: www.findthatbook.demon.co.uk. E-mail: david@findthatbook.demon.co.uk. Est: 1991. Private premises. Postal business only. Spec: Booksearch. [Updated]

Leeds Bookseller, 3 Wedgewood Drive, Roundhay, Leeds, LS8 1EF. Prop: J.B. Wilkinson. Tel: (0113) 266-7183. Est: 1980. Private premises. Postal business only. Very small stock. Spec: Academic/ Scholarly; Palaeography. PR: £1–8. [Updated]

Peregrine Books (Leeds), 27 Hunger Hills Avenue, Horsforth, Leeds, LS18 5JS. Prop: J. & M.A. Whitaker. Tel: (0113) 258-5495. Est: 1986. Private premises. Appointment necessary. Small stock. Spec: Natural History; Travel - General. PR: £5–3,000. Cata: occasionally. [09/04/2003]

David Spenceley Books, 75 Harley Drive, Leeds, LS13 4QY. Prop: David Spenceley. Tel: (0113) 257-0715 (24h. Website: www.abebooks.com/home/davidspenceleybooks. E-mail: davidspenceley@email.com. Est: 1990. Private premises. Internet and postal. Contactable. Open: **M:** 09:00–17:00; **T:** 09:00–17:00; **W:** 09:00–17:00; **Th:** 09:00–17:00; **F:** 09:00–17:00; **S:** 09:00–17:00; **Su:** 09:00–17:00; Closed for lunch: 12:00–14:00. Outside quoted opening hours - contactable at all reasonable times. Medium stock. Spec: Academic/Scholarly; Arms & Armour; Country Houses; Ecclesiastical History & Architecture; History - British; History - Middle Ages; History - Renaissance, The; History - Women; Languages - National; Medieval; War - English Civil Wars; also Booksearch. PR: £1–200. [Updated]

Graham Sykes, 81 Gledhow Park Grove, Leeds, LS7 4JW. Tel: (0113) 262-1547. Est: 1985. Private premises. Postal business only. Small general stock. Spec: Fine Art; First Editions; History - General; Natural History; Palaeontology; Photography; Topography - General; Travel - General. Cata: 3 a year on photography. Mem: PBFA. [Updated]

Woodlands Books, 65 Gledhow Wood Road, Leeds, LS8 4DG. Prop: Bill & Valerie Astbury. Tel: (0113) 266-7834. Est: 1986. Private premises. Postal business only. Small stock. Spec: Music - General; Music - Musicians. PR: £2–150. Cata: 2 a year on music and musicians. [Updated]

MIRFIELD

D. & M. Books, 5a Knowl Road, Mirfield, WF14 8DQ. Prop: Daniel J. Hanson. Tel: (01924) 495768. Fax: (01924) 491267. Website: www.dandmbooks.com. E-mail: daniel@dandmbooks.com. Est: 1989. Warehouse. Internet and postal. Telephone first. Small stock. Spec: Cartoons; Children's - General; Comic Books & Annuals; Comics; also Booksearch. PR: £10–1,000. CC: JCB; MC; V. Suppliers and manufacturers of book jacket covers and mailing supplies. Cata: 4 a year on Children's books and comics. Mem: PBFA. VAT No: GB 686 8348 71. [Updated]

OTLEY

Chevin Books, 19 Manor Square, Otley, LS21 3AP. Tel: (01943) 466599. E-mail: chevinbooks@yahoo.co.uk. Est: 1996. Spec: Architecture; Art; Fiction - Crime, Detective, Spy, Thrillers; Fiction - Fantasy, Horror; Fiction - Science Fiction; Folio Society, The; History - General; Literature; Military History; Natural History; Sport - General; Topography - General; Topography - Local. PR: £1–200. [15/05/2003]

Otley Maypole Rare Books, 98 Boroughgate, Otley, LS21 1AE. Prop: John Hepworth. Tel: (01943) 468899. [26/08/2003]

TODMORDEN

The Border Bookshop, ■ 61a & 63 Halifax Road, Todmorden, OL14 5BB. Prop: Victor H. Collinge. Tel: (01706) 814721. Website: www.borderbookshop.co.uk. E-mail: collinge@borderbookshop.fsnet.co.uk. Est: 1980. Shop open: **M:** 10:00–17:00; **W:** 10:00–17:00; **Th:** 10:00–17:00; **F:** 10:00–17:00; **S:** 10:00–17:00; Closed for lunch: 13:00–14:00. Large general stock. Spec: Children's - General; Comic Books & Annuals; Comics; Nostalgia; Periodicals & Magazines; Sport - Cricket; Sport - Football (Soccer). CC: E; JCB; MC; V. Also, new books, book tokens & book ordering service. Corresp: French. Mem: PBFA. [Updated]

John Eggeling Books, Claremont South, 56 Burnley Road, Todmorden, OL14 5LH. Prop: John Eggeling. Tel: (01706) 816487. Fax: (01706) 816487. E-mail: todmordenbooks@ndirect.co.uk. Est: 1972. Private premises. Internet and postal. Appointment necessary. Shop at: http://dogbert.abebooks.com/servlet/SearchEntry?vci=731799. Open: Medium stock. Spec: Anthologies; Calligraphy; Colonial; Countries - Australasia; Fables; Fiction - General; Fiction - Crime, Detective, Spy, Thrillers; Fiction - Fantasy, Horror; Fiction - Historical; Fiction - Romantic; Fiction - Science Fiction; Fiction - Women; and more. PR: £2–1,000. CC: MC; V. Also, a booksearch service. Cata: 6 – [Updated]

Magpie Books, Mellor Barn Farm, Peel Cottage Road, Walsden, Todmorden, OL14 7QJ. Tel: (01706) 815005. Website: http://www.ibooknet.co.uk/seller/magpie.htm. E-mail: magpie@mellorbarn.co.uk. Private premises. Internet and postal. Appointment necessary. Medium stock. PR: £5–2,000. CC: AE; JCB; MC; V. Also on Ibooknet. [18/09/2003]

Judith Mansfield, Claremont South, 56 Burnley Road, Todmorden, OL14 5LH. Judith Mansfield. Tel: (01706) 816487. Fax: (01706) 816487. E-mail: todmordenbooks@ndirect.co.uk. Est: 1983. Private premises. Internet and postal. Appointment necessary. Shop at: http://dogbert.abebooks.com/servlet/SearchEntry?vci=731799. Open: Medium stock. Spec: Crochet; Embroidery; Fashion & Costume; Knitting; Lace; Needlework; Textiles. PR: £2–500. CC: MC; V. Cata: 9 – 6 a year on embroidery & lace, 3 on costume & fash. Mem: PBFA; Textile Society. [Updated]

The Military Collector, The Manse, East Lee Lane, Eastwood, Todmorden, OL14 8RW. Prop: Ian Wilkinson. Tel: (01706) 839690. Fax: (01706) 839690. Website: www.sonic.net/~bstone/military. E-mail: military.collector@virgin.net. Est: 1978. Storeroom. Postal business only. Appointment necessary. Medium stock. Spec: Aeronautics; Alchemy; American Indians; Arms & Armour; Aviation; Colonial; Espionage; Firearms/Guns; Holocaust; Maritime/Nautical; Military; Military History; School Registers/Rolls of Honour; War - General; War - American Civil War; War - Boer. PR: £1–100. CC: AE; D; JCB; MC; V; Paypal. Also, a booksearch service. VAT No: GB 461 2500 84. [25/06/2003]

BRADFORD ON AVON

Ex Libris, ■ 1 The Shambles, Bradford on Avon, BA15 1JS. Prop: Roger Jones. Tel: (01225) 863595. Fax: (01225) 863595. Website: www.ex-librisbooks.co.uk. E-mail: roger.jones@ex-librisbooks.co.uk. Est: 1980. Shop; Internet and postal. Open: **M:** 09:00–17:30; **T:** 09:00–17:30; **W:** 09:00–17:30; **Th:** 09:00–17:30; **F:** 09:00–17:30; **S:** 09:00–17:30. PR: £1–10. CC: AE; JCB; MC. Also, new books publishing as Ex Libris Press. Mem: PBFA. [Updated]

CALNE

Clive Farahar & Sophie Dupre, Horsebrook House, XV The Green, Calne, SN11 8DQ. Tel: (01249) 821121. Fax: (01249) 821202. Website: www.farahardupre.co.uk. E-mail: sophie@farahardupre.co.uk. Est: 1978. Private premises. Internet and postal. Appointment necessary. Open: **M:** 09:00–17:00; **T:** 09:00–17:00; **W:** 09:00–17:00; **Th:** 09:00–17:00; **F:** 09:00–17:00; **S:** 10:00–13:00; Closed for lunch: 13:00–14:00. Large stock. Spec: Antiquarian; Autographs; Documents - General; Letters; Literature; Manuscripts; Photography; Royalty - General; Signed Editions; Sport - Big Game Hunting; Travel - General; Travel - Africa; Travel - Americas; Travel - Asia; Travel - Australasia. PR: £10–10,000. CC: AE; JCB; MC; V. Cata: 2 – Corresp: French. Mem: ABA; ILAB; PADA Manuscript Society. VAT No: GB 341 0770 87. [updated]

CHIPPENHAM

Vernon Askew Books, Preston East Farm, Nr. Lyneham, Chippenham, SN15 4DX. Prop: Vernon Askew. Tel: (01249) 892177 and 8. Fax: (01249) 892177. E-mail: vernonaskewbooks@tiscali.co.uk. Est: 1997. Storeroom. Appointment necessary. Very large stock. Spec: Alpinism/Mountaineering; Aviation; Bibliography; Biography; Bull Fighting; Byzantium; Churchilliana; Countries - Cyprus; Dictionaries; History - General; Literary Travel; Military History; Modern First Editions; Private Press; Pulps; Scouts & Guides. PR: £3–75. Contactable all week. Corresp: Swedish. [Updated]

Ben Bass, Greyne House, Marshfield, Chippenham, SN14 8LU. Tel: (01225) 891279. E-mail: benbassbooks@hotmail.com. Est: 1689. Storeroom. Open: **M:** 08:00–20:00; **T:** 08:00–20:00; **W:** 08:00–20:00; **Th:** 08:00–20:00; **F:** 08:00–20:00. Large general stock. Spec: Author - Machen, Arthur; Biography; Countries - Spain; Fiction - General; First Editions; Literature; also Booksearch. PR: £2–20. Corresp: French, German, Italian, Spanish. [Updated]

Chris Phillips, 28 Roundbarrow Close, Colerne, Chippenham, SN14 8EF. Tel: (01225) 742755. E-mail: batholdbooks@yahoo.co.uk. Est: 1997. Private premises. Book fairs only. Small general stock. Spec: Antiquarian; Art; Children's - Illustrated; Literature; Technology. PR: £1–500. CC: JCB; MC; V. Booksearch, Valuations for Insurance or Probate. Corresp: French. Mem: PBFA. [Updated]

DEVIZES

Garton & Co., Roundway House, Devizes, SN10 2EG. Prop: Robin Garton. Tel: (01380) 729624. Fax: (01380) 728886. Website: www.gartonandco.com. E-mail: info@gartonandco.com. Est: 1973. Spec: Catalogues Raisonnes; Fine Art. PR: £100–50,000. [15/07/2003]

MALMESBURY

Batstone Books, 12 Gloucester Street, Malmesbury, SN16 0AA. Prop: R. Batstone. Tel: (01666) 822145. Est: 1982. Private premises. Appointment necessary. Small stock. Spec: History - General; Philosophy; Religion - General; Topography - General; Travel - General. PR: £2–200. Cata: occasionally. Corresp: French. [Updated]

Earth Science Books, Old Swan House, Swan Barton, Sherston, Malmesbury, SN16 0LJ. Prop: Geoff Carss. Tel: (01666) 840995. Website: www.earthsciencebooks.com. E-mail: geoff@earthsciencebooks.com. Est: 2002. Private premises. Internet and postal. Contactable. Very small stock. Spec: Academic/Scholarly; Advertising; Animals and Birds; Geology; Hydrography; Natural History; Natural Sciences; Palaeography; Palaeontology; Salvation Army; Science - History of. PR: £3–10,000. Cata: 6 a year on Geology - specialist catalogues released occasionally. [Updated]

Richard Hatchwell, Cleeve House, Rodbourne Bottom, Malmesbury, SN16 0EZ. Tel: (01666) 823261. Est: 1952. Private premises. Small stock. Spec: Antiquarian; Early Imprints; Manuscripts; Topography - Local. Corresp: French, Italian. [Updated]

MARLBOROUGH

John Bevan Catholic Bookseller, Romans Halt, Mildenhall, Marlborough, SN8 2LX. Tel: (01672) 519817. Website: www.catholic-books.co.uk. E-mail: johnbevan@catholic-books.co.uk. Est: 1978. Storeroom. Internet and postal. Appointment necessary. Medium stock. Spec: Religion - Christian. PR: £1–500. CC: MC; V. Cata: 3 a year. Corresp: French, German. Mem: PBFA. [Updated]

Katharine House Gallery, ■ Katharine House, The Parade, Marlborough, SN8 1NE. Prop: Christopher Gange. Tel: (01672) 514040. Est: 1983. Shop open: **M:** 10:00–17:30; **T:** 10:00–17:30; **W:** 10:00–17:30; **Th:** 10:00–17:30; **F:** 10:00–17:30; **S:** 10:00–17:30. Medium stock. Spec: Antiques; Art; Illustrated; Modern First Editions. PR: £3–300. CC: MC; V. Mem: PBFA. [27/04/2003]

Nevis Railway Bookshops, ■ Katharine House Gallery, The Parade, Marlborough, SN8 1NE. Prop: N.J. Bridger. Tel: Shop (01672) 514040. Website: www.nevis-railway-bookshops.co.uk. Est: 1988. Shop open: **M:** 10:00–17:30; **T:** 10:00–17:30; **W:** 10:00–17:30; **Th:** 10:00–17:30; **F:** 10:00–17:30; **S:** 10:00–17:30; Closed for lunch: 13:00–14:15. Medium stock. Spec: Railways. PR: £1–75. Also at: Railway Book and Magazine Search, Newbury, Berks (q.v.) and Nevis Railway Bookshop, Goring-on-Thames, Oxon (q.v.). [Updated]

Anthony Spranger, ■ 6 Kinsbury Street, Marlborough, SN8 1HU. Tel: (01672) 514105. E-mail: spranger@btinternet.com. Shop open: **W:** 10:00–17:00; **Th:** 10:00–17:00; **F:** 10:00–17:00; **S:** 10:00–17:00. Medium stock. Spec: Alpinism/Mountaineering; Autobiography; Biography; Performing Arts. CC: AE; D; JCB; MC; V; SW. Corresp: French. Mem: PBFA. [22/09/2003]

RAMSBURY

Heraldry Today, ■ Parliament Piece, Ramsbury, Nr. Marlborough, SN8 2QH. Prop: Rosemary Pinches. Tel: (01672) 520617. Fax: (01672) 520183. Website: www.heraldrytoday.co.uk. E-mail: heraldry@ heraldrytoday.co.uk. Est: 1954. Shop open: **M:** 09:30–16:30; **T:** 09:30–16:30; **W:** 09:30–16:30; **Th:** 09:30–16:30; **F:** 09:30–16:30. Large stock. Spec: Biography; Ex-Libris; Genealogy; Heraldry; History - General; Royalty - General; School Registers/Rolls of Honour; also Booksearch. PR: £1–5,000. CC: E; MC; V. Also, back-numbers of journals, new books, periodicals & a booksearch service. Cata: 4 a year. Corresp: French. Mem: ABA; ILAB. VAT No: GB 238824441. [Updated]

SALISBURY

Badger, Boxwood, Broadchalke, Salisbury, SP5 5EP. Prop: Peter Bletsoe. Tel: (01722) 326033. Est: 1987. Market stand/stall. Shop at: Shop at: Antique Market, (Middle Floor) 37 Catherine Street, Salisbury. Open: **M:** 10:00–17:00; **T:** 10:00–17:00; **W:** 10:00–17:00; **Th:** 10:00–17:00; **F:** 10:00–17:00. Small general stock. PR: £5–200. CC: AE; D; E; JCB; MC; V. [Updated]

Water Lane Book Shop, ■ 24 Water Lane, Salisbury, SP2 7TE. Prop: P.J. Shouler. Tel: (01722) 337929. Website: www.drbooks.eurobell.co.uk. E-mail: drbooks@eurobell.co.uk. Est: 1981. Shop; Internet and postal. Open: **M:** 10:00–17:00; **T:** 10:00–17:00; **W:** 10:00–17:00; **Th:** 10:00–17:00; **F:** 10:00–17:00; **S:** 10:00–17:00. Medium stock. Spec: Academic/Scholarly; Antiquarian; Architecture; Art; Art - History; Art - Reference; Artists; Arts, The; Aviation; Bindings; Catalogues Raisonnes; Fine & Rare; Fine Art; Illustrated; Military; Topography - General; Topography - Local; Travel - General. PR: £1–2,000. CC: JCB; MC; V. Mem: PBFA. VAT No: GB 723 3951 38. [29/04/2003]

Trevan's Old Books, ■ 30 Catherine Street, Salisbury, SP1 2DA. Prop: John & Trevan Cocking. Tel: (01722) 325818. Fax: (01722) 341181. Website: www.abebooks.com/home/trevan. Est: 1999. Shop; Internet. Open: **M:** 09:30–17:30; **T:** 09:30–17:30; **W:** 09:30–17:30; **Th:** 09:30–17:30; **F:** 09:30–17:30; **S:** 09:30–17:30. Large stock. PR: £1–1,000. CC: AE; E; JCB; MC; V; SW, Solo. [19/03/2003]

SWINDON

Peter Barnes, 138 Ermin Street, Stratton St Margaret, Swindon, SN3 4NQ. Prop: Peter Barnes. Tel: (01793) 821327. Est: 2001. Private premises. Postal business only. Small stock. Spec: Aviation; History - General; Military; Military History; Naval; Periodicals & Magazines; Topography - General; Topography - Local; War - General; Wargames. PR: £1–50. Exhibits at book fairs. Cata: 3 a year on military. [Updated]

Bookmark (Children's Books), Fortnight, Wick Down, Broad Hinton, Swindon, SN4 9NR. Prop: Anne & Leonora Excell. Tel: (01793) 731693. Fax: (01793) 731782. E-mail: leonora.excell@btinternet.com. Est: 1973. Private premises. Book fairs only. Appointment necessary. Open: **M:** 09:00–18:00; **T:** 09:00–18:00; **W:** 09:00–18:00; **Th:** 09:00–18:00; **F:** 09:00–18:00; **S:** 10:00–18:00. Medium stock. Spec: Author - Aldin, Cecil; Author - Ardizzone, Edward; Author - Brent-Dyer, Elinor M.; Author - Crane, Walter; Author - Dahl, Roald; Author - Henty, G.A.; Author - Keeping, Charles; Author - Potter, Beatrix; Author - Uttley, Alison; Children's - General; also Booksearch. PR: £5–2,000. CC: E; JCB; MC; V; Switch. Cata: 3 a year on children's books and related juvenilia. Mem: PBFA. [Updated]

Collectors Corner, ■ 227 Kingshill, Swindon, SN1 4NG. Prop: Fred Stevens. Tel: (01793) 521545. Est: 1986. Shop open: **M:** 10:30–16:45; **T:** 10:30–16:45; **Th:** 10:30–16:45; **F:** 10:30–16:45; **S:** 10:30–16:45. Very small general stock. Spec: Collecting; Military; Railways; Topography - Local; Transport. PR: £1–100. Stock includes: postcards, cigarette cards, coins, medals, badges, toys, and ephemera. [Updated]

TISBURY

Heatons, ■ 2–3 High Street, Tisbury, SP3 6PS. Prop: Ros King. Tel: (01747) 873025 and 8. Fax: (01747) 870059. Website: www.heatons-of-tisbury.co.uk. E-mail: rosking@freenetname.co.uk. Shop; Internet and postal. Open: **M:** 09:00–16:30; **F:** 09:00–16:30; **S:** 09:00–16:30. Very large stock. PR: £1–2,000. Also, engravings, maps, Arts & Crafts, Art Nouveau & Deco furniture and decorative items epecially glass. [Updated]

WARMINSTER

Sturford Books, Landfall, 35 Corton, Warminster, BA12 0SY. Prop: Maria & Robert Mayall. Tel: (01985) 850478/85058. E-mail: robert_mayall@sturfordbooks.freeserve.co.uk. Est: 1993. Spec: Architecture; Art; Fiction - General; Foreign Texts; Literature; Poetry; Travel - General; also Booksearch. PR: £5–800. [06/06/2003]

WEST KINGTON

Peter Barnitt, Latimer's Yard, West Kington, Chippenham, SN14 7JJ. Tel: (01249) 782099. E-mail: barnitt.latlo@virgin.net. Private premises. Appointment necessary. Very small stock. Spec: Fine Printing; Private Press. PR: £20–3,000. [Updated]

WESTBURY

Aardvark Books, 50 Bratton Road, Westbury, BA13 3EP. Prop: Clive & Caroline Williams. Tel: (01225) 867723. Fax: (01225) 867723. Website: www.aardvarkmilitarybooks.com. E-mail: aardvarkbooks@blueyonder.co.uk. Est: 1998. Private premises. Internet and postal. Telephone first. Open: **M:** 09:00–19:00; **T:** 09:00-19:00; **W:** 09:00-19:00; **Th:** 09:00-19:00; **F:** 09:00–19:00; **S:** 09:00–19:00. Large stock. Spec: Military History; War - World War I; War - World War II. PR: £5–250. CC: MC; V; Switch. [Updated]

Zardoz Books, 20 Whitecroft, Dilton Marsh, Westbury, BA13 4DJ. Prop: M. & L. Flanagan. Tel: (01373) 865371. Fax: (01373) 303984. Website: www.zardozbooks.co.uk. Est: 1990. Warehouse. Internet and postal. Appointment necessary. Very large stock. Spec: Books about Books; Comic Books & Annuals; Crime (True); Early Imprints; Fiction - General; Fiction - Science Fiction; Glamour; Publishers - General; War - General. PR: £2–100. CC: MC; V. Cata: 4 a year. [18/07/2003]

WOOTTON BASSETT

G. Jackson, 10 Dryden Place, Wootton Bassett, SN4 8JP. Prop: Geoffrey Jackson. Tel: (01793) 849660. Fax: (01793) 849660. E-mail: geoffsj.jackson@tiscali.co.uk. Est: 2001. Private premises. Appointment necessary. Open: **M:** 09:30–17:30; **T:** 09:30–17:30; **W:** 09:30–17:30; **Th:** 09:30–17:30; **F:** 09:30–17:30. Small stock. Spec: Antiquarian; Antiques; Art - Reference; Irish Interest; Military History; Modern First Editions; Natural History; Sport - General; Topography - General; Travel - General; also Booksearch. PR: £25–9,000. CC: MC; V; PayPal. Cata: occasionally. [Updated]

ZEALS

Hurly Burly Books, 47 Zeals Rise, Zeals, BA12 6PL. Prop: Moira Lord. Tel: (01747) 840691. E-mail: hurlyburlybook@clara.co.uk. Est: 1995. Storeroom. Appointment necessary. Small stock. Spec: Children's - General; Children's - Illustrated; Illustrated. CC: AE; D; E; JCB; MC; V. Also at: Words Etc, Dorchester, Dorset. [09/07/2003]

WORCESTERSHIRE

BEWDLEY

Clent Books of Bewdley, Rose Cottage, Habberley Road, Bewdley, DY12 1JA. Prop: Ivor Simpson. Tel: (01299) 401090. Website: www.clentbooks.co.uk. E-mail: clent.books@btinternet.com. Est: 1977. Private premises. Internet and postal. Telephone first. Shop at: Kinver Book Fair every third Sunday in the month. Medium stock. Spec: Antiquarian; Fine & Rare; History - Local; Military; Topography - Local. PR: £10–200. Book Fair Organiser. Mem: PBFA. [Updated]

DROITWICH

Grant Books, The Coach House, New Road, Cutnall Green, Droitwich, WR9 0PQ. Prop: Bob & Shirley Grant. Tel: (01299) 851588. Fax: (01299) 851446. Website: www.grantbooks-memorabilia.com. E-mail: golf@grantbooks.co.uk. Est: 1972. Office &/or bookroom. Open: **M:** 09:00–17:00; **T:** 09:00–17:00; **W:** 09:00–17:00; **Th:** 09:00–17:00; **F:** 09:00–17:00. Small stock. Spec: Antiquarian; Sport - Golf. PR: £5–2,500. CC: AE; D; MC; V. Open at other times by appointment. Cata: 3 on golf. Mem: PBFA; BGCS; GCS(USA). VAT No: GB 275 8638 10. [Updated]

M. & D. Books, ■ 16 High Street, Droitwich Spa, WR9 8EW. Prop: Mike Hebden. Tel: (01905) 775814. Est: 1996. Shop open: **T:** 10:00–17:00; **Th:** 10:00–17:00; **F:** 10:00–17:00; **S:** 09:30–17:00. Medium stock. Spec: Topography - Local. PR: £1–250. CC: AE; JCB; MC; V; SW. [Updated]

GREAT MALVERN

The Malvern Bookshop, ■ 7 Abbey Road, Great Malvern, WR14 3ES. Prop: Howard G. Hudson. Tel: (01684) 575915. Fax: (01684) 575915. E-mail: browse@malvernbookshop.co.uk. Est: 1953. Shop open: **M:** 10:00–17:00; **T:** 10:00–17:00; **W:** 10:00–17:00; **Th:** 10:00–17:00; **F:** 10:00–17:00; **S:** 10:00–17:00; Closed for lunch: 10:00–17:00. Large general stock. Spec: Academic/Scholarly; Advertising; Antiques; Archaeology; Architecture; Art; Aviation; Bindings; Biography; Books about Books; Children's - General; Design; Literature; Military; Music - General; Natural History; Performing Arts; Poetry; Topography; also Booksearch. PR: £1–500. [Updated]

Wildside Books, Rectory House, 26 Priory Road, Great Malvern, WR14 3DR. Prop: Chris & Christine Johnson. Tel: (01684) 562 818. Fax: (01684) 566 491. Website: www.wildsidebooks.co.uk. E-mail: enquire@wildsidebooks.co.uk. Est: 1982. Private premises. Internet and postal. Appointment necessary. Small stock. Spec: Animals and Birds; Botany; Ecology; Fine & Rare; Gardening; Horticulture; Landscape; Mycology; Natural History; Natural Sciences; New Naturalist; Ornithology; Plant Hunting; Rural Life; Sport - Falconry; Zoology. PR: £15–10,000. CC: E; MC; V; SW. Gallery: specialising in wildlife and botanical art from 18th-21st Century. Cata: 4 – 3 months. VAT No: GB GB 16257375. [Updated]

KIDDERMINSTER

Lion Books, ■ 52 Blackwell St, Kidderminster, DY10 2EE. Prop: Colin Raxter. Tel: (01562) 745060. Website: www.lionbooks.co.uk. E-mail: lionbooks2@aol.com. Est: 1989. Shop; Internet and postal. Open: **T:** 10:30–17:00; **Th:** 10:30–17:00; **F:** 10:30–17:00; **S:** 10:30–14:00; Closed for lunch: 13:00–14:00. Medium stock. Spec: Sport - Angling/Fishing; Sport - Cricket; Sport - Football (Soccer); Sport - Motor Racing; Sport - Rugby; Topography - Local. PR: £1–300. CC: JCB; MC; V; Switch. specialist football book web site. Mem: PBFA. [Updated]

Salsus Books, Elderfield Gardens, 42 Coventry Street, Kidderminster, DY10 2BT. Prop: Dr. D.T. Salt. Tel: (01562) 742081. Fax: (01562) 824583. E-mail: salsus@books93.freeserve.co.uk. Est: 1991. Private premises. Internet and postal. Appointment necessary. Medium stock. Spec: Academic/Scholarly; Ecclesiastical History & Architecture; Religion - General; Theology. PR: £1–250. CC: JCB; MC; V; SW. Cata: 4 a year on theology. Mem: PBFA. [Updated]

MALVERN

Jonathan Gibbs Books, The Lakes Cottages, Drake Street, Welland, Malvern, WR13 6LN. Prop: Jonathan and Angela Gibbs. Tel: (01684) 593169. E-mail: info@jgibbsbooks.co.uk. Private premises. Appointment necessary. Open: Medium stock. Spec: Academic/Scholarly; Advertising; Aeronautics; Antiquarian; Literature; Music - General; Performing Arts; Sport - Horse Racing (all aspects). PR: £5–1,000. CC: MC; V. Cata: issued irregularly. Mem: PBFA. [Updated]

Golden Age Books, PO Box 45, Malvern, WR14 1XT. Tony Byatt, Adrian and Gillian Ainge. Tel: mail order only. Website: www.ukbookworld.com/members/goldenage. E-mail: info@goldenagebooks .co.uk. Est: 1981. Private premises. Internet and postal. Appointment necessary. Small stock. Spec: Bibles; Religion - General; Religion - Christian; Religion - Jewish; Theology. PR: £1–1,000. CC: E; JCB; MC; V; SW. Also, new Biblical books. Cata: 5 a year on Biblia, General Theology. [Updated]

Valerie Merritt, 17 Kings Road, Malvern, WR14 4AJ. Tel: (01684) 566777. Fax: (01684) 566777. Est: 1975. Private premises. Appointment necessary. Small stock. Spec: Gardening; Horticulture; Plant Hunting. PR: £20–2,000. Also, garden design. Cata: 3 a year on specialities. [Updated]

PERSHORE

Coach House Books, ■ 17a Bridge Street, Pershore, WR10 1AJ. Prop: Michael & Sue Ellingworth. Tel: (01386) 554633. Fax: (01386) 554633. E-mail: sue.chb@virgin.net. Est: 1982. Shop. Telephone first. Open: **W:** 09:00–05:00. Medium stock. Spec: Architecture; Art - Reference; Author - Lawrence, T.E.; Folio Society, The; Horticulture; Limited Editions; Military; Ornithology; School Registers/Rolls of Honour; Sport - Cricket; Topography - General; Topography - Local. PR: £5–2,000. CC: AE; D; MC; V. Also, new books, picture framing, artists materials and a booksearch service. Corresp: French. Mem: BA. Also at: 46 High Street, Pershore, Worcestershire WR10 1DP. VAT No: GB 396 2460 27. [Updated]

Sedgeberrow Books, ■ Retail Market, Cherry Orchard, Pershore, WR10 1EY. Prop: Mrs. Jayne Winter. Tel: (01386) 751830. Website: www.abebooks.com/home/SEDGEBERROW. E-mail: sales@sedgeberrowbooks.fsnet.co.uk. Est: 1985. Shop open: **W:** 09:00–17:00; **Th:** 09:00–17:00; **F:** 09:00–17:00; **S:** 09:00–17:00. Large general stock. Spec: Author - Moore, John; Author - Young, Francis Brett; Aviation; History - Local; Mind, Body & Spirit; Railways; Topography - General; Topography - Local. PR: £1–300. Cata: 1 occasional. [Updated]

Wigley Books, Morewood House, Abbey Place, Pershore, WR10 1JE. Prop: Geoffrey Whatmore. Tel: (01386) 554125. Fax: (01386) 556555. Est: 1984. Private premises. Appointment necessary. Small stock. Spec: Sport - Angling/Fishing. PR: £5–1,000. CC: MC; V. Cata: 2 a year. Corresp: French. [27/04/2003]

STOURPORT-ON-SEVERN

P. and P. Books, Dairy Cottage, Yarhampton, Stourport, Stourport-on-Severn, DY13 0UY. Prop: J.S. Pizey. Tel: (01299) 896996. Fax: (01299) 896996. E-mail: pandpbooks_jim@compuserve.com. Est: 1982. Private premises. Postal business only. Appointment necessary. Very small stock. Spec: Archaeology; Egyptology; Travel - Middle East. PR: £5–2,000. CC: JCB. Also, valuations undertaken. Cata: 3 a year on Egyptology, Archaeology & travel in The Middle East. Corresp: French. Mem: ABA; PBFA. VAT No: GB 441 7426 59. [21/07/2003]

WORCESTER

Bookworms of Evesham, ■ 81 Port Street, Evesham, Worcester, WR11 3LF. Prop: T.J. Sims. Tel: (01386) 45509. Fax: (01386) 45509. Est: 1971. Shop open: **T:** 10:00–17:00; **W:** 10:00–17:00; **Th:** 10:00–17:00; **F:** 10:00–17:00; **S:** 10:00–17:00. Medium stock. Spec: Art; History - General; Literature; Military; Topography - Local; Transport; Travel - General. Fairs attended: Cheltenham, Bath, Cirencester; and Churchdown Book Fair. Cata: occasionally on Gloucestershire topography. Mem: PBFA. [Updated]

Capuchins, ■ 37 Sidbury, Worcester, WR1 2HT. Prop: Jo Cross. Tel: (01905) 21141. E-mail: capuchins @hotmail.com. Est: 1998. Shop open: **T:** 10:00–17:00; **W:** 10:00–17:00; **Th:** 10:00–17:00; **F:** 10:00–17:00; **S:** 10:00–17:00; **Su:** 11:30–14:30. Small general stock. PR: £1–50. Also, coffeehouse. [10/05/2003]

Ann & Mike Conry, 14 St. George's Square, Worcester, WR1 1HX. Tel: (01905) 25330. Website: On www.abebooks.com. E-mail: irishallsorts@aol.com. Est: 1998. Private premises. Postal business only. Spec: Irish Interest; Literary Travel; Modern First Editions; Sport - Football (Soccer). PR: £2–400. [Updated]

Davies Fine Books, 21 Droitwich Road, Worcester, WR3 7LG. Prop: Richard Davies. Tel: (01905) 23919. Website: www.daviesfinebooks.biblion.com. E-mail: daviesfinebooks@yahoo.co.uk. Est: 2002. Private premises. Internet and postal. Contactable. Small stock. Spec: Antiquarian; Gardening; Illustrated; Natural History; Travel - General. Corresp: French. VAT No: GB 823 3339 44. [Updated]

Graduate Books, 5 Rectory Lane, Shrawley, Worcester, WR6 6TW. Tel: (01905) 620786. Fax: (01905) 620786. E-mail: davidrobertvirr@aol.com. Est: 1985. Private premises. Internet and postal. Appointment necessary. Very small stock. Spec: Esoteric; Mind, Body & Spirit; Music - Popular; Philosophy; Psychology/Psychiatry. PR: £3–200. Corresp: French. [Updated]

Priory Books, ■ 10 Church Walk, Malvern, Worcester, WR14 2XH. Prop: Paul Sheath. Tel: (01684) 560258. E-mail: priorybooks@tiscali.co.uk. Est: 1985. Shop open: **M:** 09:30–17:15; **T:** 09:30–17:15; **W:** 09:30–17:15; **Th:** 09:30–17:15; **F:** 09:30–17:15; **S:** 09:30–17:15. Medium stock. Spec: History - Local; Poetry; Railways; Topography - General. PR: £1–500. CC: AE; MC; V; Maestro. Also, free booksearch and new book ordering. VAT No: GB 819 3353 21. [Updated]

Restormel Books, 1 East Comer, St. John's, Worcester, WR2 6BE. Prop: Roy Slade. Tel: (01905) 422290. Est: 1978. Display/stand. Shop at: and shop at Reindeer Court Antiques, Mealchealen Street, Worcester. Open: **M:** 10:00–17:00; **T:** 10:00–17:00; **W:** 10:00–17:00; **Th:** 10:00–17:00; **F:** 10:00–17:00; **S:** 10:00–17:00. Small stock. Spec: Collecting; Topography - Local. PR: £1–50. Attends PBFA fairs in Midlands. Corresp: French, Spanish. Mem: PBFA. [22/08/2002]

Louise Ross Books, 28 Besford Court, Besford, Nr. Worcester, WR8 9LZ. Tel: (01368) 550461. E-mail: louise.ross@btclick.com. Est: 1977. Private premises. Postal business only. Contactable. Very small stock. Spec: Children's - General; Illustrated; Literature. PR: £25–5,000. [Updated]

Worcester Rare Books, c/o Flat 5, Coach House Lodge, Old Palace Gardens, Deansway, Worcester, WR1 2JD. Prop: D.Ieuan Lloyd. Tel: (01905) 28780. E-mail: rareboks@worcester74.freeserve.co.uk. Est: 1972. Private premises. Internet and postal. Appointment necessary. Open: Medium stock. Spec: Academic/Scholarly; Antiquarian; Architecture; Medicine; Philosophy; Science - General; Science - History of. PR: £10–500. CC: MC; V. Cata: 6 – Corresp: French German. Mem: PBFA. [Updated]

CHANNEL ISLANDS

GUERNSEY

SAINT PETER PORT

Channel Islands Galleries Limited, ■ Trinity Square Centre, Trinity Square, St. Peter Port, Guernsey, GY1 1LX. Prop: Geoffrey P. & Christine M. Gavey. Tel: Shop (01481) 723247. Fax: (01481) 714669. E-mail: geoff.gavey@cigalleries.f9.co.uk. Est: 1967. Shop and postal business. Open: **M:** 10:00–17:00; **T:** 10:00–17:00; **W:** 10:00–17:00; **Th:** 10:00–13:00; **F:** 10:00–17:00; **S:** 10:00–13:00. Small stock. Spec: Antiquarian; Atlases; History - General; Natural History; Topography - General; Topography - Local. PR: £5–4,000. CC: E; MC; V. Also, antique maps, prints, watercolours and paintings - featuring The Channel Islands, coins & CI bank notes. Corresp: French, German. [Updated]

SAINT SAMPSON

The Old Curiosity Shop, ■ Commercial Road, The Bridge, St. Sampson, Guernsey. Prop: Mrs. Adele Stevens Cox. Tel: (01481) 45324. Est: 1978. Shop open: **F:** 14:00–16:30. Small stock. Spec: Countries - Channel Islands, The. PR: £1–2,000. Corresp: French, German. [19/05/2003]

JERSEY

SAINT HELIER

Books and Things, ■ n/a, First Tower, St. Helier, JE2 3LN. Prop: Bob Burrow. Tel: 01534. Fax: n/a. Website: www.newnats.com. E-mail: bob@newnats.com. Est: 1998. Shop open: **M:** 12:00-17:00; **T:** 12:00–17:00; **W:** 12:00–17:00; **Th:** 12:00–17:00; **F:** 12:00–17:00; **S:** 12:00–17:00; **Su:** 10:00–17:00. Small stock. Spec: New Naturalist. Corresp: English. [Updated]

ISLE OF MAN

DOUGLAS

Garretts Antiquarian Books, 4 Summerhill, Douglas, IM2 4PJ. Prop: Mr. Jonathon Hall. Tel: (01624) 675065. Website: www.isleofmanbooks.com. E-mail: garrettsbooks_iom@yahoo.co.uk. Est: 1987. Private premises. Internet and postal. Telephone first. Small general stock. Spec: Countries - Isle of Man; History - Local; Topography - Local. PR: £1–1,000. CC: AE; JCB; MC; V. Mem: PBFA. [Updated]

PORT ERIN

Bridge Bookshop Ltd, Shore Road, Port Erin, IM9 6HL. Tel: 01624 833376. Fax: 01624 835381. E-mail: bbs@manx.net. [Updated]

NORTHERN IRELAND

CO. ANTRIM

BELFAST (BEAL FEIRSIDE)

Belfast Book Search, Unit A201, Portview Trade Center, 310 Newtonards Road, Belfast, Co. Antrim, BT4 1HE. Prop: Mr. William Burlingham. Tel: (028) 9045-1385. Fax: (028) 9045-1385. E-mail: belfastbooksearch@dnet.co.uk. Est: 1998. Storeroom. Internet and postal. Telephone first. Shop open daily at unit 9 North St Arcade Belfast City Centre. Open: **M:** 11:00–17:00; **T:** 11:00–17:00; **W:** 11:00–17:00; **Th:** 11:00–17:00; **F:** 11:00–17:00; **S:** 11:00–17:00. Medium stock. Spec: Irish Interest; also Booksearch. PR: £1–50. CC: JCB; MC; V; Switch. [11/05/2003]

The Bell Gallery, 13 Adelaide Park, Belfast, Co. Antrim, BT9 6FX. Prop: James Nelson Bell. Tel: (028) 9066-2998. Website: www.bellgallery.com. E-mail: bellgallery@btinternet.com. Est: 1965. Spec: Countries - Ireland; Irish Interest. PR: £10–100. Also, Irish paintings & sculpture. [12/07/2003]

Emerald Isle Books, 539 Antrim Road, Belfast, Co. Antrim, BT15 3BU. Prop: Mr. & Mrs. John Gamble. Tel: (028) 9037-0798. Fax: (028) 9077-7288. Est: 1963. Private premises. Appointment necessary. Very large stock. Spec: Antiquarian; Bindings; Countries - Ireland; Ecclesiastical History & Architecture; Fine & Rare; History - General; Irish Interest; Literature; Religion - Christian; Sets of Books; Social History; Travel - General. CC: MC; V. Corresp: French, Spanish. Mem: ABA; ILAB. VAT No: GB 252 9847 28. [Updated]

P. & B. Rowan, Carleton House, 92 Malone Road, Belfast, Co. Antrim, BT9 5HP. Prop: Peter & Briad Rowan. Tel: (028) 9066-6448. Fax: (028) 9066-3725. E-mail: peter@pbrowan.thegap.com. Est: 1973. Private premises. Appointment necessary. Large stock. Spec: Economics; Fine & Rare; History - General; Irish Interest; Law; Literature; Manuscripts; Medicine - History of; Philosophy; Science - History of; Travel - General; Voyages & Discovery. PR: £25 upwards. Cata: 3 a year. Corresp: French. Mem: PBFA; IADA. [Updated]

Stacks Bookshop, 67 Comber Road, Dundonald, Belfast, Co. Antrim, BT16 0FF. Prop: Jim Tollerton. Tel: (028) 9048-6880. E-mail: Est: 1992. Spec: Academic/Scholarly; Animals and Birds; Antiquarian; Autobiography; Children's - General; Fiction - Historical; Military; Religion - Christian; Social History; Transport; War - General. PR: £3–5. [30/08/2003]

LISBURN

Jiri Books, 11 Mill Road, Lisburn, Co. Antrim, BT27 5TT. Prop: Jim & Rita Swindall. Tel: (028) 9082-6443. Fax: (028) 9082-6443. Website: http://www.abebooks.com/home/WJS/. E-mail: jiri.books@dnet.co.uk. Est: 1978. Private premises. Postal business only. Appointment necessary. Medium stock. Spec: Antiquarian; Irish Interest; Literature; Poetry; Travel - General. CC: MC; V. Organise Annual Belfast Book Fair. Next fair 12th November 2005 and then 11th November 2006. [Updated]

CO. ARMAGH

ARMAGH

Craobh Rua Books, 12 Woodford Gardens, Armagh, Co. , BT60 2AZ. Prop: James Vallely. Tel: (028) 3752-6938. E-mail: craobh@btinternet.com. Est: 1990. Private premises. Internet and postal. Appointment necessary. Medium stock. Spec: Antiquarian; First Editions; History - National; Irish Interest; Literature; Topography - General; Travel - General; also Booksearch. PR: £1–400. CC: MC; V. Cata: 12 – monthly. Corresp: French. Mem: PBFA. [25/06/2003]

CO. DERRY

LONDONDERRY

Foyle Books, ■ 12 Magazine Street, Londonderry, Co. Derry, BT48 6HH. Prop: Ken Thatcher & Art Byrne. Tel: (028) 7137-2530. Website: www.foylebooks.freeserve.co.uk/index.html. E-mail: ken@thatcher30.freeserve.co.uk. Est: 1984. Shop open: **M:** 11:00–17:00; **T:** 11:00–17:00; **W:** 11:00–17:00; **Th:** 11:11–17:17; **F:** 11:00–17:00; **S:** 10:00–19:00. Very large stock. Spec: Academic/Scholarly; Advertising; Countries - Ireland; Foreign Texts; History - National; Irish Interest; Theology; also Booksearch. PR: £1–200. Corresp: French. [29/06/2003]

George Harris, 163 Legavallon Road, Dungiven, Londonderry, BT47 4QN. Prop: George Harris. Tel: (02877) 740012. Est: 1976. Private premises. Appointment necessary. Medium stock. Spec: Aeronautics; Arms & Armour; Aviation; Irish Interest; Military; Military History; Naval; War - General. PR: £5–500. Attends PBFA fairs. Cata: 2 a year on military. Corresp: French. Mem: PBFA. [Updated]

CO. DOWN

BALLYNAHINCH

Davidson Books, 34 Broomhill Road, Ballynahinch, Co. Down, BT24 8QD. Prop: Arthur Davidson. Tel: (028) 9756-2502. Fax: (028) 9756-2502. Est: 1958. Private premises. Appointment necessary. Medium stock. Spec: History - National; Irish Interest; Literature; Topography - Local. Cata: 3 a year. [Updated]

BANGOR

Books Ulster, 12 Bayview Road, Bangor, Co. Down, BT19 6AL. Prop: D.A. Rowlinson. Tel: (028) 914-70310. Website: www.booksulster.com. E-mail: orders@booksulster.com. Est: 1995. Private premises. Postal business only. Large stock. Spec: Irish Interest. PR: £1–500. CC: JCB; MC; V. [Updated]

DONAGHADEE

Prospect House Books, Prospect House, 4 Millisle Road, Donaghadee, Co Down, BT21 0HY. Prop: M.C. McAlister & J.M. Binney. Tel: (028) 9188-2990. Fax: (028) 9188-2990. Website: www.antiquarianbooksellersd.co.uk. E-mail: rarebooks.phb@btopenworld.com. Est: 1983. Private premises. Internet and postal. Appointment necessary. Large stock. Spec: Antiquarian; Bibliography; Biography; Countries - Ireland; Economics; Gardening; Geology; Irish Interest; Medicine; Natural History; Philology; Philosophy; Poetry; Religion - General; Scottish Interest; Theology; Travel - Africa; Travel - Asia. CC: MC; V. [18/07/2003]

DOWNPATRICK

Bookline, 35 Farranfad Road, Downpatrick, BT30 8NH. Prop: Lady Faulkner. Tel: (028) 4481-1712. Website: www.abebooks.com/home/bookline. E-mail: BooklineUK@aol.com. Est: 1988. Animals and Birds; Cats; Children's - General; Dogs; History - Irish; Illustrated; Private Press; Sport - Field Sports; also Booksearch. PR: £5–500. [Updated]

HILLSBOROUGH

Hillsborough BookHunters, 'Anna Livia', 6 Millvale Road, Hillsborough, Co. Down, BT26 6HR. Prop: Peter C. Hunter. Tel: (028) 9268-2635. Fax: (028) 9268-2268. Est: 1997. Private premises. Appointment necessary. Small general stock. Spec: Booksearch. PR: £1–800. [15/04/2003]

REPUBLIC OF IRELAND

CO. CAVAN

Cavan Book Centre, Main Street, Cavan, Co. Cavan. Prop Beatrice Maloney. Tel: (049) 436-2882. E-mail: Est: 1984. Spec: Archaeology; Biography; Irish Interest; Maritime/Nautical; Religion - General; Transport; Travel - General; also Booksearch. PR: £1–200. [20/08/2003]

COOTEHILL

Sillan Books, Drumgreen, Cootehill, Co. Cavan. Prop Mrs. Patricia Henrietta Smyth. Tel: +353 (49) 555-2343. Fax: +353 (49) 555-2343. Website: www.abebooks.com. E-mail: greenaway@eircom.net. Est: 1991. Private premises. Postal business only. Small stock. Spec: Children's - General; Irish Interest; Literature; Religion - General. PR: £3–350. CC: MC; V. [01/09/2003]

CO. CLARE

DOOLIN

Doolin Dinghy Books, ■ Fisher Street, Doolin, Co. Clare. Prop Cynthia Sinnott Griffin. Tel: (065) 70 74449. Est: 1982. Shop open: **M:** 09:00–21:00; **T:** 09:00–21:00; **W:** 09:00–21:00; **Th:** 09:00–21:00; **F:** 08:00–21:00; **S:** 08:00–21:00. Small stock. Spec: Art; Biography; Children's - General; Fiction - General; Folklore; History - National; Languages - National; Literature; Travel - Europe. PR: £1–150. Open only March-October. Other times call for appointment. Cata: 1 annually on Irish interests. Corresp: French. Mem: ASBI. [18/06/2003]

CO.CORK

BALLYDEHOB

Schull Books, Ballydehob, Co., Cork. Prop Barbara & Jack O'Connell. Tel: (+353) [0]28 37317. Fax: (+353) [0]28 37317. Website: www.schullbooks.com. E-mail: schullbooks@eircom.net. Est: 1981. Office &/or bookroom. Telephone first. Shop at: Regular exhibitor at Dublin and other bookfairs; contact for details. Open: **M:** 10:00–19:00; **T:** 10:00–19:00; **W:** 10:00–19:00; **Th:** 10:00–19:00; **F:** 10:00–19:00; **S:** 10:00–19:00. Medium stock. Spec: Irish Interest; Military History. PR: £10–500. CC: E; MC; V. Cata: 3 a year on Irish interest and military history. Corresp: French, German, Irish. Also at: Summer shop, Ballydehob village, June - Sept. [Updated]

BALLINLOUGH

Royal Carbery Books Ltd., Lissadell, 36 Beechwood Park, Ballinlough, Co. Cork. Prop G. & M. Feehan. Tel: (021) 4294191. Fax: (021) 4294191. E-mail: mgfeehan@eircom.net. Est: 1976. Private premises. Appointment necessary. Medium stock. Spec: Folklore; Guide Books; History - General; History - Local; Irish Interest; Literary Travel; Military; Music - Folk & Irish Folk; Topography - General. Cata: 4 a year on Irish interest. [20/08/2003]

CLONAKILTY

Delaney's Books, Spillers Lane, Clonakilty, Co. Cork. Prop Sheila Delaney. Tel: (023) 34363. Spec: Author - Orwell, George; also Booksearch. PR: £1–100. [17/08/2003]

DUNMANWAY

Darkwood Books, Darkwood, Dunmanway, Co. Cork. Prop Annette Sheehan. Tel: (023) 55470. Fax: (023) 55224. Website: www.darkwoodbooks.com. E-mail: darkwood@indigo.ie. Est: 2000. Private premises. Postal business only. Medium stock. Spec: Architecture; Art; Art - History; Art - Reference; Artists; Biography; Countries - Ireland; History - General; History - Irish; Irish Interest; Sport - Angling/Fishing; Sport - Hunting; Sport - Shooting. PR: £1–500. CC: MC; V. Cata: 2 a year. [Updated]

ROSSCARBERY

C.P. Hyland, 4, Closheen Lane, Rosscarbery, Co. Cork. Prop: Cal & Joan Hyland. Tel: (023) 48063. Fax: (023) 48658. Website: www.cphyland.com. E-mail: calbux@iol.ie. Est: 1966. Private premises. Internet and postal. Telephone first. Open: **M:** 10:00–17:30; **T:** 10:00–17:30; **W:** 10:00–17:30; **Th:** 10:00–17:30; **F:** 10:00–17:30; **S:** 10:00–17:30; **Su:** 12:00–17:30. Large stock. Spec: Countries - Ireland; Irish Interest; Languages - National. PR: £1–10,000. CC: MC; V. Cata: 2 a year. Corresp: Gaelic. [Updated]

SCHULL

Fuchsia Books, Main Street, Schull, Co. Cork. Prop: Mary Mackey. Tel: (028) 28016. Fax: (028) 28016. E-mail: margjmackey@ercom.net. Private premises. Internet and postal. Open: **M:** 10:00–17:00; **T:** 10:00–17:00; **W:** 10:00–17:00; **Th:** 10:00–17:00; **F:** 10:00–17:00; **S:** 10:00–17:00; Closed for lunch: 13:00–14:00. Small general stock. Spec: History - National; Irish Interest; also Booksearch. PR: £10–200. [Updated]

SKIBBEREEN

Fine Irish Books, P.O.Box 19, Skibbereen, Co. Cork.. Prop Michael Richards & Eve Chambers. Tel: (086) 8535365. Website: www.fineirishbooks.com. Est: 1995. Private premises. Internet and postal. Appointment necessary. Small stock. Spec: Antiquarian; Countries - Ireland; Fine & Rare; History - Irish; Irish Interest; Limited Editions; Private Press. PR: £100–10,000. CC: AE; MC; V; Paypal. Corresp: French, German, Spanish, Italian, Dutch, Japanese. [28/03/2003]

YOUGHAL

Alan Prim, ■ 6 South Main St., Youghal, Co. Cork. Prop: Alan Prim. Tel: (0035) 324 92781. E-mail: waprim@hotmail.com. Est: 1998. Shop open: **M:** 10:00–18:00; **T:** 10:00–18:00; **W:** 10:00–18:00; **Th:** 10:00–18:00; **F:** 10:00–18:00; **S:** 10:00–18:00; **Su:** 14:00–17:30; Closed for lunch: 13:30–14:00. Medium stock. PR: £3–100. CC: AE; MC; V. Corresp: French, Spanish. and [Updated]

CO. DONEGAL

CARNDONAGH

The Bookshop, ■ Court Place, Carndonagh, Co. Donegal. Prop: Michael Herron. Tel: (07493) 74389. Est: 1989. Shop open: **M:** 14:00–18:00; **T:** 14:00–18:00; **Th:** 14:00–18:00; **F:** 14:00–18:00; **S:** 14:00–18:00; **Su:** 14:00–18:00. Very large general stock. Spec: Antiquarian; First Editions; History - Local; Irish Interest; Medicine; Philosophy; Religion - Christian; Science - General; Theology; Topography - Local; Travel - General; also Booksearch. PR: £1–100. Also, half price sales in August, December and Easter. Cata: 3 a year. [Updated]

CO. DUBLIN

DALKEY

The Neptune, No. 5, Hyde Park, Dalkey Co. Dublin, Co Dublin. Prop: C. & A. Bonar Law. Tel: (01) 671-5021. Website: to be advised. E-mail: abl@nep.ie. Spec: Atlases; Topography - Local. PR: £1–1,000. Mem: IADA. VAT No: IE 9f60451k. [Updated]

DUBLIN

Greene's Bookshop Ltd, ■ 16, Clare St., Dublin 2, 2. Tel: 00-353-1-6762554. Fax: 00-353-1-6789091. Website: www.greenesbookshop.com. E-mail: info@greenesbookshop.com. Est: 1843. Shop; Internet and postal. Open: **M:** 09:00–17:30; **T:** 09:00–17:30; **W:** 09:00–17:30; **Th:** 09:09–17:30; **F:** 09:00–17:30; **S:** 09:00–17:00. Medium stock. Spec: Countries - Ireland; Irish Interest. CC: AE; D; MC; V. Cata: 6 – Irish Interest. Mem: PBFA. VAT No: IE 4810086O. [Updated]

Cathach Books Ltd., ■ 10 Duke Street, Dublin 2, Dublin, Co. Dublin, 15. Prop: Enda Cunningham. Tel: (01) 671-8676. Fax: (01) 671-5120. Website: www.rarebooks.ie. E-mail: cathach@rarebooks.ie. Est: 1985. Shop open: **M:** 09:30–17:45; **T:** 09:30–17:45; **W:** 09:30–17:45; **Th:** 09:30–17:45; **F:** 09:30–17:45; **S:** 09:30–17:45. Small stock. Spec: Academic/Scholarly; Archaeology; Irish Interest; also Booksearch. PR: £5–10,000. CC: AE; E; MC; V. Cata: 4 – Irish History & Literature. Corresp: Irish. Mem: ABA; Irish Antique Dealers. [Updated]

Chapters Bookstore, ■ 108/109 Middle Abbey Street, Dublin, Co. Dublin, Dublin 1. Prop: William Kinsella. Tel: (01) 872-3297. Fax: (01) 972-3044. Est: 1982. Shop open: **M:** 09:00–19:00; **T:** 09:00–19:00; **W:** 09:00–19:00; **Th:** 09:00–20:00; **F:** 09:00–19:00; **S:** 13:00–18:30. Very large general stock. Spec: Booksearch. PR: £1–1,000. CC: MC; (Alternate Tel: (01) 872-0773, 872-3024). Mem: BA. VAT No: IE 658 7410 A. [18/09/2003]

James Fenning, 12 Glenview, Rochestown Avenue, Dun Laoghaire, Dublin, Co. Dublin, Prop: Jim & Chris Fenning. Tel: (01) 285-7855. Fax: (01) 285-7919. E-mail: fenning@indigo.ie. Est: 1969. Private premises. Appointment necessary. Small stock. Spec: Antiquarian. PR: £20–100. CC: V. Cata: 6 a year. Mem: ABA. VAT No: GB IE 9T568850. [Updated]

Glenbower Books, 46 Howth Road, Clontarf, Dublin, Co. Dublin, Dublin 3. Prop: Martin Walsh. Tel: (01) 833-5305. Fax: (01) 833-5305. Website: www.abebooks.com/home/GLENBOWERBOOKS. E-mail: oldbook@eircom.net. Private premises. Postal business only. Medium stock. Spec: Academic/Scholarly; Antiquarian. PR: £3–340. CC: MC; V. [Updated]

Naughton Booksellers, 8 Marine Terrace, Dun Laoghaire, Dublin, Co. Dublin. Prop: Susan Naughton. Tel: +353 1 280-4392. Website: www.naughtonsbooks.com. E-mail: sales@naughtonsbooks.com. Est: 1976. Office &/or bookroom. Internet and postal. Telephone first. Large stock. Spec: Archaeology; Art; Countries - Ireland; Fiction - General; Fiction - Historical; First Editions; History - General; History - National; Irish Interest; Literature; Literature in Translation; Poetry; Travel - General; also Booksearch PR: £1–1,500. CC: AE; E; MC; V. [Updated]

Read Ireland, ■ 342 North Circular Road, Dublin, Co. Dublin, Dublin 7. Prop: Gregory Carr. Tel: (00353) 18309828. Fax: (00353) 18302997. Website: www.readireland.com. E-mail: gregcarr@readireland.ie. Est: 1988. Internet and postal. Shop open: **M:** 10:00–17:00; **T:** 10:00–17:00; **W:** 10:00–17:00; **Th:** 10:00–17:00; **F:** 10:00–17:00; **S:** 12:00–17:00. Large stock. Spec: Irish Interest. PR: £3–500. CC: AE; MC; V. VAT No: IE 5093937G. [19/08/2003]

STILLORGAN

Dublin Bookbrowsers, 12 Weirview Drive, Stillorgan, Co. Dublin. Prop: Dave Downes. Tel: (00353) 872636347. Fax: (00353) 1210300. Website: www.abebooks.com. E-mail: dave@dubbookbrowsers.com. Est: 1996. Private premises. Appointment necessary. Large stock. Spec: Irish Interest. PR: £1–20,000. CC: MC; V. Mem: PBFA. [Updated]

CO. GALWAY

GALWAY

Charlie Byrne's Bookshop, ■ Middle Street, Galway, Co. Galway, GW1. Tel: (0035) 391 561766. Fax: (0035) 391 561766. Website: www.charliebyrne.com. E-mail: info@charliebyrne.com. Internet and postal. Shop open: **M:** 09:00–18:00; **T:** 09:00–18:00; **W:** 09:00–18:00; **Th:** 09:00–18:00; **F:** 09:00–20:00; **S:** 09:00–18:00. [25/08/2003]

Available from Richard Joseph Publishers Ltd

MINIATURE BOOKS
by Louis W. Bondy

(A5 H/b)   221pp £24.00

Kenny's Book Export Co., Kilkerrin Park, Liosban, Tuam Road, Galway, Co. Galway. Tel: (091) 709350. Fax: (091) 709351. E-mail: terri@kennys.ie. Est: 1999. Office &/or bookroom. Open: **M:** 09:00–17:00; **T:** 09:00–17:00; **W:** 09:00–17:00; **Th:** 09:00–17:00; **F:** 09:00–17:00. Very large stock. PR: £2–16,000. CC: AE; D; JCB; MC; V. Mem: ABA. Also at: Kenny's Bookshop & Art Gallery, Galway (q.v). VAT No: IE 6328356V. [17/07/2003]

Kennys Bookshops and Art Gallery, ■ Art Galleries Ltd, High Street, Galway, Co. Galway, Prop: Managing Director: Mr. Conor Kenny. Tel: (091) 562739, 534760. Fax: (091) 568544. Website: www.kennys.ie and www.kennyscollections.com. E-mail: conor@kennys.ie. Est: 1940. Shop open. Open: **M:** 09:00–18:00; **T:** 09:00–18:00; **W:** 09:00–18:00; **Th:** 09:00–18:00; **F:** 09:00–18:00; **S:** 09:00–18:00. Very large stock. Spec: Americana; Anthropology; Archaeology; Architecture; Art - Reference; Author - 20th Century; Authors - Women; Bindings; Cinema/Film; Colonial; Countries - Africa; Countries - Arabia; Countries - Asia; Countries - Balkans, The; Countries - China. PR: £1–5,000. CC: AE; D; E; JCB; MC; V; Laser. Also, a booksearch service, in-house fine bindings & large comtemporary Irish Art Gallery. Cata: 99 a year. Corresp: French, Italian. Mem: ABA; ILAB; Also at: Kennys Export Book Co., Galway (q.v). VAT No: IE 2238521A. [25/07/2003]

MOYARD

The House of Figgis Ltd, Ross House, Moyard, Co. Galway. Prop: Neville Figgis. Tel: (095) 41092. Fax: (095) 41261. E-mail: figgisbooks@eircom.net. Private premises. Appointment necessary. Small stock. Spec: Early Imprints; Irish Interest; Literature; Modern First Editions. CC: MC; V. Cata: 2 a year on on rare books and Irish interest. VAT No: IE 9 N 543 415. [Updated]

CO. KERRY

KENMARE

Noel and Holland Books, ■ 3 Bridge Street, Kenmare, Co. Kerry. Prop: Dr. Noel Fursman and Ms. Julia Holland. Tel: (064) 42464. Fax: (064) 42464. Website: www.kenmare.com. E-mail: noelholland@eircom.net. Est: 1998. Shop open: **M:** 10:30–17:00; **T:** 10:30–17:00; **W:** 10:30–17:00; **Th:** 10:30–17:00; **F:** 10:30–17:00; **S:** 10:00–17:00. Medium stock. Spec: Biography; Children's - General; Crime (True); History - General; Irish Interest; Military; New Naturalist; Politics; Transport; also Booksearch. PR: £1–200. CC: AE; MC; V. Cata: occasionally. Corresp: Spanish, French, Irish. [11/05/2003]

CO. LAOIS

VICARSTOWN

Courtwood Books, Vicarstown, Stradbally, Vicarstown, Co. Laois. Prop PJ Tynan. Tel: (0502) 26384. E-mail: LBLOOM@EIRCOM.NET. Est: 1984. Private premises. Internet and postal. Appointment necessary. Medium stock. Spec: Academic/Scholarly; Advertising; Author - Beckett, S.; Author - Joyce, James; Author - Wilde, Oscar; Engineering; History - Local; Irish Interest; Topography - Local. PR: £1–500. CC: MC; V. Also, organiser of annual Kilkenny book fair (August). Cata: 2 a year. [Updated]

CO. LEITRIM

CARRICK–ON–SHANNON

Trinity Rare Books, ■ Bridge Street, Carrick–on–Shannon, Co. Leitrim. Prop: Nick Kaszuk. Tel: 00353 (0)78 22144. Website: www.trinityrarebooks.com. E-mail: nickk@iol.ie. Est: 1999. Shop open: **M:** 09:30–18:00; **T:** 09:30–18:00; **W:** 09:30–18:00; **Th:** 09:30–18:00; **F:** 09:30–18:00; **S:** 09:30–18:00. Large general stock. Spec: Antiquarian; Art; Arts, The; Autobiography; Avant-Garde; Beat Writers; Bindings; Biography; Books about Books; Canals/Inland Waterways; Caricature; Children's - General; Cookery/Gastronomy; Country Houses; D.I.Y (Do It Yourself); Drama; Espionage. PR: £3–150. Cata: occasionally on antiquarian, fine bindings, modern firsts. Corresp: French, German. [Updated]

CO. LIMERICK

LIMERICK

The Celtic Bookshop, ■ 2 Rutland Street, Limerick, Co. Limerick. Prop Caroline O'Brien. Tel: (061) 401155. E-mail: celticbk@iol.ie. Est: 1982. Internet and postal. Telephone first. Shop open: **M:** 10:00–17:00; **T:** 10:00–17:00; **W:** 10:00–17:00; **Th:** 10:00–17:00; **F:** 10:00–17:00; **S:** 10:00–17:00. Medium stock. Spec: Academic/Scholarly; Antiquarian; Countries - Ireland; Fiction - General; History - General. PR: £3–1,000. CC: MC; V. Cata: 1 a year on Irish. Corresp: Irish. VAT No: IE 322566i. [02/08/2003]

O'Brien Books & Photo Gallery, ■ 26 High Street, Limerick, Co. Limerick, n.a. Prop: John O'Brien. Tel: (061) 412833. E-mail: ob.books@oceanfree.net. Est: 1988. Shop open: **T:** 10:30–17:30; **W:** 10:30–17:30; **Th:** 10:30–17:30; **F:** 10:30–17:30; **S:** 10:00–17:30; Closed for lunch: 13:00–13:30. Medium stock. Spec: Art; Art - History; Biography; Cinema/Film; Fiction - General; Folio Society, The; History - General; Irish Interest; Literature; Military History; Photography. PR: £1–400. CC: D; E; JCB; MC; V. VAT No: IE 192 620 9a. [Updated]

CO. TIPPERARY

CAHIR

Glengall Books, 4/5 The Square, Cahir, Co. Tipperary. Prop: Joan Walsh. Tel: (353) 52 42896. Fax: (353) 52 42899. E-mail: jwalsh@biotipp.com. Spec: Antiques; Archaeology; Architecture; Art; Author - Baden-Powell, Lord Robert; Countries - Ireland; Genealogy; Geography; History - General; Irish Interest; Military; Military History; Royalty - General; Travel - General. [20/08/2003]

ROSCREA

Roscrea Bookshop, ■ Rosemary Square, Roscrea, Co. Tipperary. Tel: 00-353-505-22894. Fax: 00-353-505-22895. Website: http://www.roscreabookshop.com. E-mail: info@roscreabookshop.com. Est: 1997. Shop open: **M:** 07:30–19:00; **T:** 07:30–19:00; **W:** 07:30–00:20; **Th:** 07:30–19:00; **F:** 07:30–19:00; **S:** 07:30–20:00; **Su:** 07:30–14:00. Large stock. Spec: Academic/Scholarly; Africana; Agriculture; American Indians; Bibles; Children's - General; Children's - Illustrated; Christmas; Computing; Countries - France; Countries - Ireland; Crime (True); Criminology; D.I.Y (Do It Yourself); Disneyana; Fiction - Westerns. PR: £3–50. CC: AE; D; MC; V. Corresp: French. Mem: BA. VAT No: GB 327613 4P. [Updated]

CO. WEXFORD

NEW ROSS

Britons Catholic Library, Riverview, Arthurstown, New Ross, Co. Wexford. Prop: Mr. N.M. Gwynne. Tel: (51) 389111. E-mail: riverview@esatclear.ie. Private premises. Appointment necessary. Small stock. Spec: Religion - Roman Catholic. PR: £2–100. Stock majors on traditional Catholic titles. [Updated]

SCOTLAND

Including the Unitary Authorities of Aberdeenshire, Angus, Argyll & Bute, Borders, Clackmannan, Dumfries & Galloway, Dumbarton & Clydebank, Dundee, East Ayrshire, East Dunbartonshire, East Lothian, East Renfrewshire, Edinburgh, Falkirk, Fife, Glasgow, Highland, Inverclyde, Mid Lothian, Moray, North Ayrshire, North Lanarkshire, Orkney Islands, Perthshire & Kinross, Renfrewshire, Shetland Islands, South Ayrshire, South Lanarkshire, Stirling, Western Isles and West Lothian

BORDERS

INNERLEITHEN
Spike Hughes Rare Books, Willow Bank, Damside, Innerleithen, Borders, EH44 6HR. Tel: (01896) 830019. Fax: (01896) 831499. E-mail: spike@buik.demon.co.uk. Est: 1981. Private premises. Internet and postal. Appointment necessary. Small general stock. Spec: Countries - Scotland; Fine & Rare; History - General; History - Local; History - National; Literature; Philosophy; Social History. PR: £10–5,000. CC: MC; V. Cata: 6 a year. Mem: ABA. VAT No: GB 345 4470 55. [Updated]

JEDBURGH
G. & R. Stone, Hap House, 5 Allerton Court, Jedburgh, TD8 6RT. Prop: Gillian & Ralph Stone. Tel: (01835) 864147. Fax: (01835) 864147. E-mail: grstone@macunlimited.net. Est: 1972. Spec: Agriculture; Antiquarian; Natural History; Poetry; Women. PR: £5–100. [04/06/2003]

MELROSE
The Old Storytellers Bookshop, ■ The Old School, Bowden, Melrose, Borders, TD6 0SS. Prop: Brian & Carolyn Boardman. Tel: (01835) 822228. Website: www.theoldschooltearoom.co.uk. Est: 1988. Shop open: **M:** 10:00–17:00; **T:** 10:00–17:00; **W:** 10:00–17:00; **Th:** 10:00–17:00; **F:** 10:00–17:00; **S:** 10:00–17:00. Small stock. Spec: Autobiography; Biography; Fiction - General; First Editions; History - British; Illustrated; Poetry; Scottish Interest; Topography - General; Topography - Local. PR: £2–150. CC: JCB; MC; V; DE, SW. Winter opening (Nov-Mar) 11:00 to 16:00 every day. [01/07/2003]

Stroma Books, Charlesfield, St. Boswells, Melrose, Borders, TD6 0HH. Tel: (01835) 824169. Website: www.stromabooks.co.uk. E-mail: kenny@stromabooks.fsnet.co.uk. Est: 2000. Private premises. Postal business only. Medium stock. Spec: Academic/Scholarly; Art; Biography; Children's - General; Children's - Illustrated; Cinema/Film; Countries - Scotland; Entertainment - General; Literature - Scottish; Maritime/Nautical; Military; Modern First Editions; Poetry; Religion - General. CC: JCB; MC; V; M, SW, SO. [Updated]

SELKIRK
Wheen O'Books, Glyndwr, Mill St., Selkirk, Borders, TD7 5AE. Prop: Margaret Tierney. Tel: (01750) 21009. E-mail: megtie@aol.com. Est: 1997. Private premises. Internet. Telephone first. PR: £2–1,500. [01/05/2003]

WEST LINTON
Linton Books, ■ Deanfoot Road, West Linton, Borders, EH46 7DY. Prop: Derek Watson. Tel: (01968) 660339. Fax: (01968) 661701. Est: 1994. Shop open: **M:** 10:30–17:30; **T:** 10:30–17:30; **W:** 10:30–17:30; **Th:** 10:30–17:30; **F:** 10:30–17:30; **S:** 09:30–17:30; **Su:** 12:00–17:00. Small stock. Spec: Mythology; Scottish Interest. PR: £1–150. CC: E; MC; V. Closed Thursdays & Sunday in winter. [27/09/2003]

Looking for a dealer in EPHEMERA?
Then search Sheppard's on-line directories at:
www.sheppardsworld.co.uk

CENTRAL

BRIDGE OF ALLAN

Bridge of Allan Books, ■ 2 Henderson Street, Bridge of Allan, Central, FK9 4HT. Prop: Dr Andrew Jennings. Tel: (01786) 834483. Website: www.bridgeofallanbooks.com. E-mail: books@ bridgeofallanbooks.com. Est: 1985. Internet and postal. Shop open: **M:** 10:00–17:00; **T:** 10:00–17:00; **W:** 10:00–17:00; **Th:** 10:00–17:00; **F:** 10:00–17:00; **S:** 10:00–17:00. Large stock. Spec: Academic/Scholarly; Alpinism/Mountaineering; Anthroposophy; Antiquarian; Countries - Scotland; History - Local; Literature; Topography - Local; also Booksearch. PR: £1–700. Scottish history & Gaelic culture research. [11/07/2003]

CALLANDER

HP bookfinders, Mosslaird, Brig O'Turk, Callander, Central, FK17 8HT. Tel: (01877) 376377. Fax: (01877) 376377. Website: www.hp-bookfinders.co.uk. E-mail: martin@hp-bookfinders.co.uk. Est: 1986. Private premises. Internet and postal. Contactable. Very small stock. Spec: Booksearch. CC: E; JCB; MC; V; SW. [Updated]

Kings Bookshop Callander, ■ 91–93 Main Street, Callander, Trossachs, FK17 8BQ. Prop: Ian William King & Sally Evans. Tel: (01877) 339 449. E-mail: sally.king@btinternet.com. Est: 1987. Shop open: Spec: Bindings; Classical Studies; Scottish Interest. PR: £1–1,000. Shop open Monday through to Sunday. Closed Wednesday. NB When sending e-mails - add 'bookshop' to subject field. [Updated]

LARBERT

Dave Simpson, Lorne Villa, 161 Main Street, Larbert, Central, FK5 4AL. Tel: (01324) 558628. Fax: (01324) 558628. Website: dave.simpson3@virgin.net. E-mail: dave.simpson3@virgin.net. Est: 2000. Private premises. Internet and postal. Contactable. Small general stock. Spec: Antiquarian; Children's - General; Literature; Modern First Editions; Signed Editions. PR: £10–300. CC: E; JCB; MC; V; SW. [Updated]

DUMFRIES & GALLOWAY

CASTLE DOUGLAS

Benny Gillies, ■ 31–33 Victoria Street, Kirkpatrick Durham, Castle Douglas, Kircudbrightshire, DG7 3HQ. Prop: Benny Gillies. Tel: (01556) 650412. Website: www.bennygillies.co.uk. E-mail: benny@ bennygillies.co.uk. Est: 1979. Shop open: **M:** 10:00–17:00; **T:** 10:00–17:00; **W:** 10:00–17:00; **Th:** 10:00–17:00; **F:** 10:00–17:00; **S:** 10:00–18:00. Small stock. Spec: Countries - Scotland; Rural Life; Scottish Interest; Topography - Local. PR: £1–500. CC: MC; V. Cata: 2 a year. Corresp: French. Mem: PBFA. VAT No: GB 499 0638 93. [Updated]

DUMFRIES

Crescent Books, ■ 32 Church Crescent, Dumfries, Dumfries & Galloway, DG1 1DF. Prop: Martin Close. Tel: (01387) 261137. E-mail: crescent.books@virgin.net. Est: 1994. Shop open: **T:** 11:00–17:00; **W:** 11:00–17:00; **Th:** 11:00–17:00; **F:** 11:00–17:00; **S:** 11:00–17:00. Small general stock. PR: £1–50. CC: MC; V; Switch. Also, secondhand records. [10/05/2003]

Hen Hoose Bookshop, ■ Tynron, Nr. Thornhill, Dumfries, Dumfries & Galloway, DG3 4LB. Prop: J. McGregor. Tel: (01848) 200418. Est: 1994. Shop open: **T:** 11:00–17:00; **W:** 11:00–17:00; **Th:** 11:00–17:00; **F:** 11:00–17:00; **S:** 11:00–17:00; **Su:** 11:00–17:00. Medium stock. Spec: Art - History; Art - Reference; also Booksearch. PR: £1–50. CC: V. [18/06/2003]

Anwoth Books, ■ Mill on the Fleet, Gatehouse of Fleet, Dumfries, Dumfries & Gallway, DG7 2HS. Prop: Anwoth Books Ltd. Tel: (01557) 814774. Est: 1991. Shop open: **M:** 10:30–17:00; **T:** 10:30–17:00; **W:** 10:30–17:00; **Th:** 10:30–17:00; **F:** 10:30–17:00; **S:** 10:30–17:00; **Su:** 10:30–17:00. Large general stock. Spec: Art; Children's - General; Ornithology; Poetry; Scottish Interest. PR: £1–50. CC: JCB; MC; V. Winter opening: November to March open Friday to Sunday only. [Updated]

MOFFAT

Moffat Book Exchange, ■ 5 Well Street, Moffat, Dumfries & Galloway, DF10 9DP. Prop: Andy Armstrong. Tel: (01683) 220059. E-mail: dandrewarmstrong@aol.com. Est: 1998. Shop open: **M:** 10:00–16:30; **W:** 10:00–16:30; **Th:** 10:00–16:30; **F:** 10:00–16:30; **S:** 10:00–17:00; **Su:** 13:00–16:00; Closed for lunch: 13:00–14:00. Spec: Fiction - General. PR: £1–25. Stock includes large selection of paperback fiction. [Updated]

WHITHORN

Wyche Books, ■ 58 George Street, Whithorn, Dumfries & Galloway, DG8 9PA. Prop: John & Kathleen Turner. Tel: (01988) 500720. E-mail: kaytee@wychebooks.demon.co.uk. Est: 2002. Shop open: **M:** 09:00–17:00; **T:** 09:00–17:00; **W:** 09:00–17:00; **Th:** 09:00–17:00; **F:** 09:00–17:00; **S:** 09:00–17:00; **Su:** 11:00–16:00. Medium stock. Spec: Occult; also Booksearch. PR: £1–20. Winter (November to Easter), please telephone first. [31/08/2003]

WIGTOWN

AA1 Books, ■ Unit 3, Duncan Park, Wigtown, Dumfries & Galloway, DG8 9JD. Prop: Marion Richmond. Tel: (01988) 402653. Website: www.bookavenue/hosted/AA1. E-mail: AA1books@ supanet.com. Est: 2001. Shop open: **M:** 10:00–17:00; **T:** 10:00–17:00; **W:** 10:00–17:00; **Th:** 10:00–17:00; **F:** 10:00–17:00; **S:** 08:00–17:00; **Su:** 11:00–15:00. Very large stock. Spec: Children's - General; Espionage; Fiction - Crime, Detective, Spy, Thrillers; Fiction - Fantasy, Horror; Fiction - Science Fiction; Fiction - Westerns; Ghosts; History - General; Literature in Translation; Music - General; Natural History; Naval. PR: £1–150. CC: AE; MC; V. Also, new books. In association with Ming Books and Sign of the Dragon. Corresp: French, German. [18/09/2003]

A.P. & R. Baker Limited, The Laigh House, Church Lane, Wigtown, DG8 9HT. Prop: Anthony P. & Rosemary Baker. Tel: (01988) 403348. Fax: (01988) 403443. Website: www.apandrbaker.co.uk. E-mail: rosemary@apandrbaker.co.uk. Est: 1974. Private premises. Postal business only. Telephone first. Spec: Archaeology; History - General. PR: £2–500. CC: MC; V. Cata: 10 a year. [Updated]

Book Corner, ■ 2 High Street, Wigtown, Dumfries & Galloway, DG8 9HQ. Prop: Angela Langford. Tel: (01988) 402010. Website: www.book-corner.co.uk. E-mail: ian@book-corner.co.uk. Est: 1997. Internet and postal. Shop open: **M:** 10:00–17:00; **T:** 10:00–17:00; **W:** 10:00–17:00; **Th:** 10:00–17:00; **F:** 10:00–17:00; **S:** 10:00–17:00. Very large general stock. Spec: Animals and Birds; Antiques; Art; Aviation; Botany; Conservation; Cookery/Gastronomy; Ecology; Entomology; Fiction - General; Food & Drink; Gardening; Horticulture; Lepidopterology / Lepidoptery; Motoring; Natural History; New Naturalist; Ornithology. PR: £1–150. CC: MC; V; SW. Also, wildlife art by major UK artists. [18/08/2003]

The Box of Frogs, ■ 18 North Main Street, Wigtown, Dumfries & Galloway, DG8 9HL. Prop: Fiona Murphie. Tel: (01988) 402255. Fax: (01988) 402255. Website: www.froggybox.co.uk. E-mail: fiona@ froggybox.co.uk. Est: 1998. Shop open: **M:** 10:00–16:30; **T:** 10:00–16:30; **W:** 10:00–16:30; **Th:** 10:00–16:30; **F:** 10:00–16:30; **S:** 10:00–16:30; **Su:** 12:00–16:00. Medium stock. Spec: Children's - General. PR: £1–100. CC: JCB; MC; V; Switch. Mem: WBTA. [11/05/2003]

Byre Books, ■ 24 South Main St., Wigtown, Dumfries & Galloway, DG8 9EH. Prop: Laura Mustian and Chris Ballance. Tel: (01988) 402133. Website: www.byrebooks.co.uk. E-mail: info@ byrebooks.co.uk. Est: 2000. Internet and postal. Shop open: **M:** 10:00–17:00; **T:** 10:00–17:00; **W:** 10:00–17:00; **Th:** 10:00–17:00; **F:** 10:00–17:00; **S:** 10:00–17:00. Small stock. Spec: Arthurian; Cinema/ Film; Drama; Fables; Folklore; Mythology; Scottish Interest; Television; Theatre. PR: £3–100. CC: E; MC; V. From Nov-Mar irregular opening hours, phone first. Cata: 2 a year. Corresp: Spanish, French. Mem: Wigtown Book Trades Ass. VAT No: GB 789 1742 76. [13/04/2003]

G C Books, ■ The Old Bank, 7 South Main Street, Wigtown, Dumfries & Galloway, DG8 9EH. Tel: (01988) 402688. Fax: (01988) 402688. Website: www.gcbooks.demon.co.uk. E-mail: sales@ gcbooks.demon.co.uk. Est: 1990. Internet and postal. Shop open: **M:** 09:09–17:00; **T:** 00:00–17:00; **W:** 09:00–17:00; **Th:** 09:00–17:00; **F:** 09:00–17:00; **S:** 09:00–17:00. Large general stock. Spec: Academic/Scholarly; Architecture; Author - Niall, Ian; History - European; History - Local; History - National; Military History; Religion - General; Scottish Interest; War - World War II. PR: £1–1,000. CC: MC; V. Corresp: French. Mem: PBFA. [02/08/2003]

Menavaur Books, ■ 11 High Street, Wigtown, Dumfries & Galloway, DG8 1HH. Prop: Paul & Carolle Oram. Tel: (01988) 840665. Website: www.abebooks.com. E-mail: menbks@globalnet.co.uk. Est: 1993. Internet and postal. Telephone first. Shop at: Aberglass, Main Street, Kirkinner, Newton Stewart, DG8 9AN. Open: **M:** 10:00–16:00; **F:** 10:00–16:00; **S:** 10:00–16:00. Small stock. Spec: Academic/Scholarly; Advertising; Countries - Isles of Scilly; Fables; Fishes; Illustrated; Maritime/ Nautical; Natural History; Scottish Interest; Travel - General. PR: £5–1,000. CC: MC; V. Cata: 4 a year. Mem: PBFA. [Updated]

Ming Books, Beechwood House, Acre Place, Wigtown, DG8 9DU. Prop: Mrs Marion Richmond. Tel: (01988) 402653. Fax: (0709) 221-8017. Website: www.mingbooks.supanet.commcom. E-mail: mingbooks@supanet.com. Est: 1982. Office &/or bookroom. Internet and postal. Open: **M:** 10:00– 18:00; **T:** 10:00–18:00; **W:** 10:00–18:00; **Th:** 10:00–18:00; **F:** 10:00–18:00; **S:** 10:00–18:00; **Su:** 11:00– 15:00; Closed for lunch: 12:00–13:00. Very large stock. Spec: Crime (True); Espionage; Fiction - Crime, Detective, Spy, Thrillers; First Editions; History - General; Modern First Editions; Scottish Interest; Sherlockiana. PR: £4–1,000. CC: AE; MC; V; SW. Cata: 3 a year on crime fiction. Corresp: German and French. Mem: Wigtown Book Town. VAT No: GB 432 9993 15. [Updated]

Reading Lasses, ■ 17 South Main Street, Wigtown, DG8 9EH. Prop: Angela Everitt. Tel: (01988) 403266. Website: www.reading-lasses.com. E-mail: books@reading-lasses.com. Est: 1997. Shop; Open. Open: **M:** 10:00–17:00; **T:** 10:00–17:00; **W:** 10:00–17:00; **Th:** 10:00–17:00; **F:** 10:00–17:00; **S:** 10:00–00:00; **Su:** 12:00–16:00. Medium stock. Spec: Academic/Scholarly; Africana; Alternative Medicine; Anthropology; Art; Authors - Women; Autobiography; Biography; Black Studies; Cinema/ Film; Crafts; Criminology; Culture - Popular; Diaries; Drama; Economics; Education & School; Fashion & Costume. PR: £1–500. CC: AE; JCB; MC; V; S, D, Mae. Also, tea/coffee house with local produce and home baking. Sunday opening applies summer only. Corresp: French. Mem: PBFA; WBTA. Also at: [Updated]

Transformer, ■ 26 Bladnoch, Wigtown, DG8 9AB. Prop: C.A. Weaver. Tel: 0044-(0)1988-403455. Website: www.abebooks.com/home/TRANSFORMER/home.htm. E-mail: transformer@tesco.net. Est: 1998. Internet and postal. Shop open in summer. Very large stock. Spec: Academic/Scholarly; Children's - General; Culture - Foreign; Education & School; Espionage; Fiction - Crime, Detective, Spy, Thrillers; Fiction - Fantasy, Horror; Fiction - Science Fiction; Languages - Foreign; Mathematics; Psychology/Psychiatry. PR: £1–400. Corresp: French. [Updated]

FIFE

ANSTRUTHER

Rising Tide Books, 51 John Street, Cellardyke, Anstruther, Fife, KY10 3BA. Prop: Stephen Checkland. Tel: (01333) 310948. Fax: (01333) 310948. E-mail: stevecheckland@risingtidebooks.com. Est: 1997. Private premises. Book fairs only. Appointment necessary. Very small stock. Spec: Illustrated; Modern First Editions; Scottish Interest. PR: £5–500. Mem: PBFA. [Updated]

DUNFERMLINE

Larry Hutchison (Books), 27 Albany Street, Dunfermline, Fife, KY12 OQZ. Tel: (01383) 725566. Fax: (01383) 620394. Website: www.larryhutchisobooks.com. E-mail: larry@larryhutchisonbooks.com. Est: 1987. Private premises. Appointment necessary. Medium stock. Spec: Antiquarian; Countries - Scotland; Fine & Rare; Folklore; Genealogy; History - General; Literature; Military; Topography - Local; also Booksearch. PR: £5–5,000. CC: AE; MC; V. Cata: 6 a year. Corresp: most major European. Mem: PBFA. VAT No: GB 716 9500 30. [Updated]

KIRKCALDY

R. Campbell Hewson Books, 6 West Albert Road, Kirkcaldy, Fife, KY1 1DL. Tel: (01592) 262051. Est: 1996. Private premises. Appointment necessary. Small stock. Spec: Author - Burton, R.F.; Ethnography; Rural Life; Sport - Big Game Hunting; Travel - Africa; Voyages & Discovery. PR: £10–3,500. [Updated]

NEWPORT ON TAY

Gordon Bettridge, 4 Myrtle Terrace, Newport on Tay, Fife, DD6 8DN. Tel: (01382) 542377. E-mail: gordon_bettridge@lineone.net. Est: 1984. Postal business only. Spec: Advertising; Bibliography; Books about Books; Calligraphy; Illustrated; Journals - General; Papermaking; Printing; Private Press; Publishers - Penguin; Publishing; Typography. PR: £1–75. Also, back-numbers of printing & typography journals. [Updated]

Mair Wilkes Books, 3 St. Mary's Lane, Newport on Tay, Fife, DD6 8AH. Tel: (01382) 542260. Fax: (01382) 542260. E-mail: mairwilkes.books@zoom.co.uk. Est: 1969. Storeroom. Open: **T:** 10:00–16:30; **W:** 10:00–16:30; **Th:** 10:10–16:30; **F:** 10:00–16:30; **S:** 10:00–17:00; Closed for lunch: 12:30–14:00. Spec: Academic/Scholarly; Bindings; Fine & Rare; History of Ideas; Medicine - History of; Modern First Editions; Neurology; Psychology/Psychiatry; Science - History of; Scottish Interest; Topography - Local. PR: £2–1,000. CC: AE; V; SW. Cata: 3 a year on Scottish Intererst. Mem: PBFA; Also at: Scottish Antiques Ctre, Abernyte, Inchture, Perthshire. VAT No: GB 397 9923 69. [28/05/2003]

ST. ANDREWS

The Quarto Bookshop, ■ 8 Golf Place, St. Andrews, Fife, KY16 9JA. Prop: M. Squires. Tel: (01334) 474616. E-mail: quartobooks@btconnect.com. Est: 1969. Shop open: **M:** 10:00–17:30; **T:** 10:00–17:30; **W:** 10:00–17:30; **Th:** 10:00–17:30; **F:** 10:00–17:30; **S:** 10:00–17:30; **Su:** 12:00–17:00. Medium stock. Spec: Countries - Scotland; History - Local; Sport - Golf; Topography - Local; also Booksearch. PR: £1–500. CC: MC; V. Corresp: French, Spanish. Mem: BA. [Updated]

GRAMPIAN

ABERDEEN

Buchan Collectibles, South Meiklemoss, Collieston, Ellon, Aberdeen, Grampian, AB41 8SB. Tel: (+44) 1358 751774. Website: http://www.buchancollect.com. E-mail: enquiries@buchancollect.com. Est: 2000. Private premises. Internet and postal. Appointment necessary. Large general stock. Spec: Animals and Birds; Annuals; Biology; Botany; Children's - General; Comic Books & Annuals; Comics; Conservation; Entomology; Evolution; Fiction - General; Natural History; Ornithology; Poetry; Scottish Interest, also Booksearch. PR: £3–500. CC: AE; JCB; MC; V. Mem: FSB. [20/08/2003]

Elizabeth Ferguson, 34 Woodburn Avenue, Aberdeen, Grampian, AB15 8JQ. Tel: (01224) 315949. Fax: (01224) 315949. E-mail: efergusonbooks@aol.com. Est: 2000. Postal business only. Small stock. Spec: Booksearch. PR: £5–500. Cata: occasionally, on childrens, natural history. Corresp: French, German. [Updated]

Grampian Books, South Monkshill, Fyvie, Turriff, Aberdeen, Grampian, AB53 8RQ. Prop: David Fleming. Tel: (01651) 891524. Fax: (01651) 891524. E-mail: dfleming@grampianbooks.sol.co.uk. Est: 1990. Private premises. Appointment necessary. Medium stock. Spec: Academic/Scholarly; History of Ideas; Scottish Interest. PR: £2–1,000. CC: AE; MC; V. Corresp: French, Spanish. Mem: PBFA. [28/07/2003]

Kevin S. Ogilvie Modern First, 11 Wallacebrae Walk, Danestone, Aberdeen, Grampian, AB22 8YL. Tel: (07778) 637366. E-mail: kevinsogilvie@cwcom.net. Est: 1991. Postal business only. Spec: Children's - General; Modern First Editions; Fiction - Crime, Detective, Spy, Thrillers. PR: £7–100. [20/08/2003]

Clifford Milne Books, 6 Hillcrest Place, Aberdeen, Grampian, AB2 7BP. Tel: (01224) 697654. Est: 1994. Private premises. Postal business only. Small stock. Spec: Art; Countries - Scotland; Modern First Editions; Sport - Golf. PR: £1–100. Mem: PBFA. [Updated]

Winram's Bookshop, ■ 32/36 Rosemount Place, Aberdeen, Grampian, AB25 2XB. Prop: Mrs. Margaret Davidson. Tel: (01224) 630673. Fax: (01224) 631532. Est: 1977. Shop open: **M:** 10:00–17:30; **T:** 10:00–17:30; **W:** 10:00–13:00; **Th:** 10:00–17:30; **F:** 10:00–17:30; **S:** 10:00–17:30. Medium stock. Spec: Scottish Interest. PR: £1–1,000. [Updated]

BALLATER

Deeside Books, ■ 18-20 Bridge Street, Ballater, Aberdeenshire, AB35 5QP. Prop: Bryn Wayte. Tel: (01339) 754080. E-mail: deesidebk@aol.com. Est: 1998. Shop open: **M:** 10:00–17:00; **T:** 10:00–17:00; **W:** 10:00–17:00; **Th:** 10:00–17:00; **F:** 10:00–17:00; **S:** 10:00–17:00; **Su:** 12:00–17:00. Large stock. Spec: Military; Scottish Interest; Sport - Angling/Fishing; Sport - Field Sports; Topography - General; Topography - Local; Travel - General. PR: £1–100. CC: AE; E; JCB; MC; V. Mem: PBFA. [Updated]

McEwan Fine Books, Glengarden, Ballater, Aberdeenshire, AB35 5UB. Prop: Dr. Peter McEwan. Tel: (01339) 755429. Fax: (01339) 755995. Website: www.rhodmcewan.com. E-mail: art@mcewangallery .com. Est: 1968. Private premises. Postal business only. Medium stock. Spec: Academic/Scholarly; Countries - Antarctic, The; Countries - Polar; Heraldry; Literature; Natural History; Ornithology; Sport - Angling/Fishing; Sport - Big Game Hunting; Sport - Cricket; Sport - Field Sports. PR: £5–5,000. Also, works of art. Cata: quarterly. Also at: Rhod McEwan Golf Books (q.v.). [13/10/2004]

Rhod McEwan Golf Books, Glengarden, Ballater, Aberdeenshire, AB35 5UB. Tel: (013397) 55429. Fax: (013397) 55995. Website: www.rhodmcewan.com. E-mail: teeoff@rhodmcewan.com. Est: 1985. Private premises. Appointment necessary. Medium stock. Spec: Sport - Golf. PR: £3–5,000. CC: MC; V. Also, golf posters and paintings. Cata: 2 a year. Corresp: German, Hungarian, Spanish. Mem: ABA. At same premises: McEwan Fine Books. (q.v.). VAT No: GB 605 2115 89. [20/08/2003]

ELLON

Aberdeen Rare Books & Caledoni, Slains House, Collieston, Ellon, Grampian, AB41 8RT. Prop: A. J. & Mrs. P.M. Campbell. Tel: (01358) 751275 and 7. Est: 1977. Private premises. Appointment necessary. Medium stock. Spec: Archaeology; Countries - Scotland; Fine & Rare; Heraldry; History - Local; Journals - General; Law; Music - General; Periodicals & Magazines; Poetry; Topography - Local. PR: £3–3,000. Cata: occasionally. Mem: PBFA. VAT No: GB 297 2352 32. [18/09/2003]

FOCHABERS

Alba Books, Maxwell Street, Fochabers, Moray, IV32 7DE. Prop: Mike Seton. Tel: (01343) 820575. Fax: (01343) 820780. Website: www.abebooks.com/home/albabooks. E-mail: Albabooks@dial.pipex.com. Est: 1997. Warehouse; Internet and postal. Appointment necessary. Very large stock. Spec: Alternative Medicine; Art; Biology; Gynaecology; Literature; Maritime/Nautical; Medicine; Medicine - History of; Neurology; Pharmacy/Pharmacology; Psychoanalysis; Psychology/ Psychiatry; Psychotherapy; Science - General; Scottish Interest; Veterinary. PR: £2–200. CC: AE; E; MC; V; Switch. Corresp: French, German,. Also on IBooknet. VAT No: GB 751 3324 56. [Updated]

FORRES

The Moray Bookshop, ■ Logie Steading Visitor Centre, Dunphail, Forres, IV36 2QN. Prop: Pierce Roche. Tel: (01309) 611373. Website: www.moraybookshop.co.uk. E-mail: info@moraybookshop .co.uk. Est: 1999. Shop sometimes closed January & February: please ring ahead. Open: **M:** 11:00–17:00; **T:** 11:00–17:00; **W:** 11:00–17:00; **Th:** 11:00–17:00; **F:** 11:00–17:00; **S:** 11:00–17:00; **Su:** 11:00–17:01. Large general stock. Spec: Author - MacDonald, George; Author - Walsh, M.; Cookery/ Gastronomy; Countries - Scotland; Countries - Sudan, The; Food & Drink; Scottish Interest; Whisky. PR: £1–500. CC: JCB; MC; V; Maestro Switch. Cata: occasional. Mem: PBFA. [Updated]

MONTROSE

Devanha Military Books, 4 Castle Terrace, Inverbervie, Montrose, Angus, DD10 0RE. Prop: Nick Ducat. Tel: (01561) 361387. E-mail: nickducat@devbooks.fsnet.co.uk. Est: 2001. Private premises. Postal business only. Small stock. Spec: Military; Military History. PR: £5–350. [Updated]

MORAY

Marianne Simpson, ■ 61/63 High Street, Fochabers, Moray, IV32 7DU. Tel: (01343) 821192. Est: 1990. Shop open: **M:** 10:00–16:00; **T:** 10:00–16:00; **W:** 10:00–16:00; **Th:** 10:00–16:00; **F:** 10:00–16:00; **S:** 10:00–16:00; Closed for lunch: 13:00–14:00. Small general stock. PR: £1–100. Winter opening: Oct to Easter - Tues, Thurs & Sat 10:00-16:00. Closed lunch. Corresp: French. [Updated]

HIGHLAND

BRORA

Adam Gordon, Kintradwell Farmhouse, Brora, Highland, KW9 6LU. Tel: (01408) 622660. E-mail: adam@adamgordon.freewire.co.uk. Est: 1985. Private premises. Appointment necessary. Open: Large stock. Spec: Buses/Trams; Literature; Railways; Transport. PR: £1–250. Also, publisher of transport books. [Updated]

DINGWALL

Mercat Books, ■ 6 Church Street, Dingwall, Highland, IV15 9SB. Prop: Hazel MacMillan. Tel: (01349) 865593. Fax: (01349) 865593. E-mail: mercat.books@zetnet.co.uk. Est: 1995. Shop. Telephone first. Spec: Architecture; Fiction - General; Food & Drink; Gardening; Humour; Natural History; Poetry; Rural Life; Scottish Interest; Transport; War - General, also Booksearch. PR: £1–100. [Updated]

FORT WILLIAM

Don McGavin, 14 Lanark Place, Fort William, Inverness–shire, PH33 6UD. Tel: (01397) 703157. Private premises. Appointment necessary. Very small general stock. PR: £1–100. Corresp: French. [Updated]

Creaking Shelves, Arkaig Cottage, Fort William, Inverness-shire, Highland, PH33 6RN. Prop: Chris Robinson. Tel: (01397) 702886. Website: www.abebooks.com. E-mail: cr@lochaber.almac.co.uk. Est: 1998. Private premises. Postal business only. Open in summer. Very small stock. Spec: Alpinism/ Mountaineering; Countries - Scotland; Natural History; New Naturalist. PR: £5–500. [Updated]

INVERNESS

Leakey's Bookshop, ■ Greyfriars Hall, Church Street, Inverness, Highland, IV1 1EY. Prop: Charles Leakey. Tel: (01463) 239947. Est: 1979. Shop open: **M:** 10:00–17:30; **T:** 10:00–17:30; **W:** 10:00–17:30; **Th:** 10:00–17:30; **F:** 10:00–17:30; **S:** 10:00–17:30. Very large general stock. CC: E; JCB; MC; V. [27/04/ 2003]

LOCHCARRON

Blythswood Bookshop, ■ Main Street, Lochcarron, Ross-shire, IV54 8YD. Blythswood Trade. Tel: (01520) 722337. Fax: (01520) 722264. Website: www.blythswood.org. E-mail: blythswoodbookshop@ lineone.net. Est: 1984. Internet and postal. Shop open: **M:** 10:00–16:00; **T:** 10:00–16:00; **W:** 10:00– 16:00; **Th:** 10:00–16:00; **F:** 10:00–16:00. Medium stock. Spec: Biography; First Editions; Religion - General; Religion - Christian; Theology, also Booksearch. PR: £2–200. CC: MC; V. Also, new books. Mem: BA. Also at: Portree, Isle of Skye; Dingwell, Ross-shire and Stornoway, Isle of Lewis, and Cromer, Norfolk. VAT No: GB 742927906. [Updated]

LOTHIAN

EDINBURGH

Armchair Books, ■ 72-74 West Port, Edinburgh, EH1 2LE. Prop: David Govan. Tel: (0131) 229-5927. Website: www.armchairbooks.co.uk. E-mail: wlytle@ireland.com. Est: 1989. Shop open: **M:** 10:00–19:00; **T:** 10:00–19:00; **W:** 10:00–19:00; **Th:** 10:00–19:00; **F:** 10:00–18:00; **S:** 10:00–18:00; **Su:** 10:00–18:00. Large general stock. Spec: Africana; Annuals; Art; Author - Belloc, Hilaire; Author - Buchan, John; Author - Chesterton, G.K.; Author - Conan Doyle, Sir Arthur; Author - Kipling, Rudyard; Author - Lawrence, D.H.; Author - Lewis, C.S.; Countries - Ireland; Countries - Scotland. PR: £1–1,000. CC: MC; V. [Updated]

Bookworm, ■ 210 Dalkeith Road, Edinburgh, Lothian, EH16 5DT. Prop: Peter Ritchie. Tel: (0131) 662-4357. Est: 1986. Shop open: **M:** 09:30–17:30; **T:** 09:30–17:30; **W:** 09:30–17:30; **Th:** 09:30–17:30; **F:** 09:30–17:30; **S:** 09:30–17:15. Medium stock. Spec: Arms & Armour; Art - History; Egyptology; Fiction - General; Firearms/Guns; Freemasonry & Anti-Masonry; History - General; Literature; Maritime/Nautical; Military History; Naval; Scottish Interest; War - General. CC: AE; JCB; MC; V; SW. [Updated]

Blacket Books, 1 Leadervale Terrace, Edinburgh, EH16 6NX. Prop: Elizabeth Laing. Tel: (0131) 666-1542. Website: www.blacketbooks.co.uk. E-mail: liz@blacketbooks.co.uk. Est: 1985. Private premises. Internet and postal. Telephone first. Small general stock. Spec: Children's - General; Military; Scottish Interest. PR: £10–1,500. CC: JCB; MC; V. Mem: PBFA. [Updated]

Andrew Pringle Booksellers, ■ 62 West Port, Edinburgh, EH1 2LD. Tel: (0131) 556-9698. Website: www.pringlebooks.co.uk. E-mail: andrew@pringlebooks.co.uk. Est: 1988. Shop open: Medium stock. Spec: Antiquarian; Art; Biography; History - National; Literature; Modern First Editions; Scottish Interest. PR: £3–500. CC: JCB; V; Switch. Corresp: French. Mem: PBFA. [Updated]

Archways Sports Books, P.O. Box 13018, Edinburgh, Lothian, EH14 2YA. Prop: Iain C. Murray. Tel: (07990) 527942. E-mail: archways@blueyonder.co.uk. Est: 1992. Private premises. Postal business only. Small stock. Spec: Health; Physical Culture; Sport - General. CC: AE; MC; V. [Updated]

Peter Bell, ■ 68 West Port, Edinburgh, Lothian, EH1 2LD. Tel: (0131) 556-2198. Fax: (0131) 229-0562. Website: www.peterbell.net. E-mail: books@peterbell.net. Est: 1980. Shop at: Please ring if visiting on a Monday. Shop tel: (0131) 229-0562. Open: **M:** 10:00–17:00; **T:** 10:00–17:00; **W:** 10:00–17:00; **Th:** 10:00–17:00; **F:** 10:00–17:00; **S:** 10:00–17:00. Medium stock. Spec: Academic/Scholarly; Antiquarian; Biography; Ecclesiastical History & Architecture; History - General; History - British; History - European; History - Scottish; Literature - Victorian; Philosophy; Religion - Christian; Religion - Presbyterian. PR: £1–500. CC: MC; V. Cata: occasionally on academic and rare. Mem: ABA; PBFA. VAT No: GB 416 0959 50. [Updated]

Broughton Books, ■ 2a Broughton Place, Edinburgh, Lothian, EH1 3RX. Prop: Peter Galinsky. Tel: (0131) 557-8010. Est: 1963. Shop; Open. Open: **T:** 12:00–18:00; **W:** 12:00–18:00; **Th:** 12:00–18:00; **F:** 12:00–18:00; **S:** 09:30–17:30. Large stock. Spec: History - General; Humanities; Literature. PR: £2–250. Essential oils, chess sets. Corresp: Flemish, French, Frisian, German, Dutch, Spanish. [Updated]

Anna Buxton Books, Redcroft, 23 Murrayfield Road, Edinburgh, Lothian, EH12 6EP. Prop: A. Buxton. Tel: (0131) 337-1747. Fax: (0131) 337-8174. Website: www.abebooks.com. E-mail: annabuxtonb@aol.com. Est: 1989. Private premises. Internet and postal. Appointment necessary. Very small stock. Spec: Botany; Gardening; Landscape; Plant Hunting. PR: £12–5,000. CC: MC; V; SW. Cata: 1 a year. Corresp: French, Italian. Mem: PBFA. [Updated]

Jay Books, Rowll House, Roull Grove, Edinburgh, Lothian, EH12 7JP. Prop: D.J. Brayford. Tel: (0131) 316-4034. Fax: (0131) 467-0309. Website: www.jaybooks.demon.co.uk. E-mail: djb@jaybooks .demon.co.uk. Est: 1977. Private premises. Internet and postal. Appointment necessary. Open: **M:** 09:00–21:00; **T:** 09:00–21:00; **W:** 09:00–21:00; **Th:** 09:00–21:00; **F:** 09:00–21:00; **S:** 09:00–21:00; **Su:** 09:00–21:00. Small stock. Spec: Botany; Gardening; Natural History; Science - General; Science - History of; Technology. PR: £20–1,000. CC: MC; V. Also, valuations. Cata: 3 a year. Corresp: Spanish, German, French. Mem: ABA; PBFA; ILAB. [Updated]

Domhnall MacCormaig, 19 Braid Crescent, Edinburgh, Lothian, EH10 6AX. Prop: Domhnall MacCormaig. Tel: (0131) 447-2889. Fax: (0131) 447-9496. E-mail: grenitote@aol.com. Est: 1976. Private premises. Postal business only. Medium stock. Spec: Countries - Scotland; Culture - National; History - Local; Literature in Translation; Scottish Interest; Topography - Local. PR: £10–5,000. Cata: 8 a year on specialities. Mem: ABA. [24/07/2003]

Main Point Books, ■ 8 Lauriston Street, Edinburgh, Lothian, EH3 9DJ. Prop: Richard Browne. Tel: (0131) 228 4837. Fax: (0131) 228 4837. Est: 2001. Shop open: **T:** 11:00–17:00; **W:** 11:00–17:00; **Th:** 11:00–17:00; **F:** 11:00–17:00; **S:** 11:00–17:00. Medium stock. Spec: Alpinism/Mountaineering; Esoteric; Fiction - General; Literature; Poetry; Scottish Interest; Sport - Climbing & Trekking; Theology. [Updated]

McNaughtan's Bookshop, ■ 3a and 4a Haddington Place, Leith Walk, Edinburgh, Lothian, EH7 4AE. Prop: Elizabeth A. Strong. Tel: (0131) 556-5897. Fax: (0131) 556 8220. Website: www. mcnaughtansbookshop.com. E-mail: mcnbooks@btconnect.com. Est: 1957. Shop open: **T:** 09:30–17:30; **W:** 09:30–17:30; **Th:** 09:30–17:30; **F:** 09:30–17:30; **S:** 09:30–17:30. Very large stock. Spec: Antiquarian; Architecture; Art; Children's - General; Literature; Scottish Interest. PR: £1–3,500. CC: JCB; MC; V; Maestro. Mem: ABA; ILAB. VAT No: GB 327 3505 69. [Updated]

The Old Town Bookshop, ■ 8 Victoria Street, Edinburgh, Lothian, EH1 2HG. Prop: Ronald Wilson. Tel: (0131) 225-9237. Fax: (0131) 229-1503. Website: www.oldtownbookshop.co.uk. Est: 1992. Shop open: **M:** 10:30–17:45; **T:** 10:30–17:45; **W:** 10:30–17:45; **Th:** 10:30–17:45; **F:** 10:30–17:45; **S:** 10:00–17:45. Medium stock. Spec: Architecture; Art; Art - Reference; Bindings; Botany; Catalogues Raisonnes; Children's - General; Country Houses; Decorative Art; History - General; Illustrated; Literature; Natural History; Scottish Interest; Sets of Books; Topography - Local. PR: £1–3,000. CC: JCB; MC; V; SW. Exhibits at 18 book fairs around the country. Cata: 2 a year on art, architecture, Scottish and antiquarian. Mem: PBFA. [Updated]

David Page, 47 Spottiswoode Road, Edinburgh, Lothian, EH9 1DA. Tel: (0131) 447-4553. Fax: (0131) 447-4553. E-mail: page@47spot.freeserve.co.uk. Private premises. Telephone first. Small stock. Spec: Alpinism/Mountaineering; Natural History; Plant Hunting; Travel - General; Travel - Africa; Travel - Asia; Travel - Middle East; Travel - Polar. Corresp: French, German. [Updated]

Second Edition, ■ 9 Howard Street, Edinburgh, Lothian, EH3 5JP. Prop: Mrs. Maureen E. and W.A. Smith. Tel: (0131) 556-9403. Website: www.secondeditionbookshop.co.uk. E-mail: secondedition@ tiscali.co.uk. Est: 1978. Shop open: **M:** 10:30–17:30; **T:** 10:30–17:30; **W:** 10:30–17:30; **Th:** 10:30–17:30; **F:** 10:30–17:30; **S:** 09:30–17:30. Large stock. Spec: Architecture; Art; Children's - General; Fine Art; Illustrated; Literature; Medicine; Military History; Modern First Editions; Natural History; Naval; Philosophy; Scottish Interest; Topography - Local; Travel - General. PR: £10–500. Corresp: Spanish. [Updated]

Till's Bookshop, ■ 1 Hope Park Crescent, (Buccleugh Street), Edinburgh, Lothian, EH8 9NA. Tel: (0131) 667-0895. Website: www.tillsbookshop.co.uk. E-mail: tillsbookshop@btconnect.com. Est: 1986. Shop open: **M:** 12:00–19:30; **T:** 12:00–19:30; **W:** 12:00–19:30; **Th:** 12:00–19:30; **F:** 12:00–19:30; **S:** 11:00–18:00; **Su:** 12:00–17:30. Large general stock. PR: £2–20. CC: E; MC; V; De, SW, SO. Also, cinema posters. [Updated]

John Updike Rare Books, 7 St. Bernard's Row, Edinburgh, Lothian, EH4 1HW. Prop: John S. Watson & Edward G. Nairn. Tel: (0131) 332-1650. Fax: (0131) 332-1347. Est: 1965. Private premises. Appointment necessary. Medium stock. Spec: Books about Books; Children's - General; Churchilliana; Drama; Fine & Rare; Fine Printing; First Editions; Illustrated; Irish Interest; Limited Editions; Literature; Literature in Translation; Periodicals & Magazines; Poetry; Private Press; Scottish. Cata: 2 a year on specialities. Mem: ABA. [Updated]

HADDINGTON

Yeoman Books, 37 Hope Park Crescent, Haddington, East Lothian, EH41 3AN. Prop: D.A. Hyslop. Tel: (01620) 822307. Fax: (01620) 822307. E-mail: yeomanbooks@talk21.com. Est: 1924. Private premises. Appointment necessary. Very small stock. Spec: Aviation; Military; Military History; Motorbikes; Motoring; War - General. PR: £5–150. Mem: PBFA. [20/08/2003]

SOUTH QUEENSFERRY

Marion Shearer, 41 Moubray Grove, South Queensferry, West Lothian, EH30 9PB. Tel: (0131) 331-1978. Private premises. Postal business only. Very small general stock. PR: £2–200. [Updated]

STRATHCLYDE

AIRDRIE

Brown-Studies, Woodside Cottage, Longriggend, Airdrie, Strathclyde, ML6 7RU. (*) Prop: Mr. M.G. & Mrs. B.J. Brown. Tel: (01236) 843826. Fax: (01236) 842545. Website: www.brown-studies.co.uk. E-mail: brownstudies@clara.co.uk. Est: 1990. Private premises. Internet and postal. Appointment necessary. Open: **M:** 09:00–20:00; **T:** 09:00–20:00; **W:** 09:00–20:00; **Th:** 09:00–20:00; **F:** 09:00–20:00; **S:** 09:00–20:00; **Su:** 09:00–20:00. Very large stock. Spec: Artists; Author - Read, Miss; Building & Construction; Cookery/Gastronomy; D.I.Y (Do It Yourself); Ecology; Gardening; Herbalism; Knitting; Needlework; Woodwork. PR: £3–300. CC: E; MC; V; Switch. Also on Ibooknet. VAT No: GB 556 6923 05. [Updated]

AYR

Ainslie Books, ■ 1 Glendoune St., Girvan, Ayr, KA26 0AA. (*) Prop: Agnes & Gordon Clark. Tel: (01465) 715453. Fax: (01465) 715453. Website: www.ainsliebooks.co.uk. E-mail: ainslie.books@ btopenworld.com. Shop; Internet and postal. Open: **M:** 10:00–17:00; **T:** 10:00–17:00; **W:** 10:00–17:00; **Th:** 10:00–17:00; **F:** 10:00–17:00; **S:** 10:00–17:00. Large general stock. Spec: Academic/Scholarly; Advertising; Aeronautics; Africana; Shorthand; also Booksearch. PR: £1–200. CC: MC; V. [Updated]

BIGGAR

Karen Thomson, South Lindsaylands, Biggar, Strathclyde, ML12 6NR. Tel: (01899) 221991. Fax: (01899) 221955. Est: 1987. Private premises. Postal business only. Very small stock. Spec: Academic/ Scholarly; Antiquarian; Dictionaries; Medieval; Philology. Cata: 6 a year. Corresp: French, German. VAT No: GB 527 7505 33. [Updated]

CAMPBELTOWN

The Old Bookshelf, ■ 8 Cross Street, Campbeltown, Strathclyde, PA28 6HU. Prop: David and Davina Tomlinson. Tel: (01586) 551114. Website: www.theoldbookshelf.co.uk. E-mail: theoldbookshelf@ aol.com. Est: 2001. Internet and postal. Shop open: **M:** 11:00–17:00; **T:** 11:00–17:00; **W:** 11:00–17:00; **Th:** 11:00–17:00; **F:** 11:00–17:00; **S:** 10:00–16:00. Large stock. Spec: Scottish Interest. PR: £2–3,000. CC: AE; E; JCB; MC; V; Meastro. Also on ibooknet. VAT No: GB 808 8668 81. [Updated]

DALMELLINGTON

Wheen O'Blethers Bookshop, Unit 1, Dame Helen Bookcentre, 18c Ayr Road, Dalmellington, Strathclyde, KA6 7SJ. Prop: Ron Gabbott. Tel: (01292) 531723. E-mail: Est: 2000. Spec: Biography; Calligraphy; Company History; Folklore; Industry; Linguistics; Private Press. PR: £1–500. [28/08/2003]

GLASGOW

Alba Secondhand Music, ■ Otago Street, Glasgow, Strathclyde, G12 8PQ. Prop: Robert Lay. Tel: (01389) 875996. Website: www.albamusick.co.uk. E-mail: robert@albamusick.fsnet.co.uk. Est: 1994. Shop open: **M:** 11:00–17:30; **T:** 11:00–17:30; **W:** 11:00–17:30; **Th:** 11:00–17:30; **F:** 11:00–17:30; **S:** 11:00–17:30. Large stock. Spec: Music - Classical. CC: MC; V. Shop located behind Otago café & open at other times by appointment. [05/08/2003]

Caledonia Books, 483 Great Western Road, Kelvinbridge, Glasgow, Strathclyde, G12 8HL. Prop: Maureen Smillie & Charles McBride. Tel: (0141) 334-9663. Fax: (0141) 334-9663. Website: www.caledoniabooks.co.uk. E-mail: caledoniabooks@aol.com. Est: 1984. Spec: Art; Art - History; Bibliography; Biography; Cinema/Film; Countries - Poland; Drama; Fiction - General; History - General; Irish Interest; Literary Criticism; Literature; Modern First Editions; Philosophy; Scottish Interest. PR: £2–200. CC: MC; V. [26/06/2003]

Cooper Hay Rare Books, ■ 182 Bath Street, Glasgow, Strathclyde, G2 4HG. Tel: (0141) 333-1992. Fax: (0141) 333-1992. Website: www.abebooks.com/home/haybooks. E-mail: chayrbooks@aol.com. Est: 1985. Shop open: **M:** 10:00–17:30; **T:** 10:00–17:30; **W:** 10:00–17:30; **Th:** 10:00–17:30; **F:** 10:00–17:30; **S:** 10:00–13:00; Closed for lunch: 13:00–14:15. Medium stock. Spec: Art; Bindings; Countries - Scotland; Juvenile; Scottish Interest. PR: £5–10,000. CC: MC; V. Cata: 2 a year. Mem: ABA; ILAB. [27/05/2003]

Eddie's Books and Cards, Argyle Market Centre, 28 Argyle Street, Glasgow, Strathclyde, G2 8AD. Prop: Edward E. Cowan. Tel: (0141) 226-3050. Est: 1982. Market stand/stall. Open: **M:** 09:30–17:00; **T:** 09:30–17:00; **W:** 09:30–17:00; **Th:** 09:30–17:00; **F:** 09:30–17:00; **S:** 09:30–17:30. Medium stock. PR: £1–6. Also, greetings cards, remainders, calandars and jigsaws. [27/04/2003]

Erasmus Books, 34 Hamilton Park Avenue, Glasgow, Strathclyde, G12 8DT. Prop: Brian McCrossan. Tel: (0141) 334-8684. Fax: (0141) 334-8684. Website: www.abebooks.com. E-mail: erasmusbooks@ dial.pipex.com. Est: 1996. Private premises. Internet and postal. Appointment necessary. Small stock. Spec: Academic/Scholarly; Economics; History - Labour/Radical Movements; Literature; Politics; Scottish Interest; Social History; Social Sciences. PR: £5–500. CC: JCB; MC; V. Corresp: French, Italian. [05/10/2003]

The Studio, ■ De Courcy's Arcade, 5-21 Cresswell Lane, Glasgow, Strathclyde, G12 8AA. Prop: Liz McKelvie. Tel: (0141) 334 8211. Website: wwww.glasgowwestend.co.uk/shopping/antiques/studio. E-mail: lizthestudio@aol.com. Est: 1997. Shop at: wwww.glasgowwestend.co.uk/shopping/antiques/ studio.html. Open: **T:** 10:00–17:30; **W:** 10:00–17:30; **Th:** 10:00–17:30; **F:** 10:00–17:30; **S:** 10:00–17:30; **Su:** 12:00–17:00. Small general stock. Spec: Bindings; Children's - Illustrated; Decorative Art; History - Local; Publishers - Blackie. PR: £5–1,000. CC: D; E; JCB; MC; V; SW, MAE. Also, books about Glasgow and Glasgow style antiques, furnishings, metalware, textiles, ceramics - circa 1900. [Updated]

Word of Mouth, c/o Moon, 10 Ruthven Lane, Glasgow, Strathclyde, G12 9BG. Tel: E-mail: ianmrry@ aol.com. [17/08/2003]

HELENSBURGH

Brian Annesley Books of Scotti, 26 Duchess Drive, Helensburgh, Dunbartonshire, G84 9PR. Tel: (01436) 676222. Fax: (0870) 0568922. Website: www.scotbooks.demon.co.uk. E-mail: brian@scotbooks .demon.co.uk. Est: 1983. Internet and postal. Small stock. Spec: Academic/Scholarly; Countries - Scotland. PR: £5–500. CC: MC; V. [18/09/2003]

McLaren Books, 22 John Street, Helensburgh, Dunbartonshire, G84 8BA. Tel: (01436) 676453. Fax: (01436) 673747. Website: www.mclarenbooks.co.uk. E-mail: mclarenbooks@breathe.co.uk. Est: 1976. Office &/or bookroom. Open: **F:** 10:00–17:00; **S:** 10:00–17:00. Medium stock. Spec: Manuals - Seamanship; Maritime/Nautical; Maritime/Nautical - Log Books; Naval; Navigation; Ship Modelling; Shipbuilding; Sport - Canoeing/Kayaks; Sport - Rowing; Sport - Yachting; Whaling. PR: £5–2,000. CC: MC; V; Switch. Open at other times by appointment. Cata: 10 a year on maritime. Mem: ABA; PBFA; ILAB. VAT No: GB 293 0008 81. [Updated]

IRVINE

D. Webster, 43 West Road, Irvine, Ayrshire, KA12 8RE. Tel: (01294) 272257. Fax: (01294) 276322. Est: 1958. Private premises. Appointment necessary. Small stock. Spec: Circus; Physical Culture; Sport - Highland Games; Sport - Weightlifting/Bodybuilding; Sport - Wrestling; also Booksearch. PR: £5–40. Cata: 2 a year. [03/02/2003]

KILMARNOCK

Roberts Books, 8, Main Road, Waterside, Kilmarnock, KA3 6JB. Prop: Richard Roberts. Tel: (01560) 600349. Fax: (01560) 600349. E-mail: robertsbooks@btinternet.com. Est: 1976. Private premises. Internet and postal. Appointment necessary. Open: Small stock. Spec: Academic/Scholarly; Mathematics; Science - General; Science - History of; Scottish Interest; Technical; Technology. PR: £5–450. Book Market Organiser in Scotland. Corresp: French, German. [Updated]

MAYBOLE

Whitehall Antiques & Fairs, 3 Whitehall, Maybole, Ayrshire, HA19 7AJ. Tel: (01655) 883441. Est: 1996. Private premises. Postal business only. Small stock. Spec: Children's - General; Countries - Scotland; Hobbies. [04/03/2003]

OBAN

Bygone Books, Terok Nor, Ardconnel Hill, Oban, Argyll, PA34 5DY. Prop: Isaac Lipkowitz. Tel: (01631) 563928. E-mail: lipkowitz@hotmail.com. Est: 1987. Private premises. Postal business only. Appointment necessary. Very small stock. Spec: Illustrated; Mysticism; Occult; Paganism. PR: £1–200. [Updated]

PAISLEY

Barry Thurston, 3a Durrockstock Crescent, Paisley, Renfrewshire, PA2 0AW. Prop: Barry Thurston. Tel: (07986) 118480. Est: 2000. Market stand/stall; Shop at: London Road Market, The Barras, Glasgow. Open: **S:** 09:30–16:00; **Su:** 09:30–16:00. Medium stock. Spec: Children's - General; Natural History; Ornithology; Scottish Interest. PR: £2–500. Fairs: Glasgow and North of England. [17/06/2003]

SCOTTISH ISLANDS

ISLE OF ARRAN

Barnhill Books, Old Schoolhouse, Kilmory, Isle of Arran, Strathclyde, KA27 8PQ. Prop: John Rhead. Tel: (01770) 870368. E-mail: rheadz@btinternet.com. Est: 1985. Private premises. Postal business only. Spec: Alpinism/Mountaineering; Gardening; Natural History; Ornithology; Plant Hunting; Sport - Big Game Hunting; Sport - Falconry; Sport - Field Sports; Travel - General. PR: £5–2,000. Cata: 1 a year. [Updated]

Audrey McCrone, Windyridge, Whiting Bay, Isle of Arran, Strathclyde, KA27 8QT. Tel: (01770) 700564. Fax: (01770) 700564. Website: www.ukbookworld.com/members/finora. E-mail: a.mccrone@btinternet.com. Est: 1980. Private premises. Internet and postal. Telephone first. Small stock. Spec: Animals and Birds; Anthologies; Antiquarian; Archaeology; Art - History; Astronomy; Biography; Children's - General; Crafts; Divining; Earth Mysteries; History - General; Illustrated; Literature; Military; Military History; Modern First Editions. PR: £5–200. Cata: 24 a year. [Updated]

ISLE OF COLONSAY

Colonsay Bookshop, ■ Isle of Colonsay, Argyll, Isle of Colonsay, Strathclyde, PA61 7YR. Prop: Kevin & Christa Byrne. Tel: (01951) 200232. Fax: (01951) 200232. Website: www.colonsay.org.uk. E-mail: bookshop@colonsay.org.uk. Est: 1988. Shop open in summer. Very small stock. Spec: Countries - Scotland; Scottish Interest. PR: £1–300. CC: MC; V; Switch. Also, new books & publisher. [Updated]

ISLE OF IONA

The Iona Bookshop, ■ The Old Printing Press Building, Isle of Iona, Argyll, PA76 6SL. Prop: Angus L. & Alison Johnston. Tel: (01681) 700699. Est: 1978. **M:** 10:30–16:30; **T:** 10:30–16:30; **W:** 10:30–16:30; **Th:** 10:30–16:30; **F:** 10:30–16:30; **S:** 10:30–16:30; **Su:** 10:30–16:30. Small stock. Spec: Countries - Scotland; History - Local; Topography - Local. PR: £1–500. Winter: open by appointment only. Also, Celtic tapestry kits. [Updated]

ORKNEY ISLANDS

M.E.McCarty, Bookseller, ■ 54 Junction Road, Kirkwall, Western Isles, KW15 1AG. Prop: Moi McCarty. Tel: (01988) 402062. Fax: (01988) 402062. E-mail: moi@orkneybooks.co.uk. Est: 1986. Shop and Postal business. Appointment necessary. Open: **M:** 10:30–17:00; **T:** 10:30–17:00; **W:** 10:30–17:00; **Th:** 10:30–17:00; **F:** 10:30–17:00; **S:** 10:30–17:00; **Su:** 12:00–17:00; Closed for lunch: 13:00–16:00. Medium stock. PR: £1–100. Corresp: French, German, Norwegian. Mem: PBFA. Also at: 13 North Main Street, Wigtown, Scotland (q.v.). [28/04/2003]

TAYSIDE

ABERFELDY

Freader's Books, ■ 8 Dunkeld Street, Aberfeldy, PH15 2DA. Prop: Christopher Rowley. Tel: (01887) 829519. Fax: (01887) 829519. E-mail: Rowley@freaders.freeserve.co.uk. Est: 1991. **M:** 10:00–16:00; **T:** 10:00–16:00; **Th:** 10:00–16:00; **F:** 10:00–16:00; **S:** 10:00–16:00; Closed for lunch: 13:00–14:00. Very small stock. Spec: Agriculture; Author - Austen, Jane; Calligraphy; Natural History; Scottish Interest; Topography - General; Topography - Local. PR: £4–200. Mem: BA. [Updated]

ARBROATH

A Jolly Good Read, 94 Brechin Road, Arbroath, DD11 1SX. Tel: (01241) 877552. Website: www.ajollygoodread.co.uk. E-mail: books@ajollygoodread.co.uk. Est: 2004. Private premises. Internet and postal. Contactable. Small stock. Spec: Children's - General. PR: £5–500. CC: Paypal. Cata: 3 a year on Childrens. [Updated]

J. & M. Wilson, 94 Brechin Road, Arbroath, Angus, DD11 1SX. Prop: Janine Wilson. Tel: (01241) 877552. Fax: (08700) 529822. Website: jandmwilson.demon.co.uk. Est: 1986. Private premises. Internet and postal. Small stock. Spec: Author - Brent-Dyer, Elinor M.; Author - Buckeridge, A.; Author - Crompton, Richmal; Author - Dahl, Roald; Author - Needham, V; Author - Oxenham, Elsie; Children's - General; Fiction - Crime, Detective, Spy, Thrillers; Illustrated; Modern First Editions. PR: £1–500. Cata: 3 a year on Children's. [27/07/2003]

FORFAR

Hilary Farquharson, Deuchar Farm, Fern, Forfar, Tayside, DD8 3QZ. Prop: H. Farquharson. Tel: (01356) 650278. Fax: (01356) 650417. E-mail: deucharfarm@btopenworld.com. Est: 1992. Private premises. Book fairs only. Appointment necessary. Open: **M:** 08:00–21:00; **T:** 08:00–21:00; **W:** 08:00–21:00; **Th:** 08:00–20:00; **F:** 08:00–21:00; **S:** 08:00–21:00; **Su:** 21:00–22:00. Medium stock. Spec: Agriculture; Antiquarian; Countries - Scotland; Genealogy; Motoring; Scottish Interest; Topography - General; Topography - Local; also Booksearch. PR: £5–1,000. CC: JCB; V. Mem: PBFA. [Updated]

PITLOCHRY

Glacier Books, Ard–Darach, Strathview Terrace, Pitlochry, Perthshire, PH16 5AT. Prop: Chris Bartle. Tel: (01796) 470056. Fax: (01796) 470056. Website: www.glacierbooks.com. E-mail: sales@glacierbooks.com. Est: 1999. Private premises. Internet and postal. Telephone first. Medium stock. Spec: Alpinism/Mountaineering; Calligraphy; Countries - Antarctic, The; Countries - Canada; Countries - France; Countries - Greenland; Countries - Himalayas, The; Countries - Iceland; Countries - Italy; Countries - Nepal; Countries - Norway. PR: £1–3,000. Cata: 3 a year. [Updated]

WALES

The Unitary Authorities of Caerphilly, Cardiff, Carmarthenshire, Ceredigion, Conwy, Denbighshire, Dyfed, Flintshire, Gwynedd, Monmouthshire, Neath Port Talbot, Newport, Powys, Rhondda Cynon Taff, Swansea and Wrexham.

CAERPHILLY

NEW TREDEGAR

Tom Saunders, 9 Woodland Terrace, New Tredegar, Caerphilly, NP24 6LL. (*). Tel: (01443) 836946. Fax: (02920) 371921. E-mail: saunderst@cardiff.ac.uk. Est: 1989. Private premises. Postal business only. Telephone first. Small stock. Spec: Academic/Scholarly; Biography; Chess; Children's - General; Education & School; Politics; Religion - General; Sport - American Football; Sport - Rugby; Topography - General. PR: £3–50. [19/03/2003]

CARDIFF

CARDIFF

Capital Bookshop, ■ 27 Morgan Arcade, Cardiff, CF10 1AF. Prop: A.G. Mitchell. Tel: (029) 2038-8423. E-mail: capitalbooks@cardiffwales.fsnet.co.uk. Est: 1981. Shop open: **M:** 10:00–17:30; **T:** 10:00–17:30; **W:** 10:00–17:30; **Th:** 10:00–17:30; **F:** 10:00–17:30; **S:** 10:00–17:30. Large stock. Spec: Antiquarian; Countries - Wales; also Booksearch. PR: £1–500. Mem: PBFA. [Updated]

Jim Cronin, 154 Arabella Street, Cardiff, CF24 4SY. Tel: Evenings (029) 2048-. Est: 1977. Private premises. Postal business only. Very small stock. Spec: History - General; Music - General; Politics; Sport - Cycling. PR: £2–30. [27/09/2003]

Len Foulkes, 28 St. Augustine Road, Heath, Cardiff, CF14 4BE. Tel: (029) 2062-7703. Est: 1971. Private premises. Postal business only. Very large general stock. PR: £5–100. Now semi-retired. [Updated]

Whitchurch Books Ltd., ■ 67 Merthyr Road, Whitchurch, Cardiff, CF14 1DD. Prop: Mr. G.L. Canvin. Tel: (029) 2052-1956. Fax: (029) 2062-3599. E-mail: whitchurchbooks@btopenworld.com. Est: 1994. Shop; Open. Open: **T:** 10:00–17:30; **W:** 10:00–17:30; **Th:** 10:00–17:30; **F:** 10:00–17:30; **S:** 10:00–17:30; Very large stock. Spec: Anthropology; Archaeology; Art - History; Arthurian; Byzantium; Cookery/Gastronomy; Countries - Wales; Ecclesiastical History & Architecture; Egyptology; Geology; History - General; History - 19th Century; History - Ancient; History - British. PR: £1–100. CC: AE; D; E; JCB; MC; V; SW; S; EL. Also, a booksearch service. Cata: 8 a year. Mem: WBA. VAT No: GB 648 3263 23. [27/09/2003]

Nicholas Willmott Bookseller, 97 Romilly Road, Canton, Cardiff, CF5 1FN. Prop: Nicholas Willmott & Judith Wayne. Tel: (029) 2037-7268. Fax: (029) 2037-7268. Website: members.lycos.co.uk/nicholaswillmott/id17.htm. E-mail: willmott_wayne@hotmail.com. Est: 1982. Private premises. Postal business only. Contactable. Large general stock. Spec: Authors - Women; Autobiography; Biography; Drama; Feminism; Fiction - General; History - General; Humour; Literature; Modern First Editions; Music - General; Music - Classical; Music - Composers; Music - Musicians; Music - Opera; Music - Popular. PR: £2–500. Freelance tenor. Corresp: French. VAT No: GB 368 3564 19. [Updated]

CARMARTHENSHIRE

AMMANFORD

Stobart Davies Limited, Stobart House, Pontyclerc, Penybanc Road, Ammanford, SA18 3HP. Tel: (01269) 593100. Fax: (01269) 596116. Website: www.stobartdavies.com. E-mail: sales@stobartdavies .com. Est: 1989. Office &/or bookroom. Internet and postal. Open: **M:** 09:00–17:00; **T:** 09:00–17:00; **W:** 09:00–17:00; **Th:** 09:00–17:00; **F:** 09:00–17:00. Spec: Building & Construction; Crafts; D.I.Y (Do It Yourself); Forestry; Woodwork. PR: £3–20. CC: AE; D; MC; V. Cata: 2 a year. Mem: BA. [Updated]

CARMARTHEN

Sue Lloyd-Davies, 94 St. Catherine Street, Carmarthen, Carmarthenshire, SA31 1RF. Prop: Sue Lloyd-Davies. Tel: (01267) 235462. Fax: (01267) 235462. E-mail: sue@lloyd-davies.fsnet.co.uk. Est: 1979. Private premises. Internet and postal. Telephone first. Open: **M:** 10:00–16:00; **T:** 10:00–16:00; **W:** 10:00–16:00; **Th:** 10:00–16:00; **F:** 10:00–16:00; **S:** 10:00–16:00. Medium stock. Spec: Children's - General; Children's - Illustrated; First Editions; Illustrated; Literature; Travel - General; also Booksearch. PR: £5–2,000. CC: E; JCB; MC; V; Switch etc. Corresp: French Japanese Welsh. Mem: PBFA; WBA. [Updated]

CEREDIGION

ABERYSTWYTH

Economia Books, 61 Danycoed, Aberystwyth,Ceredigion, SY232hd. Prop: Peter Pavli. Tel: (01970) 624540. Website: www.abebooks.com. E-mail: peter@pavli28.freeserve.co.uk. Est: 1992. Private premises. Postal business only. Appointment necessary. Small stock. Spec: Economics; Philosophy; Politics; Science - General; Social History. PR: £5–200. CC: MC; V. [19/09/2003]

Colin Hancock, Ty'N–Y–Llechwedd Hall, Llandre, Aberystwyth, Ceredigion, SY24 5BX. Tel: (01970) 828709. Fax: (01970) 828709. E-mail: colin-hancock@wales-books.demon.co.uk. Est: 1998. Private premises. Postal business only. Appointment necessary. Small stock. Spec: Antiquarian; Archaeology; Countries - Wales; Culture - National; History - Local; Languages - National; Music - General; Topography - Local; Welsh Interest; also Booksearch. PR: £1–2,000. Also maps. Corresp: French, Welsh. Mem: Welsh Booksellers Assoc. [14/04/2003]

Ystwyth Books, ■ 7 Princess Street, Aberystwyth, Ceredigion, SY23 1DX. Prop: Mrs. H.M. Hinde. Tel: (01970) 639479. Est: 1976. Shop open: **M:** 10:00–17:00; **T:** 10:00–17:00; **W:** 10:00–17:00; **Th:** 10:00–17:00; **F:** 10:00–17:00; **S:** 10:00–17:00. Medium stock. Spec: Countries - Wales; History - Industrial; Technology; Topography - Local. PR: £2–100. CC: MC; V. Mem: BA. VAT No: GB 124 7218 86. [Updated]

CARDIGAN

Books in Cardigan, ■ 2, Pwllhai, Cardigan, SA43 1BZ. Prop: Mary Sinclair. Tel: (0121) 39682517. Website: http://cardiganbooks.hypermart.net/. E-mail: csinclair@lineone.net. Est: 1986. Internet and postal. Shop open: **M:** 09:00–17:00; **T:** 09:00–17:00; **W:** 09:00–17:00; **Th:** 09:00–17:00; **F:** 09:00–17:00; **S:** 09:00–17:00. Large stock. Corresp: Spanish, Portuguese, French. Also at: Cardigan Market Stall open 6 days a week. [Updated]

LAMPETER

Barry Thomas Poultry Books, The Vicarage, Felinfach, Lampeter, Ceredigion, SA48 8AE. Tel: (01570) 470944. Fax: (01570) 471557. E-mail: barry.thomas3@ tiscali.co.uk. Est: 1976. Private premises. Internet and postal. Contactable. M: 09:00–21:00; **T:** 09:00–21:00; **W:** 09:00–21:00; **Th:** 09:00–21:00; **F:** 09:00–21:00. Very small stock. Spec: Cockfighting; Poultry. PR: £1–1,000. Cata: 1 a year on poultry, cockfighting, waterfowl, game birds. Corresp: French, German, Welsh. [Updated]

TREGARON

Nigel Bird (Books), Bryn Hir, Llwynygroes, Tregaron, SY25 6PY. Prop: Nigel Bird. Tel: (01974) 821281. Fax: (01974) 821548. Website: www.nigelbirdbooks.co.uk. E-mail: nigelbird.books@virgin.net. Est: 1986. Private premises. Internet and postal. Appointment necessary. Medium stock. Spec: Author - Rolt, L.T.C.; Canals/Inland Waterways; Railways; Transport. PR: £1–150. CC: E; JCB; MC; V. Also, a booksearch service for specialist subjects only. Cata: 2 a year on Railways. [Updated]

CONWY

COLWYN BAY

owenbooks65, 13, Wynn Drive, Old Colwyn, Colwyn Bay, LL29 9DE. Prop: Jack Owen. Tel: (01492) 516600. E-mail: owenbooks65@hotmail.com. Est: 1989. Private premises. Internet. Appointment necessary. Small stock. Spec: Countries - Europe; Countries - France; Languages - African; Languages - Foreign; Languages - National. CC: Paypal. Cata: 4 a year on Europe and its languages. Corresp: French, Italian. Mem: WBA. Also at: Amazon. [Updated]

Colwyn Books, ■ 66 Abergele Road, Colwyn Bay, Conwy, LL29 7PP. John & Linda Beagan. Tel: (01492) 530683. E-mail: lindaandjohn@davies-beagan.freeserve.co.uk. Shop open: **M:** 09:30–17:00; **T:** 09:30–17:00; **W:** 09:30–13:00; **Th:** 09:30–17:00; **F:** 09:30–17:00; **S:** 09:30–17:00. Closed for lunch: 13:00–13:30. Very small stock. Spec: Countries - France; Foreign Texts; Theology; also Booksearch. PR: £1–15. Also, catalogue of books in French, mostly fiction and literature. Cata: 2 annually, Theology and Fiction Modern Firsts. Corresp: French, Welsh. Mem: Welsh Booksellers Assoc. [Updated]

The Bookcase, ■ 42a Seaview Road, Colwyn Bay, Conwy, LL29 8DG. Prop: David Gathern. Tel: (01492) 532569, (07799) 447772. E-mail: dagathern@btinternet.com. Shop open: **M:** 09:30–16:30; **T:** 09:30–16:30; **W:** 09:30–16:30; **Th:** 09:30–16:30; **F:** 09:30–16:30; **S:** 09:30–16:30. Medium stock. Spec: Sport - General; Sport - Baseball; Sport - Football (Soccer). Open in 7 days a week in summer 10:00–16:00. [Updated]

Rhos Point Books, ■ 85 The Promenade, Rhos–on–Sea, Colwyn Bay, Conwy, LL28 4PR. Prop: Gwyn & Beryl Morris. Tel: (01492) 545236. Fax: (01492) 540862. Website: www.ukbookworld.com/members/brynglas. E-mail: rhos.point@btinternet.com. Est: 1986. Shop; Internet and postal. Open: **M:** 10:00–17:30; **T:** 10:00–17:30; **W:** 10:00–17:30; **Th:** 10:00–17:30; **F:** 10:00–17:30; **S:** 10:00–17:30; **Su:** 10:00–17:30. Medium stock. Spec: Antiquarian; Welsh Interest. PR: £1–300. CC: AE; MC; V. Corresp: Welsh. [Updated]

Roz Hulze, Llanwst Road, Conwy, LL27 0JR. Tel: (01492) 641676. Website: www.rozhulse.com. E-mail: roz@rozhulse.com. Private premises. Appointmnet necessary. Internet and postal. Small stock. Spec: Academic/Scholarly; Antiquarian; Atlases; Colour-Plate; Illustrated; Natural History, Private Press; Travel - General; Voyages & Discovery. PR: £40–5,000. CC: MC; V.

Yesterday's News, 43 Dundonald Road, Colwyn Bay, Conwy, LL29 7RE. Prop: Elfed Jones. Tel: (01492) 53119. E-mail: lfedones@hotmail.com. Est: 1967. Private premises. Open: **M:** 09:00–21:00; **T:** 09:00–21:00; **W:** 09:00–21:00; **Th:** 09:00–21:00; **F:** 09:00–21:00; **S:** 09:00–21:00; **Su:** 09:00–00:00. Very large stock. Spec: Broadcasting; Canadiana; Churchilliana; Cinema/Film; Comic Books & Annuals; Comics; Crime (True); Entertainment - General; Feminism; Fiction - Women; Freemasonry & Anti-Masonry; Gambling; Glamour; Humour; Judaica; Literary Criticism; Literature. PR: £5–50. Majors in newspapers, periodicals and paper ephemera. Cata: up to 4 a year. Corresp: German, Welsh. [Updated]

LLANRUST

Prospect Books, 10 Trem Arfon, Llanrust, Conwy, LL26 0BP. Prop: M.R. Dingle. Tel: (01492) 640111. Fax: (01492) 640111. E-mail: mike@gunbooks.co.uk. Est: 1985. Private premises. Appointment necessary. Very small stock. Spec: Arms & Armour; Firearms/Guns. PR: £5–500. CC: E; JCB; MC; V; Maestro. Cata: 4 a year on firearms, armour and edged weapons. VAT No: GB 625 4838 25. [Updated]

OLD COLWYN

J V Owen, 13 Wynn Drive, Old Colwyn, Conwy, LL29 9DE. Tel: (01492) 516600. Fax: (01492) 516600. E-mail: owenbooks65@hotmail.com. Est: 2003. Private premises. Appointment necessary. Small stock. PR: £1–100. Specialises in European languages, and others. Corresp: French, German. [01/01/2003]

E. Wyn Thomas, Old Quarry, 9 Miners Lane, Old Colwyn, Conwy, LL29 9HG. Tel: (01492) 515336. Est: 1947. Private premises. Appointment necessary. Small stock. Spec: Countries - Wales; Fiction - General; History - General; Natural History; Topography - Local. PR: £1–1,000. Corresp: Welsh. [Updated]

DENBIGHSHIRE

LLANGOLLEN

Books, ■ 17 Castle Street, Llangollen, Denbighshire, LL20 8NY. Prop: Mr. Thor Sever. Tel: (01978) 860334. Website: www.llangollen.org.uk/pages/books.htm. E-mail: books@easynet.co.uk. Est: 1983. Shop open: **M:** 10:00–17:00; **T:** 10:00–17:00; **W:** 10:00–17:00; **Th:** 10:00–17:00; **F:** 10:00–17:00; **S:** 10:00–17:00; **Su:** 10:00–17:00. Spec: Alpinism/Mountaineering; American Indians; Art; Astrology; Cinema/Film; Countries - Melanesia; Folklore; Gardening; History - General; Literary Criticism; Military; Music - General; Occult; Oriental; Philosophy; Photography; Poetry; Politics. PR: £3–50. CC: JCB; MC; V. [Updated]

RHYL

Bookcase, ■ Unit 2 Queens Market, Sussex Street, Rhyl, LL18 1SE. Prop: David Gather. Tel: (01492) 532569. E-mail: deagathern@btinternet.com. Est: 1994. Shop open: **M:** 09:30–17:00; **T:** 09:30–17:00; **W:** 09:30–17:00; **Th:** 09:30–17:00; **F:** 09:30–17:00; **S:** 09:30–17:00; **Su:** 09:30–17:00. Medium stock. **PR:** £1–100. Open in Winter Monday to Saturday 09:30–16:30. Cata: occasionally on baseball, football and general sport. [Updated]

Siop y Morfa, ■ 109 Stryd Fawr, Rhyl, Sir Ddinbych/Denbighshire, LL18 1TR. Prop: Dafydd Timothy. Tel: (01745) 339197. Website: www.siopymorfa.com. E-mail: dafydd@siopymorfa.com. Est: 1980. Shop; Internet and postal. Open: **M:** 09:30–17:30; **T:** 09:30–17:30; **W:** 09:30–17:30; **Th:** 09:30–17:30; **F:** 09:30–16:30; **S:** 09:30–17:30; Closed for lunch: 13:00–14:00. Medium stock. Spec: History - National; Literature; Welsh Interest. PR: £5–200. CC: AE; JCB; MC; V; Solo. Cata: 3 a year. Corresp: French, Cymraeg/Welsh. Mem: PBFA. VAT No: GB 771 0696 20. [Updated]

RUTHIN

Spread Eagle Books, The Spread Eagle, 3 Upper Clwyd Street, Ruthin, Denbighshire, LL15 1HY. Prop: Janet Kenyon–Thompson. Tel: (01824) 703840. E-mail: Est: 1978. Spec: Biography; History - Local; Topography - Local; Travel - General; Welsh Interest; also Booksearch. PR: £5–200. [28/08/2003]

FLINTSHIRE

MOLD

BOOKS4U, 7 The Firs, Mold, Flintshire, CH7 1JX. Prop Norman MacDonald. Tel: (01352) 751121. E-mail: norman_macdonald@btinternet.com. Spec: Academic/Scholarly; Annuals; Antiquarian; Author - Buchan, John; Author - Conrad, Joseph; Author - Durrell, Lawrence; Author - Edwards, Lionel; Author - Fowles, John; Author - Gissing, George; Author - Greene, Graham; Author - Haggard, Sir Henry Rider. PR: £4–1,500. [15/05/2003]

GWYNEDD

BALA

White House Bookshop, ■ 99 High Street, Bala, Gwynedd, North Wales, LL23 7AE. Prop: Iona Lewis Bown. Tel: (01678) 520208. Fax: (01678) 520208. Est: 2001. Shop open: **M:** 10:00–16:30; **T:** 10:00–16:30; **W:** 10:00–12:00; **Th:** 10:00–16:30; **F:** 10:00–16:30; **S:** 10:00–16:30; Closed for lunch: 13:00–14:00. Medium stock. Spec: Natural History. [17/08/2003]

BANGOR

The Muse Bookshop, ■ 43 Holyhead Road, Bangor, Gwynedd, LL57 2EU. Prop: David Nigel Jones. Tel: (01248) 362072. Fax: (01248) 362072. E-mail: gogarth@btinternet.com. Est: 1992. Shop open: **M:** 09:30–17:30; **T:** 09:30–17:30; **W:** 09:30–17:30; **Th:** 09:30–18:30; **F:** 09:30–17:30; **S:** 10:00–16:30. Medium stock. Spec: Academic/Scholarly; Alpinism/Mountaineering; Natural History; New Naturalist; Travel - General. PR: £1–500. CC: MC; V. Also, new books. Cata: occasionally on natural history and mountaineering. Mem: BA. VAT No: GB 560 0796 45. [Updated]

BETHESDA

A.E. Morris, ■ 40 High Street, Bethesda, Gwynedd, LL57 3AN. Tel: (01248) 602533. Est: 1987. Shop; open: **M:** 10:00–17:00; **T:** 10:00–17:00; **W:** 10:00–17:00; **Th:** 10:00–17:00; **F:** 10:00–17:00; **S:** 10:00–17:00. PR: £1–100. [Updated]

CRICCIETH

Capel Mawr Collectors Centre, ■ 21 High Street, Criccieth, Gwynedd, LL52 0BS. Prop: Alun & Dee Turner. Tel: (01766) 523600. E-mail: capelmawr@aol.com. Est: 1998. Shop open: **M:** 11:00–17:00; **T:** 11:00–17:00; **W:** 11:00–17:00; **Th:** 11:00–17:00; **F:** 11:00–17:00; **S:** 11:00–17:00; **Su:** 11:00–16:00. Very large stock. Spec: Cinema/Film; Comics; Cookery/Gastronomy; Counterculture; Fiction - General; Food & Drink; Sport - General; Theology. PR: £1–100. CC: AE; E; JCB; MC; V. Winter opening Thursday, Friday, Saturday 10:00–17:00. Also, collectables & ephemera. Cata: occasionally. [Updated]

DOLGELLAU

Cader Idris Books, ■ 2 Maldwyn House, Finsbury Square, Cader Road, Dolgellau, Gwynedd, LL40 1TR. Prop: Barbara Beeby & Son. Tel: (01654) 703849. Website: www.abebooks.com/home/ dvbookshop. E-mail: beeb@dvbookshop.fsnet.co.uk. Est: 1998. Shop open: Medium stock. Spec: Arms & Armour; Firearms/Guns; Military; Sport - Archery; Welsh Interest. PR: £1–500. CC: AE; JCB; MC; V. Please telephone before calling. Cata: 4 a year on archery. Mem: WBA. Also at: Dyfi Valley Bookshop, 6, Doll St., Machynlleth, Powys,. [Updated]

DYFFRYN ARDUDWY

P. & D. Doorbar, Bron Eirian, Ffordd y Neuadd, Dyffryn Ardudwy, LL44 2DN. Prop: Mr. K.P. & Mr. D.L. Doorbar. Tel: (01341) 247191. Fax: (01341) 247191. Website: www.doorbar.co.uk/books/. E-mail: books@doorbar.co.uk. Est: 1991. Private premises. Internet. Contactable. Small stock. Spec: Art; Children's - General; Children's - Illustrated; Dogs; Gypsies; Illustrated; Rural Life. PR: £5–500. Mem: PBFA. [Updated]

MONMOUTHSHIRE

ABERGAVENNY

Books for Writers, 'Avondale', 13 Lansdown Drive, Abergavenny, Monmouthshire, NP7 6AW. Prop: Ms. Sonia A. Conway. Tel: (01873) 853967. Est: 1999. Private premises. Postal business only. Very small general stock. Spec: Biography; Fiction - General; Reference; also Booksearch. PR: £2–50. Cata: 12 – Monthly mini-lists, on writing guides, biographies. [Updated]

Monmouth House Books, Monmouth House, Llanvapley, Abergavenny, Monmouthshire, NP7 8SN. Prop: Richard Sidwell. Tel: (01600) 780236. Fax: (01600) 780532. Website: www. monmouthhousebooks.co.uk. E-mail: monmouthhousebooks@compuserve.com. Est: 1985. Private premises. Postal business only. Appointment necessary. Small stock. Spec: Architecture; Booksearch. PR: £5–1,000. Also, stock lists on architecture only. Publishes facsimile reprints of early architectural books. Cata: 6 a year on Architecture & related subjects. VAT No: GB 615 8003 63. [Updated]

TINTERN

Stella Books, ■ Monmouth Road, Tintern, NP16 6SE. Prop: Chris Tomaszewski. Tel: (01291) 689755. Fax: (01291) 689998. Website: www.stellabooks.com. E-mail: enquiry@stellabooks.com. Est: 1990. Shop open: **M:** 09:30–17:30; **T:** 09:30–17:30; **W:** 09:30–17:30; **Th:** 09:30–17:30; **F:** 09:30–17:30; **S:** 09:30–17:30; **Su:** 09:30–17:30. Very large stock. Spec: Author - Blyton, Enid; Author - Johns, W.E.; Author - Rackham, Arthur; Children's - General; Children's - Illustrated; Countries - Wales; Illustrated; Natural History; Railways; Topography - General; Topography - Local. PR: £1–3,000. CC: AE; JCB; MC; V. Wants matching. Cata: 4 a year on any subject, author, or illustrator. Corresp: French. Mem: PBFA; Ibooknet.co.uk. Also at: Rose's Books., 14 Broad Street, Hay-On-Wye, HR3 5DB. [Updated]

NEATH PORT TALBOT

NEATH

www.rugbyrelics.com, 61 Leonard Street, Neath, West Glamorgan, SA11 3HW. Prop: Dave Richards. Tel: (01639) 646725. Fax: (01639) 638142. Website: www.rugbyrelics.com. E-mail: sales@ rugbyrelics.com. Est: 1991. Private premises. Postal business only. Appointment necessary. Very small stock. Spec: Sport - Boxing; Sport - Cricket; Sport - Football (Soccer); Sport - Golf; Sport - Rugby. PR: £2–2,000. CC: MC; V. [Updated]

PEMBROKESHIRE

NEWPORT

Carningli Centre, ■ East Street, Newport, Pembs, SA42 0SY. Prop: Mrs A. Gent. Tel: (01239) 820724. Website: www.carningli.co.uk. E-mail: info@carningli.co.uk. Est: 1982. Shop open: **M:** 10:00–17:30; **T:** 10:00–17:30; **W:** 10:00–17:30; **Th:** 10:00–17:30; **F:** 10:00–17:30; **S:** 10:00–17:28. Medium stock. PR: £1–50. CC: AE; E; MC; V; Maestro. Also, an Art Gallery & Antiques. VAT No: GB 491 0134 72. [Updated]

TENBY

Cofion Books, ■ Bridge Street, Tenby, Pembrokeshire, SA70 7BU. Prop: Albie Smosarki. Tel: (01834) 845741. Fax: (01834) 843864. Website: www.cofion.com. E-mail: albie@cofion.com. Est: 1994. Shop; open: **M:** 10:30–17:30; **T:** 10:30–17:30; **W:** 10:30–17:30; **Th:** 10:30–17:30; **F:** 10:30–17:30; **S:** 10:30–17:30; **Su:** 11:30–17:30. Very large stock. Spec: Animals and Birds; Art; Art - Reference; Arthurian; Astrology; Autobiography; Biography; Esoteric; Fiction - General; Genealogy; Literature; Maritime/ Nautical; Military; Naval; Photography; Poetry; Railways; Religion - General; Sport - General. PR: £1–500. [Updated]

POWYS

BEULAH

Myra Dean Illustrated Books, Crossways, Beulah, Powys, LD5 4UB. Tel: (01591) 620647. Fax: (01591) 620647. Website: www.btinternet.com/~myra.dean/index.html. E-mail: myra.dean@btinternet.com. Est: 1984. Private premises. Internet and postal. Telephone first. Very small stock. Spec: Children's - General; Illustrated; Private Press. PR: £5–2,000. CC: MC; V; Switch. Cata: 9 every 6 weeks. Mem: PBFA. [17/06/2003]

BRECON

Andrew Morton Books, ■ 11 Lion Yard, Brecon, Powys, LD3 7BA. Tel: (01874) 620086. Fax: (01874) 620106. Est: 1999. Shop open: **M:** 09:30–17:30; **T:** 09:30–17:30; **W:** 09:30–17:30; **Th:** 09:30–17:30; **F:** 09:30–17:30; **S:** 09:30–17:30. Very large stock. Spec: Art; Children's - General; Crafts; History - General; Literature; Military. PR: £2–30. CC: MC; V; SW, SO. Also, open on Sundays in season. Also at: 7 Lion Street, Brecon. [Updated]

Michael Rainger Books, 3 Usk Terrace, St. Michael Street, Brecon, Powys, LD3 9AA. Prop:Jane Rainger. Tel: (01874) 622817 (24 h. Website: www.raingerbooks.co.uk. E-mail: michael@raingerbooks.co.uk. Est: 1993. Private premises. Internet and postal. Appointment necessary. Open: **M:** 09:00–18:00; **T:** 09:00–18:00; **W:** 09:00–18:00; **Th:** 09:00–18:00; **F:** 09:00–18:00; **S:** 09:00–18:00; **Su:** 10:00–16:00; Closed for lunch: 13:00–14:00. Medium stock. Spec: Astrology; Esoteric; Fore-Edge Paintings; Gnostics; Mysticism; Occult; Railways; Spiritualism; Witchcraft; also Booksearch. PR: £3–150. CC: MC; V. Cata: 3 a year. Mem: ABA. [14/05/2003]

A.G. & W. Wakeley, 7 The Struet, Brecon, Powys, LD3 7LL. Tel: (01874) 622714. Est: 1973. Spec: Countries - Wales; Culture - National; Topography - Local. [28/08/2003]

BUILTH WELLS

Louise Boer, Arthurian Books, The Rectory, Rhosgoch, Builth Wells, Powys, LD2 3JU. Prop: Louise Boer. Tel: (01497) 851260. Fax: (01497) 851260. E-mail: louise.boer@btinternet.com. Est: 1996. Private premises. Internet and postal. Contactable. Medium stock. Spec: Academic/Scholarly; Arthurian; Business Studies; Literary Criticism. PR: £2–150. CC: MC; V. Corresp: Dutch. [Updated]

CAERSWS

Dead Mens Minds.co.uk, Brambles, Trefeglwys, Caersws, Powys, SY17 5QG. Prop: Tristan Winston-Smith. Tel: (01686) 440730. Website: www.TPOBooks.co.uk. E-mail: deadmensminds@aol.com. Est: 2000. Private premises. Internet and postal. Very small stock. PR: £10–2,000. CC: MC; V; Switch. Corresp: Translater. [Updated]

Carol Hogben, Berthlas Chapel Cottage, The Waen, Trefeglwys, Caersws, Powys, SY17 5QG. Tel: (01686) 430653. Fax: (01686) 430447. Est: 1986. Private premises. Postal business only. Very small stock. Spec: Applied Art; Architecture; Decorative Art; Fashion & Costume; Industry; Interior Design. PR: £10–1,000. Also, trade catalgues 1840-1960. Mem: PBFA. VAT No: GB 448 7214 32. [18/06/2003]

HAY–ON–WYE (SEE ALSO HAY–ON–WYE, HEREFORDSHIRE)

The Addyman Annexe, ■ 27 Castle Street, Hay–on–Wye, HR3 5DF. Prop: Derek Addyman and Anne Brichto. Tel: (01497) 821600. Website: www.hay-on-wyebooks.com. E-mail: madder@hay-on-wyebooks.com. Shop open: **M:** 10:30–17:30; **T:** 10:30–17:30; **W:** 10:30–17:30; **Th:** 10:30–17:30; **F:** 10:30–17:30; **S:** 10:30–17:30; **Su:** 10:30–17:30. Very large stock. Spec: Bindings; Literature; Military; Modern First Editions; Music - Rock. PR: £1–100. CC: MC; V; D, Mae. [Updated]

Addyman Books, ■ 39 Lion Street, Hay–on–Wye, HR3 5AA. Prop: Derek Addyman & Anne Brichto. Tel: (01497) 821136. Fax: (01497) 821732. Website: www.hay-on-wyebooks.com. E-mail: madness@hay-on-wyebooks.com. Est: 1987. Internet and postal. Shop open: **M:** 10:00–17:30; **T:** 10:00–17:30; **W:** 10:00–17:30; **Th:** 10:00–17:30; **F:** 10:00–17:30; **S:** 10:00–17:30; **Su:** 10:30–17:30. Large general stock. Spec: Anthologies; Antiquarian; Archaeology; Architecture; Art; Arthurian; Arts, The; Astronomy; Beat Writers; Bibles; Bindings; Book of Hours; Books about Books; History - General; Literature; Military; Modern First Editions; Poetry; Theatre; Theology. PR: £1–20,000. CC: MC; V; De, SW. NB: add ' via Hereford' after Hay-on-Wye when sending by post. Also at: Murder & Mayhem, 5 Lion St., Hay-on-Wye (q.v) and The Addyman Annexe, 27 Castle St., Hay-on-Wye, (q.v.). [Updated]

C. Arden, Bookseller, ■ 'Radnor House', Church Street, Hay–on–Wye, HR3 5DQ. Prop: Chris & Catherine Arden. Tel: (01497) 820471. Fax: (01497) 820498. Website: www.ardenbooks.co.uk. E-mail: c.arden@virgin.net. Est: 1993. Internet and postal. Shop at: Open Easter to Christmas othertimes by appointment. Open: **M:** 10:00–17:00; **F:** 10:00–17:00; **S:** 10:00–17:00; **Su:** 10:00–17:00. Medium stock. Spec: Antiquarian; Biology; Botany; Conservation; Ecology; Entomology; Evolution; Fine & Rare; Gardening; Landscape; Marine Sciences; Natural History; Ornithology; Plant Hunting; Zoology. PR: £3–10,000. CC: JCB; MC; V. Cata: 3 a year. Mem: PBFA. [Updated]

Arthurian Book, Broad St. Antique & Book Centre, 6 Broad Street, Hay–on–Wye, HR3 5DB. Prop: Louise Boer. Tel: (01497) 820653. Fax: (01497) 820653. E-mail: louise.boer@btinternet.com. Est: 1997. Spec: Arthurian; Biography; Maritime/Nautical. [18/08/2003]

B. and K. Books of Hay on Wye, Riverside, Newport Street, Hay–on–Wye, HR3 5BG. Prop: Betty & Karl Showler. Tel: (01497) 820386. Website: www.hay-on-wye.co.uk/bkbooks. Est: 1966. Private premises. Appointment necessary. Small stock. Spec: Apiculture. PR: £6–600. Also at storeroom. Cata: 12 a year. [Updated]

Richard Booth's Bookshop Ltd, ■ 44 Lion Street, Hay–on–Wye, HR3 5AA. Director: Mr. Richard Booth. Tel: (01497) 820322. Fax: (01497) 821150. Website: www.richardbooth.demon.co.uk. E-mail: postmaster@richardbooth.demon.co.uk. Est: 1961. Shop open: **M:** 09:00–19:00; **T:** 09:00–19:00; **W:** 09:00–19:00; **Th:** 09:00–19:00; **F:** 09:00–19:00; **S:** 09:00–19:00; **Su:** 11:00–17:30. Very large stock. Spec: Agriculture; Archaeology; Atlases; Children's - General; Cookery/Gastronomy; Countries - Mexico; Economics; Fiction - Science Fiction; Genealogy; History - General; Languages - Foreign; Law; Literature; Military; Natural History; Performing Arts. PR: £1–1,000. CC: AE; D; JCB; MC; V. Also, paperbacks & magazines. NB: add 'via Hereford' after Hay-on-Wye when sending by post. Mem: WBA. Also at: Hay Castle, Hay-on-Wye. (q.v.). VAT No: GB 412 774 460. [Updated]

Boz Books, ■ 13a Castle Street, Hay–on–Wye, HR3 5DF. Prop: Peter Harries. Tel: (01497) 821277. Fax: (01497) 821277. Website: www.bozbooks.co.uk. E-mail: peter@bozbooks.demon.co.uk. Est: 1988. Internet and postal. Shop open: **M:** 10:00–17:00; **T:** 10:00–17:00; **W:** 10:00–17:00; **Th:** 10:00–17:00; **F:** 10:00–17:00; **S:** 10:00–17:00; Closed for lunch: 13:00–14:00. Medium stock. Spec: Author - Dickens, Charles; Literature. PR: £1–10,000. CC: JCB; MC; V. Mem: ABA. [Updated]

The Children's Bookshop, ■ Toll Cottage, Pontvaen, Hay-on-Wye, HR3 5EW. Prop: Judith M Gardner. Tel: (01497) 821083. Website: www.childrensbookshop.com. E-mail: judith@ childrensbookshop .com. Est: 1980. Internet and postal. Shop open: **M:** 09:00–17:30; **T:** 09:00–17:30; **W:** 09:30–17:30; **Th:** 09:00–00:30; **F:** 09:00–17:30; **S:** 09:00–17:30; **Su:** 09:00–17:30. Medium stock. Spec: Children's - General; also Booksearch. PR: £5–500. CC: MC; V. Corresp: French, German. Mem: Also at: Hay-on-Wye (q.v.). [Updated]

The Children's Bookshop No.2, ■ The Backfold, Hay-on-Wye, HR3 5DL. Prop: John Campbell. Tel: (01497) 821655. E-mail: johncath97@aol.com. Est: 1990. Shop open: **M:** 10:00–17:00; **T:** 10:00–17:00; **W:** 10:00–17:00; **Th:** 10:00–17:00; **F:** 10:00–17:00; **S:** 10:00–17:00. Medium stock. Spec: Children's - Early Titles; Children's - General; Children's - Illustrated. PR: £1–10. CC: JCB; MC; V. Also; children's paperbacks, modern hardbacks, picture paperbacks, non-fiction. Corresp: French, German, Spanish. [Updated]

davidleesbooks.com, ■ Marches Gallery, 2 Lion Street, Hay-on-Wye, HR3 5AA. Prop: David Lees. Tel: (01497) 822969. Fax: (01568) 780468. Website: www.davidleesbooks.com. E-mail: julie@ davidleesbooks.com. Est: 1985. Internet. Shop open: **M:** 11:00–17:00; **T:** 11:00–17:00; **W:** 11:00–17:00; **Th:** 11:00–17:00; **F:** 11:00–17:00; **S:** 11:00–17:00; **Su:** 11:00–17:00. Medium stock. PR: £0–1,000. CC: MC; V; Debit Card. VAT No: GB 488 7008 07. [Updated]

Marijana Dworski Books, Travel, 21 Broad Street, Hay–on–Wye, HR3 5DB. Tel: (01497) 820200. Fax: (01497) 820200. Website: www.dworskibooks.com. E-mail: sales@dworskibooks.com. Est: 1991. Spec: Academic/Scholarly; American Indians; Atlases; Biography; Countries - Balkans, The; Countries - East Europe; Countries - Russia; Dictionaries; Folklore; History - General; Iconography; Lace; Languages - Foreign; Languages - National; Linguistics. PR: £1–1,000. NB: add ' via Hereford' after Hay-on-Wye when sending by post. [Updated]

Francis Edwards in Hay–on–Wy, ■ The Old Cinema, Castle Street, Hay–on–Wye, HR3 5DF. Prop: Hay Cinema Bookshop Ltd. Tel: (01497) 820071. Fax: (01497) 821900. Website: www.francisedwards .co.uk. E-mail: sales@francisedwards.demon.co.uk. Est: 1855. Shop open: **M:** 09:00–19:00; **T:** 09:00–19:00; **W:** 09:00–19:00; **Th:** 09:00–19:00; **F:** 09:00–19:00; **S:** 09:00–19:00; **Su:** 11:30–17:30. Medium stock. Spec: Architecture; Art; Economics; Folklore; History - General; Law; Literature; Medicine; Military; Natural History; Naval; Philosophy; Theology; Travel - General; Voyages & Discovery. PR: £20–10,000. CC: AE; D; E; JCB; MC; V; switch. NB: add 'via Hereford' after Hay-on-Wye when sending by post. Cata: 23 regularly. Mem: ABA; PBFA; ILAB. VAT No: GB 594 2720 23. [Updated]

Greenway's Corner Bookshop, ■ Backfold Lane, Hay-on-Wye, HR3 5AJ. Tel: (01497) 820443. E-mail: georgdenfish@aol.com. Est: 2004. Shop open: **M:** 09:30–17:00; **T:** 09:30–17:00; **W:** 09:30–17:00; **Th:** 09:30–17:00; **F:** 09:30–17:00; **S:** 09:30–17:00. Large stock. Spec: Biography; Fiction - General; Fiction - Crime, Detective, Spy, Thrillers. PR: £1–100. [Updated]

Hancock & Monks Music Emporium, ■ 6 Broad Street, Hay–on–Wye, HR3 5DB. Prop: Eric Hancock & Jerry Monks. Tel: (01591) 610555. Fax: (01591) 610555. Website: www.hancockandmonks.co.uk. E-mail: jerry@hancockandmonks.co.uk. Est: 1974. Internet and postal. Shop open: **M:** 10:00–17:00; **T:** 10:00–17:00; **W:** 10:00–17:00; **Th:** 10:00–17:00; **F:** 10:00–17:00; **S:** 10:00–17:00; **Su:** 10:00–17:00. Medium stock. Spec: Music - General; Music - Classical; Music - Composers; Music - Jazz; Music - Music Hall; Music - Musicians; Music - Opera; Music - Printed; Musical Instruments. PR: £1–250. CC: MC; V; Maestro. Also, CDs, DVDs, sheet music & scores. VAT No: GB 139 8108 51. [Updated]

Hay Castle (Booth Books), ■ Hay Castle, Hay–on–Wye, HR3 5DL. Prop: Hope Booth (Richard Booth Bookshops Ltd.). Tel: (01497) 820503. Fax: (01497) 821314. Website: www.boothbooks.co.uk. E-mail: books@haycastle.freeserve.co.uk. Est: 1987. Shop open: **M:** 09:30–17:30; **T:** 09:30–17:30; **W:** 09:30–17:30; **Th:** 09:30–17:30; **F:** 09:30–17:30; **S:** 09:30–17:30; **Su:** 09:30–17:30. Very large stock. Spec: American Indians; Architecture; Art; Cinema/Film; Crafts; Humour; Photography; Railways; Transport. PR: £1–2,500. CC: AE; MC; V. Also, photographic images from 1850s onwards. NB: add 'via Hereford' after Hay-on-Wye when sending by post. Corresp: French. Mem: WBA. Also at: 44 Lion Street, Hay–on–Wye (q.v.). [Updated]

Hay Cinema Bookshop Ltd., ■ Castle Street, Hay–on–Wye, HR3 5DF. Tel: (01497) 820071. Fax: (01497) 821900. Website: www.haycinemabookshop.co.uk. E-mail: sales@haycinemabookshop.co.uk. Est: 1982. Shop open: **M:** 09:00–19:00; **T:** 09:00–19:00; **W:** 09:00–19:00; **Th:** 09:00–19:00; **F:** 09:00–19:00; **S:** 09:00–19:00; **Su:** 11:30–17:30. Very large general stock. PR: £1–25. CC: AE; D; JCB; MC; V. Fine and Antiquarian books in all subjects via our sister business Francis Edwards. Mem: ABA; PBFA. Also at: Quinto, 48a Charing Cross Road, London WC2H 0BB (q.v.) and Quinto, 63 Great Russell Street, London WC1B 3BF. VAT No: GB 594 2720 23. [Updated]

HCB Wholesale, Unit 2, Forest Road Enterprise Park, Hay–on–Wye, HR3 5DS. Prop: Andrew Cooke. Tel: (01497) 820333. Fax: (01497) 821192. E-mail: sales@hcbwholesale.co.uk. Est: 2002. Storeroom. open: **M:** 09:00–18:00; **T:** 09:00–18:00; **W:** 09:00–18:00; **Th:** 09:00–18:00; **F:** 09:00–18:00. Very large stock. CC: AE; D; E; JCB; MC; V. Main stock: publishers' returns, academic overstocks, and remainders. NB: add 'via Hereford' after Hay-on-Wye when sending by post. Cata: on demand, please ask. [Updated]

Murder & Mayhem, ■ 5 Lion Street, Hay–on–Wye, HR3 5AA. Prop: Derek Addyman & Anne Brichto. Tel: (01497) 821613. Fax: (01497) 821732. Website: www.hay-on-wyebooks.com. E-mail: madness@hay-on-wyebooks.com. Est: 1997. Shop open: **M:** 10:30–17:30; **T:** 10:30–17:30; **W:** 10:30–17:30; **Th:** 10:30–17:30; **F:** 10:30–17:30; **S:** 10:30–17:30. Medium stock. Spec: Crime (True); Criminology; Fiction - Crime, Detective, Spy, Thrillers; Fiction - Fantasy, Horror; Sherlockiana. PR: £1–1,000. Also at: Addyman Books, 39 Lion Street, Hay-on-Wye (q.v.). [Updated]

Outcast Books, ■ 15a Broad St., Hay–on–Wye, HR3 5DB. Prop: David Howard. Tel: (01497) 820265. Website: www.ukbookworld.com/members/outcastbooks. E-mail: outcastbooks@supanet.com. Est: 1993. Shop open: **M:** 10:30–17:00; **T:** 10:30–17:00; **W:** 10:30–17:00; **Th:** 10:30–17:00; **F:** 10:30–17:00; **S:** 11:30–17:00; **Su:** 12:00–14:00. Small stock. Spec: Academic/Scholarly; Alternative Medicine; Medicine; Psychoanalysis; Psychology/Psychiatry; Psychotherapy; Social Sciences. PR: £1–150. NB: add 'via Hereford' after Hay-on-Wye when sending by post. [Updated]

The Poetry Bookshop, ■ Ice House, Brook Street, Hay-on-Wye, HR3 5BQ. Prop: Christopher Prince. Tel: (01497) 821812. Fax: (01497) 821812. Website: www.poetrybookshop.co.uk. E-mail: info@poetrybookshop.co.uk. Est: 1998. Internet and postal. Shop open: **M:** 10:00–18:00; **T:** 10:00–18:00; **W:** 10:00–18:00; **Th:** 10:00–18:00; **F:** 10:00–18:00; **S:** 10:00–18:00; **Su:** 11:00–17:00. Large stock. Spec: Academic/Scholarly; Anthologies; Antiquarian; Autobiography; Beat Writers; Bindings; Biography; Counterculture; Fine & Rare; First Editions; Folio Society, The; Fore-Edge Paintings; Foreign Texts; Humour; Illustrated; Irish Interest; Letters; Litera PR: £1–10,000. CC: MC; V; Maestro. All subjects that relate to poets and poetry inc criticism, biography, readers guides, work in translation and anthologies. VAT No: GB 831 777 901. [Updated]

Rose's Books, ■ 14 Broad Street, Hay–on–Wye, HR3 5DB. Tel: (01497) 820013. Fax: (01497) 820031. Website: www.rosesbooks.com. E-mail: enquiry@rosesbooks.com. Est: 1982. Internet and postal. Shop open: **M:** 09:30–17:00; **T:** 09:30–17:00; **W:** 09:30–17:00; **Th:** 09:30–17:00; **F:** 09:30–17:00; **S:** 09:30–17:00; **Su:** 09:30–17:00. Large stock. Spec: Children's - General; Children's - Illustrated; Illustrated. PR: £1–2,000. CC: AE; JCB; MC; V; SW. Also, bookmatch service - we can let you know when a book comes into stock. Cata: 4 by various subjects, authors or illustrators. Mem: PBFA; www.ibooknet.co.uk. VAT No: GB 667 0422 36. [Updated]

Mark Westwood Books, ■ High Town, Hay–on–Wye, HR3 5AE. Tel: (01497) 820068. Fax: (01497) 821641. E-mail: mark@markwestwoodbook.co.uk. Est: 1987. Shop open: **M:** 10:30–17:30; **T:** 10:30–17:30; **W:** 10:30–17:30; **Th:** 10:30–17:30; **F:** 10:30–17:30; **S:** 10:30–17:30; **Su:** 10:30–17:30. Very large stock. Spec: Folio Society, The; History - General; Mathematics; Medicine; Medicine - History of; New Naturalist; Philosophy; Psychology/Psychiatry; Science - History of; Technology; Theology. PR: £5–1,000. CC: E; JCB; MC; V. Corresp: French. Mem: ABA; PBFA. VAT No: GB 315 3343 88. [Updated]

Y Gelli Auctions, Broad Street, Hay-on-Wye, HR3 5DB. Prop: Michael Bowers. Tel: (01497) 821179. Fax: (01497) 820978. Website: www.invakuable.com/ygelli. E-mail: auction@ygelli.demon.co.uk. Est: 1988. Saleroom. Open: **T:** 10:00–18:00; **W:** 10:00–18:00; **Th:** 10:00–18:00; **F:** 10:00–18:00. CC: MC; V. Cata: 9 plus a year. [Updated]

LLANDRINDOD WELLS

Udo K.H. Polczynski, Rose & Crown, Llanbadarn Fynydd, Llandrindod Wells, LD1 6YH. Tel: to come. Fax: to come. Est: 1984. Private premises. Appointment necessary. Medium stock. Spec: Anthropology; Archaeology; Classical Studies; Folklore; Journals - General; Medieval. PR: £10–5,000. Also at: Philologus - Fine & Rare Books, London SW16. Cata: 2 a year. Corresp: French, German, Malay, Polish, Russian, Spanish. [12/03/2004]

LLANGAMMARCH WELLS

Dally Books & Collectables, Berthllwyd, Beulah, Llangammarch Wells, Powys, LD5 4UN. Prop: Andrew Dally. Tel: (01591) 610892. Website: www.dallybooks.com. E-mail: andrew@thedallys.com. Est: 2001. Market stand/stall. Internet and postal. Contactable. Small stock. Spec: Memorabilia; Military; Military History; War - General; War - World War I; War - World War II; Welsh Interest. PR: £1–200. [13/04/2003]

LLANIDLOES

Dusty Books, The Old Woollen Mill, Shortbridge Street, Llanidloes, Powys, SY18 6AD. Prop: Bernard Conwell. Tel: (01686) 411247. Fax: (01686) 411247. Website: www.dustybooks.co.uk. E-mail: alex@dustybooks.co.uk. Postal business only. Spec: Author - Farnol, Jeffery; Author - Forester, C.S.; Author - Heyer, Georgette; Author - Sabatini, R.; Author - Shute, Neville; Cookery/Gastronomy; Crafts; Food & Drink; Gardening; Rural Life; Sport - Angling/Fishing; Welsh Interest; Wine; also Booksearch. PR: £5–250. [Updated]

The Great Oak Bookshop, ■ Great Oak Street, Llanidloes, Powys, SY18 6BW. Prop: K. Reiter & B. Boswell. Tel: (01686) 412959. Website: www.midwales.com/gob. E-mail: booksales@midwales.com. Est: 1988. Internet and postal. Shop open: **M:** 09:32–17:30; **T:** 09:31–17:30; **W:** 09:29–17:30; **Th:** 09:31–17:30; **F:** 09:30–17:30; **S:** 09:31–16:30. Very large general stock. Spec: Autobiography; Biography; Countries - Wales; Welsh Interest; also Booksearch. PR: £1–50. Also, new books, & greetings cards. Corresp: German, French. Mem: BA; WBA. Also at: [05/10/2004]

MACHYNLLETH

Coch-y-Bonddu Books Ltd., ■ Papyrus, Pentrerhedyn Street, Machynlleth, Powys, SY20 8DJ. Prop: Paul Morgan. Tel: (01654) 702837. Fax: (01654) 702857. Website: www.anglebooks.com. E-mail: paul@anglebooks.com. Est: 1982. Internet and postal. Shop open: **M:** 09:00–17:00; **T:** 09:00–17:00; **W:** 09:00–17:00; **Th:** 09:00–17:00; **F:** 09:00–17:00; **S:** 09:00–17:00. Large stock. Spec: Animals and Birds; Conservation; Dogs; Fishes; Forestry; Natural History; Ornithology; Rural Life; Self-Sufficiency; Sport - Angling/Fishing; Sport - Falconry; Sport - Hunting; Welsh Interest; also Booksearch. PR: £1–2,000. CC: AE; D; E; JCB; MC; V. We stock new books in our fields, as well as remainders, s/hand and antiquarian. Cata: occasional. Corresp: French, German, Spanish, Portuguese, Welsh. Mem: PBFA; BA. [Updated]

Dyfi Valley Bookshop, ■ 6 Doll Street, Machynlleth, Powys, SY20 8BQ. Prop: Barbara Beeby & Son. Tel: (01654) 703849. Website: www.abebooks.com/home/dvbookshop. E-mail: beeb@ dvbookshop.fsnet.co.uk. Est: 1988. Shop open: **M:** 09:30–17:00; **T:** 09:30–17:00; **W:** 09:30–17:00; **Th:** 09:30–17:00; **F:** 09:30–17:00; **S:** 09:30–17:00; Closed for lunch: 12:00–12:30. Medium stock. Spec: Firearms/Guns; Literature; Rural Life; Sport - Archery; Sport - Field Sports; Sport - Shooting; also Booksearch. PR: £1–300. CC: AE; E; JCB; MC; V. Cata: quarterly. Mem: PBFA; WBA. Also at: Cader Idris Bookshop, Finsbury Square, Dolgellau. [14/04/2003]

MONTGOMERY

Castle Bookshop, The Old Rectory, Llandyssil, Montgomery, Powys, SY15 6LQ. Prop: C.N., E.J. & S.J. Moore. Tel: (01686) 668484. Fax: (01686) 668842. Website: www.archaeologybooks.co.uk. E-mail: castlebooks@dial.pipex.com. Est: 1987. Office &/or bookroom. Telephone first. Large stock. Spec: Archaeology; Architecture; Countries - Wales; Welsh Interest. PR: £5–1,000. CC: JCB; MC; V; Switch. Cata: 10 a year on Archaeology, Architecture, Wales. Mem: ABA; PBFA; ILAB. VAT No: GB 482 4054 51. [Updated]

NEWTOWN

David Archer, The Pentre, Kerry, Newtown, Powys, SY16 4PD. Prop: David Archer & Alison Brown. Tel: (01686) 670382. Website: www.david-archer-maps.co.uk. E-mail: david@david-archer-maps.co.uk. Est: 1985. Private premises. Internet and postal. Telephone first. Open: **M:** 08:30–20:00; **T:** 08:30–20:00; **W:** 08:30–20:00; **Th:** 08:30–20:00; **F:** 08:30–20:00; **S:** 09:00–16:00. Very large stock. Spec: Cartography; Geography; Geology; Transport. PR: £1–50. Mem: Welsh Booksellers Assoc. [Updated]

Carta Regis Ltd, Mochdre Industrial Estate, Newtown, Powys, SY16 4LE. Prop: David Pugh. Tel: (01686) 624274. Website: www.davidp@cartaregis.com. E-mail: davidp@cartaregis.com. Est: 1997. Warehouse. Internet and postal. Appointment necessary. Open: **M:** 10:00–17:00; **T:** 10:00–17:00; **W:** 10:00–17:00; **Th:** 10:00–17:00; **F:** 10:00–17:00; **S:** 10:00–17:00. Large stock. Spec: Academic/Scholarly; Agriculture; Alpinism/Mountaineering; Animals and Birds; Antiques; Arts, The; First Editions; Fore-Edge Paintings; Literary Criticism; Literature; Medicine; Modern First Editions; Music - General; Religion - General. CC: AE; E; MC; V; Paypal. New Books. Altenative web site: [Updated]

D.M. Newband, Drefor Cottage,Kerry, Newtown, Powys, SY16 4PQ. Prop: D.M. Newband. Tel: (01686) 670205. Fax: please ask. Website: www.davidnewbandbooks.co.uk. E-mail: enquiries@ davidnewbandbooks.co.uk. Est: 1983. Office &/or bookroom. Internet and postal. Appointment necessary. Open: **M:** 09:00–19:00; **T:** 09:00–19:00; **W:** 09:00–19:00; **Th:** 09:00–19:00; **F:** 09:00–19:00; **S:** 09:00–19:00; **Su:** 10:00–18:00. Small stock. Spec: Railways; Steam Engines; Transport; also Booksearch. PR: £1–200. CC: Paypal. Also, a valuation service on Railways books only. Cata: 2 – January & July. Corresp: None. [Updated]

PRESTEIGNE

Kingshead Books, ■ 45 High St., Presteigne, Powys, . Prop: Ivan Monckton. Tel: (01547) 560100. (Hom. Est: 1983. Shop open: **M:** 10:00–17:00; **T:** 10:00–17:00; **W:** 09:00–17:00; **Th:** 10:00–17:00; **F:** 10:00–17:00; **S:** 10:00–17:00. Medium stock. Spec: Natural History; Welsh Interest. PR: £1–250. Open as above in summer. Winter: Saturdays & various others. Phone first. [Updated]

TALGARTH

The Strand Bookshop, ■ Regent Street, Talgarth, Powys, LD3 0DB. Prop: Mr. & Mrs. I. Perry. Tel: (01874) 711195. Shop open: **M:** 09:00–17:00; **Th:** 09:00–17:00; **F:** 09:00–17:00; **S:** 09:00–17:00; **Su:** 09:00–17:00. Medium stock. PR: £1–50. Also at: The New Strand Bookshop, Eardisley. [28/05/2003]

WELSHPOOL

Len Lewis, Plas Y Coed, 3 Smithy Meadow, Guilsfield, Welshpool, Powys, SY21 9ND. Tel: (01938) 552023. E-mail: len.lewis5@virgin.net. Est: 1986. Private premises. Postal business only. Telephone first. Very small stock. Spec: Sport - Athletics; Topography - Local. Booksearch service for any subject. [21/07/2003]

D. & J. Young, Fairview Cottage, Groes Llwyd, Welshpool, Powys, SY21 9BZ. Prop: David & Joy Young. Tel: (01938) 553149. Website: www.abebooks.com. E-mail: joy_young@lineone.net. Est: 20. Private premises. Postal business only. Appointment necessary. Small stock. Spec: Calligraphy; Embroidery; Fashion & Costume; Knitting; Lace; Textiles. PR: £1–300. [Updated]

RHONDA CYNON TAFF

FERNDALE

Norman F. Hight, 149,North Road, Ferndale, CF43 4RA. Tel: (01443 756552. E-mail: norman.f.hight@care4free.net. Est: 1998. Private premises. Internet and postal. Appointment necessary. Open: **M:** 10:00–19:00; **T:** 10:00–18:00; **W:** 10:00–19:00; **Th:** 10:00–19:00; **F:** 10:00–18:00; **S:** 10:00–14:00. Small stock. Spec: Fiction - Crime, Detective, Spy, Thrillers; Fiction - Fantasy, Horror; Fiction - Science Fiction; Modern First Editions. PR: £1–200. CC: PayPal. [Updated]

SWANSEA

SWANSEA

Mollie's Loft Books., 31 Cilmaengwyn, Pontardawe, Swansea, SA8 4QL. Prop: M.J.P. Evans. Tel: (01792) 863556. Website: www.Molliesloft.com. E-mail: books@mollies.freeserve.co.uk. Est: 1998. Private premises. Internet and postal. Appointment necessary. Small stock. Spec: Science - General; Technology; Welsh Interest. PR: £5–150. CC: MC; V; Switch. Corresp: French. [28/08/2003]

Dead Zone Books, 23 Quarry Road, Treboeth, Swansea, SA5 9DJ. Prop: Stephen Mallory. Tel: (01792) 795509. E-mail: stephenmallory@hotmail.com. Private premises. Postal business only. Very small stock. Spec: Academic/Scholarly; Advertising; Aeronautics; Author - King, Stephen; Countries - Mexico; Fiction - Science Fiction. PR: £10–1,000. [27/03/2003]

Dylans Bookstore, ■ Salubrious House, 23 King Edward Road, Swansea, SA1 4LL. Prop: Jeff & Elizabeth Towns. Tel: (01792) 655255 & 360. Fax: (01792) 655255. Website: www.dylans.com. E-mail: jefftowns@dylans.com. Est: 1970. Shop. Medium stock. Spec: Antiquarian; Author - Thomas, Dylan; Erotica; Folklore; History - Local; History - National; Literature; Topography - Local. PR: £5–500. CC: MC; V. Mem: PBFA. Also at: Dylans Thomas Centre,Somerset Place, Swansea SA1 1RR. [Updated]

J.M. Farringdon, Ariel Cottage, 8 Hadland Terrace, West Cross, Swansea, SA3 5TT. Prop: M.G. Farringdon. Tel: (01792) 405267. Fax: (01792) 405267. E-mail: bellbooks@aol.com. Est: 1970. Private premises. Internet and postal. Appointment necessary. Very small stock. Spec: Antiquarian; Author - Masefield, John; Author - Ransome, Arthur; Bell-Ringing (Campanology); also Booksearch. PR: £20–1,000. Also, publisher of 'Ariel House Publications'. Cata: 4 a year. VAT No: GB 558 2330 40. [Updated]

D. Ieuan Lloyd, 452 Mumbles Road, Mumbles, Swansea, SA3 4BY. Tel: (01792) 363175. Website: www.ukbookworld.com/members/dilloyd. E-mail: dilloyd@rbooks.fsnet.co.uk. Est: 1974. Private premises. Appointment necessary. Small stock. Spec: Academic/Scholarly; Antiquarian; Philosophy. PR: £15–5,000. CC: MC; V. Cata: regularly. Corresp: French. Mem: PBFA. [Updated]

TORFAEN

BLAENAVON,

The Battle of New Orleans /Pea, ■ 56 Broad Street, Blaenavon, Torfaen, NP4 9NH. Tel: (01495) 792417. Est: 2003. Shop open: **M:** 06:00–17:00; **T:** 06:00–18:00; **W:** 06:00–18:00; **Th:** 06:00–18:00; **F:** 06:00–18:00; **S:** 06:00–18:00; **Su:** 05:00–18:00. Large general stock. PR: £1–60. Also, toys, new magazines, groceries. [07/08/2003]

Blaenavon Books, ■ 86 Broad Street, Blaenavon, Torfaen, NP4 9HA. Prop: James Hanna. Tel: (01495) 793093. E-mail: fci2@ix.netcom.com. Est: 2003. Shop open: **M:** 10:00–17:00; **T:** 10:00–17:00; **W:** 10:00–17:00; **Th:** 10:00–17:00; **F:** 10:00–17:00; **S:** 09:00–17:00; **Su:** 10:00–17:00. Spec: Art; Design; Photography. PR: £1–100. CC: MC; V; SW, SO. [11/07/2003]

Broadleaf Books, ■ 12 Broad Street, Blaenavon, Torfaen, NP4 9ND. Prop: Joanna Chambers and Latagrifrith-Unny. Tel: (01495) 792852. E-mail: broadleaf12@aol.com. Est: 2003. Shop open: **M:** 10:00–17:00; **T:** 10:00–17:00; **W:** 10:00–17:00; **F:** 10:00–17:00; **S:** 10:00–17:00; **Su:** 11:00–16:00. Medium stock. Spec: Children's - General; Design; Natural History; Photography. PR: £1–50. CC: V. [10/07/2003]

Browning Books, ■ 33 Broad Street, Blaenavon, Torfaen, NP4 9NF. Prop: Stephanie and Andrew Nummelin. Tel: (01495) 790089. Website: http://www.browningbooks.co.uk. E-mail: info@browningbooks.co.uk. Est: 2001. Internet and postal and shop, open: **T:** 10:00–17:00; **W:** 10:00–17:00; **Th:** 10:00–17:00; **F:** 10:00–17:00; **S:** 10:00–17:00. Medium stock. Spec: Children's - General; Children's - Illustrated; Languages - National; Mining; Railways; Steam Engines; Transport; Welsh Interest. PR: £1–150. CC: AE; E; JCB; MC; V; MAE, ELEC. Mem: BA. [Updated]

Chatterton's Books, ■ 35 Broad Street, Blaenavon, Torfaen, NP4 9NF. Prop: Jo Wyborn. Tel: (01495) 793141. Website: www.booktownblaenafon.com. E-mail: jo@chattertonsbooks.co.uk. Est: 2003. Shop open: **M:** 10:00–17:00; **T:** 10:00–17:00; **Th:** 10:00–17:00; **F:** 10:00–17:00; **S:** 10:00–17:00; **Su:** 11:00–16:00. Small general stock. Spec: Drama; Erotica; Fiction - General; Fiction - Romantic; Health; History - General; Homosexuality & Lesbianism; Humanities; Literary Criticism; Literature; Poetry; Politics; Sexology; Welsh Interest; Women. PR: £1–100. CC: MC; V; SW, SO. [07/08/2003]

The Left Bank, ■ 10 Broad Street, Blaenavon, Torfaen, NP4 9ND. Prop: Mark Bennett. Tel: (01495) 791300. Website: www.leftbank.org.uk. E-mail: leftbankents@aol.com. Est: 2003. Shop open: **M:** 09:30–17:30; **T:** 09:30–17:30; **W:** 09:30–17:30; **Th:** 09:30–17:30; **F:** 09:30–17:30; **S:** 09:30–17:30; **Su:** 11:00–16:00. Spec: Cinema/Film; Entertainment - General; Fiction - General; Fiction - Science Fiction; Music - General; Television; Theatre. PR: £1–150. [07/08/2003]

Llyfrauffur Books, ■ 63 Broad Street, Blaenavon, Torfaen, to come. Prop: Alan Phillips. Tel: to come. E-mail: alaniphillips@hotmail.com. Shop. Spec: Biography; Culture - National; Travel - General. [10/07/2003]

The Railway Shop, ■ 13a Broad Street, Blaenavon, Torfaen, NP4 9ND. Prop: Peter Hunt. Tel: (01495) 792263. E-mail: railway@pontypoolandblaenavon.freeserve.co.uk. Est: 1998. Shop open: **M:** 11:00–17:30; **T:** 11:00–17:30; **W:** 11:00–17:30; **Th:** 11:00–17:30; **F:** 11:00–17:30; **S:** 11:00–16:00. Small general stock. Spec: Aviation; Railways; Shipbuilding; Transport. PR: £1–20. Also: model railways, jigsaws and Thomas toys. [10/07/2003]

WREXHAM

WREXHAM

J.C. Poole Books, 7 Stonewalls, Rossett, Wrexham, LL12 0LG. Tel: (01244) 571557. E-mail: john@cooperpoole.freeserve.co.uk. Est: 1999. Private premises. Appointment necessary. Spec: Antiquarian; Bindings; Fine Printing; Media; Military. PR: £5–250. [17/08/2003]

ALPHABETICAL INDEX BY NAME OF BUSINESS

(Business name followed by county, some of which have been abbreviated)

ALPHABETICAL INDEX OF DEALERS WITH WEB SITES

Leigh Gallery Books, (See page 108) .... www.abebooks.com/home/BOO/
Lewcock (John), (See page 65)... www.abebooks.com/home/maritime
Lewis (J.T. & P.), (See page 73) .... http://ukbookworld.com/members/JTLANDPL
Lewis (John), (See page 107) .... www.abebooks.com
Lewis First Editions, (See page 136)............................... www.abebooks.com/home/davidfordyce/
Libra Books, (See page 147) .... : http://www.ukbookworld.com/members/LibraBooks
Liebreich Antique Maps & Prints (Kitty), (See page 170) .... www.kittyprint.com
Lion Books, (See page 251) .... www.lionbooks.co.uk
Little Bookshop (The), (See page 118)............................... http://thantatosbooks.seekbooks.co.uk
Little Stour Books, (See page 134)... www.littlestourbooks.com
Lloyd (D. Ieuan), (See page 287)................................... www.ukbookworld.com/members/dilloyd
Lost Books, (See page 197)... www.lostbooks.net
LSA Books, (See page 234).................................. www.ukbookworld.com/members/lesanscombe
Lucas (Roger), (See page 148) .... www.rogerlucasbooksellers.com
Lund Theological Books, (See page 63) .... www.lundbooks.co.uk
Lymelight Books & Prints, (See page 92)............................... www.lymelight-books.demon.co.uk
LyngHeath Books, (See page 188) .... www.lyngheathbooks.co.uk

Macfarlane (Mr. H.), (See page 110) .... www.tudorblackpress.co.uk
Maggs Brothers Limited, (See page 170) .... www.maggs.com
Maghreb Bookshop (The), (See page 175) .... www.maghreview.com
Magis Books, (See page 145)... www.magis.co.uk
Magna Gallery, (See page 206) .... www.magna-gallery.com
Magpie Books, (See page 246).................................. http://www.ibooknet.co.uk/seller/magpie.htm
Main–Smith & Co. Ltd. (Bruce), (See page 144) .... www.brucemainsmith.com
Mandalay Bookshop, (See page 165)... www.mandalaybookshop.com
Marcet Books, (See page 161) .... www.marcetbooks.co.uk
March House Books, (See page 94) .... www.marchhousebooks.com
Marco Polo Travel & Adventure Books, (See page 91) .... www.marcopolobooks.co.uk
Marrin & Sons (G. & D.), (See page 136) .... www.marrinbook.co.uk
Martin - Bookseller (Colin), (See page 104)..................................... www.colinmartinbooks.com
Martin Bookshop & Gallery (Richard), (See page 122) .... www.richardmartingallery.co.uk
Mason (Mary), (See page 202)... www.masonpeett.co.uk
Maynard & Bradley, (See page 145)............................... www.maynardandbradley.com
McConnell Fine Books, (See page 135)....................... www.abebooks.com/home/sandwichfinebooks
McCrone (Audrey), (See page 274) .... www.ukbookworld.com/members/finora
McEwan Fine Books, (See page 268) .... www.rhodmcewan.com
McEwan Golf Books (Rhod), (See page 268) .... www.rhodmcewan.com
McGlynn (John), (See page 141) .... www.vintagetechnology.org
McKay Rare Books (Barry), (See page 76) .... www.abebooks.com/home/barrymckayrarebks
McKelvie (Ian), (See page 155)................................... http://ukbookworld.com/members/Dudley1
McKenzie (J.W.), (See page 230)... www.mckenzie-cricket.co.uk
McLaren Books, (See page 273)... www.mclarenbooks.co.uk
McNaughtan's Bookshop, (See page 271)............................... www.mcnaughtansbookshop.com
Meadowcroft Books, (See page 239) .... www.meadowcroftbooks.demon.co.uk
medievalbookshop, (See page 179) .... www.medievalbookshop.co.uk
Meekins Books (Paul), (See page 234) .... www.paulmeekins.co.uk
Menavaur Books, (See page 266) .... www.abebooks.com
Merlin Books, (See page 240).. www.merlinbooks.com
michaelsbookshop.com, (See page 138) .... www.michaelsbookshop.com
Milestone Publications Goss & Crested China, (See page 122)........... www.gosschinaclub.demon.co.uk
Military Bookworm, (See page 161) .... www.militarybookworm.com
Military Collector (The), (See page 247) .... www.sonic.net/~bstone/military
MilitaryHistoryBooks.com, (See page 137).............................. www.militaryhistorybooks.com
Mills Rare Books (Adam), (See page 63)... www.abebooks.com
Ming Books, (See page 266).. www.mingbooks.supanet.commcom
Minster Gate Bookshop, (See page 194)............................... www.minstergatebooks.co.uk
Mobbs (A.J.), (See page 238) .... www.mobbs.birdbooks.btinternet.com
Mogul Diamonds, (See page 238).................................. www.ukbookworld.com/members/mogul
Mollie's Loft, (See page 287) .... www.Molliesloft.com
Monmouth House Books, (See page 280)............................... www.monmouthhousebooks.co.uk
Moore (Eric T.), (See page 130) .... www.erictmoore.co.uk

ALPHABETICAL INDEX BY NAME OF PROPRIETOR

SPECIALITY INDEX
Index of dealers by stock speciality followed by county

ADVERTISING

ANTHROPOSOPHY

ANTIQUARIAN

ANTIQUES

APICULTURE

APPLIED ART

- HISTORY

- REFERENCE

- TECHNIQUE

- THEORY

ART DECO

ART NOUVEAU

ARTHURIAN

ARTISTS

ARTS, THE

ASSASSINATIONS

ASTROLOGY

ASTRONAUTICS

ASTRONOMY

ATLASES

AUTHOR
- GENERAL

- 20TH CENTURY

- ALCOTTS, THE

- ALDIN, CECIL

- ARDIZZONE, EDWARD

- ARNOLD, MATTHEW

- AUSTEN, JANE

- BADEN-POWELL, LORD ROBERT

- BALLANTYNE, ROBERT M.

- BARING-GOULD, S.

- BARKER, CECILY M.

- BARNES, WILLIAM

- BATES, H.E.

- ILLUSTRATED

CHRISTMAS

CHURCHILLIANA

CINEMA/FILM

CIRCUS

CITIES

CITY OF LONDON

CIVIL ENGINEERING

CLASSICAL STUDIES

COCKFIGHTING

COUNSELLING

COUNTERCULTURE

COUNTRIES
- AFGHANISTAN

- AFRICA

- ALBANIA

- AMERICAS, THE

- ANDORRA

- ANTARCTIC, THE

- ARABIA

- ARCTIC, THE

- ARMENIA

- ASIA

DEEP SEA DIVING

DESIGN

DIARIES

DICTIONARIES

DISNEYANA

DIVINING

DOCUMENTS
- GENERAL

DOGS

DOLLS & DOLLS' HOUSES

DRAMA

DRAWING

DRUGS

EARLY IMPRINTS

EARTH MYSTERIES

EARTH SCIENCES

ECCLESIASTICAL HISTORY & ARCHITECTURE

ECOLOGY

ECONOMICS

EDUCATION & SCHOOL

EGYPTOLOGY

ELECTRONICS

EMBLEMATA

EMBROIDERY

ENCYCLOPAEDIAS

ENGINEERING

ENGRAVING

ENTERTAINMENT
- GENERAL

ENTOMOLOGY

ENVIRONMENT, THE

EROTICA

FARRIERS

FASHION & COSTUME

FEMINISM

FICTION
- GENERAL

- CRIME, DETECTIVE, SPY, THRILLERS

- FANTASY, HORROR

- HISTORICAL

- ROMANTIC

FINE ART

FINE PRINTING

FIRE & FIREFIGHTERS

FIREARMS/GUNS

FIRST EDITIONS

GEMMOLOGY

GENEALOGY

GEOGRAPHY

GEOLOGY

- 19TH CENTURY

- AMERICAN

- ANARCHISM

- ANCIENT

- BRITISH

- BYZANTINE

- DESIGN

- EUROPEAN

- MIDDLE AGES

- MODERN

- NATIONAL

- RENAISSANCE, THE

- ROMAN

- SCOTTISH

- SOUTH AFRICA

- WOMEN

HISTORY OF CIVILISATION

HISTORY OF IDEAS

HYDROGRAPHY

HYMNOLOGY

ICONOGRAPHY

ILLUMINATED MANUSCRIPTS

ILLUSTRATED

IMPRINTS

INCUNABULA

INDUSTRY

INTERIOR DESIGN

INTERNATIONAL AFFAIRS

IRISH INTEREST

JEWELLERY

JOURNALISM

JOURNALS
- GENERAL

- NATIONAL

LAW

LEPIDOPTEROLOGY / LEPIDOPTERY

LETTERS

LIMITED EDITIONS

LINGUISTICS

LITERARY CRITICISM

LITERARY TRAVEL

LITERATURE
- GENERAL

- LOG BOOKS

MARQUE HISTORIES (SEE ALSO MOTORING)

MARXISM

MATHEMATICS

MEDIA

MEDICINE

MILITARY HISTORY

MONOGRAPHS

MOTORBIKES

MOTORING

MUSIC
- GENERAL

- CLASSICAL

- COMPOSERS

- COUNTRY & WESTERN

- FOLK & IRISH FOLK

- JAZZ

- MUSIC HALL

- MUSICIANS

- OPERA

NATURAL HISTORY

NATURAL SCIENCES

NATURISM

NAVAL

PERIODICALS & MAGAZINES

PHARMACY/PHARMACOLOGY

PHILATELY

PHILOLOGY

PHILOSOPHY

POLICE FORCE HISTORIES

POLITICS

- FORENSIC

- HISTORY OF

SCIENTIFIC INSTRUMENTS

SCOTTISH INTEREST

SCOUTS & GUIDES

SCULPTURE

SELF-SUFFICIENCY

SETS OF BOOKS

SEXOLOGY

SHEEP/SHEPHERDING

SHERLOCKIANA

SHIP MODELLING

SHIPBUILDING

SHORTHAND

- CYCLING

- DIVING/SUB-AQUA

- DUELLING

- FALCONRY

- FENCING

- FIELD SPORTS

- FOOTBALL (SOCCER)

- GOLF

THEOSOPHY

TOPOGRAPHY
- GENERAL

- LOCAL

TOPOLOGY

TOWN PLANNING

TOYS

TRACTION ENGINES

TRADE UNIONS

TRANSATLANTIC ARTS

TRANSPORT

WOODWORK

YOGA

ZOOLOGY

BOOKSEARCH SERVICE
Index of dealers who offer a booksearch service

LARGE PRINT
Dealers who stock books in large print

Index of Advertisers